About the Editor

Director of Research at the National Center of Scientific Research in Paris and Adjunct Director of the Center of Research in the History of Science and Technology, École des Hautes Études, Paris, René Taton is widely recognized as one of the world's leading historians of science. Secretary General of the International Union of the History and Philosophy of Science since 1955, Professor Taton is the author of six previously published works, including *Reason and Chance in Scientific Discovery*.

History of Science

THE BEGINNINGS OF MODERN SCIENCE

HISTORY OF SCIENCE

THE BEGINNINGS OF MODERN SCIENCE

From 1450 to 1800

Edited and with a preface
by RENÉ TATON

Translated by A. J. Pomerans, B.Sc.

With 55 black and white plates and 36 line illustrations

BASIC BOOKS, INC. NEW YORK

Library of Congress Catalog Card Number: 63–21689

CONTENTS

(*For a full list of contributors to this volume, see p.* 666)

Part II The 17th Century

Part III The 18th Century

The Theoretical Sciences

The Physical Sciences

Biological and Geological Sciences

Part IV Science outside Europe

ILLUSTRATIONS

Figure *page*

PREFACE

WHEREAS *Ancient and Medieval Science* dealt with the development of science from its early beginnings to the end of the Middle Ages, the present volume covers a very much shorter period, stretching from about the middle of the 15th century to the end of the 18th. The justification for this apparent lack of balance is, of course, the profound importance of the three and a half centuries which form the subject of this volume. Contemporary science, which is universal in the sense that its findings are accepted and taught throughout the world, is the direct outcome of a trend which the Renaissance inaugurated. What previous bursts of scientific activity there had been—as, for example, at the beginning of the Alexandrian period—were short-lived, sporadic and restricted to only a few branches of science. The bold and original work of European scientists at the time of the Renaissance, on the other hand, not only embraced science as a whole but set in train an irreversible movement which had only to be broadened and accelerated in the centuries to come.

Our distinction between modern science, as we have called it, and contemporary science (that of the 19th and 20th centuries), which will be the subject of the next two volumes, may appear purely artificial. However, this distinction, which was in any case imposed by technical considerations, is a very real one. Contemporary science differs characteristically from modern (as opposed to classical) science in that it introduced a profound change of attitude in regard to the meaning and social significance of scientific endeavour. As new methods of teaching and research became general, as laboratories multiplied, as more and more specialized scientific journals appeared in growing numbers and as discoveries were increasingly put to practical use, the interest in science ceased to be predominantly aesthetic and formal. As a result, the 19th and 20th centuries, though they did not neglect fundamental research, paid greater heed to the technological progress of mankind than any previous age.

* * *

Since this volume is the result of the collaboration of many experts, it may be criticized for excessive fragmentation of the subject matter. While recognizing this objection, we believe that any other plan would have been open to equal, if not more serious, criticism.

It may be worth pointing out that, although we have deliberately kept all references to practical skills to a minimum, we have felt justified in including the history of medicine because it is inseparable from the history of biology.

The chronological periods which we have been forced to introduce must obviously not be taken too rigidly. They were chosen after very careful consideration and we hope that we have been successful in combining them in a coherent presentation. All the contributors to this volume have gladly submitted to the fairly strict discipline which a collective effort of this kind demands. Apart from them, we should like to thank all those who have kindly given us the benefit of their specialized knowledge, and the publishers who have spared no effort in preparing this work for the press.

PART I

The Renaissance

LIKE ALL ARTIFICIAL DIVISIONS of history, the Renaissance has no definite beginning or end, nor are its characteristic features as clear-cut as is sometimes claimed. True, the 150 years or so dividing the schoolmen from the first great scientists of the 17th century—Vieta, Galileo, Kepler, Gilbert, Bacon and Harvey—represent an important stage in the rise of modern science, but the nascent humanism and the great achievements of the Renaissance must not blind us to its deficiencies. On the one hand there were the invention of printing, the return to classical sources, the study of nature at first hand, the great voyages of discovery and the Reformation, and on the other a great revival of superstition, the bloody excesses of the *conquistadores* and the bitter wars of religion—to cite but a few of the deplorable aspects of the age. In short, the Renaissance was an effervescent and stimulating mixture of the most far-reaching innovations and a most irrational backwash from the Middle Ages. It was also an encyclopedic age. To describe the growth of science in this confused situation we have had to introduce rather artificial divisions between the various scientific disciplines, for only in this way could we show what real advances were made in any one of them, and hence in science as a whole.

Humanism and Encyclopedism

SCIENCE WOKE FROM ITS LONG medieval slumber when, by returning to the sources of antiquity, it learned to supplant speculative book-learning with experiment and observation.

THE MEDIEVAL HERITAGE

In the scholastic syllabus formulated by Albertus Magnus, theoretical science was subdivided into *metaphysics*, *mathematics* (including astrology) and *physics* or natural philosophy. Physics was the study of the essence, genesis and corruption of movable objects in general, throughout the universe, of atmospheric phenomena, and of such compounds or mixtures—either inanimate (mineral) or living (plants, animals)—as were governed by vegetative, sensitive or reasonable souls. St. Thomas Aquinas made a further distinction between *speculative* and *effective* knowledge, the former corresponding to theoretical, and the latter to applied, science, though he defined neither clearly. Thus, he called alchemy and medicine speculative *and* effective.

At the dawn of the Renaissance, therefore, scholastic precepts were still applied to the totality of things: *visibilium omnium et invisibilium*. All science was general science, and the ideal man of science was a universal scholar like Pico della Mirandola.

When Charles de Bouelles drafted a new syllabus in his *Metaphysicum introductorium* (1503), he included morals, mathematics, music, astronomy and physics. When the medieval *Summae* came to be printed, Vincent of Beauvais' *Speculum naturale* (1475–1478), and Albertus Magnus' *De virtutibus herbarum, lapidum et animalium* found a wide circle of erudite readers, and so did such apocryphal texts as the *Secrets of Albert the Great* and the *Secrets of Albert the Lesser*, veritable sorcerers' handbooks. Johann von Cube's *Gart der Gesundheit* (*Hortus sanitatis*), first published in Mainz in 1485, was followed by a number of further editions in German, French, Italian and Latin. In 1556, Jehan Corbichon republished the writings of Bartholomew the Englishman (13th century), whose *De proprietatibus rerum* had dealt with 'heaven and earth, beasts, birds, stones, metals and other substances'. Bersuire's vast *Reductorium morale*, written in the 14th century and first published in 1489, treated of God, the angels, the devil, man, hygiene, the constellations, meteors, storms, animals, the earth, stones, vegetables, *etc.*, and was republished in Venice in 1583. Others were John of San Geminiano's *Summa de exemplis et rerum similitudinibus* (Antwerp, 1629), and Louis of Granada's *Catechism or Introduction to the Symbol of the Faith* (Paris, 1654). Medicine was still largely in the hands of monks, and the very title of *physicus* reflected the 15th-century belief that medicine was the daughter of *physica* or natural science.

The Church endorsed the medieval view that science embraced metaphysics, astrology and visible natures, which was expressed, for instance, in Lefèvre d'Étaples' theory of the three worlds: Intelligence, Celestial Bodies and Matter.

The prevailing cosmological ideas continued to be those of Aristotle and Ptolemy, adapted to Christian dogma. All the traditional celestial spheres were kept intact; above them lay what Brunetto Latini called the azure vault of the firmament, the crystalline heaven and the purple Empyrean, from which the rebellious angels had fallen. Below the heavens was the world of the living—infidels or members of the militant church. Lower still were the fires of hell, the world of demons where the damned roast eternally for their sins. Fernel, who was otherwise a Galenic rationalist, would occasionally hold forth on the mysteries of hell—*de abditis rerum causis*—and blame cacodemons for man's illnesses. In 1546, Calvin preached his fiery sermon on Satan's personal abduction of a sinner. G. Emiliano, who had studied the works of Plato and Plotinus, felt he could divide the fauna of hell into five categories: igneous, ethereal, aerial, aquatic and terrestrial.

But between the Creator and His works stood that ancient symbol of universal harmony: Nature, which, as *natura naturata*, perpetuates the divine order in the created world (Giordano Bruno). That order is first of all aesthetic. 'Physics', Rabelais said, 'gave birth to beauty and harmony.' It is also benevolent, the seal of God's demonstrable purpose. 'What fool is he', Erasmus declared, 'who feigns to correct or direct her efforts.' As *natura medicatrix*, she helps the sufferer to be made whole, placing the remedy by his side, or, as Paracelsus would have it, causing salubrious plants to spring up by the side of diseases, and to reveal their presence by special 'signatures'.

In time, Nature gained her secular independence, and became what Erasmus called 'Mother Nature, the ingenious worker'. Still, Nature remained full of whims, of airs and graces—even in man himself, who is a microcosm, a tiny replica of the world in which he lives. In him, she resurrects parasites born from the slime, thus perpetuating the miracle of spontaneous generation, and stones in the bladder as reminders of the mineral world. Nature produces her prototypes in the very entrails of the earth, where the fossil shells are either mockeries or abortive attempts at creation. Who would deny that Nature's wondrous instincts reflect her irrepressible creative urges?

Nature, whom Ambroise Paré still called the 'handmaiden of God Almighty', had ceased to be the passive 'seal and witness of God's elementary plan'. Even in the heavens, where, according to Louis of Granada, the Almighty as the Prime Mover had bestowed motion on the planets and stars, God's direct influence was gradually being whittled down. The Arabs had been the first to introduce an agent between the Prime Mover and His sublunary world: a series of intelligences governing the motion of the spheres. These astral powers were now personified in neo-Platonic ways to resemble the genii and demiurges of the East, or else merged into what René Bretonnayau called the 'universal plastic virtue', into Cardan's cosmic animism, or into Bruno's pantheistic dynamism, in which spirit becomes matter and matter spirit throughout eternity.

While the *conquistadores* advanced on the earth, and astronomers penetrated the stellar world, mysticism thus continued unabated. The century of Erasmus and Montaigne was also that of Cardan, Paracelsus and Cornelius Agrippa. Gnosticism was resuscitated, joining God to spirit and matter. Marsile Ficin was a staunch defender of this union; Lefèvre d'Étaples made it the basis of his theories about natural magic, planetary harmonies and number mysticism. Primitive thought and ancient incantations survived as astrology, geomancy, chiromancy and metopomancy.

The Rediscovery of the Classics

However, an intellectual revolution was maturing as copyists were gradually ousted by printers, illuminators by xylographers or chalcographers, Latinists by Hellenists, clerical physicians by lay practitioners, and the theologians of the *Summae* by human encyclopedists.

After the fall of Constantinople in 1453, Byzantine scientists forced to flee to Italy took with them those classical treasures which the printing presses were soon to pour forth in an unending stream. From Italy, the new light spread, first to France and then to the entire West, revolutionizing art and manners, arousing new interest in natural and spiritual problems, and resurrecting the glory that was Greece. It was from this return to Hellenic values that humanism was born, first of all in the purely philological work of restoring, publishing and distributing the ancient texts. Just as the Reformation produced and popularized the Authorized Version of the Bible, so lay scholars supervised and authorized the general publication of the Greco-Latin texts.

From 1450 to 1500, some 13,000 incunabula were published. From 1473, when German printers opened a printing press in Saragossa, printing shops sprang up like mushrooms. Michel Servet, working for Frellon in Lyons, and Jean Hauhin, working for Frobel in Basle, felt no loss of dignity in acting as mere proof-readers.

Actually, Greek scientific texts had been published before. Albertus Magnus and his successors had read the works of Aristotle in Michael Scot's and Gerard of Cremona's translations from the Arabic, or from William of Moerbeke's translation from the Greek, but these were generally second-hand documents, altered by translators and copyists and full of scholastic jargon and glosses. Now the originals became generally available, though at first they remained chained to library shelves. One of the first classical writers to be resurrected was Pliny (published by Johannes de Spira, Venice, in 1469). Other authors appeared in rapid succession from the presses of Estienne (Henri Estienne published the collected works of Plato from the first complete manuscript to reach the West in 1438), of Aldo Manuzio (who published the works of Aristotle in five volumes, 1495–1498) and of Gryphus and Plantin. Restored and purged by competent exegetists and philologists, these texts, previously stored in musty monastic *scriptoria*, now reached the studies of secular scholars where they were eagerly received.

The Secularization of Science

At the universities a new wind had begun to blow—science was becoming secular. While the Middle Ages had considered the study of ancient science and thought no more than a means of advancing the Christian life, the 16th century studied them for their own sake and brought them down to earth. The servants of a decadent and corrupt Church, shortly to be rent by the religious wars, made way for scholars in lay garb with a far wider horizon, though at first with a far smaller audience. Thus, though England produced Turner, Linacre and Wotton, Oxford and Cambridge paid little heed to science, largely ignoring it until 1598, when Gresham College was opened in London. France, on the other hand, more directly in touch with Italian culture, was much quicker to break with the past; the schools of Bourges and Orleans were dazzlingly, if briefly, successful. True, the great French universities remained immersed in scholastic disputes and the Sorbonne frowned on the new doctrines, but science took a great step forward when Francis I founded the *Collège de France* in 1530. It was of this College that Gargantua wrote to

Pantagruel, 'Now all the disciplines are restored, and the languages soundly installed. There is an abundance of scholars, of very learned preceptors . . . of very rich libraries.'

Outside the official universities, many European cities organized public lectures and supported literary clubs where brilliant men could display their encyclopedic knowledge. Florence counted no less than fourteen such clubs, including the short-lived *Accademia Platonica* founded by Marsile Ficin, the *Accademia della Crusca* (1583) and the *Alterati*. Other clubs were opened in Padua (Academy of Science, 1520), at Mantua (with the support of Vittorino da Feltre), at Perugia (*Insensati*), at Siena (*Intronati*), at Venice (*Fama*, 1558, *Accademia Aldine*, *Ricoverati*) and at Bologna (*Oziosi*, 1563). The *Accademia Pontania* flourished at Naples, where G. B. della Porta also founded the *Accademia dei Segreti* which opened its doors to none but original discoverers of new medical or biological facts. Not all these institutions fared alike, for the Inquisition looked upon some of them with especial disfavour. The most long-lived of all was the *Accademia dei Lincei* (1603–1630), founded in Rome with the support of Prince Cesi.

As a result, the encyclopedic idea smouldered on. Paolo Giovio tried his hand at writing annals, Aldrovandi at archaeology, Pierre Giles at geography, Fernel at geodesy, and Peletier at grammar and mathematics. Physicians, following the example of Galen, Serapion, Ibn al-Bayṭār and Avicenna, studied nature at large by investigating the cosmic and climatic causes of diseases and the curative powers of medicaments derived from the three kingdoms of nature. Rondelet, while caring for his patients, found time to study plants and fishes, and Richer de Belleval's chair at the University of Montpellier (1593) was a combined chair of anatomy and botany.

Vernacular Encyclopedias

Since Latin was the international language of science, itinerant teachers or masters of science could address university audiences throughout Europe. But while the humanists tried to restore Latin to its pristine purity, other scholars responded to popular interest by translating the classics into the vernacular. The work which had been begun in the 14th century by Raymond Lulle and Nicole Oresme was continued by Aldrovandi and Gesner, whose *Nomenclator* contained a long list of synonyms in the most common languages of the day. Classical Jewish culture woke from its long torpor when Nathan Ha-me'ati's Hebrew translation of Avicenna's *Canon* (1279) was published in 1479. European languages, too, laid claim to being heard, beginning with Italian in Ugo Benzi's *Tractato utilissimo* of 1491, and later in Paccioli's *Summa* and in the work of F. Imperato.

An Italian version of Pliny was published in Venice in 1489 by C. Landino. A Castilian translation (*Compendio de la salud humana*) of J. von Ketham's *Fasciculus medicinae* appeared in 1517; Dürer published his books on proportion in German (*Vier Bücher über die Proportion*), and Agricola's *De re metallica* was translated into German almost as soon as it was written. In 1654, Dodoens' great botanical treatise was published in Flemish, and so were Stevin's works at the end of the century. In his *Defence and Illustration of the French Language* (1549) Joachim du Bellay boasted 'that all the sciences can be faithfully and amply treated in that tongue'. Pierre Belon and Rondelet were not too proud to accompany their Latin texts, '*ad usum eruditorum*', with French translations for the use of laymen, and Gargantua taught his son the French names of 'all the fishes in the sea and all the birds of the air'.

The Scrutiny of Classical Texts

As classical knowledge spread, its sources came under closer scrutiny. When he translated the Gospels into German, Luther freed the German genius from the shackles of Rome and brought critical scholarship back to honour. The religious awakening triggered off the great intellectual revolution, so that the classical ideas had hardly reached France from Italy before they were thoroughly re-examined. Rabelais refused to bow to any authority other than Hippocrates, while Paracelsus, imitating Luther who had publicly burned the Papal Bull in 1520, consigned to the flames the collected works of Avicenna and Galen before the assembled citizens of Basle in 1527. No wonder that the scientific debates of the time were often riotous, and went far beyond the walls of the universities. Intellectual swashbucklers faced one another in public, Aristotle and Hippocrates in their pockets and less harmless weapons up their sleeves.

Yet science benefited greatly from public interest in these disputes. In 1543, Vesalius laid the foundations of modern anatomy when he dared to reject the Galenic system. In 1509, Leoniceno criticized Pliny's most blatant medical errors. Clearly, the ancients had neither seen nor known everything there was to see and know. Many of their descriptions were vague and full of gaps, and the gaps could only be bridged by observation.

Naturalists combed the Mediterranean basin and the Near East for botanical specimens, which they sent to the many botanical gardens which had sprung up in Italy; intrepid voyagers extended the geographical horizons of the Old World. When Christopher Columbus discovered America in 1492, the old geography had to be thrown out almost overnight. The East and West Indies revealed a treasure of plants, animals and human races which the great authors of the past had not even suspected, so that all their encyclopedias needed to be rewritten. Many attempts to do so were made, including particularly those of Gesner and Aldrovandi, two men of exceptional erudition. Henceforth, no single scholar would ever again dare to tackle all branches of human knowledge, and the best of them restricted their investigations to given fields. The polygraphers had to make way for the monographers. Ichthyology was turned into an independent discipline by Belon, Rondelet, Gilles d'Albi, Salviani and Paolo Giovio; ornithology by Belon, W. Turner and Longolius; mammalogy by G. Emiliano; herpetology by N. Leoniceno; and entomology by Penny, Wotton and Moufet. Geology was developed by Agricola and Palissy. Botany became more exact and more specialized, and gradually threw off its clerical and medical shackles.

In mathematics, the rediscovery of the rich heritage of the past went hand in hand with attempts to establish an independent algebra. While Stevin set statics and hydrostatics on firm foundations, Benedetti produced less spectacular results in dynamics, which nevertheless enabled him to cast doubt on Aristotle's physics. In astronomy, Copernicus made a radical break with past ideas on the structure of the universe. However, the full consequences of the Copernican system would not be appreciated until the 17th century, when the new physics of Galileo, Descartes and Newton would weld terrestrial phenomena and celestial motions into one gigantic framework. Meanwhile, two great astronomers—Tycho Brahe and Johannes Kepler—pursued different but convergent paths to pave the way for their illustrious successors.

Encyclopedism and Scientific Humanism

While greater specialization led to the deeper study of natural phenomena, general knowledge also increased. Works of literary popularization in Low Latin or in the vernacular reached an ever-wider public as printing presses poured out a never-ending stream of texts. Greater familiarity with the classical sources brought not only a greater love of nature, but also literary elegance. Few scientists hid their artistic lights under a bushel. Thus Salviani was not only a great ichthyologist, but the author of the rather obscene *La Ruffiana* (1554), and Fracastoro used the metre of Virgil and Lucretius to write his famous *Syphilis sive morbus gallicus* (Verona, 1530). Ambroise Paré also ventured to produce verses (though he may have borrowed them from Jean Lyège, author of 1,000 Latin verses on human physiology). In 1533, René Bretonnayau published a French poem on the *Generation of Man*. Indeed, there was no single erudite work that was not provided with a rhetorical preface or with a *Liber amicorum*, in which bilingual or trilingual compliments were freely exchanged.

While many poets took familiar animals as their themes, others went further afield. In a cosmogonic and biblical poem, the *Sepmaine*, the Huguenot Salluste du Bartas described all the animals, plants and minerals of God's creation. His lengthy alexandrines included so many strangely compounded names that Simon Goulart was forced to add a special glossary. Another Huguenot, Charles de Gamon, criticized Bartas' conception in his own *Sepmaine* or 'Creation of the World', in which he denied the existence of the griffin, the basilisk and the phoenix, the alleged power of the remora to stay the course of any ship to which it attaches itself, and the fable that the pelican feeds her young with her own blood.

THE EXACT SCIENCES

WE SHALL EXAMINE THE HISTORY of the exact sciences during the Renaissance under three headings—mathematics, astronomy, and physics or mechanics—even though the term 'exact' cannot be properly applied to them, except in anticipation of future developments.

Needless to say, this division is highly artificial. The history of astronomy cannot be studied apart from that of mathematics—or even of physics. Nevertheless, our approach has the advantage of emphasizing the inherent logic of historical processes that would otherwise seem quite haphazard.

In fact, many of the external influences which historians have called turning-points in the history of science are completely illusory. Thus the appearance of the cannon did not cause the emergence of the new dynamics—it was precisely the behaviour of cannon-balls that Leonardo da Vinci, Tartaglia and Benedetti were unable to explain. The needs of navigators, of ecclesiastical calendar computers and of astrologers ought to have led to the correction of existing astronomical tables, but they did not; nor did they persuade Copernicus to change the traditional order of the celestial spheres and to place the sun at their centre. Commercial needs and the rise of banking certainly helped to spread elementary mathematical knowledge, but they cannot explain the spectacular advances made by early 16th-century Italian algebraists, nor their systematic attempts to 'symbolize' arithmetical and algebraic operations.

However, though the series of events constituting the evolution of mathematics, astronomy and physics cannot be explained in isolation—it is always vain to 'explain' an invention or a discovery—they can at least be made intelligible. The history of scientific thought cannot content itself with less or demand more.

CHAPTER 1

Mathematics

THE REVIVAL OF MATHEMATICAL STUDIES

FIFTEENTH-CENTURY MATHEMATICIANS devoted most of their energies to the discovery and study of medieval, Arabic and, later, of Greek texts, and to the widest possible dissemination of their newly-acquired knowledge.

Two events, in particular, helped to hasten this development: the fall of Constantinople, which drove a host of scholars with their Byzantine manuscripts into Italy; and the invention of printing. However, the first printed books were little concerned with mathematics, and many works written in the middle of the 15th century (for example, those of Nicholas of Cusa, Peurbach and Regiomontanus) were not printed until very much later. Those of Chuquet and Piero della Francesca were not printed at all, but in 1472 Sacrobosco's *Sphaera* was published at Ferrara and at about the same time Peurbach's *Theoricae novae planetarum* appeared in Nuremberg. While Ptolemy's *Quadripartitum* was printed in Venice as early as 1484 and 1493, no Latin edition of the *Almagest* was printed before 1515 (Venice) and no Greek edition until 1538 (Basle). Euclid's *Elements* (in the Campanus edition) was published in 1482 at Venice and in 1491 at Vicenza. Medieval mathematicians were not forgotten, for though the works of Leonardo of Pisa were not published before the 19th, nor those of Levi Ben Gerson before the 20th century, some of the writings of Thomas Bradwardine, of Jordanus Nemorarius and even of Nicole Oresme appeared much earlier. Jordanus' *Arithmetic* was printed in 1496, 1503, 1507, 1510 and 1514; Bradwardine's *Arithmetic* in 1495, 1498, 1502, 1503, *etc.* Bradwardine's *Geometry* in 1495, 1516 and 1530; and Oresme's *De latitudine formarum* in 1483 and 1496. At the same time, there appeared the first popular textbook: an anonymous arithmetic published in Treviso in 1478. There followed a host of Italian and German works of a similar kind.

These textbooks, which handed down the oral tradition of the Italian abacists and the German *Rechenmeister*, grew more and more comprehensive. When Luca Pacioli's *Summa* was published in Venice fifteen years after the Treviso textbook, it contained all the mathematical knowledge of the day.

Nicholas of Cusa

Although better known as a philosopher than as a scientist, and although he made no original contribution to science, Nicholas of Cusa, or Cusanus (1401–1464), was to influence Leonardo da Vinci, Giordano Bruno, Copernicus and Kepler. His belief in the absolute value of the principle of continuity, and his formal identification of the circle with a polygon having an infinite number of sides became the basis of Kepler's *Stereometria doliorum*, and hence of 17th-century differential geometry.

Cusa held that, though all finite and relative thought is based on opposites and contraries, the mind is capable of seizing on the 'dialectical concordance of these contraries in infinity' by an act of intuition which he called 'learned ignorance'.

All thought consists of comparisons and the discovery of relationships. Now, numbers express the relationship between small and great. While we can always increase or decrease numbers, we can never reach infinity—a maximum than which no number can be greater, or a minimum than which no number can be smaller. Infinity can be grasped only by the intuitive act of identifying maxima and minima.

The concordance of contraries in infinity holds also in geometry, where we meet such apparent opposites as the straight line and the curve, or the continuous and the broken line. However, such oppositions hold only in the finite realm. Thus the curvature of a circle, which decreases as the radius increases, and increases as the radius decreases, never reaches a *finite* minimum or maximum. Yet it disappears altogether at infinity.

From these metamathematical speculations, Cusa concluded that only through mathematics can the mind reach certainty. Hence mathematics is the basis of all physics, even though, strictly speaking, nature cannot be completely reduced to number. Cusa therefore tried to apply his dialectics directly to physical problems.

The purely mathematical work of Nicholas of Cusa was rather unfruitful, probably because he tried to tackle the impossible task of squaring the circle. His solution, based on the arcuation of the straight line and on the rectification of the arc of a circle, led him to very poor approximations, which Regiomontanus soon dismissed as such. However, in his *De mathematica perfectione* (1458) he gave the excellent approximation (in modern notation):

$$\varphi = 3 \sin \varphi / (2 + \cos \varphi)$$

Cusa realized that a line cannot be divided into a series of points, but only into a series of smaller line segments, just as a plane can be divided only into planes and a volume into volumes. These ultimate indivisibilities reflect the absolute indivisibility of the point. He also knew that two sets of polygons, one inscribed in, and the other circumscribed to, a circle, though approaching each other and the circle as the number of their sides is increased, can never coincide with each other or with the circle. His principle of the concordance of maxima and minima did, however, lead him to postulate a dialectical concordance of opposites between the triangle (minimum number of sides) and the circle (absolute maximum of number of sides).

These considerations led him to the adoption of the principle of continuity—previously stated by Campanus—according to which any magnitude which increases continuously between two limits must, at a given moment, become equal to the upper limit. From this principle, and his principle of the concordance of maxima and minima at infinity, which can be grasped intuitively by the mind (*visio intellectualis*), Cusa concluded that what is true of maxima and minima is also true of intermediate values.

Peurbach's Contribution

The renewal of mathematical and astronomical studies in Europe is rightly associated with the name and the work of Georg von Peurbach (1423–1461), who carried humanism into astronomy and who preached a general return to the Greek sources.

Peurbach was born near Vienna, and studied at the university of that city before going to Italy, where he met Nicholas of Cusa and the Italian mathematician and astronomer Giovanni Bianchini. He returned to Vienna in 1453, was appointed Astronomer-Royal by Ladislaus of Hungary in 1454, and later taught astronomy, arithmetic and classical literature at the University of Vienna. His *Algorismus*, reprinted in 1492 as the *Opus algorismi jucundissimus*, ran to many editions and replaced Sacrobosco's *Algorismus* as the principal university textbook. In truth, Peurbach's book was no great advance over Sacrobosco's, for he, too, gave rules without proofs and considered *mediation* and *duplication* as independent operations. Moreover, he dealt only with integral numbers. Algorisms, let us recall, were calculations using Arabic numerals, unlike abacist calculations with counters (on the line), which were invariably associated with Roman numerals. Until the 17th century the abacist method was the one most commonly used in practical life (by merchants, money-changers, *etc.*). Public authorities insisted on Roman numerals on all official documents, claiming that Arabic numerals were much easier to forge.

As a result, the abacists were able to fight a long rearguard action against the algorists. Their method was still taught in most 17th-century practical arithmetics and is used in many parts of Asia and Russia to this day.

Much more important than Peurbach's *Algorismus* was his *Tractatus . . . super propositiones Ptolemaei de sinibus et chordis*, one of the first European textbooks on trigonometry. It included a sine table of unprecedented accuracy.

Sines, an Indian invention, had gradually come to replace the Greek chords, but though translations of Arabic astronomical texts had familiarized European scholars with the new concept, they had no adequate tables to implement it. Peurbach decided to fill the gap. Using Arabic methods, particularly those of Arzachel (al-Zarqālī), he established a sine table for all angles (arcs) from 0° to 90°, at 10-minute intervals, with the radius (*sinus totus*) equal to 600,000.

Peurbach's own tables, however, were never published. His pupil Regiomontanus rejected them as inadequate and intended to replace them with his own, in which the angles (arcs) varied by much smaller intervals and the radius was equal to six million and later to ten million. His premature death put an end to his project and Peurbach's *Tractatus*, with his pupil's tables, was not published until 1541. Peurbach also invented an astronomical instrument, the *quadratum geometricum*, which could be used in conjunction with sine tables. (Modern instruments are usually associated with tangent tables.)

Regiomontanus

Born in 1436, in Königsberg (Duchy of Coburg), Regiomontanus (Johann Müller) was admitted to the University of Leipzig at the age of eleven. He left Leipzig in 1450 to continue his studies under Peurbach at Vienna. When Peurbach entrusted him with the completion of the translation of Ptolemy's works Regiomontanus repaired to Italy, where he studied Greek under Cardinal Bessarion. Working with George of Trebizond at first, and later by himself, he copied a number of Greek manuscripts, including the *Almagest*. He also toured all Italy, accompanying Bessarion on astronomical expeditions, in the course of which he collaborated with Bianchini and also with the humanists Guarini and Theodore of Gaza. After revising the *Almagest* and completing his *De triangulis omnimodis*, he returned to Vienna. Later, Matthias Corvinus, King of Hungary, appointed him Keeper of the Royal Collection at Ofen, and in 1471 he went to Nuremberg where a rich burgess, Bernhard Walther, provided him with an observatory, a tool-shop and a printing works. There he meant to concentrate on the writing and publication of his own work. However, in 1475 Pope Sixtus IV summoned him to help reform the calendar and appointed him titular bishop of Ratisbon. Regiomontanus died in Rome on the 6th July 1476, having bequeathed his books and manuscripts to Bernhard Walther, his former benefactor. Many of them were later acquired and saved for posterity by the German humanist Willibald Pirckheimer.

Regiomontanus' scientific work, though vast, was far less original than was formerly thought. He was greatly influenced by the writings of his predecessors, particularly by a number of Arabic and Jewish authors whom modern scholars only rediscovered in the 19th century, including Levi Ben Gershon, al-Battānī and Naṣir al-Dīn al-Ṭūsī. Even so, he was the first mathematician to treat trigonometry as an independent discipline.

His publications, for which he had acquired and copied numerous manuscripts, included the works of Ptolemy, most of the mathematical and mechanical texts of antiquity, a number of medieval treatises, the works of Peurbach (*Theoricae novae planetarum*, *Tractatus super propositiones Ptolemaei de sinibus et chordis*) and his own writings.

Of the last, the 'Five Books on Triangles' (*De triangulis omnimodis libri quinque*, Nuremberg, 1533) was the most important, both inherently and also by its great influence on other mathematicians. Thus, while the treatise of Naṣir al-Dīn al-Ṭūsī, by which Regiomontanus' work was most directly influenced, may be called a conclusion, the *De triangulis* may be called a new beginning.

Books I and II dealt with plane trigonometry, while Books III and IV and most of Book V covered spherical trigonometry. After some general propositions, trigonometry as such was introduced by Proposition X, which states that the sides of similar triangles are proportional to the angles they subtend. Regiomontanus applied this fundamental theorem (known previously to Levi Ben Gershon) to the numerical solution of many problems.

Book III and the beginning of Book IV repeated the subject-matter of Menelaos' and Theodosios' *Spherics*. Two of its propositions state that the sum of the sides of a spherical triangle is smaller than a great circle and that the sum of its angles is greater than two right angles.

Regiomontanus went on to prove the theorem of sines, first for the case of a right spherical triangle, and then for spherical triangles in general. By means of examples and very difficult calculations, he showed how the sides of a spherical triangle can be obtained from the angles, and *vice versa*.

Book V solved a number of old problems by methods which seem to have been influenced by al-Battānī, and especially by means of the *sinus versus*, defined as the difference between the *sinus totus* and the *sinus complementi* (our cosine, first introduced by Rheticus and called *co-sinus* by E. Gunter in 1620).

1 Self-portrait by Leonardo da Vinci

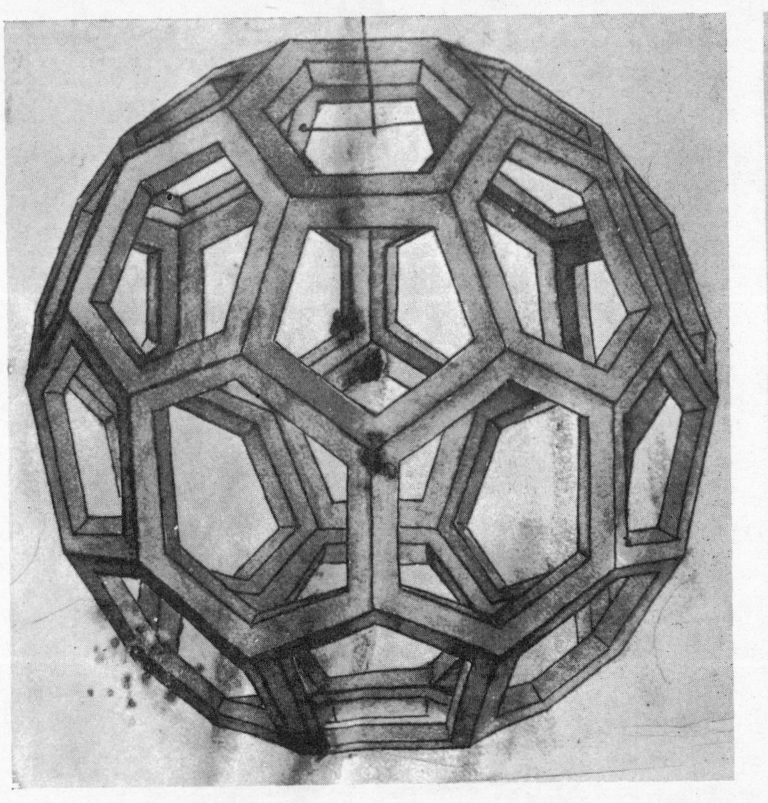

2 Hollow polyhedra, by Leonardo da Vinci

It seems likely that Regiomontanus intended to revise the entire book after al-Battānī's writings, particularly on the tangent,[1] were rediscovered *c.* 1464, for in 1467 he published a table of tangents—the 'Fertile Table' of his astronomical *Tabula directionum*. However, he had time to revise and prepare for printing only Book I. Regiomontanus also wrote an *Introduction to Euclid's Elements* and engaged in a vast scientific correspondence.

Early Textbooks

The last two decades of the 15th century witnessed an upsurge of literary and, above all, of typographical activity. Unfortunately, the mathematical works which came off the French, Italian and German presses were rather unoriginal and fell far below the level of the great 13th- and 14th-century mathematicians—Jordanus Nemorarius, Leonardo of Pisa and Nicole Oresme. Even so, they give us a fair idea of the state of mathematics and illustrate, in particular, how much the alliance between practical mathematics and algebra has helped to raise algebra to the rank of an independent science. They also reflect a keen desire to introduce an abridged notation into algebra.

The *Treviso Arithmetic* (1478) was the earliest of a series of practical textbooks. Its anonymous author, who claims that his small book was written at the request of young people preparing to enter a commercial career, lists the rules for performing common calculations.

While he dwells very briefly on addition and subtraction, he offers a number of different methods for performing multiplications and divisions, operations which must have presented great difficulties to medieval and later mathematicans. One multiplication method was called 'by the column' (*per colonna*) and was prescribed for all cases where the multiplier consists of one digit only. Another was 'cross multiplication' (*per croxetto*) and a third, which could be used in five different ways, one similar to our own, was the 'chessboard' method (*per scachiero*). Division was performed 'by the column', or, when the divisor consisted of more than one digit, by the 'galley method' (*per galeo* or *per batello*) in which the partial answers were first written above the dividend and then erased and amended at each successive stage—a procedure doubtless derived from the ancient method of making calculations in the sand or on wax tables.

[1] Although it was widely used by Arab astronomers, the advantages of the tangent (with which they were familiar) do not seem to have occurred to early Western scientists. In the 13th century Robert the Englishman referred to it as the *umbra*; in the 14th century Levi Ben Gershon discussed it in his *De sinibus, chordis, et arcubus, item instrumento revelatore secretorum*, the first Western textbook of trigonometry. However, Regiomontanus was the first to appreciate its usefulness. As for the term *tangent*, it first appeared in Thomas Fincke's *Geometria rotundi* (1583).

The check of nines was an integral part of all these operations. Other important methods discussed were the rule of three (*regola de tre cose*), the rule of mixtures (proportion of precious metals in alloys), and the computation of the Golden Number, on which the ecclesiastical calendar was based. Among the subjects treated, some of which go back to antiquity, were problems of pursuit, including the famous hound-and-hare problem (first discussed by Alcuin) and also that of one person overtaking another. The *Treviso Arithmetic* was the first of a series of similar Italian works, the most famous of which was the *Arithmetic* of Pietro Borgi (or Borghi), published in 1484 at Venice.

The German counterpart of the *Treviso Arithmetic* was the *German Arithmetic* (1483) and the *Bamberger Rechenbuch* (1483), in both of which the Italian influence is unmistakable. The latter, which is the more comprehensive and systematic of the two, deals with the enumeration, addition, subtraction, multiplication (by five different methods) and division (by a number of methods) of integral numbers (with the check of sevens) and of fractions, the summing of arithmetical and geometrical progressions, the rule of three and the 'golden rule' (*die gulden Regel*).

One chapter is devoted to *Toletrechnung* ('Calculations with the Counting Frame'), whose very name emphasizes the Italian inspiration (*Tolet=tavoletta*). It deals with rates of exchange, alloys and partnerships. Tables give the immediate solutions of a number of general problems.

Johann Widmann's *Behend und hübsch Rechnung auf allen Kauffmannschafften* (1489), which is more comprehensive than the *Rechenbuch* on which it is freely modelled, is of a fairly high level. It heralds that alliance between arithmetic and algebra of which Luca Pacioli's *Summa* is the best witness. The most interesting thing about Widmann's book is his use of the signs + and − to refer, not to addition and subtraction or to positive and negative numbers, but to deficiencies and surpluses and to premiums and discounts—three ells lacking (−) two inches; three pennies over (+) the shilling. Following in the tradition of their Eastern and medieval precursors, 15th-century mathematicians usually combined given problems and special rules for solving them into special classes, *e.g. la regula pulchra, inventionis fusti, sententiarum, etc.*

The word 'algebra' (*Regel Algebre oder Cosse*)[1] crops up during Widmann's discussion of problems involving simple and compound interest, or the rule of (double) false position.

[1] The word *Coss*, by which German writers referred to algebra in general, was simply the *cosa* (thing) by which the Italians described unknown quantities.

Though Widmann did not use Latin algebraic terms (*res*, *census*) or, for that matter, any algebraic formulae, he put forward a number of notions which belong to the common stock of algebraic ideas.

The real level of mathematical knowledge at the time may be gleaned from two manuscripts, the Munich manuscript (1461) and the Dresden manuscript. The first, containing various texts by Oresme, Bradwardine and Nicholas of Cusa, is a *Geometria practica cum figuris*, a small treatise on fractions and a German-Latin arithmetic which, following Boethius, starts with a discussion of odd and even numbers, and prime and perfect numbers, and ends with progressions, the *regula falsi*, the *regula aurea vel de tre*, and with a list of special rules and examples. Finally, a partial translation of al-Khwārizmī's *Arithmetic* divides equations into the following six types (in modern notation):

1. $ax=b$ 2. $ax^2=b$ 3. $ax^2=bx$
4. $ax^2+bx=c$ 5. $ax^2+c=bx$ 6. $ax^2=bx+c$.

The Dresden manuscript, which is the more comprehensive of the two, contains, *inter alia*, Jordanus Nemorarius' *De numeris datis*, two algebras (one in Latin and one in German), which give special symbols for the first four powers of x, and a new classification of equations involving an additional eighteen cubic and biquadratic types. These vast classifications are typical of medieval and Renaissance algebraists and arose from the misunderstanding of the nature of negative numbers and the need to express all equations exclusively in positive terms.

Chuquet's 'Triparty'

The *Triparty en la science des nombres*, drafted in 1484 by the Parisian physician Nicolas Chuquet, is much superior to Widmann's textbook and to the Munich and Dresden algebras. It represents a half-way stage between the latter and Luca Pacioli's *Summa*, and since none had any direct influence on any of the others their similarities stamp them as belonging to one and the same tradition.

Chuquet's work contains three sections devoted, respectively, to rational numbers, irrational numbers, and the theory of equations. Following in the tradition, Chuquet begins with a discussion of *numeration*, *i.e.* of number and notation. The role of the zero symbol is clearly explained. In order to facilitate the process of numeration, Chuquet divides numbers into groups (by points) and gives each group a special name by which its rank can be easily recognized.

Instead of speaking of a thousand thousands, we shall say Million, instead of speaking of millions of millions we shall say Byllion, Tryllion,

Quadrylion . . . Septylion, Octylion, Nonylion, and so on as far as we wish to proceed.

Chuquet's technical terminology was so well devised that much of it has been retained by modern mathematicians. His multiplication table, or 'algorismic guide', was set out in a triangle. He rejected the method of casting out nines as unreliable, and preferred casting out sevens, 'for seven has less familiarity with number than nine'. Chuquet noted that multiplications by two, three, *etc.*, are particular instances of a general operation and not particular operations. He clearly defined arithmetical and geometrical progression and—this is one of Chuquet's greatest claims to fame—related them to each other.

If an arithmetical progression be the series of natural numbers, and a geometrical progression begin with any number whatsoever but have its *denominator* equal to that (natural) number (*i.e.* if the natural series is 0, 1, 2, 3, 4, 5 and the geometric series 1, 2, 4, 8, 16, 32, or 2^0, 2^1, 2^2, 2^3, 2^4, 2^5), any product of two numbers of the second series is part of that series, and its ordinal number (given by the natural series) will be the sum of the ordinal numbers of its factors.

Here we have the first glimmerings of logarithms. In his treatment of the rule of three and the rules of false and double false positions, Chuquet made systematic use of positive and negative numbers (*ung moins*) and gave rules for operating with them.

Whosoever multiplies plus by minus, or *vice versa,* will always arrive at a minus. Whosoever divides plus by plus, or minus by minus, will always arrive at plus. And whosoever divides plus by minus or minus by plus will arrive at minus.

Chuquet introduced the symbols $\tilde{p}$ and $\tilde{m}$ to distinguish not only between positive and negative numbers but also between addition and subtraction. Further symbols appear in the later part of the work. Thus the square root is expressed by ℞ (previously used by Leonardo of Pisa and Regiomontanus), to which Chuquet added exponents, *e.g.* ℞^{2} (square root), ℞^{3} (cube root), *etc.*

Chuquet extended his exponential notation from roots to the powers of unknown numbers, or to those 'first numbers' which the ancients called 'things' (*res* and *cosa*). He invariably omitted them in his formulae, writing 12^1 for $12x$, 12^2 for $12x^2$, *etc.* Now, despite this deficiency, Chuquet had no difficulty in multiplying and dividing expressions of the type a^n, a^m. Thus, he put $12^3 \times 10^5 = 120^8$, *i.e.* $12x^3 \times 10x^5 = 120x^8$. Nor was he in any way put out by the appearance of negative or zero exponents.

His method of extracting square and cube roots (by methods very similar to our own) was far superior to any other known in the 15th century. In his theory of equations, which, unlike that of all his contemporaries, was designed to reduce and not to increase the number of special cases, Chuquet established four canonical groups of quadratic equations, or of equations that can be reduced to quadratic equations, namely (in modern notation):

$$ax^{m} = bx^{m+n} \qquad ax^{m} + bx^{m+n} = cx^{m+2n}$$
$$ax^{m} = bx^{m+n} + cx^{m+2n} \qquad ax^{m} + bx^{m+2n} = cx^{m+n}$$

Some of the examples involved negative solutions which Chuquet considered to be perfectly admissible; others led to indeterminate equations. The manuscript also contained a set of collected problems, a section dealing with the algebraic treatment of geometry, and finally a commercial arithmetic.

Unfortunately, the *Triparty* remained in manuscript form and, though it did not pass entirely unnoticed and though its ideas were occasionally repeated, particularly in Etienne de La Roche's *Larismethique* (Paris, 1520 and 1538), the work failed to influence the development of algebra as much as it ought to have done. Hence it was Luca Pacioli, and not Chuquet, whom historians were to call the first of the great modern mathematicians.

Luca Pacioli

Luca Pacioli (Luca di Borgo, or Luca di Borgo S. Sepolcro) was born in Borgo San Sepolcro, Umbria, *c.* 1445. In 1464, he moved to Venice where he acquired the commercial knowledge so ably reflected in his *Summa.* He became a Franciscan monk, completed his studies, and then taught mathematics at Perugia (1475) and later at Florence, Naples, Pisa, Bologna, Venice and, finally, at Rome, where he died in 1517.

The *Summa de aritmetica geometria proportioni et proportionalità*, which followed in the wake of three shorter textbooks, was completed in Perugia in 1487 and published in Venice in 1494. It was a very large work for the time (600 pages or 300 folios). In addition to the subjects mentioned in the title, it contained a full course in commercial arithmetic, and it was this comprehensiveness which explains the enormous success of a work that was otherwise disorganized and difficult to read.

The *Summa* was divided into five parts, each subdivided into special treatises and distinctions. The whole work was published in two volumes, the first of which dealt with theoretical and practical arithmetic and algebra (224 folios) and the second with geometry (76 folios).

Pacioli's vast compilation was almost completely unoriginal, and the author frankly acknowledged the many sources from which he had taken his ideas: Plato, Aristotle, Euclid, Archimedes, Boethius, Thābit, Aḥmad ibn Yūsuf, Leonardo of Pisa, Bradwardine, Blaise of Parma, Albert of Saxony, Jordanus Nemorarius, and John of Sacrobosco. Among his contemporaries he quoted Prodoscimo de Beldomandi (whose *Algorismus de integris*, written in 1428, was published in 1483).

Part I of the *Summa* dealt with the traditional theory of arithmetic and algorisms: it discussed the distinction between square, oblong, triangular, perfect, 'friendly' and other numbers, and the theory of the five regular polyhedra.

Arithmetical operations were said to be of seven distinct types: numeration, addition, subtraction, multiplication, division, progression, extraction of roots. Mediation and duplication were deliberately excluded. There was only one method of addition (symbolized by the sign $\tilde{p}$). To check the result, the addition was reversed or else more learned methods—casting out nines or sevens—were used. Subtraction, symbolized by $\tilde{m}$, was performed according to three different methods: multiplication according to eight, division according to four (including the galley method, identical with that of the *Treviso Arithmetic*), and the *danda* method which, according to Pacioli, was used by professional men and which was very similar to the one we use today. There followed chapters, inspired by Leonardo of Pisa, on progressions and the extraction of square and (rational) cube roots. Pacioli went on to study fractions, using a notation very similar to our own.

He explained the abbreviations used in everyday calculations and others (*caratteri algebrici*) which were used only in the *regola della cosa*.

Among his *caratteri* was the root sign, R̷. R̷ *prima* is identical with the number, R̷ or R̷2 is the square root, R̷3 the cube root. Unlike Chuquet, Pacioli wrote his indices on the line and went no further than the cube root.

Unknown numbers were not described by special symbols; their higher powers were usually given by the following abbreviations: *res* or *cosa*=*co.*; *censo*=*ce.* (square); *cubo*=*cu.*; *censo de censo*=*ce. ce.* (square of square or x^4); *primo relato*=*p°r°* (x^5); *censo de cubo*=*cubo de censo*=*ce. cu.* (x^6); *secundo relato*=*2°r°* (x^7); *censo de censo de censo*=*ce. ce. ce.* (x^8); *etc.*

Since these names were based on the multiplication of the powers and not on their addition, Pacioli was forced to introduce the so-called *relati* for the 5th, 7th, 11th powers, *etc.* With roots, however, he used addition, if somewhat inconsistently: $\sqrt[7]{}$ = R̷ R̷ R̷ *cuba*; $\sqrt[5]{}$ = R̷ *relata*; $\sqrt[6]{}$ = R̷ *cuba de* R̷ *cuba* and $\sqrt[8]{}$ = R̷ R̷ *cuba de* R̷ *cuba*.

The root of an algebraic expression was written ℞*u* (*radix universalis*).

Equality was expressed by the word *eguale*, or by a dash, and sometimes not all. The constant of an equation was called *numerus*. Whenever one expression had more than one unknown the second, or *quantità*, was expressed by the special symbol $\overline{q\beta}^{a}$.

Pacioli began his study of algebra, as such, by giving a series of mnemonic rules for the use of the symbols $\tilde{p}$ and $\tilde{m}$ (plus and minus; *più e meno*). He explained that the *pratica speculativa*, vulgarly called the 'cossike art' (*regola della cosa*) or the 'great art' (*arte maggiore*) is also called *algebra* and *almucabala*. In his theory of equations he distinguished between the three simple types: $ax^2=bx$; $ax^2=c$; $bx=c$, and the three compound types: $ax^2+bx=c$; $bx+c=ax^2$; $ax^2+c=bx$.

Their solutions could be obtained from the mnemonic rules. Equations of a higher order (cubic or biquadratic equations) were classified into eight groups, of which two were called 'impossible'.

Pacioli went on to pose a gaming problem, and was possibly the first mathematician to do so. A game, which is won on gaining six points, has to be abandoned when one of the players has gained five and the other two points. How must the stake be divided between them? Pacioli explained that it must be shared out in proportion to the points gained.

The book ends with a discussion of double-entry book-keeping, and a table of current Italian coins, weights and measures taken from Giorgio Chiarini's *Libro di mercantie e usance di paesi* (Florence, 1481).

Part II of the *Summa* dealt with various problems of metric geometry and discussed over one hundred 'very useful' questions. It also contained a 'Special Treatise on Regular and Common Bodies'. Most of the problems are solved arithmetically and not by geometrical constructions. It would, however, be wrong to call Pacioli's approach 'analytical', for he invariably studied particular problems and never rose above the level of mere calculation.

In 1509, Pacioli published his *Divina proportione, Opera a tutti gl'ingegni perspicaci e curiosi necessaria*, a work in three parts based almost word for word on an (unpublished) book of Piero della Francesca. In Part I, which is, in fact, the only one to deal with the 'divine proportion' of the title (the division of a line in extreme and mean ratio), Pacioli goes into raptures about its properties and justifies its 'divine' nature by quotations from Plato and Christian theologians. He explains the immense part which the divine proportion plays in the structure of the universe in general and of the human body in particular. He adds a series of propositions on this type of proportion (taken from Euclid) and discusses its uses in architecture, printing and in the construction of regular and semi-regular bodies.

He then mentions various collections, each containing sixty models of divinely proportioned bodies, in Florence, Milan and Venice. He himself prepared a similar collection and presented it to the Duke Guidobaldi d'Urbino in April 1489. (His famous portrait by Jacopo de' Barbari depicts two of these models—one a regular, and one a semi-regular polyhedron.) For the figures in his treatise Pacioli enlisted the help of Leonardo da Vinci.[1]

Leonardo and Mathematics

The work of Leonardo da Vinci, like that of his friend Luca Pacioli, spanned the 15th and 16th centuries. A universal genius without equal, the greatest of great amateurs, as J. Coolidge has called him, Leonardo da Vinci left his mark on all branches of science: geometry, mechanics, geology, geography, biology, anatomy, botany and optics. Nothing escaped his inexhaustible curiosity and nothing remained unchanged after his intervention.

Leonardo da Vinci (15th April 1452–2nd May 1519) was not the product of a university or of Italian humanism. Though Pierre Duhem, in his famous *Études sur Léonard de Vinci, ceux qu'il a lus et ceux qui l'ont lu* (Paris, 1909–13), depicted him as a great scholar imbued with the tradition of medieval science and instrumental in handing it on to his 16th- and 17th-century successors, modern historians have rejected this interpretation almost unanimously. For them, as for his contemporaries, Leonardo was an *uomo senze lettere*, an unlettered man, lacking a classical education and with no Latin and no Greek. He was a self-taught scholar, albeit one of genius.

The historians—and Leonardo's contemporaries—are both right and wrong. They are wrong to underplay the lessons which the young Leonardo must have learnt from Andrea del Verrocchio, in whose workshop he served as an apprentice and to whom he owes his scientific background. Great workshops like Verrocchio's, where not only painters but bronze-casters, stonemasons, draughtsmen, architects, builders and civil and military engineers were taught their respective trades, were far more akin to modern technical colleges

[1] We must also mention Pacioli's Latin translation of Euclid's *Elements*, published at Venice in 1508. Campanus' version of the *Elements* (from the Arabic) had been published in 1482; in 1505, Bartolomeo Zamberti found fault with its many errors and its barbarous terminology, and published a new translation from a Greek manuscript. So great, however, was the renown of Campanus—it was commonly believed that the problems alone were by Euclid, that the demonstrations in the Latin version were by Campanus and those in the Greek text by Theon—that Pacioli, dissatisfied with Zamberti's translation, republished Campanus after having corrected the worst errors. The common confusion between the Euclid of the *Elements* and the philosopher Euclid of Megara was not finally removed until 1572, in Commandino's edition.

than to painters' studios. Clearly the practice of all these 'arts'—including painting, which involved familiarity with perspective—called for a great deal of scientific and mathematical preparation.

Historians are right to insist on the predominantly practical nature of Leonardo's training, for it is in this way that his concrete approach and vocabulary are best explained. At heart, Leonardo was a constructor of engines rather than a theorist. Thus, his geometry was generally that of the engineer, and his answers were practical solutions, rough and ready, capable of being implemented with existing instruments, and not elegant abstractions. For him, as for many of his contemporaries, science meant action rather than contemplation.

A good example of his pragmatic approach is his method of inscribing regular polygons in a circle as a means of squaring it. Inscribing polygons with 3, 6, 8 and 24 sides is an easy matter, and Leonardo performed it with a fixed compass. (Such constructions, which had been studied by Pappos and particularly by Abū'l Wafā, became very popular in Italy during the 16th century.) The inscription of heptagons and pentagons, however, is much more difficult, and Leonardo had to make do with approximate solutions. He rectified and squared the circle by rolling it along a straight line. This solution indicates a complete misunderstanding of the theoretical problem involved, but is fully justified in engineering practice.

Undoubtedly it was from Luca Pacioli, whose *Summa* he was one of the first to read and with whom he later contracted a firm friendship, that Leonardo gained most of his mathematical knowledge. But he was also indebted to Albert of Saxony, Jordanus Nemorarius, whom he frequently quotes, and to Nicholas of Cusa. It seems most unlikely that he studied Archimedes at first hand, but there is little doubt that he knew of his writings through Eutocios and Valla, with whose *De expetendis et fugiendis rebus* he was certainly familiar.

It seems odd that Leonardo never studied algebra. Perhaps he found it too difficult or too abstract. By contrast, he was a born geometer and his extraordinary practical gifts in this field more than made up for his theoretical shortcomings. His interesting musings on the fundamental concepts of geometry reflect a strong Aristotelian and Cusanian influence.

Leonardo was not afraid to introduce infinitesimal concepts (limiting values) into his work. To determine the centre of gravity of a semicircle, for instance, he assumed that it could be divided into 'so many pyramids [triangles] that the concavity of their base would become almost imperceptible, almost a straight line'. In general, however, Leonardo's methods were simpler, more straightforward and more elementary. It was no doubt intuition which led him to his most remarkable discovery: the determination of the centre of gravity of a pyramid. It seems that, applying to solids the same arguments that held for plane figures, he was able to find the centre of gravity of the tetrahedron—at the point of intersection of its 'axes' (the straight lines joining any angular point to the centre of gravity of the opposite face). He then discovered that the straight lines joining the centres of the opposite faces of a tetrahedron also intersect in its centre of gravity; finally, he generalized this into the theorem that the centre of gravity of any pyramid is found on its axis, at a distance of one quarter of the axis from the base.

Though Leonardo's studies on the transformation of one solid into another 'without diminution or increase of matter' were inspired by Nicholas of Cusa's *De transmutationibus geometricis* (1450), he solved Cusanus' problems (the transformation of a number of cubes into a single cube, and the transformation of a cube into a right prism, and conversely) by Valla's method of mean proportionals. Leonardo also studied original transformations, *e.g.* the transformation of a cube into a pyramid.

Leonardo was fascinated by the lunes of Hippocrates. Apart from mentioning them frequently in his *Notebooks*, he began a special treatise on them, the *De ludo geometrico*, which, like all his other works, was left uncompleted. His interest in them is best explained by his appreciation of their aesthetic properties and by the ease with which they could be combined in all sorts of ways with other geometrical figures. As he went along, he discovered a number of their very simple properties, previously unknown in the West. Thus he established that the sum of the lunes constructed on the sides of a right-angled triangle is equal to the area of the triangle itself.

Let us finally mention the highly ingenious mechanical solution (by means of a special compass) of a problem in optics, known as Alhazen's problem, which was not to find a geometric solution for another 150 years (Huygens). Leonardo's solution involved a very profound knowledge of the properties of conic sections, and such knowledge was exceptional in his day.

THE 16TH CENTURY: FROM RHETORICAL TO SYNCOPATED ALGEBRA

The importance of Luca Pacioli's *Summa* is due mainly to its method of presentation and its historical role. To Pacioli any problem, no matter how complicated, that could be reduced to a quadratic equation with *real and positive* roots, was a problem capable of solution. Moreover, he indicated the path of his successors in the solution of equations of a higher degree, which marked the apogee and end of the kind of 'syncopated' algebra he himself had practised.

Apart from the solution of equations, Pacioli and other 16th-century mathematicians also tackled the problems of the simplification and unification of basic arithmetical and algebraic operations, and of the development of a consistent terminology and an appropriate notation. Now, curiously enough, the pursuit of these two tasks led to a national 'division of labour'. While Germany, above all, concentrated on developing the notation, Italy forged ahead in the task of consolidating the new-found knowledge.

Humanism and the Teaching of Mathematics

In most respects, the general trend of early 16th-century scientific thought differed little from that of the 15th century. The main task in both periods remained the digestion of medieval and classical texts and their diffusion to an ever-larger public. However, this general trend of printing and reprinting the great works of the past[1] and of producing textbooks in Latin and in the vernacular had gathered momentum, with the result that mathematics assumed increasing importance in the education of all cultured men, and not only in the occupations of experts.

Though mathematics had always been included in the arts curriculum of medieval universities, the level of teaching had never been very high. The universities produced very few great mathematicians during the 13th and 14th centuries. Even in the 15th century, the teaching of mathematics and physics involved no more than a little arithmetic (algorithm), a little geometry and a little astronomy—very little, indeed, when all is said and done.

During the second half of the 15th century, Bologna and Cracow were practically the only universities where the teaching of mathematics, as a stepdaughter of astronomy or astrology, was properly organized. Cracow was the first university to have, in addition to a chair of astronomy (1450), a chair of mathematics (1476) of which

[1] Thus, Euclid was published in Latin in 1505, 1506, 1509, 1510, 1516, 1537, 1546, 1557, 1572, 1574; in Greek (with Proclos' *Commentaries*) in 1533; in Italian in 1565 and 1574; in French in 1564 (the first nine books only); in English in 1570. Even an Arabic edition was published in 1594 and there were numerous other partial editions containing the first six books only. A very poor Latin translation of Apollonios was published in 1537, followed in 1566 by Commandino's excellent version. Some of the most important writings of Archimedes were published in 1503 by L. Gaurico; in 1543, Tartaglia published William of Moerbeke's version as his own; in 1544, Venatorius published Jacopo da Cremona's complete Latin version; in 1572, Commandino published a new translation. Pappos' works were published in 1588. Ptolemy was published in 1515 by George of Trebizond; a revised edition of this translation was published by Erasmus Schreckenfuchs in 1539, followed by an edition of the Greek original in 1538, and by the complete works in 1551. In addition, there were many editions of the works of Theodosios, Menelaos, Eutocios, Hero *et al.*

the occupant, Albert of Brudzewo, not only 'read' Aristotle's *De coelo* and Sacrobosco's *Sphaera*, but also taught pure geometry and algebra.

This situation became radically changed at the turn of the 15th century. At Bologna, Scipione del Ferro was appointed to the newly-created chair of pure mathematics in 1496. In 1500 he was joined by Scipione of Mantua and Dominico Maria of Novara, holders of two newly-established chairs of astronomy. Tübingen had a chair of mathematics in 1494; a Professor-in-Ordinary was appointed in 1510. An 'astronomer' (who also taught astrology) joined the staff of the University of Ingolstadt in 1494; in 1524, the then holder of this office, Petrus Apianus, was appointed Professor-in-Ordinary. Wittenberg had a chair of mathematics from its foundation in 1502; a second chair of mathematics was established in 1532. Vienna, in which Peurbach and Regiomontanus had taught previously, was given a *Collegium poetarum et mathematicorum* by the Emperor Maximilian I in 1501. Though this college was short-lived, it was the forerunner of the University of Vienna. The older universities—Heidelberg, Erfurt, Leipzig—followed suit, though with some delay. Chairs of mathematics were established at the Parisian *Collège Royal* in 1532, and at the University of Coimbra in 1544.

Philipp Melanchthon and Willibald Pirckheimer established a chair of mathematics in Nuremberg in 1526. Its first occupant was Johann Schöner who, in 1533, published Regiomontanus' *De triangulis omnimodis*. Among the group around Pirckheimer and his library—one of the leading centres of German humanism—were two of the most original men of the time: Johann Werner and Albrecht Dürer.

The German School and Notational Reforms

The Work of Johann Werner

Johann Werner (1468–1528), a Nuremberg priest, began his scientific career as a geographer and cartographer, and it was thus that he became interested in mathematics and especially in trigonometry.

In 1522 he published a collection of mathematical works, including the *Commentarius seu paraphrastica enarratio in undecim modos conficiendi ejus problematis, quod cubi duplicatio dicitur*, and the *Libellus super vigintiduobus elementis conicis*. In the *Libellus*—the first original study of conics written in the West—Werner discussed the parabola and the hyperbola but ignored the ellipse, probably because he looked upon his study of conics as a prelude to that of the duplication of the cube. He defined conics in the manner of Apollonius, namely as the surfaces described by a straight line, one end of which rotates about the circumference of a circle while the other passes through a fixed point outside the plane of the circle. However, he treated conic sections not as plane figures but as figures traced out on the cone and related to it. His *Commentary . . . concerning the duplication of the cube* was a very free translation of Eutocios' *Commentary* with many original observations. Werner also wrote a book on spherical trigonometry, *De triangulis per maximorum circulorum segmenta constructis libri quinque*, based on the work of Regiomontanus. This book mentions a great discovery—*prostapheresis*—and explains the prostapheretic method based on the following equalities (in modern notation):

$$\sin\alpha \cdot \sin\beta = \tfrac{1}{2}[\cos(\alpha - \beta) - \cos(\alpha + \beta)]$$
$$\cos\alpha \cdot \cos\beta = \tfrac{1}{2}[\cos(\alpha - \beta) + \cos(\alpha + \beta)]$$

This method, which was developed further by Rheticus, and by Tycho Brahe and his collaborators, served 16th-century mathematicians much as logarithms serve us today.

Werner's treatise, like most original writings of the time, remained unpublished. After his death it passed into the hands first of Georg Hartmann and, in 1542, of Rheticus, who incorporated it into his own work. The manuscripts were rediscovered in the Vatican Library in 1902.

Dürer and Mathematics

Albrecht Dürer (1471–1528), though overshadowed in most respects by Leonardo da Vinci, was at least his equal when it came to mathematics. His *Underweysung der Messung mit dem Zirckel und Richtscheyt* ('Instructions on measuring with compass and ruler', Nuremberg, 1525), holds a very high place in 16th-century geometrical literature.

The 'Instructions' was not a theoretical work, but taught the art of drawing geometrical figures to artisans, painters, and architects. However, Dürer did not intend his work to be a mere collection of precepts and rules. His main object was to base the art—or the practice—of geometry on science, hence all his figures were accompanied by proofs, and hence his book may be called the first work on applied mathematics written for the benefit of practical men. Small wonder that his original German version was translated into Latin soon after its first appearance.

The first of the four books of the 'Instructions' dealt with curves. Dürer, who was fascinated by the aesthetic aspects of spirals, showed how they could be constructed with compasses. He also studied other, more complicated curves, including the epicycloid and the conchoid, which he called *Muschellinie* (mussel-line) and which he produced by sliding a given line across a set-square, one of whose arms cuts the line at a fixed point. Dürer constructed conics by plotting points, for

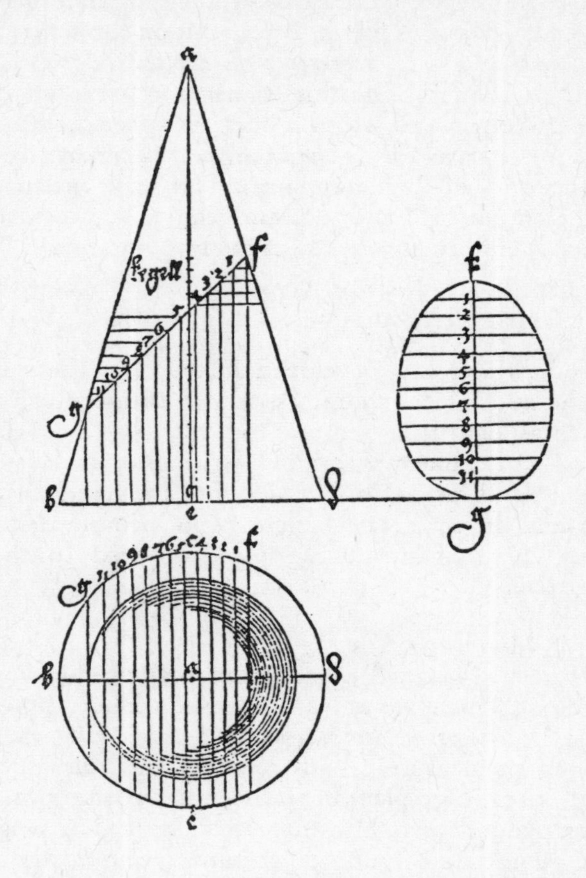

fig. 1 *Dürer's treatment of an elliptic section of a cone of revolution.*

which purpose he employed the method of double orthogonal projection. Hence he may be considered a precursor of Monge.

Book II studied the construction of regular polygons including the heptagon, the nonagon and the 15-sided polygon. In Book IV, Dürer dealt with regular and semi-regular solids, treating them as surfaces which can be unfolded on a plane. The 'Instructions' ends with the description of two technical inventions by which Alberti's methods of perspective were greatly improved. Dürer also published a book on defence works and one on the proportions of the human body.

The 'Margarita Philosophica'

Let us now examine some 16th-century books written for the 'man in the street' who, it appears, must have been exceptionally undemanding. True, Giorgio Valla (the translator of a number of Greek scientific texts into Latin) wrote a popular *De expetendis et fugiendis rebus* (published posthumously in Venice, 1501), containing three books on arithmetic (based on Maximos Planudes) and six on geometry (which he took—for the first time in the West—as far as conic sections), and also translations of Eutocios' *Commentary on Archimedes* and of Simplicios' *Commentary* on the lunes of Hippocrates, but his work was exceptional rather than typical of the times. Far more characterististic was the *Margarita Philosophica* written by a Carthusian monk, Gregorius Reisch, first published in Freiberg in 1503 and frequently reprinted in the course of the 16th century (Freiberg, 1504; Basle, 1508; Strasbourg, 1508, 1512, 1515, *etc.*). In the thirty or so pages each devoted to theoretical and practical arithmetic and geometry, Reisch does little more than summarize the work of Boethius.

Reisch was, in fact, much less interested in the theoretical aspects than in the practical applications of mathematics. Thus he looked upon arithmetic—which he discussed as far as the rule of three—as the art of practical calculation, based both on the method of 'reckoning on the lines' (abacus) and 'reckoning with the pen'—the latter in its common as well as the sexagesimal form, which was indispensable for ecclesiastical and astronomical computations and was for this reason taught throughout the 16th century. Similarly, he treated geometry as the art of mensuration and gauging which, as such, could well afford to dispense with theoretical perfection. His practical approach is clearly illustrated by the allegorical drawings forming the title-pages of the various sections. Among the objects surrounding 'Geometry', for instance, and symbolizing her usefulness, were a barrel and a gauge. In Germany, the art of gauging barrels was, in fact, considered to be as important in geometry as the art of 'reckoning on the line' was in practical arithmetic.

Arithmetical Textbooks and the Development of Notation. Christoph Rudolff

The hundreds of mathematical works that poured from 16th-century presses consisted mainly of practical textbooks which, though producing nothing new, played an important role in the consolidation and digestion of past writings and in the development of an algebraic notation.

Among the foremost 16th-century mathematical textbooks in the German language were the manuals of Adam Riese, a teacher of arithmetic (*Rechenmeister*) at Erfurt and at Annaberg (1525). His books were so popular that his name became synonymous with 'reckoner'. Fully conscious of the difficulties involved in learning the very 'complicated and subtle art' of handling counters and numbers, Riese wrote with exceptional clarity. His works included a textbook on 'reckoning on the lines' (*Rechnung auf der Linihen* . . . 1518), which he later incorporated into his *Rechnung auf der Linihen und Federn* . . . ('Reckoning on the line and with the pen', Erfurt, 1522). In 1550, he published a complete textbook of arithmetic: *Rechnung nach der Lange auf den Linihen und Federn* . . . in which he came down squarely in favour of the pen method. This book, the best of its kind in the 16th century, was extremely popular, 38 editions appearing in the course of the century.

The first German textbook of algebra was that of Christoph Rudolff, *Behend und hübsch Rechnung durch die kunstreichen Regeln Algebre so gemeinicklich die Coss genennt werden* ('Handy and elegant reckoning by the ingenious rules of algebra, commonly called the rule of coss', Strasbourg, 1525; republished by Stifel in 1553). Rudolff based his *Algebra* on Riese's unpublished work of that name, and also on an early 16th-century manuscript whose use of the + and − signs shows that these symbols had passed into common practice. Anxious to simplify the traditional tools of algebra, Rudolff objected to the needless profusion of its rules. He was also conscious of the imperative need to introduce consistent symbols for algebraic quantities and operations. Nevertheless his own notation was not entirely new—he continued to use the 'cossic characters' made up from the first letters of the names of the powers (though he replaced such names as *zensicubus* or *cubocubus* with symbols standing for *sursolidus* and *bisursolidus*): 1, 1 ℞. 1 ʒ. 1 ce. 1 ʒʒ. 1 ß. 1 ʒce. 1 bß. 1 ʒʒʒ.

When it came to roots, he was much more revolutionary. Abandoning the symbol R7, he introduced new symbols, on which our own notation is based: square root: √ ; cube root: ⱱⱱ√ ; fourth root: ⱱ√ . Stifel considered this rather unsatisfactory and tried to improve upon it.

The *Eyn Neue und wolgegründte Underweisung aller Kauffmans Rechnung* (Ingolstadt, 1527) by Petrus Apianus (Bienewitz or Benewitz) was a very remarkable work if only because its author, like Chuquet and probably under his influence, began his arithmetical progressions with zero and associated them with various geometrical progressions. He stressed the fact that to multiply any number of terms of the geometrical series it suffices to add their exponents, *i.e.* the terms of the corresponding arithmetical series, which he called 'signatures'. Another remarkable feat—and this makes Apianus' book a landmark

3 Arithmetic according to the *Margarita Philosophica*

4 Copernicus. School of Holbein

in the history of European mathematics—was the inclusion of the arithmetical triangle (the so-called 'Pascal's triangle') which, though known to the Chinese and to the Arabs, had not previously been described in the West. The importance which Apianus attached to this triangle may be gauged from the fact that he depicted it on the cover of his book.

Apianus' scientific work covered a large field. He published Jordanus Nemorarius' *De ponderibus*, Peurbach's *Theoricae* (1534) and Witelo's *Optics* (1535). His *Cosmographia* (Landshut, 1524), republished by Gemma Frisius in 1533, was frequently reprinted and translated into various languages in the course of the 16th century. In addition, he published a treatise on astrological astronomy (*Astronomicum Caesareum*, Ingolstadt, 1540), a splendid work in which the mechanism of planetary motion was illustrated by remarkable mobile figures. In 1533, he printed the first sine tables (for angles from 0 to 90°, by minute intervals with *sinus totus* = 100,000). They were based on Regiomontanus, whose complete tables Schöner was to publish in 1541. Apianus' *Instrumentbuch* (Ingolstadt, 1533; Latin translation, 1534) contained a description of an instrument for finding the *sinus* and *sinus versus* of first quadrant angles mechanically.

Gemma Frisius (1508–1555), Professor of Medicine at Louvain, is best known for suggesting the present method of determining longitude by differences in local time, and for having taken one of the first steps towards modern methods of triangulation (*Libellus de locorum describendorum ratione*, Antwerp, 1533). However, in his own day he was famed above all for his *Arithmeticae practicae methodus facilis* (Antwerp, 1540), the most popular of all the 16th-century university arithmetics. (Some sixty editions were published before 1600, and many more in the 17th century.) The work was exceptionally lucid and simple, particularly in its method of extracting square roots.

The Work of Stifel

Michael Stifel (1487?–1567) was the author of an *Arithmetica integra* with a preface by Philipp Melanchthon (Nuremberg, 1544), of a *Deutsche Arithmetica* (1545), and of a commentary on Rudolff's *Die Coss* (1553–1554). Like Johann Werner, he must be considered one of the most gifted German mathematicians of his day—one in whom the trend towards the simplification and systematization of theory and notation, so characteristic of the German 'cossists' of the time, found its most marked expression. Being neither a professional mathematician nor the product of a university, Stifel, a fanatical Lutheran and for many years an itinerant preacher, was attracted to mathematics by his interest in number-mysticism. His first work (1532), a numerical interpretation of Daniel's prophecies, predicted the exact hour and day (in 1532) of the end of the world. When this prediction failed to materialize, and when Luther reproached him with it, Stifel abandoned his prophetic activities and turned to pure mathematics and particularly to the works of Rudolff, Nicholas of Cusa, Riese, Dürer and Cardan. He was also familiar with some of Chuquet's ideas.

The most striking aspect of Stifel's *Arithmetica integra* was its treatment of arithmetical and geometrical progressions. He not only devoted an entire chapter to this subject, but stressed time and again that the correlation of the two kinds of progression holds the key to arithmetic and algebra. Though this idea, inspired by Chuquet, had crept into many arithmetical texts, no other author had taken it to its logical conclusion, extending the series to include negative numbers as well. Stifel did so without hesitation, allowing even the negative 'exponents' of an arithmetical series—it was he who coined the term exponent (*exponens*)—to correspond with positive 'exponents' of a geometrical series:

$$\begin{matrix} \ldots -3 & -2 & -1 & 0 & 1 & 2 & 3 & 4 & 5\ldots \\ \ldots \frac{1}{8} & \frac{1}{4} & \frac{1}{2} & 1 & 2 & 4 & 8 & 16 & 32\ldots \end{matrix}$$

Moreover, Stifel explained that the two series could be extended *ad infinitum*.

The *Arithmetica integra* also dealt with rational and irrational numbers and with algebra as such. For the extraction of roots, Stifel employed his 'arithmetical triangle', which he calculated as far as the seventeenth line though, as he pointed out, there was no reason to stop there. Quoting Euclid, he averred that irrational numbers could not be *true* numbers. True, they were real enough but they were as indeterminate as infinite numbers. Applying these ideas to geometry, Stifel, following Nicholas of Cusa, distinguished between the fundamental properties of mathematical and real circles.

In Book III, under the influence of Rudolff and possibly of Cardan as well, Stifel tried to combine the vast number of cossic rules into a single one:

> To solve any problem, express it as an equation, in which the term containing the highest power of the unknown quantity is written on the left side and all the other terms on the right; divide the equation through by the coefficient of the highest power, and finally extract the root of the equation.

The simplicity of this rule is, however, more apparent than real, and Stifel was frequently forced to use traditional methods when it came to practical examples. In fact, Stifel rejected equations in which positive terms are equal to negative terms and ignored all negative roots.

This approach seems odd in one who otherwise felt quite at home with negative numbers. The explanation is that he looked upon them not as *true* numbers but as *absurd* numbers that are merely feigned (*fingunt*) to be smaller than nothing (*nihil*).

The book ends with a series of difficult problems, many of which were taken from Cardan's *Practica arithmeticae* and some of which lead to cubic and biquadratic equations. Stifel used the symbols + and − throughout the book and followed Rudolff's notation with respect to indices. He used the symbol $\sqrt{\ }$ for ℞, but in conjunction with special cossic signs, *viz.*:

$$\sqrt{\mathfrak{z}},\ \sqrt{\mathfrak{c}},\ \sqrt{\mathfrak{zz}} = \sqrt{\ },\ \sqrt[3]{\ },\ \sqrt[4]{\ },$$

probably to emphasize the connection between powers and roots.

In his Commentaries on Rudolff's *Die Coss*, Stifel simplified the notation further by dropping the cossic sign for the square root, which thus became our own $\sqrt{\ }$. This notation was quickly and widely adopted in Germany, France, England, and even in Italy.

Where more than one unknown quantity appeared in an equation Stifel called them *radices primae, secundae, tertiae, etc.*, and expressed them by the letters A, B, C, repeated twice for the square, three times for the cube, *etc.*, or else followed by a number.

With Stifel we have come to the threshold of our own notation and it seems odd that he himself failed to cross it. This omission is due to the fact that, before the 'syncopated' notation could give way to a symbolic notation, a major obstacle had to be cleared: the *abstraction of algebraic operations* from their *objects*. Hence, it is not surprising that it took the genius of Vieta and Descartes to take the final step.

The Italian School and the Development of Algebra

Textbooks

While early 16th-century German mathematicians tried to simplify the rules of algebra and to develop a more consistent and systematic notation, Italian mathematicians seemed to be marking time. Pietro Borghi's *De arte mathematiche* (3 editions in the 15th and 12 editions in the 16th century) and Pacioli's *Summa* were frequently reprinted. Among the newer textbooks, those of Girolamo and Gianantonio Tagliente (*Opera che insegna a fare ogni ragione de mercantia*, Venice, 1515; 30 editions in the 16th century), of Francesco Feliciano da Lazecio (*Libro de abaco*, Venice, 1517), and of Francesco Ghaligai (1521) deserve special mention, though none of them contained any real innovations.

Ghaligai tried to re-introduce the use of geometric figures as algebraic symbols, but his method was too clumsy to have any followers, and most Italian mathematicians continued to use Pacioli's notation.

The Italian Algebraists

Nevertheless, Italy eventually produced a number of brilliant mathematicians—Scipione del Ferro, Tartaglia, Cardan, Ferrari and Bombelli—so outstanding that the rest of Europe was left far behind. It was these men who effected the break-through that bore Western mathematics to heights reached by neither the ancients nor the Arabs, and who paved the way for the much-needed transformation of 'syncopated' into symbolic algebra. The decisive contribution was the solution of cubic and biquadratic equations by del Ferro, Tartaglia, Cardan and Ferrari. Though it seems obvious to us that, once quadratic equations had been solved, mathematicians would quite naturally attempt to solve higher-degree equations, it required a great deal of courage (and talent) to engage on so uncharted a course in the 16th century.

The Cubic Controversy

The solution of cubic equations gave rise to one of the first great mathematical battles, the forerunner of the many bitter and sterile priority disputes that were to poison the atmosphere of the Republic of Letters during the 17th and 18th centuries. Despite the many studies that have been devoted to it, the whole affair remains shrouded in mystery. The crucial documents are missing and the witnesses—Tartaglia, Cardan and Ferrari—all pleaded their own cause and must therefore be treated with circumspection.

Of the protagonist in this obscure drama—Scipione del Ferro (1465–1526)—we know no more than that he was a professor at the University of Bologna from 1496 to 1526. Niccolò Tartaglia was born at Brescia *c.* 1500. In 1512 his face was badly slashed during the sack of his native town by the troops of Gaston de Foix. For many years his injury impeded his speech, whence he obtained his name, which means 'stutterer'. He gave private and public lectures at Verona, Mantua and Venice, where he settled in 1534, and died in 1557. The third contestant, Gerolamo Cardano, better known as Cardan, was a true son of the Italian Renaissance—physician, philosopher, astrologer, mathematician, dabbler in magic and prolific writer, and hence the living proof of Seneca's *nullum unquam magnum ingenium sine mixturae dementiae*. He was born at Pavia in 1501, and studied in his native city and later at Padua, where he took his medical degree. Cardan was renowned as a physician throughout Europe. He taught at the universities of Milan, Pavia and Bologna, deserting each as a result of a dramatic incident. In 1570 he fled to Rome, where he was given an annuity by the Pope and where he died in 1576.

Lodovico Ferrari, a dissolute and impious fellow and an inveterate gambler to boot, began as Cardan's attendant and later became his pupil. At the age of 21, he was appointed Professor at the University of Milan and was commissioned to survey the local region. He discovered the solution of biquadratic equations when he was only 23 years old. He left Milan for Bologna, where he obtained his doctorate in 1565, was appointed Professor and died in the same year, having been poisoned, as the story has it, by his own sister.

The First Discoveries

Towards the end of the 15th century, Scipione del Ferro managed to solve an equation of the type $x^3+ax=b$. Instead of publishing his discovery, he sent it, no doubt under the seal of secrecy, to some of his friends, including Pompeo Bolognetti and Anton Maria Fior. In 1535, Fior issued a mathematical challenge to Tartaglia, in which he posed a series of problems involving del Ferro's equation. Tartaglia, who had been studying similar problems after he was introduced to them by Zuanne de Tonini da Coi (Colla) some years earlier, had, by a remarkable effort, managed to find the solution of del Ferro's equation, $x^3=ax+b$. As a result, he was able to solve the thirty problems posed by Fior only a few days after the challenge was issued. Of the problems he himself put to Fior, the latter failed to solve a single one—at least, according to Tartaglia. Curiously enough, instead of publishing his great discovery, Tartaglia, too, kept it to himself. His *Nova Scientia* (1537) dealt exclusively with ballistics.

Cardan

It was at this point that Cardan appeared on the scene. In 1538, he asked Tartaglia for his 'rule', which he promised to acknowledge in a treatise of algebra he was preparing. Tartaglia refused outright.

When Cardan's *Practica arithmeticae generalis* (Milan, 1539) finally appeared, it proved to be a brilliant if somewhat unoriginal work. It contained a comprehensive treatment of progressions and of the laws of exponents; the use of negative numbers and roots was admitted, though all mathematicians since Chuquet had rejected it, but imaginary roots were called 'impossible' and *tunc questio ipsa est falsa*. One chapter was devoted to the problem of interrupted games, which Cardan solved differently from Pacioli, though equally erroneously. Cardan handled his notation, which was based on Pacioli's though much more complex, with remarkable dexterity. The most striking aspect of the work was its treatment of concrete problems by means of special formulae, and its reduction of cubic to quadratic equations by completion and factorization. Cardan's keen interest in cubics was the main reason why he kept pressing Tartaglia for his rule despite the latter's obvious reluctance to supply it. In the end Cardan succeeded, for Tartaglia revealed the information in cryptic verse. This solution, which came to be known as Cardan's formula, involved the following steps: If $x^3+px=q$, let $u-v=q$. Then $x=\sqrt[3]{u}-\sqrt[3]{v}$, for $(\sqrt[3]{u}-\sqrt[3]{v})+p(\sqrt[3]{u}-\sqrt[3]{v})=u-v$. Hence

$$x=\sqrt[3]{u}-\sqrt[3]{v}=\sqrt[3]{\frac{q}{2}+\sqrt{\left(\frac{q}{2}\right)^2-\left(\frac{p}{3}\right)^3}}-\sqrt[3]{\frac{q}{2}-\sqrt{\left(\frac{q}{2}\right)^2-\left(\frac{p}{3}\right)^3}}$$

The same method can also be used when $x^3=px+q$.

The 'Ars Magna'

In 1539, Tartaglia refused to supply further information, this time on the 'irreducible case' of $\left(\frac{p}{3}\right)^3>\left(\frac{q}{2}\right)^2$, in which the expression $\sqrt{\left(\frac{q}{2}\right)^2-\left(\frac{p}{3}\right)^3}$ becomes impossible (imaginary). Cardan discovered that, even in this case, the equation leads to at least one—and sometimes three—'true' solutions. No doubt imagining that he had developed the theory much further than Tartaglia, Cardan published his *Ars Magna sive de regulis algebraicis liber unus* (Nuremberg, 1545), without advising his rival, though acknowledging his debt to him and also to Scipione del Ferro. Cardan remarked that the sum of the roots is equal to the coefficient of x^2, while their product is equal to the constant, thus inaugurating the modern theory of algebraic equations. He was also the first European mathematician to deal with the approximate solution of numerical equations and, despite his refusal to grant negative numbers the status of 'true' numbers, he did not mind working with the roots of negative numbers (our imaginary numbers), provided they could be eliminated from the results. He himself failed to appreciate the importance of the extraordinary fact that real numbers could be engendered by 'impossible' numbers. Bombelli took full advantage of this fact a few years later.

The *Ars Magna* also contained a summary of Ferrari's solutions of biquadratic equations by a method that was to become classical.

When Tartaglia published his *Quesiti et inventioni diverse* (Venice, 1546) one year after the appearance of the *Ars Magna*, he accused Cardan of having done no more than reveal methods entrusted to him under the seal of secrecy. Ferrari replied with a scurrilous pamphlet (*Cartello di fida*, 1547) in which he accused Tartaglia of plagiarizing del Ferro, and issued a mathematical challenge. Tartaglia's reply (*Risposta*) was not long in coming, and six *Cartelli* and *Risposti* were exchanged which, while doing nothing to settle the priority question, gave dazzling proof of the rivals' skill in solving a host of difficult problems.

Tartaglia's and Cardan's Last Publications

The *General trattato di numeri et misure* (Venice, 1556–1560), Tartaglia's uncompleted and posthumous work, is an enormous volume in six parts, modelled on Pacioli's *Summa* but presented with far greater lucidity. The author, who was obviously anxious to outshine Cardan and Stifel, used the arithmetical triangle to solve a problem in combinatorial analysis and also to study higher roots.

Cardan's later mathematical works were singularly unsuccessful and, when Bombelli's *Algebra* appeared in 1572, they became outdated overnight. Even so, his *Ars magna arithmetica* (uncertain date) contained an anticipation of Descartes' rule of signs, and his *Opus novum de proportionibus* (1570) a discussion on the angle of contingence. In his *De subtilitate* (1550) Cardan had upheld Campanus' view that the angle of contingence is an example of an infinitely small magnitude *in actu* and not simply *in potentia.* This false conception went unchallenged until 1559, when Jacques Peletier showed that the angle is zero. Finally, Cardan wrote the (posthumous) *De ludo aleae* in which, drawing upon his own gambling experience, he discussed the games of his day, the probabilities of various throws of dice, *etc.*

Bombelli's 'Algebra'

With Rafael Bombelli, Italian algebra reached its highest peak. The illustrious author of the *Algebra* (*Algebra, parte maggiore dell'aritmetica, divisa in tre libri*) was the first, and for a long time the only, mathematician bold enough to accept the 'existence' of imaginary numbers and hence to throw some light on the enigma of 'irreducible' cubic equations. Bombelli, who was born in Bologna, was a hydrographer by profession. The first draft of his work (prepared about 1550) was rediscovered and published by E. Bortolotti in 1929. It was in the course of his translation of a manuscript of Diaphantos' *Arithmetic* that Bombelli was filled with the tremendous enthusiasm that went into the final version of his *Algebra*, published in Bologna in 1572.

The *Algebra* is divided into three books, the first of which deals with roots and exponents. In the 1550 manuscript, roots were expressed by the traditional symbols ℞, $℞^2$, $℞^3$, *etc.*, but in the printed version, Bombelli unfortunately reverted to the abbreviations *R.q.* for $\sqrt{}$, *R.c.* for $\sqrt[3]{}$. The expression whose root is to be extracted was, in the manuscript, enclosed in straight lines, and in the book between the symbols L and ⅃. For example:

Manuscript:	R̸³ |52.*p*.R̸ |0.*m*.2209||	stood for	$\sqrt[3]{52+\sqrt{0-2209}}$
Book:	*R.c.*L.71.*p.R.q.*1088⅃	stood for	$\sqrt[3]{71+\sqrt{1088}}$

The operations of addition and subtraction were symbolized by the letters *p* and *m*, multiplication by the word *via*, products and sums by the word *fa*.

Quite apart from many minor advances, Bombelli made one contribution to algebra that was to prove of incalculable value. He admitted the square roots of negative quantities when he wrote R̸|0.*m*.1|: *più di meno* (abbreviated to *p.di.m.*), which signified $\sqrt{0-1}$ $(=i)$; and *meno di meno* signified $-\sqrt{0-1}$ $(=-i)$.

Bombelli operated with these new mathematical entities much as we do, except that he wrote the coefficient behind the symbol, *i.e.* *p.di.m.* 2, where we write $2i$. He was undoubtedly led towards this revolutionary innovation by certain passages in Cardan and Tartaglia, but his great originality is proved by the fact that Cardan continued to deny the possibility of calculations with these 'sophistical' numbers. In Book II of Bombelli's *Algebra*, which gives the complete theory of linear, quadratic, cubic and biquadratic equations, Diaphantos' influence is unmistakable. Bombelli called the unknown quantity *tanto* or *quantità*, the square, *potenza* (δύναμις) and the degree of the equation *dignità* (a term first introduced by Tartaglia). Bombelli represented powers in a manner similar to that of Chuquet, but he placed the exponent in a small semicircle above the corresponding coefficient:

$$\overset{\smile}{\underset{}{3}}\quad\overset{\smile}{2}$$
$$1.\ p.\ 4.\ m.\ 3=x^3+4x^2-3.$$

Though he used the rule $x^n \times x^m = x^{n+m}$, Bombelli neglected the cases of $n=0$ and $n<0$, and was therefore behind Stifel, at least in this respect. He was greatly hampered by his lack of symbols for unknowns and constants. Another limitation was his failure to grasp the nature of negative numbers, as a result of which he was forced to distinguish between three traditional types of quadratic equation and six (trinomial) types of cubic equation, *i.e.*:

$$x^3+px=q;\ x^3=px+q;\ x^3+q=px$$
$$x^3+px^2=q;\ x^3=px^2+q;\ x^3+q=px^2.$$

He treated the first three by Tartaglia's method and reduced the last three to the first by putting $z=\frac{1}{x}$. His use of imaginary numbers enabled him to solve the 'irreducible case', and Cardan's method of introducing an auxiliary unknown helped him to reduce the complete cubic equation (with four terms) to a trinomial. Bombelli solved biquadratic equations (of which he distinguished 44 types) by Ferrari's method of first reducing the equations to polynomials of four terms.

Bombelli's virtuosity emerges further from the way in which he handled specific problems. These were concrete in the manuscript version, but had become more abstract in the printed version, to which he added further examples taken from Diophantos. Finally, Book III of his *Algebra* contained an essay on the geometrical solution of algebraic problems.

MAUROLICO

Among other 16th-century Italian mathematicians of note were Maurolico, Benedetti, Commandino and Clavius (who, although of German extraction, spent most of his life in Italy).

Francesco Maurolico (1494–1575) had one of the most brilliant minds of his time. He was a mathematician, engineer, optician, historian and a prolific author. Unfortunately, most of his work was not published until after his death and hence came too late to influence the development of mathematical thought. For instance, his summary of the works of Archimedes did not appear until 1681, the first edition, printed in Messina in 1594, having been lost at sea.

His translation of Apollonios (Books I–IV from extant Greek manuscripts and a reconstruction of Book V) was not published until 1654 (by Borelli), at the very time when Viviani was presenting his own version. The *Photismi de lumine et umbra*, a most original work which anticipated a great deal of Kepler's *Optics*, did not appear until 1611, after the appearance of Kepler's own *Ad vitellionem paralipomena*.

During his own life, Maurolico published a *Cosmographia* (Venice, 1543), a *Gnomonica* (1553), a collection of translations of Greek mathematical texts (including Theodosios' and Menelaos' *Spherics*, Autolycos' *De sphaere mobili*, Theodosios' *De habitationibus* and Euclid's *De phaenomenis*). His own *Opuscula mathematica* and *Arithmeticorum libri duo* appeared in Venice in 1575. In his *Gnomonica*, Maurolico proved that the shadow cast by the tip of the gnomon invariably describes a conic section, whose nature varies with the plane of projection. He also wrote the first complete treatise on conic sections in which, like Werner and unlike Apollonios, he considered conics as plane sections. In the *Opuscula* he discussed the determination of the centres of gravity of various figures (pyramid, spherical sector, paraboloid of revolution), and was the first to suggest that the faces and vertices of regular polyhedra could be related by a formula. In his *Arithmetic*, he made systematic use of letters instead of numbers, and gave one of the first examples of the kind of argument that would later be called *mathematical induction.*

Benedetti

Giambattista Benedetti (1530–1590), philosopher, mathematician and engineer in the service of the Duke of Savoy, was a geometer of precocious genius. His first publication was the *De resolutione omnium Euclidis problematum aliorumque una tantummodo circuli data apertura* (Venice, 1553), followed by a *Treatise on the Gnomon* (1575) and, finally, by the *Diversarum speculationum mathematicarum et physicarum liber* (Turin, 1585), which was devoted chiefly to a critique of Aristotle's dynamics, but covered also geometrical arithmetic, music and perspective. He solved quadratic equations elegantly by the methods of classical geometry and gave a method of inscribing a quadrilateral with four given sides into a circle.

Commandino's Translations

Federigo Commandino (1509–1575), physician and mathematician to the Duke of Urbino, was not a great mathematician, and his studies of the centres of gravity of solids by Archimedes' infinitesimal procedure (Bologna, 1565) were inferior to Maurolico's. On the other hand, he was an outstanding and indefatigable translator of the Greek mathematicians: Archimedes (Venice, 1558; Bologna, 1565); Apollonios, together with the commentaries of Pappos and Eutocios (Bologna, 1556); Ptolemy's *Analemma* (Rome, 1562); Aristarchos of Samos (Pisa, 1572); Euclid into Latin (Pisa, 1572) and into Italian (Pesaro, 1575); Heron's *Pneumatics* (Urbino, 1575); and Pappos' *Mathematical Collections* (Pisa, 1585). While Commandino was thus engaged, Xylander was translating Diophantos (Basle, 1575), so that, by the end of the 16th century, the most important Greek mathematical texts were available to Western scholars.

Clavius and the Teaching of Mathematics

Christophorus Clavius (Christoph Klau, 1537–1612), professor of mathematics at the *Collegium* of the Society of Jesus in Rome, played a leading part in establishing the Gregorian calendar. His *Opera mathematica* (Mainz, 1612) consisted of five folio volumes; his excellent translations and commentaries of Euclid (1574) quickly became the standard text and remained so until the 17th century. His large textbooks of arithmetic, geometry, algebra, harmonics and astronomy were used in all Jesuit Colleges, thus making Clavius the instructor of the mathematicians of Catholic Europe.

The Contribution of the Other Schools

French Mathematical Texts

Outside Germany and Italy, the 16th century produced few mathematical writers. Until the time of Vieta, whose work was not generally appreciated before the 17th century, French mathematicians lagged behind their Italian and German colleagues, whom they generally emulated.

Jacques Lefèvre d'Étaples published Jordanus Nemorarius' *Arithmetic* and Boethius' *Arithmetic* in 1496 and 1503, respectively, and edited Sacrobosco's *Sphaera* (1499 and numerous later editions) and the *Works* of Nicholas of Cusa (1514), which were widely read and appreciated. In 1516, he published an edition of Euclid's *Elements* containing Campanus' and Zamberti's translations.

His pupil, Charles de Bouelles (Bovillus) who was well known as a philosopher and theologian, published a Latin *Introduction to Geometry* (1500), a French textbook of practical geometry (*Livre singulier et utile touchant l'art et la pratique de la géométrie*, Paris, 1511) which was frequently republished both in the original French and in Latin translation, and a *Geometricum opus* in two books (Paris, 1557). In addition, he published detailed studies of regular convex and stellar polygons. As for the cycloid, whose discovery is attributed to him, he confused it, in fact, with an arc of a circle and, following Cusanus, he used it in his attempts to square the circle.

The first commercial arithmetics appeared at the beginning of the century. All were of a rather poor standard, except Étienne de la Roche's *Larismethique* . . . (Lyons, 1520), which was based largely on Chuquet's *Triparty* (though it ignored zero and negative exponents), and on Pacioli's *Summa*. It was an excellent textbook for the time and may well have helped to popularize many of Chuquet's ideas, thus suggesting to mathematicians, and to Bombelli in particular, the advantages of the exponential notation.

Oronce Fine (1494–1555), the first Professor of Mathematics to be appointed to the *Collège Royal* (*c.* 1532), was greatly renowned among his contemporaries. Unfortunately, his work was second-rate. He republished the *Margarita philosophica*, Peurbach's *Theoricae novae planetarum*, a Greco-Latin edition of Euclid, Books I–VI, and an elementary textbook on pure and applied mathematics called the *Protomathesis* (1532). Parts of this work were frequently republished in Latin, French and other languages. Fine concentrated particularly on sexagesimal arithmetic and on the construction of geometrical figures and their mutual transformations. In a posthumous work, he claimed to be presenting a rigorous method of squaring the circle and to have solved various other famous problems of antiquity (duplication of the cube, multisection of angles, *etc.*)—all by means of the divine proportion (*De rebus mathematicis hactenus desideratis*, Paris, 1556). The book had many critics, the most famous of whom were Pedro Nuñez and Joannes Buteo.

The latter, also known as Jean Butéon, Bateon, Borrel and Borell, while pouring scorn on Fine and Stifel's attempts to square the circle, developed a strange method of duplicating the cube by successive approximations. In his *Logistica quae et arithmetica vulgo dicitur* (Lyons, 1559), he attempted to re-introduce a geometrical notation into algebra. Thus, he replaced the term 'radix' with 'latus', expressed the unknown quantity (*res* or *cos*) by the Greek letter ρ, the square sign by a square standing on one of its vertices, and so on. Equality was expressed by a square bracket [. When an equation had more than one unknown, Buteo, following Stifel, wrote the unknown quantities in capital letters.

Jacques Peletier du Mans (Peletarius), whom the reader will remember as the critic of Cardan's views on the angle of contingence, was a strange combination of poet, philosopher and mathematician. He edited Horace, fought for the reform of orthography, published an *Arithmetic* (Poitiers, 1549, and frequently republished), and an *Algebra* (Lyons, 1554) based chiefly on Cardan and Stifel. From Stifel he took the arithmetical triangle, the zero exponent and also the system of expressing unknowns by the first letters of the alphabet. Peletier also presented a method of determining the rational roots of an equation with rational coefficients. Finally, he published the first six books of Euclid with very interesting commentaries of his own (Paris, 1559).

Another edition of Euclid was published by François de Foix-Candale (1566). It contained the traditional books I–XV, together with three of the author's own books dealing with different types of polyhedron. Pierre Forcadel (d. 1576), whom Ramus helped to make Professor of Mathematics at the *Collège Royal*, published a French translation of the first nine books of Euclid (1564) and also some of the mathematical and astronomical works of Archimedes, Proclos, Autolycos, Oronce Fine, Gemma Frisius, *et al.* He was also the author of an excellent *Arithmeticque* [*sic*] in three books (1557–1558). In the first edition, he used the usual abbreviations, Chuquet's root symbols, and the + and − signs, but in the last edition he returned to more traditional methods.

The third book of Jean Trenchant's *Arithmetique . . . departie en trois livres . . . avec l'art de calculer aux getons* ('Arithmetic divided into three books, with the art of calculating with counters'; 1557, 4th edition 1573) contained a treatise on algebra explaining the 'cossic' notation, the arithmetical triangle, *etc.* Finally, we must mention Guillaume Gosselin's treatise on algebra (*De arte magna sive de occulta partem numerorum*, Paris, 1577) and his abbreviated French translation of Tartaglia's *General trattato*.

Ramus

Pierre de la Ramée, or Ramus, was not so much a creative mathematician as a defender of mathematics—the elegance of which he contrasted with the sterility of logic and scholastic dialectics—and an historian of mathematics. The first three books of his *Scholarum mathematicarum libri XXXI* (Basle, 1569) were devoted to mathematical history. He was killed during the St. Bartholomew's Day massacre on 26th August 1572, and is remembered above all as a great humanist, philosopher and polemicist. Even so, his *Arithmetic* went into numerous editions and was translated into English. His treatment of negative numbers was based on classical logic: a double negative assertion is equivalent to a positive assertion. Ramus was less successful in geometry. His hostility towards the scholastic tradition—his thesis was 'All that Aristotle has said is false'—and his determination to replace logic with rhetoric led him to the project of reforming the work of Euclid which, he argued, fell far short of the rational teaching of science and ignored the natural development of thought. Arithmetic, he wrote, must be taught before geometry, and axioms may be put forward only as the need for them arises. For the rest, Ramus held that commercial arithmetic as practised by the merchants of St. Denis was far more useful than the hair-splitting demonstrations given in Book X of Euclid's *Elements*. Though his views sprang quite logically from the pedagogical and pragmatic position he defended, they represented a profoundly retrograde step in terms of scientific and philosophic thought.

The Beginnings of the English School

England lagged further behind Germany and Italy even than France. The first English mathematical treatise, Cuthbert Tunstall's *De arte supputandi libri quattuor* (London, 1522), was a commercial arithmetic based on the Italians and chiefly on Pacioli's *Summa*, whose general arrangement and presentation it followed. As it was written in Latin, the *De arte* was not very popular in England, but ran to seven editions on the Continent.

Robert Recorde was far better known, thanks mainly to his *The Ground of Artes* (*c.* 1540 and 11 editions in the 16th century), *The Pathwaie to Knowledge* (1551) and, above all, *The Whetstone of Witte . . . containing the extraction of Rootes: the Cossike practice, with the rule of Equation: and the woorkes of Surde Nombers*. In the *Whetstone* he used the + and − signs and, what was even more important, was the first to print the = sign. For the rest, Recorde simply adopted Stifel's notation.

Mention must also be made of Leonard and Thomas Digges, who wrote a number of works on military arithmetic (including the *Stratioticos*) and on practical geometry. Finally, there was an English translation of Euclid's *Elements* by Sir Henry Billingsley and John Dee (1570). The latter, like Commandino, reconstructed Euclid's ideas on the division of geometrical figures from an Arabic translation.

The Work of Nuñez

The foremost Iberian mathematician of the 16th century was the Cosmographer-Royal Pedro Nuñez (Nonius) (1492–1577), for whom a chair of mathematics was founded at the University of Coimbra. A brilliant and inventive man, Nonius left his mark on more than one branch of scientific endeavour. In his *Livro de algebra en arithmetica y geometria* (Antwerp, 1567), he used the greatest common divisor of algebraic expressions as a means of solving a number of cubic equations. He was also the first to solve the problem of the minimum duration of twilight (*De crepusculis liber unus*, Lisbon, 1542), and was the inventor of the *nonius*, an instrument for the accurate measurement of small angles. The *nonius* was, however, too fragile an instrument to be widely adopted and was therefore replaced in the 17th century by the far simpler and more robust *vernier* (invented in 1631). In his *De arte atque ratione navigandi* (Coimbra, 1456), Nonius challenged the common belief of sailors when he argued that it was the Great Circle Route, and not the rhumb line (*i.e.* the line cutting all meridians at a constant angle) which represented the shortest distance between two points on the surface of the earth. The rhumb line, which he studied at length, was to play an important role in the history of 17th-century mathematics, where it became known as the *loxodrome*, a term coined by Snellius.

Simon Stevin

The end of the 16th century marked a period of relative stagnation in Italian science; the centre of scientific thought had moved northwards. Simon Stevin (1548–1620) may be called the true heir of Bombelli and of Benedetti.

Like them, he was both a theorist and a practical man; he was an accountant and a constructor of mills, sluice-gates and fortifications. In his youth, he was cashier in an Antwerp merchant house. In 1577, after having travelled in Prussia, Poland and Norway, he became a port official in his native Antwerp. In 1581 he went to Leyden, where he enrolled as a student of literature. Later, he became a quartermaster general in the Dutch Army and was appointed inspector of dykes. In 1600, he began teaching mathematics in Dutch at the Leyden School of Engineering. In 1603, with the support of Maurice of Nassau, whom he had taught mathematics and whose firm friend he had become, he was appointed Intendant of the Dutch Army. He died at The Hague in 1620.

Early Writings

Stevin's earliest work (*Tafelen van interest*, Antwerp, 1582), the first interest tables ever to be printed, reflected his ambition to divulge to the community what had previously been kept a secret, and to put mathematics to practical use. According to Stevin, the real inventor of his tables was Jean Trenchant, whose authorship he acknowledged in the preface. In his *Bookkeeping . . . in the Italian manner* (Leyden, 1608), Stevin advocated the double-entry system. In contradistinction to the *Tafelen*, his *Geometrical Problems* (*Problematum geometricarum . . . libri V*, Antwerp, 1583) was the purely theoretical work of an accomplished geometer. The book included a highly advanced study on the inscription of regular and semi-regular solids (like Dürer, Stevin 'unfolded' their surfaces on a plane), and stressed the 'great analogy' and 'manifest correspondence' between continuous and discontinuous quantities. Stevin developed this subject further in his later writings.

In 1585, Stevin published *The Arithmetic of Simon Stevin of Bruges* which contained, in addition to a long treatise on arithmetic and algebra, the famous *Disme* and a shortened translation of Diophantos' *Algebra* [*sic*] based on Xylander's version. (Diophantos clearly exerted a marked influence on both Stevin and Bombelli.) The *Arithmetic* holds an important place in the history of mathematics, for in it Stevin achieved a far higher degree of systematization and simplification than any of his predecessors. He introduced two outstanding innovations: the systematic use of decimal fractions and a new approach to numbers that freed algebra of its subjugation to geometry, while yet tightening the interdependence of the two disciplines.

Decimal Fractions

Stevin introduced decimal fractions in a small practical treatise, published in Dutch under the title *De Thiende* (1585) and far better known by its French title, *La disme enseignant facilement expedier par nombres entiers sans rompus tous comptes se recontrant aux affaires des Hommes*. Stevin did not 'invent' decimal fractions—they had been used long before him by Immanuel ben Jacob Bonfils of Tarascon (in 1350), and subsequently by Regiomontanus (in 1463), by

Rudolff (in 1525), by Elijah Misrachi (in 1532) and, shortly before the appearance of the *Disme*, by Vieta (in 1579). But with the exception of the great Arab mathematician Jemshīd al-Kashī, whose works were not known in the West, he was the only mathematician to use them consistently instead of vulgar fractions and to develop a notation involving no special rules. Unfortunately his notation, based on Bombelli's *Algebra*, was cumbersome in the extreme. In it, the symbols $\textcircled{0}$, $\textcircled{1}$, $\textcircled{2}$, $\textcircled{3}$, *etc.*, represented $(\frac{1}{10})^0$, $(\frac{1}{10})^1$, $(\frac{1}{10})^2$, $(\frac{1}{10})^3$, *etc.*, possibly by analogy with sexagesimal fractions in which $\frac{1}{60}{}^\circ = 1'$ and $\frac{1}{60}{}' = 1''$. In Stevin's notation, 15.378 would therefore be written 15 $\textcircled{0}$ 3 $\textcircled{1}$ 7 $\textcircled{2}$ 8 $\textcircled{3}$.

It seems most odd that Stevin did not appreciate the redundancy of these 'exponents' and that he failed to separate the units from the fractions by a single sign, as we do. This step was taken soon afterwards by G. A. Magini who, in his *De planis triangulis* (1592), wrote 15.378 in the modern style. In 1593, Clavius followed suit in his *Astrolabium*.

Stevin's use of decimal fractions (though not his notation) was quickly and widely adopted. The further suggestion of the *Disme*, *viz.* the introduction of a uniform decimal system of weights, measures and coins, was not implemented for another two centuries, and then only in some countries; there are countries which have not adopted it to this day.

Stevin's View of Unity

Stevin's second great innovation was to treat zero rather than unity as the principle governing all numbers. According to Stevin, zero represents the geometrical point, the basis of all continuous magnitudes. Hence 'any square root is a number', and such numbers as $\sqrt{2}$ or $\sqrt{8}$ are neither 'absurd, irrational, irregular, nor inexplicable'. True, they are incommensurable, 'but incommensurability does not cause absurdity'. This theory of numbers was revolutionary and prepared the way for the great developments of algebra and of analytical geometry.

Stevin's Contribution to Algebra

Stevin's algebraic notation was based on those of Stifel and Bombelli. Exponents (like decimals in arithmetic) were placed in circles and written after the coefficient. Unknowns were not written down. Thus 2 $\textcircled{1}$ represented $2x$, and 3 $\textcircled{4} = 3x^4$. Though Stevin admitted fractional exponents in principle, he preferred to use the conventional root signs, *viz.:* $\surd$, $\surd\surd$, $\surd\textcircled{3}$ for $\sqrt[2]{}$, $\sqrt[4]{}$ and $\sqrt[3]{}$.

Addition, subtraction, multiplication and division were expressed by the signs +, −, M and D. *Nomen* and *multinomen* stood for monomial and polynomial.

Among the special problems studied by Stevin was the greatest common divisor of two polynomials (a problem previously studied by Nuñez). But Stevin's greatest claim to algebraic fame was undoubtedly his simplification of the rules for solving algebraic equations or, to use his own words, 'the rules of three governing quantities'. We may best illustrate his procedure by considering his solution of a quadratic equation:

> Given three terms, of which the first is ②, the second ①⓪, and the third any algebraic number, find the fourth proportional term. [*I.e.*, given $x^2 = ax + n$, find x.]

Now, earlier algebraists had considered all quadratic equations as belonging to one of three fundamental and irreducible types, and were therefore unable to formulate a general solution. Stevin changed all that when he wrote:

> The *binomen* of the second term of the problem may stand for three different expressions, to wit: ①+⓪ [$=ax+n$]; −①+⓪ [$= -ax+n$]; ①−⓪ [$=ax-n$]. These have previously been treated as three different operations . . . but we shall show that there is a single manner whereby, without varying one syllable, the operation becomes the same in all three cases.

Stevin succeeded where his predecessors—Stifel, Cardan and Peletier—had failed, because he clearly accepted the legitimacy of negative numbers. Not only did he admit negative solutions of equations, but—and this for the first time in the history of algebra—he expressly equated the subtraction of a positive number with the addition of a negative number, thus reducing the three types of quadratic equation to a single one. He similarly reduced cubic and quartic equations, though his failure to accept imaginary numbers made his contribution in this sphere far less impressive than his work on quadratic equations.

Stevin's Last Publications

After the publication of the *Arithmetic*, Stevin seems to have turned from pure mathematics first to physics and later to purely practical pursuits. However, in 1594 he published the *Algebraic Appendix*, in which he gave an approximate method of solving equations, and the *Practice of Geometry*, an enlarged Dutch version of his *Problematum geometricarum libri* of 1583.

In his *Dialectike* (1584), Stevin propounded the thesis that the Dutch language is particularly suited to the study of science. Hence he published his three books on mechanics (1586), his treatise on fortifications (1594) and many other technical works in Dutch. All these texts were dedicated to Maurice of Nassau and were collated into a gigantic work, the *Wisconstige gedachtenissen*, covering the theory and practice of dynamics and all the mathematical and physical sciences of his time. The Dutch version (Leyden, 1608) appeared in five volumes, and the work was immediately translated into Latin and published by Willebrord Snell as the *Hypomnemata mathematica*. A partial French translation by Jean Tuning (*Memoires mathematiques* . . .) appeared in 1608 and was republished by A. Girard in 1634 as part of his *Œuvres mathematiques de Stevin*. Although their publication date stamps them as 17th-century works, their contents were written during the previous century and we have therefore treated them as such.

* * *

With Simon Stevin, Renaissance algebra had reached the final term of its evolution. Hence, this may be a good point to survey its achievements and to describe its basic structure.

During the Renaissance, mathematicians accumulated a vast store of new algebraic knowledge in unusually quick time. Among other accomplishments, they developed a very compact and convenient notation—certainly more convenient than, for instance, Vieta's. However, they failed to take the essential step of abstracting *algebraic operations* from their objects, and hence mistook their true nature.

This omission strikes us as exceedingly curious, for nothing seems simpler to us than the notion of algebraic or arithmetical operations. Moreover, medieval and Renaissance textbooks were quite familiar with these and taught all the steps involved in multiplication, division, the extraction of square roots, and the solution of simple equations. However, despite the sporadic use of operational symbols (letters) by Aristotle (in logic), by Leonardo of Pisa and by Jordanus Nemorarius (in proportional theory), the operation and the object (the *res*) to which it was applied were thought to form so indivisible a whole that it seemed impossible to dissociate them. *Res*, *radix*, *census* stood, respectively, for the unknown quantity, the root and the square; but the *radix* and the *census* were never considered as the root or the square of the *res*, although they were extracted from and raised to it; they were and remained *radix* and *census* in their own right. It is for this reason also, and not because only a single unknown was involved in most equations, that the *res*—our *x*—was never expressed in equations.

As a result, Renaissance algebra, instead of producing *formulae*, offered *rules* and *examples*. Like the grammarians who also gave well-chosen *rules* and *examples* for declining nouns and conjugating verbs, mathematicians produced paradigms that somehow never turned into formulae. Renaissance mathematicians and grammarians alike thought in terms of cases, varying from concrete noun to concrete noun, or from concrete problem to concrete problem.

Hence the introduction by Vieta and Descartes of symbols expressing the unknown marks a decisive stage in the history not only of notation but of algebraic thought in general, for it reflects the passage from grammatical to logical abstraction. In other words, abbreviation had turned into symbol, or—as Vieta put it—*logistica numerosa* had become *logistica speciosa*.

CHAPTER 2

The Copernican Revolution

HUMANISTIC ASTRONOMY

The Cosmology of Nicholas of Cusa

An important chapter in the history of cosmology was written when Nicholas of Cusa challenged the classical conception of a closed and hierarchical universe. As against this cosmology, which had held sway for almost two thousand years, he introduced a universe 'of which the centre is everywhere and the circumference nowhere'. Rejecting the view that the celestial spheres revolve about the earth as their centre, he was also forced to reject the distinction in the universe between 'sublunary' and 'celestial' regions. The universe is indivisible and the earth is but one of many celestial bodies, as noble as any other. Like them, it radiates light and has its proper motion.

In his *De docta ignorantia* (1440), Nicholas of Cusa attacked the 'presumptuous science' of the astronomers and philosophers with unprecedented boldness, denying the existence of privileged directions and places in the universe; 'above' and 'below' had ceased to be anything but relative terms. An observer placed on the sun or a planet would invariably see the earth revolving about and above him, and hence believe he was at the centre of its motion. Motion itself is not absolute, but varies from one apparently immobile reference system to the next.

The destruction of the classical cosmos was a prerequisite of the scientific revolution of the 17th century—hence the great historical importance of the *De docta ignorantia*. Small wonder that Cusa's contemporaries and successors—except Leonardo da Vinci—opposed it with all their might. Not until Giordano Bruno did Cusa's great work begin to exert any appreciable influence on astronomy, for it was only then that Cusa's unlimited universe finally became the infinite universe of modern thought. In fact, since Cusa denied the existence of fixed points and of perfectly uniform motions, and hence the periodicity of celestial events, 15th- and 16th-century observational astronomy would have become paralysed had astronomers adopted his views without any qualifications. Cusanus himself seems to have gone back on them when he wrote in his *De venatione sapientiae* (1462):

> God has endowed every body with its own nature, orbit and place, and has set the earth in the middle of all, decreeing that it be heavy and deviate neither upwards nor sideways.

Even so, he left the earth free to rotate on its own axis. In an earlier note in his own handwriting, written on the last sheet of an astronomical treatise issued at Nuremberg in 1444, Cusanus had claimed that the starry sphere revolves from east to west in twelve hours, while the earth revolves in the same direction in twice that time. Hence it travels round the poles of the world, 'as Pythagoras says', once in a day and a night, 'but the eighth sphere revolves twice, and the sun a little less than twice, in a day'.

In other words, to an observer on the earth, this would produce the same effect as if the earth were immobile while the starry sphere revolved once in twenty-four hours. The annual motion of the sun is the result of its lagging slightly behind the other stars.

From these brief remarks it will have become clear that Nicholas of Cusa cannot be considered a direct precursor of Copernicus.

Peurbach and Regiomontanus

In the 15th century, the development of mathematical astronomy was greatly influenced by efforts, initiated by Peurbach and Regiomontanus, to return to the original Greek and Arabic manuscripts, or to revise earlier translations of the great astronomical classics, particularly of Ptolemy, and to prepare *compendia* that might replace Sacrobosco's *Sphaera*, the inadequacy of which had become more and more apparent. These efforts culminated in the publication of Gerard of Cremona's version of the *Almagest* in 1515, of George of Trebizond's new version in 1528 and, finally, in S. Grynaeus' publication of the Greek text together with the commentaries of Pappos and Theon (edited by J. Camerarius in 1538). Peurbach, who, on the advice of Bessarion, had begun the translation of the *Almagest* and the writing of a summary (*Epitome*) of the works of Ptolemy, left much of the work to Regiomontanus, who failed to finish the translation but completed the *Epitome*, which was printed posthumously at Venice in 1496. This work represents the theoretical complement to Peurbach's *Theoricae novae planetarum* (Nuremberg, 1472), an elementary textbook in which the author's simple planetary theories are stated without any proofs. The *Theoricae* was meant to replace Sacrobosco's *Sphaera*,[1] which enjoyed a great deal of popularity until

[1] However, Sacrobosco's *Sphaera* was not supplanted by the *Theoricae*. It was reprinted time and again with more and more learned commentaries.

fig. 2 The elements of the earth according to Aristotle.
(From O. Fine: 'Théorique de la huictième sphère et sept planètes', 1528.)

the end of the 16th century and was very often republished, usually with new commentaries (for instance, by Oronce Fine). It formed the basis of the astronomical section of Reisch's *Margarita philosophica* and was translated into Italian by Toscanelli in 1566.

In his writings, Peurbach proved a strict Ptolemaist except in two respects. Following the Arabs, he (1) added trepidation to the six Ptolemaic motions of the celestial spheres, and (2) substituted solid crystal spheres for the purely mathematical circles of the *Almagest*. This substitution—which Ptolemy had, in fact, made himself in his *Hypotheses of the Planets*—seems to reflect a deliberate refusal to accept mathematical abstractions and to acquiesce in the misalliance between Aristotelian physics and Ptolemaic astronomy.

Peurbach was not only a theorist, for he made astronomical observations with a *quadratum geometricum* of his own design. His trigonometrical investigations, and those of Regiomontanus, provided astronomers with efficient and accurate mathematical methods. It was mainly because of them that early 16th-century astronomers and algebraists were able to assimilate the classical authors.

Leonardo and Astronomy

Though Leonardo da Vinci was not an astronomer, and though he did not make those astronomical discoveries which some over-enthusiastic historians have attributed to him, he was one of the first, if not the first, Western writers to have realized that moonlight is reflected light. Again, though he did not invent the telescope, as has sometimes been claimed, he made a very important discovery (unrecognized in his day) by which he became the precursor of Galileo: he appreciated the subjective nature of the halo of the fixed stars and consequently of their apparent dimensions.

Leonardo's cosmological views, though never fully elaborated, fell between those of Cusanus and Copernicus. Despite the famous phrase in the *Notebooks*, *Il sole non si muove* (the sun does not move), it seems unlikely that Leonardo subscribed to the heliocentric doctrine. On the other hand, it is clear that, following Nicholas of Cusa, he abandoned the geocentric view and, by the double step of likening the moon to the earth and the earth to the moon, he inferred the terrestrial character of the moon and the celestial character of the earth. In effect, he said that the moon consists of the same elements as the earth, namely earth, air and water. He also claimed that because it resembles the moon, the earth must enjoy the dignity (*noblesse*) of a star.

> The earth is not in the centre of the universe [the influence of Cusanus is unmistakable] but is in fact in the centre of the elements which accompany it and are united to it. And if one were to be upon the moon, then to the extent to which it together with the sun is above us, so far below it would our earth appear, with the element of water performing the same office as the moon does for us.

Moreover, it seems most likely that Leonardo thought of the earth as spinning on its axis, and that he defended this view against classical objections. This is borne out by a reference to the motion of 'a heavy body falling through the air while under the action of a circumvolutory motion with a period of twenty-four hours'.

Fracastoro and Amici: the System of Homocentric Spheres

Girolamo Fracastoro (1483–1553) owes his fame to his writings on astronomy, on medicine and, above all, to his poem on syphilis. He was a fellow-student of Copernicus at the University of Padua, and it seems likely that the two young men discussed astronomical questions and agreed both on the inadequacy of the Ptolemaic system and on the necessity of replacing it with a better cosmology. But while Copernicus tried to base his reforms on Aristotelian ideas,

Fracastoro decided to follow Callipos. His first work, the *Homocentricum sive de stellis liber* (Venice, 1538), was dedicated to the same Pope (Paul III) to whom Copernicus was to dedicate his *De revolutionibus orbium coelestium*; it was the fulfilment of a deathbed promise to Giovanni Battista della Torre (the brother of Marco Antonio della Torre, Leonardo's friend and anatomical collaborator). In it, Fracastoro tried to represent the motions of the planets without recourse to either eccentrics or epicycles and by relying solely on circular motions about a single centre (homocentric spheres). The axes of these spheres were placed at right angles to one another, and while this condition was of great mathematical and systematic importance, it led to a great increase in the number of spheres: 76 for the planets and the moon and an additional sphere below, which, unlike the others, was not homogeneous but denser in some places than in others. The heterogeneous sphere was meant to counter the strongest objection to the homocentric system, namely that the changes in brightness of the planets must result from changes in distance. The objectors were told that these effects were, in fact, due to changes in the density of the medium through which the planets are seen from the earth.

At the same time as, but independently of, Fracastoro, the homocentric system was also resurrected by Giovanni Battista Amici, whose *De motibus corporum coelestium iuxta principia peripatetica sine excentricis et epicyclis* was published in Venice in 1536. Though Amici did not stipulate orthogonal planetary axes, he imposed other, still more complicated, conditions. Appearing as they did on the eve of the Copernican revolution, Fracastoro's and Amici's systems were at best historical curiosities.

Calcagnini

The same is also true of the far more remarkable attempt by Celio Calcagnini (1479–1541) to prove *quod coelum stet, terra moveatur* (1525). In an essay, which first appeared as part of his complete works (1544), Calcagnini, who had probably heard of the work of Copernicus and who quoted Nicholas of Cusa, claimed that it is the earth, and not the heavens, which revolves. His arguments in support of this thesis were, however, purely metaphysical: the earth as the seat of imperfections was far more likely to change than the heavens whose perfection and divine nature stamped them immutable and immovable. Moreover, since the earth is both heavy and unable to drop down further from its lowly place in the universe, it must continue to revolve once it has been set in motion, whereas there is no means of moving the weightless heavens. In other words, Calcagnini's reversal of traditional dynamics was based on the correct appreciation that a body without mass cannot receive an impetus. Had the essay been published in 1525, when it was written, it would probably have played an important role in the astronomical revolt against the ideas of Aristotle and Ptolemy, but when it appeared in 1544, a year after the publication of Copernicus' *De revolutionibus orbium coelestium*, it came decidedly too late to have any influence on astronomical developments.

COPERNICUS

The work of Copernicus marks a turning-point in the history of Western thought, for it initiated the 17th-century 'scientific revolution' when it replaced the closed and hierarchical cosmos of Antiquity and of the Middle Ages, with the homogeneous and infinite universe of modern science. Curiously enough, the 'Copernican revolution' appeared like a bolt from the blue, for neither Nicholas of Cusa (whom Copernicus knew) nor Leonardo da Vinci (whom he did not know) was 'precursor' of Copernicus. Though the rotation of the earth about its axis had occurred to Nicole Oresme, no one since Aristarchos of Samos and Seleucos had even dreamt of placing the sun in the centre of the planet's orbit.

The *De revolutionibus orbium coelestium* therefore resurrected classical thought from two thousand years of oblivion. However, it was only because of his familiarity with Ptolemaic mathematics that Copernicus could finish what his ancient predecessors had vaguely begun.

Biography

Nicolaus Copernicus was born on the 19th February 1473 in the city of Thorn on the Vistula (Pomerania). His father, who was also called Nicolaus, had emigrated from Cracow to Thorn before its annexation by the King of Poland, and was a merchant of some social standing. His mother, Barbara Watzelrode, belonged to an old-established patrician family of the region. Having lost his father when he was ten years old, young Copernicus was adopted by his maternal uncle, Lucas Watzelrode, later Bishop of Ermland. Historians have argued at length whether Copernicus was a German or a Pole, and though there seems little doubt that he was Polish, the whole controversy strikes us as singularly fruitless since it is neither by his racial origin nor his education—in which Italy played an incomparably greater role than Poland—that his genius can be explained. Intellectually, Copernicus was undoubtedly a *proles sine matre*.

In 1491, Copernicus enrolled in the University of Cracow, then the most important university in Eastern Europe and justly famous as a centre of scientific and humanist ideas. We do not know what courses Copernicus attended, though there seems little doubt that he studied astronomy in addition to dialectics and philosophy, which formed part of the general arts curriculum of all universities.

One of the most famous of Copernicus' teachers at the University was Albert of Brudzewo (Brudzewski), an astronomer and a distinguished mathematician, and the author of a commentary (1482) on Peurbach's *Theoricae novae planetarum*. Although many historians have suggested that Copernicus turned to astronomy on the advice of Brudzewski, their claim is, at best, unsupported.

In 1496 Copernicus returned to Thorn, whence he left for Italy in the same year as a prospective law student. On 6th January 1497, his name was entered among the students of the *Natio Germanorum* in the University of Bologna, which does not, however, mean that the authorities looked upon Copernicus as a German.

Copernicus spent about three and a half years in Bologna. His astronomical studies must have proceeded apace, for the famous astronomer Domenico Maria da Novara described him 'rather as a friend and assistant than as a pupil' (*non tam discipulus quam adjutor et testis observationum*). Copernicus also studied law, medicine and philosophy, learned Greek and read Plato.

In 1500 he went to Rome, where he gave a series of lectures on mathematics (and probably astronomy). In 1501, he returned home to take up a canonry at the Cathedral of Frauenburg, to which he had been admitted through the patronage of Lucas Watzelrode. Immediately after his official appointment he obtained leave of absence and returned to Italy, this time to Padua, where he studied medicine and law; on 31st May 1503, he obtained the degree of Doctor of Canon Law at Ferrara. After a total stay in Italy of about nine years, Copernicus returned to his native Ermland where he lived until his death.

He went first to Heilsberg, to be near his uncle Lucas Watzelrode, for whom he became personal secretary and physician. When his uncle died in 1512 he settled in Frauenburg, where he administered the property of his chapter (whence his treatise, *De monetae cudendae ratione*) and practised medicine, apparently with great success. He also acquired a *triquetrum* (*instrumentum parallacticum*), an armillary sphere and a quadrant, with which he made many of the astronomical observations described in his *De revolutionibus*.

Towards the 'De Revolutionibus'

Copernicus seems to have arrived at the main idea of his system fairly soon. In the preface to the *De revolutionibus*, he states that he kept his work secret not for nine years (as the Pythagoreans enjoined) but for four times nine years. This assertion must not, however, be applied to the book itself but only to its fundamental, heliocentric idea. Moreover, Copernicus did not, in fact, guard his 'secret' for nearly as long as he claimed. L. Birkenmajer has shown that some years after his return from Italy (about 1512) Copernicus wrote a clear summary of his new astronomy in *De hypothesibus motum coelestium a se constitutis Commentariolus*, which he circulated among his friends. However, he did not print this work (the *Commentariolus* was first published in 1878), for he realized that it was not enough to formulate new ideas, or (as he apparently thought he had done) to revive Pythagorean notions; what was needed was to present a planetary theory as complete and as useful as that of Ptolemy. That theory he finally presented in his *De revolutionibus orbium coelestium libri sex*, of which Book I contains a general exposition of his system and a treatise of trigonometry, Book II an account of spherical astronomy and a star catalogue (compiled from old data and modern observations) and Books III and IV the detailed theory of the (apparent and real) motions of the sun, moon and planets. Not surprisingly, the elaboration of this work took Copernicus until 1532, or even later, and for the rest of his life he continued modifying and correcting it.

Copernicus' Scruples

When the *Commentariolus* reached Rome in 1533, some twenty years after it was written, the Austrian scholar Johann Widmanstadt used it to explain the Copernican system to Pope Clement VII. At the time, neither the Pope nor any other Church dignitary raised any objections to either the theory or to its author. On the contrary, in 1536 a member of the Curia, Nicolas Schönberg, Cardinal Archbishop of Capua, offered to pay for the publication of Copernicus' discoveries. Copernicus did not comply, and continued to refuse even when all his friends, and particularly his 'very dear Tiedemann Giese, Bishop of Kulm', kept insisting that the publication of his work was a duty towards science and humanity. Copernicus was most anxious to avoid any breath of scandal, or giving any offence to the theologians, an attitude which, in his case, was probably carrying prudence too far.

In 1539, a young professor at the University of Wittenberg, Georg Joachim Rheticus (1514–1576), came to Frauenburg in order to study the new cosmology at first hand. Significantly enough, the Ermland authorities raised no objections to the visit of a professor from the heretical University of Wittenberg, nor did those of Wittenberg see any reason for vetoing the journey. Barely two months after his arrival, Rheticus wrote a brief and enthusiastic summary of the

Copernican doctrine in a letter to his teacher, Johann Schöner, which was later printed in Danzig (1540).

This letter—the *Narratio prima*—was so great a success that it had to be reprinted in Basle one year later. Henceforth, scientists could study the basis of the new doctrine for themselves and, once the secret was out, Copernicus saw no reason for prolonging his own silence. He entrusted the manuscript of his *magnum opus* to Tiedemann Giese who sent it to Rheticus, now back in Wittenberg. Rheticus had it published by Johannes Petreius of Nuremberg, and Giese reports that Copernicus was handed the first printed copy of his work on his deathbed, on 24th May 1543.

Osiander's Preface

However, Rheticus did the job very badly. When he was appointed professor at the University of Leipzig in 1542, he left the editing to his friend Andrea Osiander, a famous though somewhat heretical Lutheran theologian. Osiander, who had first-hand experience of religious persecution and who feared a violent reaction on the part of his fellow-theologians and die-hard Aristotelians, decided to take a number of precautions. In fact, he himself was uneasy about Copernicus' ideas; the new cosmology was clearly contrary to the Bible, whose literal inspiration he was too good a Lutheran to doubt.

As early as 1541, therefore, he suggested to Copernicus an elegant escape route. Astronomy, Osiander argued, is solely concerned with 'saving the appearances' (*salvare apparentias*). Its aim is not to discover the hidden causes or the real motions of the heavens—which it is, in any case, unable to do—but to combine and arrange its observations by means of simple mathematical hypotheses for the accurate prediction of the real and apparent positions of the planets. These hypotheses are neither true nor demonstrable, as Osiander explained in an anonymous preface entitled, *To the reader about the hypotheses of this work*, which was for a long time considered as Copernicus' own work. Thus many readers, including Cardinal Bellarmin, attributed Osiander's ideas to one to whom the motion of the earth was a physical fact and not a mere working hypothesis.

The Foundations of the New Theory

In his dedication to Pope Paul III, which forms his own introduction to the *De revolutionibus*, Copernicus explained the reasons why he felt impelled to present a new planetary theory. These included the failure of mathematicians to agree on the old theories, the variety and multiplicity of astronomical systems, and the inability of all these systems to give an accurate account of the apparent motions by means of uniform circles. Clearly, the 'mathematicians' had neglected some essential principles, or else had based their systems on a false idea.

His studies of the philosophers had made Copernicus familiar with the writings of those who, like Hiketas, Heraclides of Pontos, and Ecphantos, had argued that the earth is a moving body. He decided to test this hypothesis despite its apparent absurdities, and found that it provided not only an excellent explanation of celestial phenomena but also a coherent cosmology. He concluded that mathematicians had been wrong to consider the earth as the centre of the universe and of all celestial motions.

His fundamental objections to the Ptolemaic system were, firstly, that in order to save the fundamental principle of uniform circular motion it had to introduce the unnecessary complication of equants and, secondly, that it drew an irrational picture of the universe.

During a discussion of the inherent problems of the motions of Venus and Mercury (Book I), Copernicus mentioned Marcianus Capella's view that these planets might revolve about the sun. He added that this conception might be extended to explain the motions of all the planets. This was so short a step to take in Ptolemaic astronomy, in which the sun played so great a role, that Copernicus might very well have made it the starting-point of his own system.

This view is suggested by the *Narratio prima*, in which Rheticus explained that it was the considerable variations in brightness of Mars, inexplicable by the geocentric theory, which had convinced Copernicus that the planet revolved about the sun. However, if Copernicus had, in fact, argued in that way, he would have developed Tycho Brahe's system rather than his own. To go beyond it, to place the sun at the centre of the universe and the earth among the planets, something else was needed, *viz.* a profound acceptance of Pythagorean theories. In fact, the first book of the *De revolutionibus* calls the sun the 'spirit, ruler and visible god of the universe'. Moreover, the very argument by which the sun was placed at the centre of the universe, because of its perfection—'who in this universal temple would place this splendid light in another or better place than whence it can shine on all at once?'—was a radical transformation of the orthodox geometrical and hierarchical approach. Far from taking the Aristotelian and Christian view that the central place was the lowest and humblest, Copernicus, like the Pythagoreans, thought it the only fit place for the most beautiful and most honourable of all celestial bodies.

Simplification of Planetary Theory

Copernicus also criticized contemporary astronomy for its superfluity of circles. Far better assume a moving earth, he wrote, no

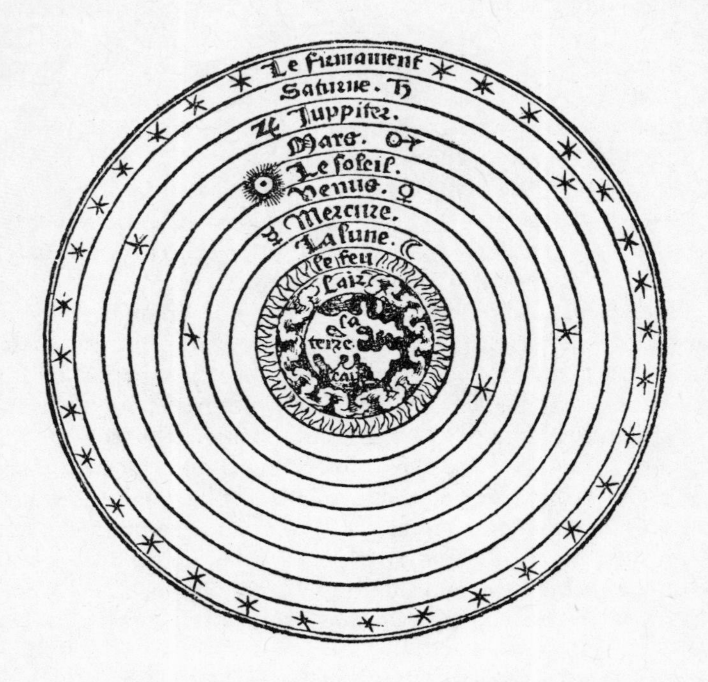

fig. 3 The medieval Universe: Ptolemy's celestial spheres.
(From O. Fine: 'Théorique de la huictième sphère et sept planètes', 1528.)

matter how absurd it might appear, than let one's mind be rent by the almost infinite number of circles and orbs of geocentric astronomy. By contrast, his own scheme was said to be seductively elegant and simple. Actually, the simplification was not as great as Copernicus made out. Instead of Peurbach's forty-two circles Copernicus used thirty-four, so that the total saving was eight circles.

In fact, Copernicus' mathematical technique was identical with Ptolemy's, or, seeing that he discarded the equants, even with that of Hipparchos. Now, since the planets do not move about the sun, nor the moon about the earth, with uniform velocity along perfect circles, Copernicus, like his predecessors, was forced to combine a number of circular motions—epicycles, and mobile deferents—in order to 'save the appearances', *i.e.* to explain the observations. His transfer of the diurnal motion from the celestial sphere to the earth was a tremendous achievement, but it did not diminish the number of motions. Even the transfer of the annual motion from the sun to the earth saved no more than one circle per planet—the deferent of inferior planets and the epicycle of superior planets. On the other

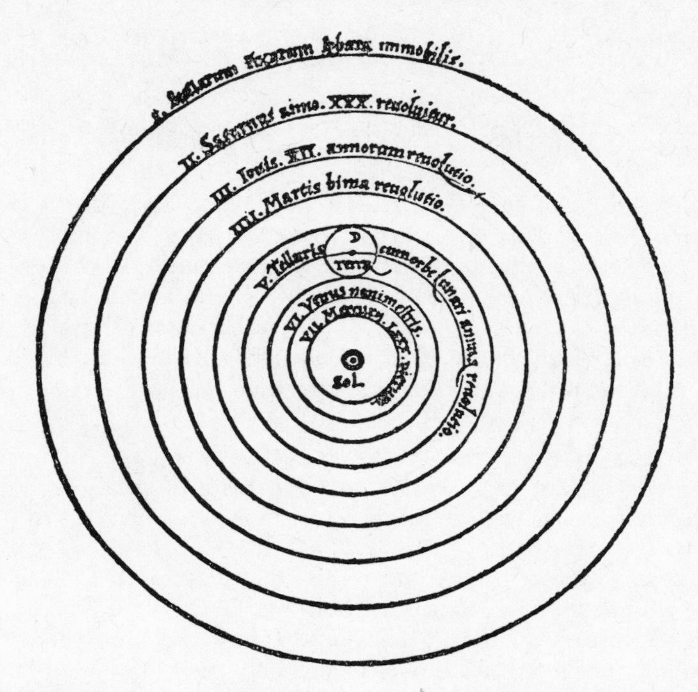

fig. 4 The Universe of Copernicus. ('*De revolutionibus . . .*', *1543.*)

hand, the rejection of the equant, this great feat of Copernican astronomy, introduced further complications and called for the introduction of 'supplementary circles'. When it came to the motion of the earth, Copernicus—who continued to believe that the planets were moved by material wheels (orbs)—was forced to introduce, over and above the diurnal and orbital motions, a third 'conical' motion responsible for keeping the earth's axis pointing towards the Pole Star. By making this third motion somewhat slower than the orbital motion, he was able to offer an ingenious explanation of the precession of the equinoxes. Paradoxically, it was in lunar theory, which was quite unaffected by his heliocentric innovations, that Copernicus' rejection of equants led to the greatest simplification and the most realistic model.

The Regularization of Planetary Motions

Hence it was not so much in the reduction of the number of celestial motions (and of the corresponding circles) that the great superiority of Copernicus' system must be sought. Its greatest achievement was the regularization and systematization of these motions, *viz.* the realization that a planet's period varies with its distance from the sun, and that the irregularity of the apparent motions (stations, retrogradations, *etc.*), is due to the changing perspective of the observer himself. Rheticus stressed this fact when he explained how the moving-earth hypothesis simplifies the explanation of celestial phenomena:

> In effect, the planets appear each year as following a direct or retrograde motion, as being stationary, close or distant from the earth, *etc.* As my teacher has shown, all these phenomena can be explained by the regular motion of the spherical earth about the sun, a motion which it has pleased him to call the 'great circle'.... In truth, it seems divinely ordained that the certain understanding of celestial phenomena should depend on the regular and uniform motion of the terrestrial sphere.

The Immobility of the Celestial Sphere

Copernicus' polemics against traditional astronomical and cosmological ideas are extremely interesting. They show us that in passing from geocentrism to heliocentrism he was less concerned with substituting one system of celestial circles for another than with initiating an intellectual revolution that went far beyond a mere astronomical reform. Against Ptolemy and, above all, against Aristotle, Copernicus argued that it was absurd to move the *locus* and not the *locatum*, and that the heavens which, according to Aristotle, were the *locus* of the universe must needs be considered immobile.

This argument strikes us as being perfectly logical. In effect, we feel that it is unreasonable to have the immense (for us, infinite) universe turning about a small grain of dust. But while we are convinced, the Aristotelians (or Ptolemaists) were not. Their universe, although large—about 20,000 terrestrial radii—was not immense and they were opposed to what they considered its gratuitous extension by Copernicus. For, in order to counter their objection that a moving earth would necessarily cause the appearance of stellar parallax, Copernicus was forced to increase the radius of the universe by at least two thousand times and to affirm that, compared with the sphere of the fixed stars, the earth's orbit and not, as Ptolemy had postulated, the earth itself, was like a point. This argument, which was bound to appear to Aristotelians as a *petitio principii*, strikes us as a brilliant example of Copernicus' intuitive powers.

The Rotation of the Earth. Copernicus' Reply to Traditional Objections

Moreover, the traditionalists felt that there was a fundamental and qualitative distinction between the heavy and inert earth and the weightless celestial spheres: while the former could be moved only by a material force from without, the latter moved by virtue of their perfection, by their very nature. Copernicus, on the other hand, held that the earth was qualitatively identical with the planets, and that what was true of them was true of it as well.

To the objection that the rotation of the earth must engender a centrifugal force so great that the earth would burst asunder, Copernicus replied that the same objection could be raised against the motions of the heavens, the more so since the velocity of the sphere of fixed stars must be infinitely greater than that of the earth.

Ptolemy's astronomy and Aristotle's physics were commonly cited in support of the immobility of the earth. Since heavy bodies drop downwards, *i.e.* towards a centre, the earth, too, must drop to its natural place—the centre of the universe. Copernicus countered by pointing out that gravity is merely the natural tendency of parts to return to the whole from which they have been separated. As terrestrial bodies return to the surface of the earth, so parts wrenched from the moon and from the other planets would return to their respective surfaces. Clearly, Copernican space had ceased to be the physical space of Aristotle, and though it remained limited it had become geometrical space.

But what of the old objection that, if the earth moved, stones thrown up into the air (or dropped from a tower) would not fall down vertically, but would 'be left behind', and that the air would turn into a terrible hurricane, perpetually blowing from east to west? Copernicus' answer was quite simple: stones, birds, clouds, the air and even fire participate quite naturally in the motion of the earth and are carried along with it. For this reason, though 'things falling and rising' undergo a mixed motion with rectilinear and circular components, they appear to move perpendicularly when seen from the moving earth.

The Importance of Uniform Circular Motion

No doubt following Nicholas of Cusa, Copernicus held that since the sphere is the most perfect geometrical form, which all natural bodies tend to assume because of its very perfection, it is not only the form best suited to motion—on which everyone was agreed—but also a sufficient cause of the most perfect and most natural of all motions, *i.e.* circular motion.

This explains why Copernicus based his celestial mechanics on the principle of uniform circular motion, the only possible means of keeping the *machina mundi* going. Once a spherical body was placed in space, it would keep turning without an external mover or even without an Aristotelian centre. No such centre is therefore found in Copernicus' astronomy.

Place and Role of the Sun

Though Copernicus placed the sun at the centre of the universe, his planetary spheres did not revolve about the central point in the sun. While Copernicus' universe was therefore heliocentric, his astronomy was not—he related the motions of the planets to the centre of the terrestrial orbit, which was not coincident with the centre of the sun. His orbital centre itself revolved about the sun—or, more precisely, it described a small epicycle whose deferent had the sun as its centre, but its motion was so slow—the epicycle had a period of 3,434 and the deferent of 53,000 years—that it had no practical significance. As a result, we have the paradox that the sun played a rather minor role in Copernicus' celestial mechanics. Its main function was rather to illuminate the heavens, whereby alone it secured pride of place in the universe.

The Universe of Copernicus

Copernicus was no modern physicist; his universe did not fill infinite space. True, it was much larger than Aristotle's, but though immeasurable (*immensum*), it was finite, contained in—and limited by—the sphere of the fixed stars. The sun was in the middle and around it revolved the wheels carrying the planets, which were just as real to him as the crystalline spheres had been to medieval cosmologists. The orbs revolved because of their form, and the planets were set in them like jewels in their mounting and were governed by Ptolemaic laws of celestial mechanics, though shorn of Ptolemy's errors.

Thus, curiously enough, as happens so frequently in history, a revolution had sprung from a mere reform, and progress from a desire to return to the past. This, in any case, is how Copernicus' contemporaries judged his work: the resurrection of Pythagoreanism by a new Ptolemy.

THE DIFFUSION OF COPERNICAN IDEAS

In his work, Copernicus had combined a new cosmology with a new scientific system, and it was largely because of this combination that Copernicanism spread so slowly.

In fact, though the system aroused so much interest that a second edition of the *De revolutionibus* (including Rheticus' *Narratio prima* as an introduction) had to be published in 1566, few astronomers were prepared to adopt it. Contrary to expectation, it was much admired and certain of its methods of calculation were used selectively, but it had few wholehearted disciples. Moreover, among those who did adopt it, some merely used it as an improved mathematical technique for the construction of tables and the computation of ephemerides. Lastly, there were those who treated the astronomical hypotheses of Copernicus and Ptolemy as being of equal importance.

Germany, the Netherlands and Italy

Among the foremost Copernicans in Germany were Rheticus, Christoph Rothmann, astronomer to the Landgrave William IV of Hesse-Cassel, and Michael Mästlin, Kepler's teacher and publisher of Kepler's *Mysterium cosmographicum* (1596). Even so, when Rheticus, modelling himself on Paracelsus, prepared to write a 'German Astronomy' towards the end of his life, he did not propose to make it a Copernican treatise. Erasmus Reinhold, again, author of the famous *Tabulae Prutenicae* (1551), which was based exclusively on the Copernican system, and of an (unfinished) commentary on the *De revolutionibus*, failed to accept the physical truth of heliocentrism, and while he called Copernicus the 'second Atlas', he gave no theoretical exposition of the Copernican system in his *Tabulae*.

Paul Crusius and Erasmus Schreckenfuchs, who had published Ptolemy, were full of praise for Copernicus and thought that there might be 'some justification' for discarding geocentrism. Finally, there was Rudolf Wursteisen (Urstitius of Basle) who, according to Galileo, gave Copernican lectures in Italy.

In the Netherlands, Gemma Frisius saw no absurdity in the notion of a moving earth, but he was less interested in the physical truth of the new doctrine than in its mathematical usefulness in calculating more accurate tables. In Italy, Benedetti rejected Aristotle's cosmology and spoke of Copernicus with undisguised admiration, but he knew little about the heliocentric doctrine and cannot be considered a true Copernican. Giordano Bruno, on the other hand, was a true disciple and may be called the only Italian Copernican before Galileo, even though his philosophical and literary work was set in France, England and Germany, and not in Italy.

England

In England, Robert Recorde's *Castle of Knowledge* (London, 1551) was full of praise for Copernicus, whom it hailed as a new Pythagoras. John Field, who computed his *Ephemerides* (1566) '*juxta canones Copernici et Reinholdi*', prudently shared the reserve of Reinhold. On the other hand, John Dee, who wrote the preface to the *Ephemerides*, openly proclaimed the truth of Copernicanism. However, L. Thorndike has pointed out that in his *Propedeumata aphoristica* . . . (London, 1558), Dee spoke of the rapid motion of the celestial vault and of the sun.

Thomas Digges may be called a true Copernican. In the preface to his *Alae seu scalae mathematicae* (1573), a work devoted mainly to the study of the nova of 1572, Digges attacked the error of the Ptolemaic system. In 1576, in the *Perfitt Description of the Coelestiall Orbes, according to the most Ancient Doctrine of the Pythagoreans: lately revived by Copernicus and by Geometrical Demonstrations approved*, which Digges appended to his republication of his father Leonard's *Prognostication*, he went much further still. In effect, the *Perfitt Description* marks an important date in the history of scientific thought, for Digges not only translated a few pages of the *De revolutionibus* and gave an excellent summary of Copernicus' planetary system, but going further than even Copernicus himself, he denied the existence of the sphere of fixed stars and proclaimed that the 'orb' in which the stars are set extends infinitely 'upwards'. Undoubtedly, he still identified this infinite orb with the Kingdom of Heaven and peopled it with saints and angels, but it is none the less true that he was the *first*—even before Bruno—to have proclaimed that the stellar universe is infinite, and to have removed its constricting vault. Digges was also the first to destroy the classical objection that, were the earth to move, a stone dropped from a tower would be 'left behind', for he argued that a stone dropped from the mast of a moving ship drops to the bottom of the mast and not into the ship's wake.

Unfortunately, Digges' *Description* failed to attract the attention it deserved. It was probably read by William Gilbert who, more resolutely even than Digges, denied the existence of the celestial spheres and affirmed the infinity of space and of the stars within it. Gilbert, who mentioned the diurnal rotation of the earth in the *De magnete* (1600), said nothing about its annual revolution. Like Patrizzi and Ursus, Gilbert must therefore be called a semi-Copernican.

France

Oddly enough, France failed to produce a single true Copernican. Though Pontus de Tyard, Jean Péna and Jacques Peletier were open admirers of the new doctrine, they refused to become its formal adherents. Pierre Ramus, whose opposition to Aristotelianism should have driven him towards Copernicus, rejected the new astronomy outright as 'teeming with physical and metaphysical hypotheses, like Aristotle's'. Ramus called instead for a purely mathematical astronomy, shorn of all cosmological trappings, like that of the ancient Chaldeans and Egyptians. True, Copernicus was an admirable astronomer, for he had rejected such erroneous hypotheses as concentric spheres, epicycles and eccentrics, but what a pity that he did not reject all hypotheses, and concentrate on the true positions of the stars, rather than move the earth 'with a giant's hands'. What was needed was a new astronomy based exclusively on observation and developed by means of logic and mathematics, to the exclusion of all ancient ideas. Kepler, we know, would claim to have done just that when he rejected 'all hypotheses, including that of circular motion which Copernicus retained'.

The Slow Diffusion of Copernicanism

While Copernicans were few and far between in the 16th century, works on the Copernican doctrine were even more so; to all intents and purposes, Rheticus' *Narratio prima* was the only commentary on the new doctrine. In fact, none of Copernicus' admirers or disciples —including Urstitius, Mästlin and Schreckenfuchs, all of whom published commentaries on Sacrobosco's *Sphaera* or on Peurbach's *Theoricae novae*—ever wrote accounts of the Copernican revolution. Rothmann, too, kept silent, and it was not until 1596, when Tycho Brahe (in his *Epistolarum astronomicarum liber*) published Rothmann's letters in defence of Copernicus against the attacks of the Danish astronomers, that Rheticus' example was followed. As for Rheticus himself, though he published his openly Copernican *Ephemerides* in 1551, he failed to produce the *Narratio secunda* which he had promised in his *Narratio prima*, and which the publication of the *De revolutionibus* —as difficult a work as the *Almagest*—had by no means rendered redundant. Rheticus seems to have lost interest in astronomy as he grew older, and to have turned all his attention to the development of trigonometry—in the history of which, by the way, he played as great a role as the Danish mathematician Thomas Fincke (*Geometria rotundi*, 1583). Rheticus was, in fact, the first to give a systematic account of the six trigonometrical functions and his *Opus palatinus de triangulis* (Heidelberg, 1596), completed by his pupil Valentin Otto, was an enormous volume (1,466 folios) in which trigonometrical functions were calculated by minute intervals for a radius (*sinus totus*) equal to 10^{15}.

The Chief Difficulties

The surprising lack of Copernican texts was, of course, partly due to the fear, honestly admitted by Schreckenfuchs, of offending against the combined authority of Aristotle and the Church. However, the threat to heliocentrism from religion has been exaggerated by far too many historians.

In fact, the Catholic Church seems to have been not only quite unperturbed by Copernicanism before the advent of Giordano Bruno —who, moreover, by introducing an infinite universe went much further than Copernicus—but altogether unaware of its inherent challenge. In 1581, Clavius was apparently the first to accuse Copernicus not only of having presented a physically absurd doctrine, but also of having contradicted numerous scriptural passages. Even so, Clavius hailed Copernicus as the second Ptolemy and based his calendar reform on Reinhold's *Prussian Tables*. A Spanish theologian, Diego de Zúñiga, published a *Commentary on the Book of Job* in which he tried to show that the Bible was in full agreement with 'the ideas of the Pythagoreans renewed in our day by Copernicus'.

The Protestant Churches seem to have been far more alive to the potential challenge, and proclaimed their opposition publicly. Even before the publication of the *De revolutionibus*, Luther and Melanchthon condemned the new doctrine as repudiating the Scriptures, and Calvin followed suit later. Protestant scientists—Peucer (1551) and Theodoric (1564)—attacked Copernicanism on physical and Biblical grounds, and so did Tycho Brahe.

But even among Protestants, the religious objections were not the most important ones; there seemed to be quite enough physical evidence to refute the absurd and inconceivable notion that the earth was a moving body, an idea which offended common sense at least as much as it offended the authority of the Scriptures. No wonder that not only Schreckenfuchs and Mästlin, but even Stevin, the author of the first and—until the publication of Blaeu's *Institutio astronomica* in 1688—the only scientific summary of the Copernican doctrine (*cf.* his *Hypomnemata mathematica* and his *Opera mathematica*), described Copernicus' system not as simpler, as we should, but as more difficult than the traditional systems, not only because it introduces a factor—the revolution of the earth—which contradicts the evidence of man's eyes and requires a superhuman effort of abstraction, but also because Copernicus' explanation of the 'phenomena' as mere 'appearances' produced by the combined motions of the planets and the earth seemed far more complicated than the explanations of geocentric astronomy.

Thus, it was argued that Copernican astronomy must not be taught until the end of the astronomy course, and Copernicans could quite legitimately continue to teach Ptolemaic astronomy, as Galileo still did in Padua. This situation was to change in the 17th century, when better telescopes, the development of a new physics and the decline of Aristotelianism helped astronomers to outgrow the traditional approach. It was only then that religious arguments came to the fore and that the previous situation was reversed: the Catholic Church entrenched itself in violent and sterile opposition while the Protestant Churches abandoned the struggle, possibly because the rising tide could no longer be stemmed. In the 16th century, however, it was still the universities and the philosophers, rather than the theologians, who were in the vanguard of the anti-Copernican struggle. While they had no qualms about exploiting the technical advantages of the new system, they refused to teach a doctrine that was so obviously unreasonable.

The Reform of the Calendar

The second half of the 16th century witnessed the introduction of a new calendar—the Gregorian—almost universally used today.

The reform of the calendar reflected the wish to co-ordinate the civil and ecclesiastical years with astronomical events, and particularly to fix the date of Easter on which the dates of all other church festivals depend. Now, the Julian year of 365¼ days (three years of 365 days followed by a 'bissextile' year of 366 days), adopted by the Council of Nicaea in 325 B.C., was not a true tropical year (365 days, 5 hours, 48 minutes and 46 seconds). The difference of 11 minutes 14 seconds per year leads to an accumulated error of one day in 128 years, and the vernal equinox which, at the time of Julius Caesar, fell on the 26th March, occurred five days earlier in the year in which the Nicaean Council met. In the 8th century, the Venerable Bede remarked that the calendar had slipped three days forward with respect to the Nicaean dates. In the 13th century, Sacrobosco in his *De anni ratione* held this advance to be equal to seven or eight days. Moreover, in his *De reformatione calendarii*, Roger Bacon suggested to Pope Clement IV that he co-ordinate the calendar with astronomical events, a proposition to which the Pope paid no heed.

With advances in astronomy and the appreciation that the accumulated error was becoming irksome, a calendar reform became imperative. It was urged by Matthias Vlastar and Nicephoros Gregoras in 14th-century Byzantium, but for political reasons the Emperor Andronicos refused to listen to them. In 1414, Peter of Ailly made similar representations to the Council of Constance and to Pope John XXIII, and Nicholas of Cusa followed suit. In 1475, Regiomontanus was called to Rome by Pope Sextus IV for the express purpose of preparing the reform, but the great astronomer died before he could finish the work. In the 16th century, the question was discussed by the Lateran Council (1512) and, though a great many papers were written on it, no solution was found.

Finally, in 1582, Gregory XIII introduced a new calendar (known as the 'Gregorian' or 'New style' calendar) based on the system of the Neapolitan physician and astronomer Luigo Lilio. Since Lilio died before the official adoption of his system, it fell to Clavius to carry out the immense calculations involved and to publish them in an enormous volume, the *Romani calendarii a Gregorio XIII P. M. restituti explicatio* (Rome, 1603; 680 folios).

To correct the systematic error of the Julian calendar, all that was needed was to drop three bissextile days every 400 years (this was done by dropping the 366th day of all completed centuries whose first two figures are indivisible by 4, *e.g.* 1700). The correction of the accumulated advance of the civil year on the astronomical year was a simple matter; the calendar was put forward by ten days. In 1582, Gregory XIII instructed all Catholic states to call the day following St. Francis' Day the 15th, instead of the 5th, of October.

It was much more difficult to compute the date of Easter, for to do so solar and lunar data had to be co-ordinated. Now, the Council of Nicaea had stipulated that Easter must be held on the first Sunday after the 14th day of the moon that occurred next after the vernal equinox, though, if the full moon fell on a Sunday, Easter must be held on the following Sunday. Moreover, Easter must never be allowed to coincide with the Jewish Passover.

Lilio carried out the necessary calculations by ignoring the usual method of 'golden numbers' (based on the Metonic cycle) and concentrating instead on the epact, *i.e.* the number of days of the moon's age on the first day of the year. This method, though very complicated and unreliable—the 'full moon' can differ by one or two days from the real full moon—had the great advantage of fulfilling the conditions laid down by the Council of Nicaea. With some purely formal modifications, it was finally adopted by all the Western Churches.

As for the Gregorian calendar, it was adopted by Italy, Spain and Portugal on the date appointed by Rome; France followed suit in December 1582 and Catholic Germany during the next year. The Protestant states of Germany held out for more than a century against what they termed the 'Papist Calendar', but finally adopted it in 1700. England did not adopt the Gregorian calendar officially until 1752, when the 2nd day of September 1752 was followed by the 14th, and New Year's Day was moved from the 25th March to the 1st January. The Greek Orthodox Church held out much longer still, and it was only in 1923 that the 'new style' calendar was definitely adopted by Russia.

Giordano Bruno's Infinite Universe

Giordano Bruno (1548–1600) was neither an astronomer nor a mathematician, but by a stroke of sheer intuition, foreshadowing the great discoveries of Galileo and going much further than Digges or Benedetti, he seized upon the idea of the infinite universe without reliance on accepted astronomical data. In contrast with the ordered and finite cosmos of medieval astronomers—traces of which persisted even in the work of Copernicus and Kepler—his cosmos was 'immense and innumerable' and peopled by an infinity of 'worlds' (*De l'infinito universo e mondi*, 1584; *De innumerabilis, immenso et infigurabili*, 1591; *etc.*). It was this vision, joined to uncompromising hostility towards Aristotle, that he preached throughout Europe with the zeal of an apostle, and for which he paid with his life.[1]

In his *Cena de la ceneri* (1584), Bruno presented an account and a defence of Copernican astronomy—an account which, despite some errors, was remarkably well informed, and a defence in which he extended the ideas of his master by introducing dynamical concepts in a remarkably intelligent way. The classical arguments against the motion of the earth—that winds, clouds and birds would be 'left behind'—were worthless, Bruno explained, because the air surrounding a moving body must needs follow the body's motion. The argument of the falling stone was dismissed in the same way: seen from the earth, 'all things of the earth move with it' and behave exactly as if the earth were at rest.

While Copernicus distinguished between the 'natural' motion of the earth and the 'violent' motion of terrestrial objects, Bruno stated that no such distinction exists. Far from considering the 'natural' character of the earth's rotation as exceptional, he expressly likened it to a boat gliding across the surface of an ocean: the motion of the boat has no effect on the motions of objects on the boat. Similarly on earth; only an observer standing apart from the earth could observe the effects of the earth's motion. To the fundamental objections of Aristotelian physics, based on such notions as heaviness and lightness, natural places and natural motions, Bruno replied that such terms as heavy and light do not apply to 'natural bodies naturally constituted' (*i.e.* taken by themselves), nor to complete spheres like the earth or the planets. Heaviness is nothing but the tendency of parts to return to a given place; heaviness and lightness are relative terms.

Nor had Bruno any respect for 'natural' places. In fact, his world, or more precisely his universe—which he believed was peopled with a host of material worlds and mechanical systems of worlds like our solar system—was not only 'unbounded' but infinite, and hence devoid of privileged places or privileged directions. He went much further than Nicholas of Cusa, whose universe was his stepping-stone. 'High' and 'low' were merely relative concepts and the 'centre' of the universe was a meaningless term. The inhabitants of other planets have as much right to consider themselves at the centre of their world as we have to be at the centre of ours.

[1] Bruno was arrested by the Inquisition in 1593, and held a prisoner for seven years. He was then excommunicated and burned at the stake on 17th February 1600, in Rome.

As much or as little right, for in Bruno's universe not only the earth but even the sun has lost its privileged place. The sun is no more than the centre of our own mechanical system, one star among a host of others, all of which are suns.

We cannot but marvel at the hardiness of Bruno's thought, and at his complete rejection of all the established Aristotelian concepts. By his infinite universe he not only introduced a revolutionary transformation of the traditional cosmology, but also presented a radically new view of physical reality. With the infinite universe, the unity of nature, the geometrization of space, and the consequent view that all motion is relative, the medieval cosmos had ceased to exist. Its doom was shared by Aristotelian physics which was swept away by the 'new science'—that of Galileo, Descartes and Newton—which Bruno had ushered in.

TYCHO BRAHE

Tycho Brahe's Opposition to the Copernican System

Bruno's anti-Aristotelianism convinces us because we accept his infinite universe and his view of space from which his arguments derive their greatest force. This is precisely why they were rejected in their own day, not only by Tycho Brahe, who attacked Copernicus with traditional arguments in new guise, but even by Kepler, who defended Copernicus against Tycho Brahe with original arguments. To Bruno's contemporaries his infinite universe seemed entirely unnecessary, unsupported by astronomical observations, and hence even less acceptable than the system of Copernicus which he professed to support.

The example of Tycho Brahe is a clear illustration of the formidable obstacles which the new astronomy had to overcome, and shows that the chief prerequisite of its general acceptance was the development of a new physics in which terrestrial and celestial phenomena would be treated as one. Though Kepler himself failed to produce this unification, he fully appreciated its immense importance. It was only because of its absence that Tycho Brahe could propound his own system. For though Tycho was indignant that that system, in which the planets revolved about the sun while the sun itself revolved about the earth, should be called a modified Copernican one, the two were mathematically, though not physically, identical. His system, he claimed, was based directly on observation, but there is no doubt that he presented it after reading Copernicus, who had suggested it as a possibility, and after having accepted the justice of Copernicus' criticism of Ptolemaic astronomy. Tycho would most

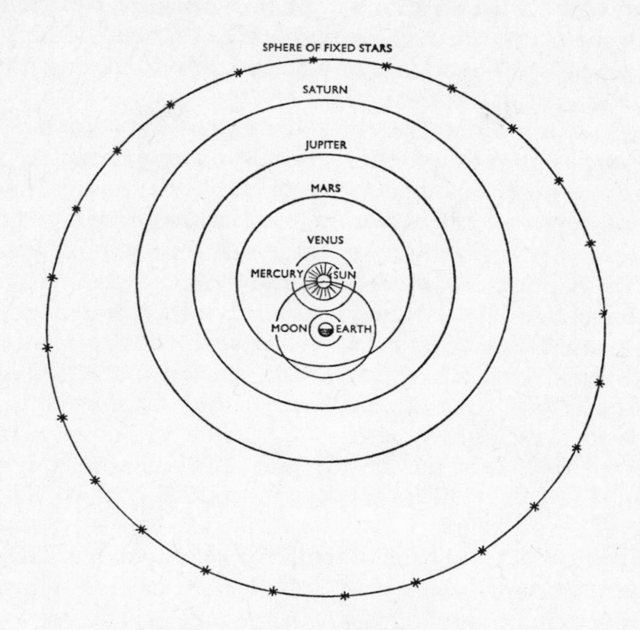

fig. 5 The Universe of Tycho Brahe.
(*After O. von Guericke: 'Experimenta nova', 1672.*)

certainly have accepted the Copernican system had he not been prevented from doing so by what he considered to be insurmountable obstacles, among which Copernicus' tacit refutation of the Bible was not the least. But the decisive stumbling-block was the absence of any discoverable parallax of the fixed stars, with even the best instruments of the time. Tycho stressed this point in his polemics with Rothmann, a staunch Copernican.

Tycho was not content to refute Rothmann with classical arguments, but introduced a recent invention, the cannon. He showed that if identical projectiles were fired by the same cannon and under the same conditions, one towards the east and the other towards the west, they would cover the same distance. This he considered a decisive argument against the hypothesis that the earth was in motion.

Now, from the point of view of the old physics, and even from that of Bruno's impetus dynamics, Tycho's argument was perfectly valid. Hence he had good reason to hold that the earth must be supposed immobile until new or incontrovertible arguments had shown that violent motion is in no way affected by the natural motion of freely falling bodies or by the rotation of the earth; in other words until a new physics, based on a new conception of motion, had been established. Tycho's arguments were discussed at length by Kepler and Galileo, though only the latter was able to refute them.

The Historical Importance of Tycho's System

Tycho Brahe's opposition to the Copernican system must not mislead us into misjudging the importance of his work nor its role in the subsequent development of astronomy. Early 17th-century astronomers looked upon Tycho's system as one which combined the advantages of those of Copernicus and Ptolemy—even Pascal continued to speak of *three* systems between which it was impossible to choose—and which was in many respects superior to the other two because it combined the experimental accuracy and the common sense of the second with the elegance of the first. Moreover, it was Tycho's work which gave the *coup de grâce* to traditional cosmology, reversing the dogma of the immutability of the heavens, destroying the solid orbs of Peurbach and Copernicus and, finally, assembling all the valid parts of earlier astronomies into an observational science of unrivalled accuracy which enabled Kepler to establish an entirely new astronomy as well as a new cosmology.

Tycho's Astronomical Tables

Tycho Brahe (1546–1601) was the son of a Danish nobleman who took not the slightest interest in science. The Danish nobility, one of the richest in Europe, was also one of the most uncultured. Tycho was attracted to astronomy while still a young boy. Thrilled by the idea that that science enabled one to predict the future positions of the stars, he enrolled at the University of Copenhagen at the age of thirteen, and continued to study astronomy at the universities of Leipzig, Basle and Rostock. He spent many a night observing the sky. In 1563, at the age of seventeen, he made his first important observation—the conjunction of Saturn and Jupiter—and, on that occasion, he began to appreciate how inaccurate the existing astronomical tables really were.

In fact, this shortcoming was generally known and Bernhard Walther and Regiomontanus had already tried to remedy it by taking new observations into account. Their work was resumed when Reinhold published his famous *Prussian Tables* in 1551. To improve these tables further, the Landgrave William IV of Hesse built an observatory in 1561 in which (first by himself and in 1564 with the help of Christoph Rothmann and the Swiss mathematician and horologist Jost Bürgi) he carried out a long series of observations to correct the positions of the fixed stars and also the motions of the planets. The results were published by Snellius in 1618.

Tycho, for his part, became convinced that all this work was futile and that what was needed was entirely new tables. His first step towards compiling these was to reform the methods of observation. While Copernicus held that a margin of error of ten minutes was an inaccessible ideal, Tycho thought in terms of seconds, and accordingly started his work by constructing observational instruments of unprecedented accuracy. The first of these, built at Augsburg (where Tycho lived from 1569 to 1571), was financed by Paul Hainzel, a former burgomaster of that town. It was a great quadrant with a radius of about 19 feet for measuring the altitudes of stars. To measure angular distances Tycho also constructed a sextant with a radius of 14 feet, and later marked his results on a celestial sphere 10 feet in diameter. While still at Augsburg, he decided to make a complete map of the sky.

The Nova of 1572 and the Comet of 1577. Their Influence on Tycho's System

After his return to Denmark (in 1571), Tycho made detailed studies of the nova of 1572 and of the great comet of 1577.

The appearance of that nova, brighter than Sirius or even Venus, made a great impression on Tycho's contemporaries. Tycho decided first of all to determine if it was, in fact, a new star—in which case, the dogma of the incorruptibility of the heavens would collapse once and for all—or merely a comet, *i.e.* a 'sublunary phenomenon'.

The nova remained visible until March 1574. In 1573, Tycho Brahe was able to show that, in the absence of any observable parallax, the nova was situated well above the sphere of Saturn, and at least 13,000 terrestrial radii from the earth (Tycho gauged the radius of the sphere of Saturn to be 12,800, and that of the fixed stars 14,000, terrestrial radii). Hence it could not possibly be a comet.

He explained all this in his *De nova stella*, which he published at Copenhagen in 1573, and which he included in his *De mundi aetherei recentioribus phaenomenis* . . . . More important still was the appearance of the great comet of 1577, not so much because it was particularly impressive and provoked a good deal of astrological speculation, as because it was the first comet to have been studied systematically, and particularly by Tycho Brahe and Mästlin. Each of these two men determined independently that its parallax was exceedingly small, and that the comet, too, must be placed not only above the sphere of the moon, but even above that of Venus. The acceptance of the 'superlunary' or celestial character of comets—a further proof of the mutability of the heavens—met with a great deal of resistance. Curiously and paradoxically enough, one of its opponents was Galileo. In addition, Tycho discovered that the paths of various comets which he was able to observe intersected the planetary spheres, which he eventually rejected altogether. This was not, of course, an entirely new discovery, for the Averroists, followed by Pontus de Tyard and Péna, had already argued that Ptolemy's circles were no more than mathematical abstractions. However, most astronomers—and philosophers—believed in their physical reality, so that their rejection by Tycho Brahe became an important event.

In this way Tycho was able to let his planets move freely through space and encroach upon their neighbours' territories, and hence he could greatly reduce their orbits. As a result, Tycho's universe was much smaller than that of Copernicus and less than half the size of Ptolemy's. One might say that the universe had thus to shrink before it could once again expand.

Tycho Brahe did not discuss his studies of the comet of 1577 until 1588, when he published the *De mundi aetherei recentioribus phaenomenis liber secundus*, which also contained a critical review of all the main publications on that comet, and an explanation of Tycho's ideas about the construction of the universe, which, he explained, he discovered 'by inspiration' in 1583.

Because of this delay in presenting his system, Tycho was forestalled by Nicolai Reymers Bär (Ursus), who had visited him a few years earlier and who, in his *Fundamentum astronomicum* (Strasbourg, 1588), proposed ideas which Tycho recognized as modifications of his own. In Ursus', as in Tycho's, system the planets revolve about the sun and the sun about the earth, but Ursus also allowed that the earth rotates on its own axis. When Tycho accused him of plagiarism, Ursus, who had meanwhile been appointed 'Caesarian mathematician', replied with an extremely violent pamphlet in which he accused Tycho of having copied Apollonios, Copernicus and Ursus himself (*De astronomicis hypothesibus*, Prague, 1597).

The Uraniborg Observatory

Tycho's delay in publishing the *De mundi aetherei* can be explained by the truly royal offer of Frederick II, King of Denmark, in 1576, to 'confer and grant to our beloved Tyge Brahe our land of Hveen, with all rent and duty which comes from that'. Tycho was also given an annual pension and a special grant to build and equip an observatory. Hence he was kept busy for years erecting on the island of Hveen his château of 'Uraniborg', with its assistants' quarters, chemical laboratory and observatory, and planning a detailed programme of observation. It was not until ten years later that he felt free to publish his work in a printing shop of his own.

Tycho's astronomical instruments, which he described in his *Astronomiae instauratae mechanica* (Wandsbeck, 1598), were so numerous that four years after the completion of Uraniborg he was forced to build an annexe, Stjerneborg, with subterranean chambers in which the instruments were shielded from atmospheric effects. They included an impressive collection of armillary spheres (simplified and improved by Tycho), quadrants, sextants and octants, all supported by masonry or wooden beams. Most impressive of all was Tycho's great mural quadrant which was provided with two sights that could slide along the arc.

The Value of Tycho Brahe's Astronomical Observations

But it was not so much in the unrivalled accuracy as in the systematic nature of his observations that Tycho's greatness must be sought. He was one of the first astronomers to realize that sporadic observations, no matter how precise, were of little value and that the sky must be watched continuously, night after night. Only after revising the map of the sky on the basis of an adequate number of precise observations could a new and better planetary theory be propounded. Hence it was mainly to observation that he devoted the twenty years he spent at Hveen. No wonder that his star catalogue became the basis of Kepler's *Rudolphine Tables* (1627) and that his ten observations of Mars helped Kepler to solve the riddle of the planet's motion and thence to carry out his radical reform of astronomy.

Tycho's observations were undoubtedly as perfect as they could be with the available instruments. They were not to be bettered for a hundred years—until Flamsteed was able to repeat them with far more powerful telescopes. Tycho determined the position of the nine main stars of his celestial map with an error (due mainly to his misjudgment of atmospheric refraction) of less than one minute. His estimate of the length of the tropical year was out by a mere two seconds; he calculated the precession of the equinoxes to be 51″ and discarded the mistaken notion of trepidation; he gave the inclination of the ecliptic as $23\frac{1}{2}°$; he established the longitude of the sun's apogee at 95° 30′, with an annual motion of 45″ (it should be 61″), thus greatly improving on Copernicus' value (24″).

Though an admirable observer, Tycho Brahe was not a great theorist, and while he helped to improve lunar theory (by introducing, among other refinements, two new inequalities: the inequality in longitude (variation) and the annual equation), he made no contribution to the theory of the solar planets. Moreover, apparently obsessed by a desire to effect a maximum reduction of the dimensions of the solar system, he systematically decreased the orbital radii (and the volumes) of the sun and planets, claiming that Copernicus had greatly exaggerated the size of the sun and its distance from the earth.

Tycho's Disgrace and Exile

Tycho Brahe seems to have been a singularly disagreeable man and a spendthrift to boot. While Frederick II was alive all was well, but the situation changed radically on the accession of Christian IV. True, Tycho's large debts were settled, but he was warned not to contract new ones. Tycho managed to carry on, and thanks to a considerable inheritance was even able to set up a paper mill and to print his scientific correspondence in 1596. But his fortunes declined as more and more of his fiefs were withdrawn. In 1597, Christian even stopped the annuity which Frederick II had granted.

In these circumstances, Tycho was forced to leave his beloved Uraniborg, first for Copenhagen and then for Rostock and Wandsbeck, where he stayed for nearly two years and where he printed his remarkable *Astronomiae instauratae mechanica* (1598), copies of which he sent to all those rich and powerful enough to further the aims of astronomy—and of Tycho Brahe. To the copy addressed to the Emperor Rudolph II he appended a handwritten catalogue of 777 stars, which, he suggested, was a great improvement on the existing tables.

In 1599, Rudolph II signified that he was prepared to appoint Tycho as imperial mathematician and to supply all his needs. The move to Prague was a most laborious affair, but gradually everything was arranged to Tycho's satisfaction and his team, weakened by the departure of his lieutenant Longomontanus but strengthened by the addition of Kepler, could set to work again in 1601. The printing of the *Astronomiae instauratae progymnasmata* was resumed. When it appeared in Augsburg, in 1602, it contained a catalogue of Tycho's 777 stars plus 228 stars added by Kepler. Work was also begun on the *Rudolphine Tables*, the most difficult section of which —the study of the motions of Mars—was entrusted to Kepler.

The future looked bright indeed, when Tycho Brahe died on 22nd October 1601. Rudolph II gave him a resplendent state funeral and charged Kepler with continuing the great work.

* * *

Kepler always spoke of his meeting with Tycho Brahe as a special act of divine Providence. In view of the tremendous consequences of this meeting—the birth of the 'New Astronomy' and the upsurge of scientific thought which, without it, might have been delayed for decades—one is tempted to agree with this judgment, and even to

5 Tycho Brahe's great mural quadrant

6 Jost Bürgi's celestial sphere

add that Providence also chose the right moment for Tycho Brahe's death. For, having accomplished his work, having collated and handed on all the material which Kepler needed to substitute a celestial physics for the kind of stellar kinematics of which Tycho had been the last and purest representative, Tycho had played his part, and so had kinematic astronomy.

CHAPTER 3

Physics

PHYSICS IN THE 15TH CENTURY

THE HISTORY OF PHYSICS during the 150 years separating Nicholas of Cusa from Simon Stevin is not nearly as dramatic as the history of mathematics or astronomy of the same period. The scientific revolution for which the ground was then being prepared was not to bear fruit until the 17th century, and Galileo and Descartes' science, in any case, was based purely on Copernican astronomy—its 'prologue in heaven'—and not on any striking advances in physics.

Moreover, physics derived little benefit from the return to the Greek sources, since—with the exception of Archimedes' studies in statics—the ancients had not greatly bothered with its mathematical basis. Worst of all, Aristotelian physics as presented particularly in the (probably apocryphal) *Problems of Mechanics* was considered in such good agreement with common sense that it needed little further improvement. Admittedly, it had a few minor weaknesses; for instance, its explanation of the motion of objects separated from their moving agents by the reaction of the surrounding air seemed improbable. But John Philoponos' notion of *impetus*, which was developed in the Middle Ages mainly by the Parisian Nominalists, seemed to reconcile the facts within the general Aristotelian framework.

This modified Aristotelian doctrine survived the Middle Ages and was adopted by most philosophers, though the Paduan Averroists who kept to the strict letter of Aristotle, and some backward Alexandrians, rejected it out of hand.

Nicholas of Cusa

CUSANIAN DYNAMICS

The *impetus* school had a staunch advocate in Nicholas of Cusa. However, in his *De ludo globi* (1463), Cusanus argued that a non-spherical and partially evacuated ball would, under the joint and simultaneous action of a circular *impetus* and its natural gravity, describe a helicoidal path on the surface over which it rolled. Such motion, which is inadmissible in modern dynamics, was, if anything, more in accordance with Aristotle's dynamics than with the theory of *impetus*, in which two motions—one natural and one violent, or both violent—cannot be present in the same body except in the special case of the projectile, where the violent motion of the throw gradually abates before the natural motion of the fall. In the case of the ball, the rolling motion would therefore have had to be 'natural', which it clearly could not have been. In effect, in the *De possest* (1460), which dealt with the gyroscopic motion of a top, Cusanus was forced to revert to a more traditional explanation.

Moreover, the analogy drawn by Cusanus between a 'spirit of life' animating a non-living body and the *impetus* activating a body in motion shows clearly how much of a traditionalist he really was. To him, *impetus* was a purely transitory phenomenon that opposed the natural tendency of the body. Nevertheless, the ideas propounded in the *De ludo globi* had a great influence on Leonardo da Vinci and Copernicus, and hence played an appreciable role in the history of dynamics.

The Beginnings of Quantitative Physics

Having conceived the brilliant idea that the universe consists of like parts and that reason is eminently suited to their comparison and measurement (that *mensura* is derived from *mens*, he stressed time and again), Cusanus deduced that the study of nature must be based on mensuration and particularly on weights and related quantities.

Thus, he called the balance the measuring instrument *par excellence*, and in his curious dialogue, *De staticis experimentis* (1450), he explained its many uses in physics, meteorology and medicine. By weighing the blood and the urine, one can readily diagnose the state of health; variations in the weight of a piece of linen give the degree of humidity of the air; air itself can be weighed, either by determining the difference in weight between an empty and an inflated bladder, or else by measuring the time taken by two bodies to fall from equal heights.

To measure the time of their fall and also the pulse of a patient, Nicholas of Cusa weighed the water collected in a clepsydra during the time of the experiment. He suggested that the depth of a lake could be deduced from the time it took a light object pushed to the bottom to rise to the surface, or the speed of a ship by the time taken by an object thrown into the sea from the prow to travel to the poop. His other measuring projects were considerably more far-fetched but, despite some of his naïve notions, his basic idea proved profoundly valuable to succeeding generations.

The Paris and Oxford Traditions

Some 15th-century scholastics carried on the traditions of the medieval logicians and kinematicians, commenting, editing and developing their works.

Pierre Duhem has shown that the schools of Paris and Oxford—led by Oresme, Swineshead and William of Heytesbury—distinguished not only between motion (*motus*) and velocity (*latitudo motus* or *velocitatis*), but also between velocity and acceleration (*latitudo acquisitionis latitudinis motus*). Cajetan of Tienen made similar distinctions between motion (*motus*) and velocity (*latitudo* or *velocitas motus*), and between *velocitas* and *velocitatio* or *acquisitio motus* (acceleration). In his *De motu locali*, Angelo de Fossembrone also distinguished between motion (*motus*) and *intensio motus*, and between velocity (*velocitas motus*) and *velocitas intensionis motus*. His commentaries show that he was familiar with the ideas of uniform and 'uniformly varying' motion.

'Uniformly Varying' Motion and Medieval Thought

Duhem has rightly equated the expression 'uniformly varying motion' with 'uniformly accelerated motion'. According to him, Italian scholars were well-acquainted with the laws of uniformly accelerated or uniformly retarded motion, in the middle of the Quattrocento, but it seems that none of them (not even Leonardo da Vinci) was led to assume that the fall of bodies was uniformly accelerated. The reason why all the schoolmen, with the notable exception of Dominic de Soto, failed to 'consider the motion of falling bodies as subject to . . . the laws of uniformly varying latitude', was simply that medieval theorists considered the two as distinct as mathematical abstraction and physical reality.

The modern historian takes little interest in what to him are the senseless discussions of medieval logicians. The only part of the large volumes devoted to the study of the 'latitude of forms' or to 'calculations', 'predicaments' and 'sophisms' which interests him is the section dealing with motion in general, and translational motion in particular. Thus he is inclined to forget that that section was at best of minor importance to its authors. Translational motion was considered just one case of physical change in general, including growth, alteration, generation and corruption, *etc.* Moreover, the medieval theory of motion tried to combine not only the 'motions' of temperature, light or sound, which were considered subject to *intensio et remissio* just like *motus localis*, but also such 'motions' as the intensification of divine grace or changes in the concupiscence of a sinner's soul.

The Physical Problem of the Motion of Projectiles

Meanwhile, the 'physicists' concentrated on entirely different subjects: the motion of projectiles, the acceleration of moving bodies, air resistance, the study of *impetus*, and the interpretation of the famous Aristotelian thesis that the velocity of a moving body is proportional to the motor force and inversely proportional to the resistance. The discussion of this theory led them to a closer investigation of the respective roles of impetus and gravity in vertical throws. It was generally held that a body rises up through the air whenever its upward *impetus* is greater than the downward pull of its weight and that its ascending velocity varies with the difference (inequality) between the two. This difference decreases continuously as the *impetus* grows weak until, finally, gravity becomes larger than *impetus* and the body drops down with a velocity that varies with the excess of gravity over *impetus*.

In other words, the vertical motion of projectiles was thought to be compounded of a violent and a natural component, whereas horizontal motion was not. Aristotle had taught, and everyone, with the single exception of Benedetti, accepted his opinion until the middle of the 17th century, that there was one moment in a projectile's up-and-down motion when it was poised immobile in the air. This belief in a position of intermediate rest (the *quies media*) was said to be only common sense and easily observable, for, as Juan Luiz Vives pointed out, everyone knows that an arrow shot vertically into the air stands still before it begins to descend.

Moreover, archers, arquebusiers and gunners alike were apparently agreed that projectiles increase their speed at the beginning of their course. Though Jean Dullaert and Luiz Coronel refuted this claim, they, too, were convinced that a bullet strikes with greater force at some distance from the cannon than it does near the cannon's mouth, since 'in a given projectile no fixed relationship exists between the violence of the shot and the velocity of the motion'.

Leonardo da Vinci

Leonardo da Vinci's contribution to physics was indubitably the most original of the period. While there is no doubt that many discoveries (for instance the discovery of the principle of inertia and of the law of falling bodies) have been wrongly attributed to him by Venturi, Libri, Pierre Duhem and, more recently, by V. Somenzi, there is no doubt that Leonardo's work was far more important than the views of such hypercritical scholars as Olschki and Dugas would suggest.

From Technique to Science

Leonardo da Vinci was a man of unrivalled technological genius. His transformation of mere technique into technology was foreshadowed by his famous remark that experiment is vastly superior to speculation and book-learning, and is the true basis of all scientific theories. Thus, he was able to describe mechanics as the paradise of mathematics, in which the latter comes into its own and turns empirical art into applied science. This transformation was hastened by his many drawings and plans of engines which were never presented in the form of pictures, as in 15th- and 16th-century technical albums, but as geometrical scale-drawings. One might say that, though Leonardo's geometry was often the geometry of the engineer, his engineering technique was invariably that of the geometer.

Despite his praise of theory, Leonardo did not publish a single theoretical work, or if he did, no such work has come down to us. What we have, instead, is a mass of fragments of uncertain date, repeating, completing and often contradicting one another. Their study, though greatly improved by Guido Ucelli's admirable edition of the *Scritti della mecanica* (Milan, 1940), remains extremely difficult because of their fragmentary nature, their inaccurate terminology and their vague formulation. Hence, Leonardo's contribution to mechanics must not be sought in his general formulae and definitions, but rather in his analysis of concrete or semi-concrete cases. Leonardo da Vinci's strength lay in his exceptionally acute perception of concrete reality, and not in his powers of abstraction.

'Virtual Velocities' and Simple Machines

Leonardo's mechanics were based on Aristotle—or rather on the apocryphal *Problems of Mechanics*—to which he added a number of amendments, notably his own doctrine of *impetus*.

Leonardo used the basic principle of Aristotle's statics—which we might call the 'principle of virtual velocities'—to explain the behaviour of simple machines: pulleys, tackles, levers, balances, *etc.* In addition, he used the principle of virtual displacements, the discovery of which has been wrongly attributed to him. He would sometimes speak of both principles in the same breath, no doubt because he believed them to be identical. In fact, the difference between them was first appreciated by Descartes.

Leonardo was an expert on the workings of simple machines. He considered the lever and the balance as the rational models of mechanical relationships, all of which were said to be based on mechanical equilibrium.

He found that the pull of a weight placed on the end of a lever decreases as the lever is tilted from the horizontal, and that it is proportional to the distance of the weight from the vertical drawn through the fulcrum. Hence, in a balance with bent arms, it is not the length of the *real* arms which matters but that of the *potential* arms. Like all his predecessors, Leonardo was keenly interested in the problem of the inclined plane. Studying the equilibrium of two heavy bodies connected by a thread and placed on two intersecting planes, he showed that the two bodies are in equilibrium when their weights are proportional to the 'obliquity' of the planes, a term which he unfortunately failed to define. However, a drawing in *Manuscript H*[1] shows that the relative weight of a body placed on an inclined plane is inversely proportional to the gradient of the plane.

Though Leonardo's studies of the tension of threads were not very profound, it was through them that he was led to the parallelogram of forces. This discovery would have been of tremendous importance had he been able to generalize the solution. But once again his brilliant intuition was not joined to a correspondingly great gift for theoretical abstraction.

Leonardo's Dynamics

Leonardo made his greatest contribution to science in dynamics, though over-enthusiastic historians have exaggerated its importance more even than that of his contribution to statics.

As Pierre Duhem has shown, Leonardo's dynamics were, in fact, based on the *impetus* doctrine, and his concrete formulations were clearly influenced by Albert of Saxony and by Nicholas of Cusa. From Albert he took his method of calculating the ratio of the motive force to the internal or external resistance, and from Cusanus the notion of compound *impetus*. Leonardo considered *impetus* as 'a virtue created by motion' and 'impressed by the motor on the moving body'. Though *impetus* can be produced in various ways, in every case a force bestows upon the moving body a derived force similar to itself. '*Impetus* is the impression of motion which is transmitted from the motor to the moving body.'

The motion of a projectile can be resolved into three phases. In the first, the motion is purely violent—the projectile moves in a straight line; in the second, the motion is part violent and part natural, *i.e.* the violence of the throw is counteracted by the projectile's natural tendency to fall back under the action of its own weight, and the projectile describes an arc; in the third phase, where nature's laws are restored, the projectile drops in a straight line towards the centre of the earth.

[1] Leonardo's was the typical drawing of the engineer. Thus he introduced rollers to minimize friction between the heavy bodies and the inclined planes on which they were placed.

In the case of a hemisphere rolling along a plane, Leonardo agreed with Cusanus and eliminated the rectilinear part of the trajectory. Had he extended his remarkable realization that a trajectory can be completely described by mixed motion to the case of projectiles, Leonardo would have forestalled Tartaglia by some 50 years. As it was, he failed to do so, though he admitted the possibility of completely curved motion in the case of water jets, and though, on one occasion, he even abandoned the fundamental theory of the rectilinear character of violent motion altogether, contending that:

> Everything movable thrown with fury through the air continues the motion of its mover; if, therefore, the latter move it in a circle and release it in the course of this motion, its movement will be curved.

Acceleration and Air Resistance

Leonardo adopted the Aristotelian principle that the velocity of a moving body is proportional to the motive force and inversely proportional to the resistance the moving body meets. 'If a power move a certain weight a certain distance, it will move double that weight through half the distance.' Aristotle's principle can also be applied to the excess of the 'power' over the resistance rather than to their ratio, and it is this method which Leonardo generally used. He argued that the reaction of the ambient air has two opposite effects: on the one hand it helps the acceleration of the descent by setting up a direct wave in front of the falling body, thus reducing the resistance in its path and, by means of a reflex wave, surrounding the body and pushing it from behind; on the other hand, it resists the motion though, since its density is uneven, the air resistance is not uniform. Hence it follows that the motion of a falling body is neither uniform nor even uniformly accelerated; uniform acceleration is effected by a compensatory mechanism which Leonardo discusses at length, confusing the respective roles of time and distance. In fact, this confusion was characteristic of Leonardo's day.

Impact, Action and Reaction

Though Leonardo discovered neither the law of falling bodies nor the principle of inertia, he came very close to the discovery of Newton's third principle, that an action is always opposed by an equal reaction. Thus, in his studies of percussion, he stated that 'everything striking against a resisting object leaps back from this object with equal force', and it was on this principle that he based his analysis of impact phenomena. Though a century ahead of his time in this respect, Leonardo failed to formulate the new conception of motion which his approach implied. Percussion was to him a special case of violent motion, opposed to natural forces and causes. It is produced whenever a body in rapid motion meets a resisting object. A heavy body hitting a plane is hit, in turn, by an equal force and deflected at an angle equal to the angle of percussion. The reflected motion is governed both by the simple force of the *impetus* (which controls the incident motion) and by the simple 'percussive' force. Analysis shows that the reflected motion is composed of two motions according to the principle of the parallelogram of velocities. Hence the two motions, or the two motor forces, can coexist in one and the same moving body without impeding each other. From this view it was but a short step to the principle of the conservation of momentum.

Leonardo denied that *impetus* is lost in percussion, and claimed that the conservation of *impetus* or of motive force governed the impact of elastic bodies, a view which has obvious similarities with that of Descartes. However, Leonardo's conservation of *impetus* was not absolute, for he held that the resulting motion was restricted to a limited distance.

The conservation of motor force, and the equality of action and reaction in percussion formed the basic theory of Leonardo's analysis of different cases of percussion. Despite certain errors of calculation, his solutions were astonishingly accurate, which is the more surprising since he distinguished between the impacts of elastic and 'soft' bodies.

He argued that impact leads not only to the formation of two equal and opposite forces, but also to the total or partial transfer of 'force' from the percussing body to the object of the percussion. This transfer may appear as the exchange of 'reciprocal forces', or else as the sharing out of the total force available between the agent and the object.

The mechanics of the 16th century has nothing to offer that is comparable with the level of Leonardo's analytic thought, and such heights were not reached again until the advent of Jan Marcus Marci von Kronland a hundred years later.

PHYSICS IN THE 16TH CENTURY

Contrary to the widespread opinion that Leonardo da Vinci's work had a considerable influence on his contemporaries or immediate successors, it seems to have attracted very little, if any, attention. In any case, no one seems to have benefited from his most original and fruitful ideas, namely his treatment of the acceleration of heavy bodies and his theory of percussion. In fact, 16th-century physical thought seems to have been singularly stagnant; what progress was made was due almost entirely to Tartaglia and Benedetti.

Tartaglia

Tartaglia's *New Science* (1537) was the science of ballistics. While he was wrong to call himself its inventor—Leonardo had, in fact, studied the subject long before him—he was undoubtedly the first to offer a *theoretical* discussion of what had previously been a purely empirical 'art'. It is for this reason that Tartaglia's work deserves attention even though the theories he developed were completely false.

The 'Nova Scientia'

Though Tartaglia's dynamics was almost completely traditional, his method of presenting it was not. He modelled himself on the Greek geometers, beginning with a series of definitions followed by 'suppositions' (axioms) and 'common statements', from which he deduced the 'propositions' of the new science. He avoided any kind of metaphysical speculation on the concepts he used and on the causes of the phenomena he studied, if only because his work was addressed to 'practical men' and not to philosophers.

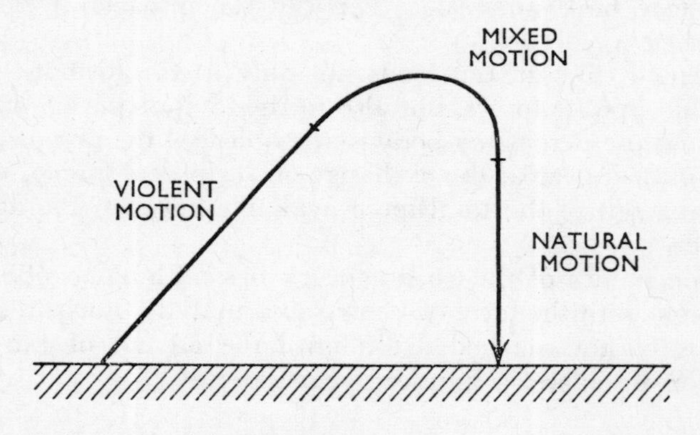

fig. 6 Analysis of the trajectory of projectiles before Tartaglia.

The 'new science' was chiefly concerned with the motion of bodies 'of even weight', *i.e.* bodies which 'because of the gravity of their matter and because of their form are not subjected to appreciable opposition when they move through the air'. Such bodies are balls made of dense material.

The motion of 'evenly heavy' bodies can be natural or violent. Now, for Tartaglia the falling motion of an evenly heavy body was its *only* possible natural motion. During natural motion all evenly heavy bodies travel 'the faster the farther they are from their starting-point or the nearer they approach to their destination'. As a result, a falling body has a maximum velocity when it hits the earth, and the velocity of its natural motion of descent varies with the space it has traversed.

Violent motion has quite different characteristics, for a violently propelled body begins to slow down the instant it is released from the moving force. Hence, Tartaglia opposed the common belief that projectiles were subject to an initial acceleration.

Tartaglia's study of the trajectory of an evenly heavy body in violent motion, based on the absolute incompatibility of natural and violent motions, should have led him to an angular trajectory: straight upwards as far as the point of minimum velocity marking the end of the violent motion, and then vertically downwards in natural motion.

However, Tartaglia failed to take his own principles to their logical conclusion. Instead, he presented a trajectory with three phases, arguing that the violent motion of the ball becomes curved under the influence of the ball's own weight. Why, then, should not the whole trajectory have been curved?

Tartaglia got round the difficulty by claiming that the apparently rectilinear parts of the trajectory are, in fact, imperceptibly curved. It seems that having adopted the traditional view of the trajectory, he then tried to adapt his theoretical conceptions to it—with deplorable results. In fact, since the motion of a ball remains 'violent' until the beginning of its 'natural' descent, it is there, and not at the summit of Tartaglia's curve, that the point of minimum velocity must be sought. Since the maximum trajectory in a given plane depends both on the length of the rectilinear part and on that of the circular part, Tartaglia concluded that the trajectories of evenly heavy bodies projected upwards at an equal angle are proportional to their initial velocities.

The rest of the *Nova scientia* dealt with such practical questions as the determination of distances and contained a description of an instrument for measuring elevations.

Important Corrections: Towards a New Ballistics

In 1546, Tartaglia published his *Quesiti et inventioni diverse*, the first two books of which complete and modify the ballistic theories of the *Nova scientia*.

The most important modification was the rejection of the axiom of the incompatibility of natural and violent motions, and hence the rejection of all (except vertical) motion in a straight line. Unless a cannon-ball is fired vertically into the air, its trajectory has no rectilinear component.

Tartaglia defended this theory against all those who maintained that it was refuted by 'experience'. Thus one of the *dramatis personae* in the *Quesiti*—which is written in the form of a dialogue—is told that the 'common experience' that cannon-balls travel in a straight line is based on an optical illusion and on the weakness of the human intellect. The claim that the gigantic velocity with which the ball leaves the mouth of the cannon assures its continuance in a straight line is refuted by the argument that that very velocity helps to lighten the ball, which is the more firmly supported the greater is its velocity, without ever being completely deprived of its weight. Tartaglia went on to prove by a *reductio ad absurdum* that no part of the trajectory, no matter how small, can ever be straight.

Let us suppose that the part *ab* of the trajectory is rectilinear and that *c* is its midpoint. According to the principles we have stated, the segment *ac* would then be traversed more quickly than the segment *cb*, which would lead to the absurd conclusion that the segment *ac* is straighter than the segment *cb*.

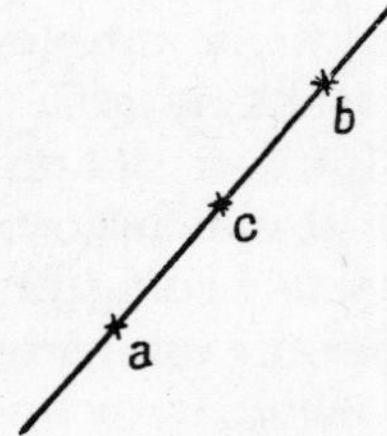

Though obstinate in his defence of theoretical truth against the so-called experience of gunners, Tartaglia could not ignore their claims completely. Thus he was forced to give reasons for their alleged observations that if, of two identical cannon-balls fired from a cannon with identical charges and elevations, the second travels farther than the first, the ball which strikes the nearer object does so with less force than the other strikes the more distant object.

The statics in the *Quesiti* were 'borrowed' from Jordanus Nemorarius without acknowledgment, for which Tartaglia was bitterly reproached by Ferrari. However, historians owe Tartaglia a great debt for handing his manuscript of Jordanus' original text to Curtius Trojanus, who published it in 1665 under the title *Jordani opusculum de ponderositate, Nicolai Tartalea studio correctum.*

Tartaglia's attempt to base ballistic theory on experiment while at the same time rejecting the so-called everyday 'experiences' of gunners was both premature and a little too radical. Thus, while the triple trajectory of his earlier *Nova scientia* was widely adopted, the completely curved trajectory of the *Quesiti* was not. No one, not even such great mathematicians as Cardan, Baldi, or even Benedetti, who opposed tradition with the solid foundations of his mathematical philosophy and who was familiar with Tartaglia's theories, bothered to discuss (let alone to adopt) his views. This lack of interest illustrates the strength of the empirical and technical traditions and shows once again what tremendous obstacles Galileo would have to overcome.

Changes in the Meaning of 'Impetus'

CARDAN

Jerome Cardan's famous *De subtilitate* (1550) was a moderate defence of *impetus* dynamics and included a long account of the Aristotelian theory together with the traditional objections to it, which Cardan himself shared. In his discussion of the behaviour of an object thrown obliquely into the air, Cardan, like Tartaglia, distinguished three phases, but unlike his predecessor (and more logically) he directed his attention to the *velocities* and not to the trajectory. He was wrong to reject the idea that the body describes an arc in the 'mixed' phase.

Cardan also proved a traditionalist when he accepted the 'fact' of the initial acceleration of projectiles which, according to him (as also to Leonardo and Aristotle), reach their maximum velocity and striking power when they have covered half their paths. This happens because the action of the *impetus* must be added to the reaction of the air.

Cardan's *Opus novum de proportionibus* (1570) added little to his *De subtilitate*. Pure natural motion was said to be necessarily uniform since it is produced by a constant cause, whereas violent motion must gradually vanish because its cause ceases to act upon it. As a consequence of the reaction of the medium which pushes and pulls the projectile in a forward direction, all natural motion has a lasting phase of acceleration, unlike violent motion in which acceleration stops after 'a certain point' (Cardan no longer said 'half-way along the trajectory'). Before the motion ceases completely, it gradually dies down; hence it is at a minimum at the peak of the curve. Cardan also affirmed, no doubt following Benedetti, that if two like spheres are dropped from a tower, they will hit the ground simultaneously.

PICCOLOMINI

Unlike Cardan's semi-Aristotelian dynamics, those of Alessandro Piccolomini (*In mechanicas questiones Aristotelis paraphrasis paulo quidem plenior* . . . Rome, 1542) were based squarely on the doctrine of *impetus*. *Impetus* is impressed on a naturally moving body by a motor which increases its 'natural gravity' and hence its velocity. On the other hand, the '*impetus* of violent motion' impresses 'superficial lightness' on the moving body, so that the body is kept up while the action continues. The moment the action ceases, or when the 'true weight' of the body exceeds it, the violent motion ceases and the body descends by virtue of its 'proper motion'.

Scaliger

In his *De subtilitate ad Hieronymum Cardanum* (*Exotericarum exercitationum libri XV*, Paris, 1557), Julius Caesar Scaliger launched a violent attack on Cardan and particularly on his theory of air reaction in conjunction with *impetus*, showing that when a thin wooden disk is set spinning inside the plank from which it has been cut out, what little air is left between the two cannot possibly support the motion. The cause of its motion is 'an entity which is implanted in the moving body and which can remain there even when the prime mover is taken away'. According to Scaliger, the acceleration of bodies under the continuous action of a motor is due to the impression of a succession of motions.

Scaliger's traditionalist reaction against the eclecticism of his day —he was opposed to Cardan's glorification of Archimedes and vigorously defended John Duns Scotus, Heytesbury and Swineshead against Cardan's attacks—is, in fact, of no more than purely historical interest.

Bernardino Baldi

The same is true of the work of Bernardino Baldi, who based his theories on Cardan's and Piccolomini's, and whose only new contribution was the assertion that motion is engendered by motion. In his *In mechanica Aristotelis problemata exercitationes* (written in 1582 and published in 1621) he explained that the motion of projectiles results from the action of a violent and characteristically transitory *impetus*. It is this *impetus* which causes moving bodies to assume a measure of 'gravity by violence', whereby motion is added to motion and whereby projectiles are accelerated at the beginning of their course.

The Enigma of Dominic de Soto

Duhem has described Dominic de Soto, the great Spanish Schoolman, famous in his day and since forgotten, as one of the first scholars to look upon the ascent and descent of heavy bodies as instances of 'motion which is uniformly deformed [varying] with respect to time'. De Soto was not a great philosopher—his physics were traditionalist and eclectic. Hence it is surprising that he held that:

> Motion which is uniformly deformed with respect to time is that in which the deformity is such that if it is divided according to time, that is according to intervals which succeed one another in time, in each part

the motion at the central point exceeds the weaker terminal motion in this part by an amount equal to that by which it is itself exceeded by the more intense terminal motion.

This kind of motion is one which is appropriate to bodies which have a natural motion, and to projectiles.

Indeed, each time that a mass falls from the same height in a homogeneous medium, it moves more quickly at the end than at the beginning. And similarly, the first motion is uniformly accelerated and the second uniformly retarded. [*Quaestiones super octo libri physicorum*, Salamanca, 1572.]

In other words, de Soto held that the distance covered by a moving body is equal to that which it would have covered in the same time travelling with a uniform velocity equal to the mean between the actual maximum and minimum velocities.

How did de Soto come to consider the motion of falling bodies as an example of uniformly accelerated motion, and to describe physical reality in the kind of mathematical terms that the Oxford mathematicians and logicians had always rejected as a matter of course? It is extremely difficult to give a satisfactory answer, particularly since de Soto himself seems to have misunderstood the exact nature of uniformly varying motion.

According to Duhem, de Soto merely repeated the shallow views of early 16th-century Parisian schoolmen and of their disciples. But if this is the case, why was de Soto alone in putting them down on paper? And why did no one else before Galileo—not even Benedetti, who made a deliberate and consistent attempt to found physics on the firm and solid basis of 'mathematical philosophy'—adopt them?

In Search of a Mathematical Philosophy of Nature: Benedetti

Giambattista Benedetti (1530–1590) was not only the most interesting of all 16th-century Italian physicists, he was also the most influential; so much so, that when the young Galileo wrote his *De motu* he followed Benedetti step by step. True, it was Galileo and not Benedetti who made the final break with medieval science, but Benedetti came much nearer to modern science than Tartaglia, his teacher and immediate predecessor, when, in conscious opposition to the empiricist and qualitative physics of Aristotle, he attempted to found physics on Archimedes' statics and, to use his own phrase, to establish a 'mathematical philosophy of nature'.

His attempt was bound to fail since, unlike Galileo, he was unable to rid himself of the confused idea that *impetus* is a cause of motion.

Even so, he managed—and this was no mean achievement—to give a mathematical refutation of the *quies media* and to prove that *impetus* is conserved in a straight line. He also broke with a thousand years of tradition when he argued that two bodies of equal 'nature' (*i.e.* bodies of equal density) fall with the same velocity irrespective of their individual weights, though he left it to Galileo to apply the theory to *all* bodies, irrespective of their 'natures'.

Early Work

In the preface to his 'Resolution of all Euclid's Problems' which he published separately as the *Demonstratio proportionum motuum localium contra Aristotelem* (Venice, 1554) and which was shamelessly plagiarized by J. Taisnier (1569), Benedetti explained that Aristotle's doctrine that a body twice as heavy as another falls twice as quickly through the air is to be corrected in two essential points. First, it is not the body's weight but its excess of weight over that of the medium which determines the velocity of its fall; second, it is not the weight of the body but its density which must be considered.

Benedetti demonstrated the first of these propositions by means of Archimedes' Principle: a heavy body immersed in a medium lighter than itself (*e.g.* in water) becomes lighter by an amount equal to the weight of the volume of water it displaces.

He proved the second proposition by taking the case of a ball weighing four pounds, and comparing it with that of four balls weighing one pound each. Clearly, the centre of gravity of the ball weighing four pounds would fall with the same velocity as the combined centres of gravity of the four balls. Hence the balls themselves must fall with the same velocity.

The second proposition, Benedetti declared with justification, 'does not agree with the doctrine of Aristotle or that of any of his commentators whom I have had occasion to see or read, or with whom I have been able to converse'. The first proposition, however, had been discussed by some commentators of Aristotle's *Physics*, particularly by John Philoponos.[1] Hence Benedetti's original contribution was simply his substitution of the Archimedean for the Aristotelian scheme.

Further Developments

In his *Diversarum speculationum mathematicarum et physicarum liber* (1585), Benedetti replaced the Aristotelian notion of *absolute* heaviness and lightness with the notion of *relative* heaviness and lightness. Since all bodies are heavy, any one of them can merely be said to be heavier or lighter than the medium into which it is immersed, and not to be

[1] See *Ancient and Medieval Science* in this series, pp. 508–10.

7 The Metallotheca Vaticana

8 Prospecting for minerals in the 16th century

heavy or light in itself. He had thus replaced Aristotelian qualities with Archimedean quantities.

Benedetti's physics were, moreover, based on the wholehearted acceptance of the doctrine of *impetus*. Like all his immediate predecessors, he developed his *impetus* theory by first criticizing the Aristotelian view of missiles, but more radical than most, he condemned that view out of hand: the air is *never* the motor of, but *always* an obstacle to, the missile's motion.

The conception of *impetus* as the internal cause of the motion of heavy bodies has been discussed elsewhere.[1] Benedetti subsequently rejected the earlier notion of circular *impetus*, arguing that the hand or the sling imparts to heavy bodies a tendency to move in straight lines. The same is true of a spinning top or of a rotating millstone, each of whose constituent particles is given a rectilinear *impetus* by the mover. Only because of violence (resulting from the constraining forces) are the top and the wheel forced to describe circles. Benedetti claimed that the poverty of Aristotelian physics arises from Aristotle's failure to understand the role of mathematics in physical science. Only by building on the 'unshakable foundations' of mathematical philosophy—*i.e.* on Archimedes and Plato—can physics be *founded on verities that the human intellect can grasp intuitively.*

Benedetti's Critique of Aristotle

To that end, Benedetti devoted most of his energies. Aristotle, he showed, was ignorant of motion. In the matter of natural motion he had held that the velocity of a body falling depends on its proximity to its final goal, when in fact it depends on its distance from its starting-point. Aristotle also failed to appreciate that 'the rectilinear upward and downward motion of natural bodies is not natural *per se*', but is the result of a violent force and the action of the medium in which the bodies have been placed. In the case of violent motion, again, Aristotle had failed to see that the up-and-down motion is continuous and ceaseless, or that motion in a straight line may be infinite in time while yet being finite in space.

But Aristotle's greatest error in physics was to deny the possibility of a vacuum on the grounds that a moving body in a vacuum, meeting no resistance, would assume an infinite velocity. Nothing could be further from the truth, Benedetti countered, since, in fact, the velocity is proportional to the relative weight of the body, *i.e.* to its absolute weight diminished (and not divided) by the resistance of the medium. It follows that the velocity does not increase indefinitely even when the resistance is zero. On the contrary, the velocities of different bodies (*i.e.* composed of different materials) are proportional

[1] *Ibid.*

to their densities. As for bodies composed of one and the same substance, they have identical natural velocities in a vacuum.

Benedetti proved this point with the following argument:

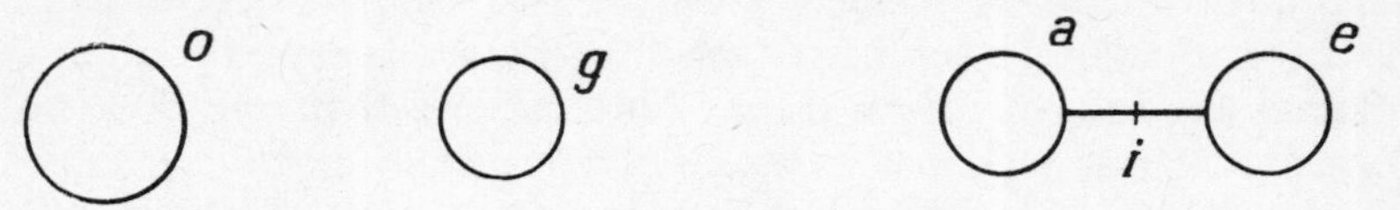

fig. 7 The simultaneous fall of heavy bodies according to Benedetti.

Let *o* and *g* be two homogeneous bodies and let the weight of *g* be half that of *o*. Let *a* and *e* be two other bodies of the same material as *o* and *g*, and each identical in weight to *g*. Imagine *a* and *e* placed at the extremities of a bar of negligible weight with centre *i*. Clearly, *i* would weigh as much as *o*, and hence would move with the same velocity through a vacuum as *o*. Now, removing *a* and *e* from the bar would not change their velocities. Hence *g* must have the same velocity as *o*.

With his motion in a vacuum and the simultaneous fall of homogeneous bodies Benedetti had indeed travelled a long way from Aristotle. But his dream of laying the unshakable foundations of mathematical philosophy did not allow Benedetti to stop there. Aristotle had, in fact, constructed a false image of the world and transplanted it into his physics. His false cosmology, based on the theory of 'natural places', had necessarily vitiated his dynamics. According to Benedetti, there were no obstacles to the existence of infinite bodies 'beyond the heavens'. Aristotle's objections had no greater validity than had his denial of a plurality of worlds, of the mutability of the heavens and of many other things as well. Aristotle's views were wrong simply because he did not understand mathematics; only thus could he deny infinity.

To disprove Aristotle, Benedetti divided a segment into two equal parts, then halved the parts and argued that since the infinite repetition of this operation was possible in principle, infinity was a fact.

As one can see, Benedetti came within hailing distance of Galileo and Descartes, from whom he was nevertheless separated by a deep gulf. In fact, he shared Aristotle's gravest error in dynamics: he, too, considered motion as a *change* of state. Hence Benedetti's 'mathematical philosophy' must be placed on the wrong side of the line dividing Renaissance from modern science.

A New Archimedes: Simon Stevin

Stevin's sole contribution to dynamics was his experiment with Jean Grotius in 1585 to determine whether heavy bodies descend more quickly than light bodies, as Aristotle had taught, or whether they fall with the same velocity, as Taisnier and Cardan had claimed they did. The experiment proved that though two lead balls of different weights fall with the same velocity, a thread of cotton falls more slowly than a cotton ball. Both theories were therefore false.

It seems odd that Stevin should have felt satisfied with this result. Possibly, he was held back by the difficulty he faced in attempting the same kind of theoretical explanation of the relationship between resistance and force in dynamics as he was able to give in statics and hydrostatics. This is not surprising, for statics, though ostensibly concerned with the practical behaviour of balances and simple machines (lever, winch, *etc.*), is, in fact, a theoretical science—a branch of mathematics on a footing with arithmetic and geometry.

Stevin's first works on statics (1586) included the *De beghinselen der weeghconst* ('Elements of the Art of Weighing'), his *De weeghdaet* ('Weighing Practice') and his *De beghinselen des waterwichts* ('Elements of Hydrostatics'). An enlarged version, published in 1605 as the *Wisconstige gedachtenissen* ('Scientific Thoughts'), was translated into Latin by Snellius (*Hypomnemata mathematica*). Albert Girard's French translation was not published until 1634.

Distinction between Statics and Dynamics

As Duhem has pointed out, Stevin's statics were purely Archimedean—the geometer of Bruges was a faithful disciple of the great Syracusan. Hence, he condemned the traditional marriage between statics and dynamics consummated in the pseudo-Aristotelian *Problems of Mechanics*, according to which the problem of the equilibrium of the lever is the problem of finding the arcs described by its extremities.

Stevin's opposition to all attempts to found statics on dynamics, and thus to explain immobility by motion, extended not only to the principle of virtual velocities but also to the principle of virtual work. Thus, when, in a second appendix to his *Statics*, he stated that systems of pulleys can be treated by the principles of statics—'*Ut spatium agentis ad spatium patientis, sit potentia patientis ad potentiam agentis*'—it was the *actual* work which he referred to, and not, as Duhem and Dugas have suggested, the *virtual* work.

Stevin's Statics: the Lever

The *Statics* is divided into two books, the first dealing with the equilibrium of weights and the second with centres of gravity. Book I is subdivided into two parts, one containing the definitions and postulates, and the other propositions on the behaviour of heavy bodies on horizontal and inclined planes.

By a very ingenious and elegant argument, Stevin reduced the equilibrium of all levers to the simplest case, *i.e.* the balance.

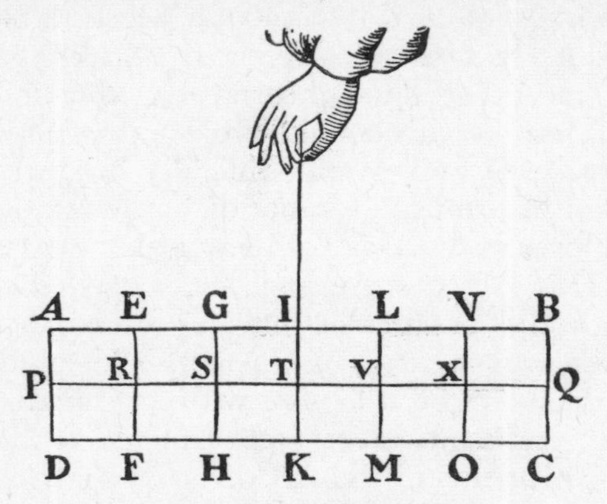

fig. 8 Stevin's proof of equilibrium.

Let a homogeneous right parallelepiped be suspended from its geometrical centre, and hence its centre of gravity, T *(fig. 8)*. It will clearly be in equilibrium. Imagine it divided into six equal parts by the lines AD, EF, GH, IK, LM, NO, BC. Now imagine the four left sections and the two right sections respectively joined together, with their several centres of gravity placed in S and X. Replace each of them with an equal weight suspended from the respective centres of gravity and join these centres by a rigid bar: the equilibrium would not be affected. Now, the distance separating T from S and X is inversely proportional to the suspended weights. Similarly, it can be proved that any body of whatever

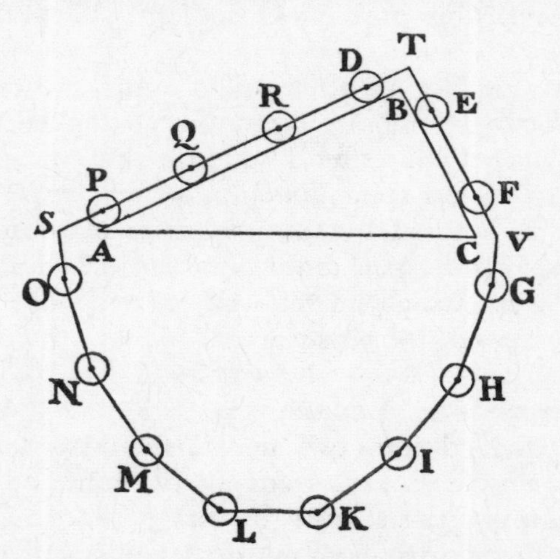

fig. 9 Stevin's inclined plane.

shape or however suspended from the [rigid] arm of a balance will be in equilibrium under these conditions.

The Inclined Plane: 'The Magic Is Not Magical'

Stevin was not, as some historians have claimed, the first to solve the problem of the equilibrium of heavy bodies on an inclined plane, for, as Duhem has shown, the solution was found by Jordanus Nemorarius and then 'borrowed' by Tartaglia. Even so, Stevin's name must be linked with the solution, for he arrived at it quite independently and far more incisively than his historical precursors. His solution was based on the impossibility of *perpetual motion*, which he thereby transformed into a fundamental principle of mechanics, using intuitive arguments that brook no contradiction.

Stevin was so rightly proud of his famous proof that he reproduced the associated diagram in the frontispiece of his work with the legend '*Wonder en is gheen wonder*' ('The magic is not magical').

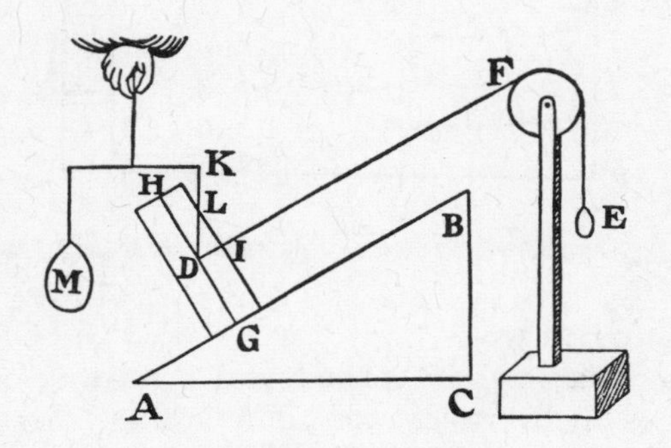

fig. 10 Body in equilibrium on an inclined plane. (*After Stevin.*)

Let ABC be a triangle whose plane is perpendicular, and whose base AC is parallel, to the horizon. Let AB=2BC. Round the triangle, arrange a chain of fourteen spheres equal in weight and size, and equidistant from each other at the points D, E, F, G, H, I, K, L, M, N, O, P, Q, R (*fig. 9*), so that two of the spheres lie on the side BC, four on the side AB, and the eight remaining spheres are suspended symmetrically beneath. The whole system must necessarily be in equilibrium for if the 'apparent weights' [a notion corresponding to the *gravitas secundum situm* of medieval statics] of the spheres E and F were not equal to that of the spheres P, Q, R, D, the 'heaviest' would begin to fall and the 'lightest' would rise, with the result that the spheres will have the same disposition as before, and the process would be continued *ad infinitum*, which is clearly absurd. Hence the 'apparent' weights placed on an inclined plane are inversely proportional to the length of the sides on which they rest, so that the weight E will balance twice the weight D.

In *fig. 10*, therefore, the thread DF parallel to AB would balance the weight D provided $E = D\frac{AB}{BC}$, just as the vertical thread DK would balance D, provided M=E.

Stevin also studied more complicated cases, including oblique elevation, and in the last part of the *Statics* (*Spartostatics*) he arrived at the rule of the parallelogram of forces for the case where the two forces are at right angles.

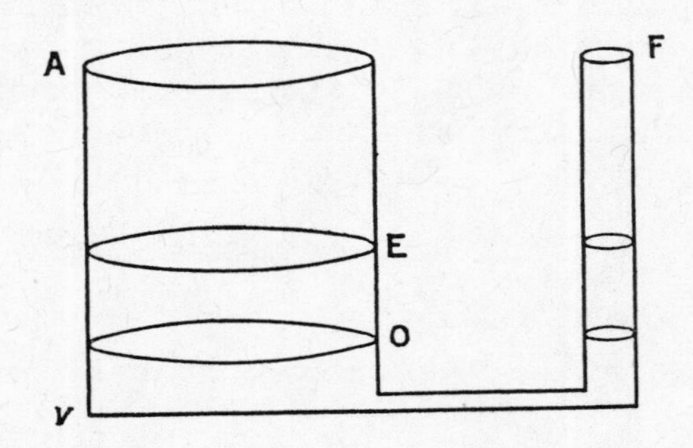

fig. 11 Benedetti's study of communicating vessels.

Stevin's Hydrostatics

While Stevin's *Statics* rightly earned him the name of 'the second Archimedes', his hydrostatics was, if anything, more remarkable still. Hydrostatics had, in fact, stood almost completely still since Archimedes.

The only other advance had been made by Benedetti, who had shown in his *Diversarum speculationeum . . . liber* that the water levels of two communicating vessels must necessarily be equal. Hence, if the chamber of the pump AV *(fig. 11)* is joined to the tube F, 'the water in F will suffice to resist the thrust of the water in AV, and conversely, even though the quantity of water in AV greatly exceeds that in F'. Moreover, Benedetti had shown that the water pressure on the bottom of any vessel is proportional to the cross-section. From these observations, Benedetti deduced that if the pump chamber AV has ten times the cross-section of the tube F, a weight of one pound in F would balance a weight of ten pounds in AV. Benedetti thus foreshadowed Pascal's hydraulic press.

Since Stevin had not read Benedetti, his work must be considered independent and original. In any case, it led him to results of far wider scope, for from the equilibrium of liquids in two communicating vessels he deduced that the *pressure* exerted on each vessel must be equal. By elegant and original arguments, he was then able to prove that the water pressure on the bottom of a vessel depends neither on the shape of the vessel nor on the volume of water contained in it, but exclusively on the height of the water. This led him to his famous 'hydrostatic paradox'—that a fluid, by means of its pressure, can exert on the bottom of a vessel a total effort many times greater than its weight.

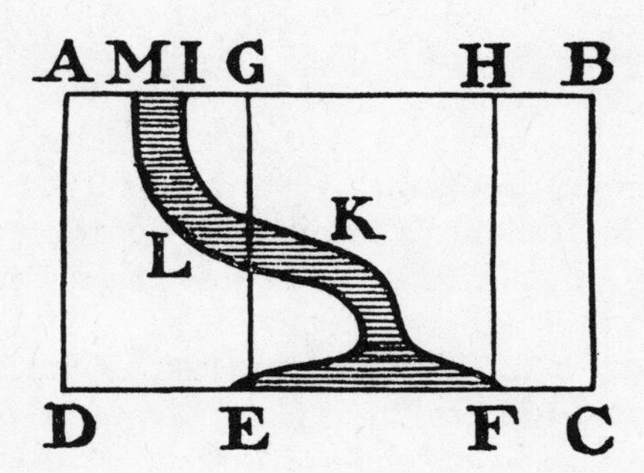

fig. 12 Stevin's determination of liquid pressure on the bottom of a vessel.

Stevin based his argument on the principle of solidification (Th. IV, Prop. IV), according to which a solid body of any shape and of the same density as water remains in it at equilibrium whatever its position may be. He then showed that the water pressure in any channel left in the solidified mass and in contact with the base is independent of the shape of the channel and depends only on the height *(fig. 12)*. In other words, the pressure in any one channel is equal to that of a right parallelepiped constructed on the element of the base under consideration. To balance the pressure exerted on each such element by a very small quantity of water, we should therefore need a weight many times greater than that of the liquid. Conversely, a small quantity of water can support a weight much greater than its own.

Stevin went on to determine the pressure of liquids on the walls of the containing vessels.

To do so, he considered the total pressure as the sum of the partial pressures exerted on small horizontal slices of the wall, which vary with the depth. Having constructed two series based respectively on the upper and lower values of each element, the first smaller and the second larger than the required value, he showed that the correct value could be found by increasing the number of slices *ad infinitum*, and that the total pressure exerted by a liquid on a vertical wall is equal to the weight of half the right prism of which it is the base and whose height is equal to that of the water in the vessel.

By a similar procedure, Stevin determined the pressure of liquids on inclined walls and even on curved walls, adding numerical proofs to his geometrical demonstrations.

Stevin and His Contemporaries

Though Archimedes' influence over Stevin was undeniable, it remains to Stevin's lasting credit that he was the first to apply Archimedean principles in a field in which no one before him had suspected their relevance.

Compared with his other contributions, Stevin's theory of navigation might seem unimportant. Nevertheless it was Stevin who first proved, not only that a ship's stability depends on its having a low centre of gravity, but also that its centre of gravity must be lower than that of the water which it displaces.

Oddly enough, Stevin's contemporaries did not so much admire him for his statics and hydrostatics as for the wind-propelled chariot which he constructed in 1600 for Maurice of Nassau, and which could carry 28 passengers much faster than a horse.

THE DESCRIPTIVE SCIENCES

CHAPTER 1

Geology

Ancient and Medieval Sources

The syllabus which Gargantua drafted for Pantagruel 'so that he might achieve knowledge of the facts of nature', included the art of detecting 'all the metals hidden in the belly of the abyss, and all the stones of the east and the south'. Luckily, Pantagruel did not have to start from scratch, for he could consult the ancient polygraphers: Aristotle, Theophrastos (Περὶ λίθων), Dioscorides and Pliny the Elder, all of whom had been translated by Jewish and revised by Arabic scholars. He could also consult the commentaries of Solin (*Polyhistor*), who had plagiarized Pliny, and of Isidore of Seville (*Etymologies*), or the compilations known as *Lapidaries*, the most famous of which was that of Marbode, Bishop of Rennes, at the end of the 11th century; or the medieval *Summae*, including those of Albertus Magnus, who wrote the *De mineralibus et rebus metallicis libri quinque*, republished in Cologne in 1569; or, finally, the *Hortus Sanitatis* of Johann von Cube, which was reprinted in Venice in 1538 and which contained the *De lapidibus et in terrae venis nascentibus*.

With great eloquence, all these works boasted of their scientific spirit, and John of San Geminiano even used 'scientific' mineralogy to show sinners the way towards repentance and perfection.

Nor was poetic inspiration lacking in these works—science had been embraced by the Muse.[1] Clumsily fingering the lyre of Lucretius and Virgil, the new versifiers poured out a stream of cosmological, mineralogical and mythological jingles. Scévola de Sainte-Marthe, Rémy Belleau, Duchesne (*Chants lyriques*), Daubinier (*La Création*), all tried their hands at the new verse, not to mention such hermetic poets as Augurelli. Some passages in du Bartas' *Sepmaine* and in Ronsard's *Daimons* show clearly how much soul-searching went into their authors' occult attempts to associate our sublunary world with the sphere of the stars.

[1] *Cf.* A. M. Schmidt, *La poésie scientifique en France au XVIe siècle*, Paris, 1938.

The First Specialists

Some 'physicians' who prided themselves on their erudition became engineers and geologists rather than doctors. Such men were Agricola, and Encelius of Saalfeld. They were joined by a humble practitioner who, relying on experience and common sense alone, was able to see clearly what his learned contemporaries failed to discern in their books. His name was Bernard Palissy, and it was due to him as much as to the learned Agricola that geology was given the form which enabled Steno and Leibniz in the 17th century, and Buffon in the 18th, to develop it with so much success.

Born in 1494 at Glauchau in Saxony, Georg Bauer, *alias* Agricola, studied the classics at Zwickau and Leipzig, medicine at various German and Italian universities, and chemistry at Venice. In 1626, he settled in the Riesengebirge on the borders of Bohemia where, more interested in geology than in medical practice, he made a detailed study of mines and mining which he published in his famous *De re metallica*.

With this book Agricola (who died at Chemnitz in 1556) became the first great modern mineralogist. He was also—and long before Ramazzini—an expert on industrial diseases, studying and classifying miners' complaints at first hand, describing in particular the cutaneous lesions so common in salt miners, and protesting against unnecessary accidents, over-exertion and premature senility.

The Huguenot Bernard Palissy (1510?–1589) was a most romantic figure. He was a potter who so loved his art that he ruined himself and his family in its pursuit. He was famed for his clay figures which, though coveted by kings and queens, earned him nothing but penury. In the end, he died for his faith in the Bastille. Palissy, the humble autodidact, combined a keen eye with peasant shrewdness to the profit of science. Instead of reading books he looked at the ground; instead of splitting hairs he watched his kiln and wandered through the mines.

After long reflection on all he had observed, Palissy was persuaded in 1575 (probably by his friend François de Choisnyn) to give Paris, and hence France, its first course of geological lectures. The course, consisting of three lessons on 'fountains, stones, metals and other natures', was open to 'learned and curious listeners' for a fee of one talent.

Early experts in field geology also included the itinerant physician and naturalist Pierre Belon who, after roaming through Brittany and the Auvergne, moved on to Italy and the East where he made a number of observations on the nature of the soil, the sources of rivers, *etc.*

THEORETICAL SPECULATIONS

Biblical and Occult Cosmology

Palissy pleased himself by writing a dialogue in which Theory confronted Practice. While Theory offered traditional dogmas and generalizations, her opponent offered positive knowledge and the useful results of experiment.

In fact, geology was still a mere adjunct of mathematical, astronomical, physical, chemical and biological theories, and had not yet become an independent discipline. Its early history was that of cosmology, and cosmology was still steeped in Ptolemy's geocentric doctrine. In the 16th century, geological periods were still defined in terms of the Book of Genesis, and all nature was held to have developed along the three planes of the Cabbalists: the spiritual, the astral and the elementary.

The Spiritual Powers

The ancients had had no need of demiurges—Aristotle assumed that the world was as it always had been, and Lucretius, following Democritos, believed that it had emerged from chaos by pure chance. But Christianity took quite a different view, and Calvin stressed the permanent action of the Sovereign Judge, whose wrath causes the earth to shake so that the mountains skip like rams and the little hills like lambs. True, these Biblical metaphors referred to a prehistoric past that no human being had witnessed, but the Almighty's avenging angels, prophets and saints continued to have the power of using natural catastrophes for the punishment of sinners, or of withholding them to reward the prayers of the repentant.

Nor was the heavenly host the only visitor, for Satan, too, had his minions on earth. John Tritheimus described them at length. They were the igneous spirits, prowlers of the air, magicians and hobgoblins, who carry the lost traveller into the abyss; the aquatic spirits, whose clamours in raising the tempest terrified Brother Jean of Entommeures; or the infernal army which darkens the light of the bright sun and which revels in playing evil tricks on mankind. Maliciously, these powers nibble at the roots of the 'devil's-bit' scabious plant (*morsus diaboli*), depriving suffering mankind of its benefits, or send their excrements in the form of black pitch, the *stercus daemonum* of Encelius and Agricola. In his *Bermannus*, Agricola tells how demons killed twelve workers in the Annaberg silver mine, which had to be abandoned. Though Palissy rejected all these fables, and though Belon received them with scepticism, most people continued to believe in the existence of spirits haunting the mines: the '*Kobolds*' and '*Nickels*'. The miners of Liège were convinced that goblins kept blowing firedamp into their shafts. Ambroise Paré devoted Chapter XXVII of his *On monsters* to proving that 'demons infest stone quarries', and Scévola de Sainte-Marthe attributed earthquakes to the subterranean exhalations of gnomes.

The Astral Powers

These spiritual powers had their astral assistants. 'From the coming and going of the VII planets through the XII signs', Bartholomew the Englishman wrote, 'comes generation and corruption and all that nature performs below the heavens.' Celestial and terrestrial events were held to be linked together and, Agricola's objections notwithstanding, it was generally agreed that the stars participated in the generation of stones and metals. Stellar signatures were, after all, plain to see on the star-shaped encrinites or 'star-stones' and in the colour of metals, stones and jewels, whose emanations could be transmitted to human beings.

Thus Christian miracles receded before cosmic forces, and Baudin, like Campanella, had no hesitation in endowing the planets with sensitive and rational souls.

The Elemental Power: 'Mother Nature'

Those who were offended by this Pantheon of fallen angels embraced another idol: Nature. Her handiwork could be felt right down to the mineral kingdom, where she copied the stars (*astroites*), the brain (*cerebrites*), the tongue (*glossopetres*), and even the alphabet (*graptolites*). Belon recognized 'some naturally written Hebrew characters' on a stone he had found near Suez, and others spoke of the omnipresent hand of the *spiritus mundi* causing stones to produce stones and metals to generate metals. Thus, Cardan endowed rocks with a kind of vegetative soul, causing them to grow much like trees, and Campanella attributed the creation of such mountain chains as the Pyrenees, the Alps and the Apennines to the same force.

Geogenesis and the Four Elements

Since ancient times, terrestrial matter was supposed to be built up from the four elements, air, fire, water and earth, in accordance with various classical theories: the Aeolian Hypothesis propounded by Anaximenes and by Diogenes of Apollonia; the Plutonian Hypothesis propounded by Zeno and Heraclitos; and the Neptunian Hypothesis propounded by Thales and Aristotle. In the 16th century, all these imposing theories were made to fit in with the views of the nature poets.

Aeolus

Aeolus was held responsible for the production of respirable air, which miners fanned into their shafts with flapping sails in order to dispel the mephitic vapours.

According to Palissy, winds are formed by the compression of air. They exist even below ground, for miners are familiar with strong air currents in certain galleries and with draughts in caves. No wonder that Peletier followed Pliny and Strabo in explaining that earthquakes are caused by the 'wind forces encompassed within the earth'. According to Agricola, subterranean winds are responsible for igniting pyrites, bitumen or sulphur, thus producing the 'boiling vapours which shake the ground when they condense'. Palissy argued that earthquakes cannot occur unless 'fire, water, and air be first joined together', as, for example, when the wind in a cave is compressed by the rising of the subterranean waters, or when water vapour is produced during subterranean combustion.

Earthquakes, which are so frequent in the Mediterranean basin and the Near East, did more than merely inspire myths and legends. The environs of Naples, which had suffered great damage in 1198, witnessed further disasters in 1488, 1527 and, particularly, in 1538. In 1573, a new island—Mikra Kameri—rose up in the Gulf of Santorin. In his *Hymn to Savoy*, J. Peletier mentioned two recent earthquakes at Moutier, and the *conquistadores* discovered that the New World was no firmer (1580, 1581, 1586, 1588).

Agricola classified seismic phenomena into four categories: *tremor* (shaking in various directions); *concussio* (an alternating up-and-down movement); *arietatio* (a bucking or simultaneous up-and-down movement; and *inclinatio* (oblique heaving of the ground). His classification bears some resemblance to the modern analysis of earthquakes into preliminary ripples, horizontal or lateral shocks, and undulatory movements.

Vulcan and Pluto

From time immemorial, men have held that the bowels of the earth are the seat of subterranean fires. Accordingly, Palissy explained that will-o'-the-wisps arise 'from the ignition of sulphur below the earth'. Moreover, miners, particularly in Liège, 'knew' that firedamp resulted from the combination of subterranean sulphur and water vapour. Then there were those ephemeral fires seen in the 'burning fountain near Grenoble' which Tardin made the subject of a *Natural History Augmented by an Ample Treatise on Subterranean Fires*

(Tournon, 1618), and which were reported more frequently still in Italy. Belon remarked on the escape of inflammable gases from the mouth of the Salso Maggiore oil wells, and the ancients had been terrified of the Phlegrean Plain between Naples and Cumae, a field of tepid mud studded with thermal springs and craters. In the *Phaido*, Plato attributed volcanic eruptions to the overspill of flaming matter from the Pyriphlegethon, whose fiery streams kept Tartarus imprisoned. Moreover, he held that the fires of Etna and the Aeolian Islands came from the forge of Cyclops or from the mouth of the giant Encelados.

The Italian peninsula had been the scene of a great many such 'fires', and the terrible eruption of Vesuvius in 1136 had left its unforgettable traces for all to see. It was also known that Hecla in distant Iceland had spewed out its fiery charge in 1436, 1510, 1554 and 1597. Spanish sailors reported similar phenomena from the New World. On the arrival of the *conquistadores* in Central America, a volcano (which was studied by G. Hernandez de Oviedo in 1520) was in full eruption, and they learned that the natives were in the habit of throwing young girls into its crater to appease their subterranean gods. In 1534, Cortés' army was showered with the ashes of Pichincha, 50 leagues away, and in 1541, Agua in Guatemala spat out gigantic streams of lava.

The causes of these eruptions remained a subject of keen controversy. In the middle of the 15th century, Jacobo Mariano (Taccola) of Siena blamed a central fire—'the soul of the earth'—and, foreshadowing L. von Buch's theory, he declared that 'the fire and the air locked in the cavities and pores of the earth cause the earth to heave up, seeing that the fiery flames and the air tend naturally to rise up'. Others believed in purely local phenomena: the ignition of deposits of oil, sulphur, pyrites, bitumen and petroleum. This theory seemed to be borne out by the presence of mineral oil in a number of volcanic areas.

The chapters on petroleum in Belon's *De admirabili operum antiquorum . . . praestantia* (Paris, 1553) are among the oldest writings on mineral oil. During a visit to Italy, he observed a fountain of white petroleum (called Parma petroleum) gushing from a well in Salsa (Salso Maggiore?). The white oil was a mixture of rock oil and salt water, but at Monte Gibbio (which was also visited by Aldrovandi) Belon observed red petroleum as well. Petroleum was of little economic importance at the time, though Agricola mentions that it was used as lamp oil in Sicily, Cilicia, Babylonia, in the Indies and in Ethiopia, and that Saxon peasants put it in their nuptial torches. In addition, it was greatly praised by 'many great doctors of medicine, not only of Rome but also of Naples and Bologna' as a specific against 'cold maladies' and as being 'excellent for the curing of wounds'.

According to Palissy, petroleum congeals to engender bitumen, 'which is so abundant on the shores of the Dead Sea and which the ancient architects sought out for its binding properties'. In the 7th century, bitumen was used as a component of Gregorian fire. Ambroise Paré recorded the presence of *asphaltum* in a fountain at Beauregard, which was in fact the famous Puy de la Poix on the outskirts of Clermont-Ferrand.

Neptune

Early geologists were also interested in hydrology, and particularly in water as the chief means by which Proteus produces his metamorphoses. Albert of Saxony wrote as early as the 14th century that erosion was the chief cause of the shape of the earth's crust. Congealed into immobile snow and ice on the mountains at one moment, water breaks free at the next and pulls the soil with it as it pours into the valleys.

Landslides were well known in the Savoy. In 1218, Mont Granier began to crumble, burying the town of St. André and five surrounding villages, and strewing its debris over an area which is called the 'Abyss of Myans' to this day. Leonardo da Vinci spoke of the choking of lakes by mountain rubble.

Natural springs were said by Scaliger to result from the infiltration of sea water into the earth under the pressure of the oceans, and, by Cardan, from the humidity of the subterranean atmosphere. Peletier, too, subscribed to the Lucretian view that springs must be of marine origin, for many of them contain salt.

More originally, Palissy argued that springs are caused when vapours, generated by the sea and in humid places, become condensed in the atmosphere and come down again as rain, so that 'the waters rise and fall ceaselessly'. 'In flat regions and fields, the pluvial waters penetrate through sandy, friable or spongy earth as far as the rocks or clay beneath, whence they emerge as fountains, brooks or rivers'. Peletier also appreciated that the level of water tables keeps rising and falling.

Theories about the nature and composition of water abounded. In certain regions of France the water was said to be 'noxious and goitrogenous', and Peletier and Palissy warned against drinking it. They recommended instead springs which, by virtue of the principles dissolved in them or because of their temperature, 'have rightly and since olden times been considered a fit means of relieving the suffering of mankind'. Palissy held that thermal springs are 'heated by the subterranean combustion of sulphur, coal, lumps of earth and bitumen, probably ignited by a spark from a falling stone'. Agricola, too, looked upon bitumen as the source of heat. Early hydrologists analysed water by distillation, concentration and evaporation, thus probing the secrets of its virtues. Such men were Gunther of Andernach, Leonhardt Turneiser and, particularly, Paracelsus, who classified matter and diseases into mercury, sulphur and salt, each with specific hydrothermal virtues. Paré distinguished between sulphurous, albuminous, bituminous, cuprous, ferrous, plumbous and gypseous springs. Iron was thought to be particularly beneficial and common salt to add flavour, but oils and such salts as blue and green vitriol and alum were held to produce pernicious effects (Palissy and Peletier).

The health-giving properties of various spas and mineral springs were praised by Savonarola (*De omnibus mundi balneis*, Bologna, 1493), Remaclus Fuchs of Liège (*Historia omnium aquarum*, Paris, 1542), Gesner (*De balneis*, 1553), Fallopius (*De thermalibus aquis libri VII*, Venice, 1564), Martin Ruland (*Hydriatice*, 1568) and Andrea Bacci, physician to Pope Sextus V (*De thermis libri VII*, Venice, 1571). A host of sufferers began to converge on these miraculous spas, previously frequented by the Gauls (*e.g.* Plombières and Luxeuil) and by the Romans. Albrecht Dürer has immortalized the scene of bathers emerging from a pool in Aix-la-Chapelle to the sound of music. Carlsbad attracted mainly wounded soldiers. Sixteenth-century Frenchmen went to Pouges and Borvo; the ancient protector of Gallic fountains was resurrected in Bourbon-l'Archambault and in Bourbon-Lancy. In Southern France, there were Balaruc and Barèges; Henri II expected the Bourbon waters to heal the wounds he had sustained at Pavia; Margaret of Navarre took the waters at Cauterets in 1546 and 1547, and Montaigne made a long, if fruitless, tour of all the spas of Europe.

There were also purely spectacular springs. 'In some places', Belon reported, 'the water turns into its own excrement and hence into stone.' A case in point was the natural bridge 'excreted' by the fountain of Saint-Allyre (Clermont), which Belleforest described in his *Cosmographie universelle* (1575).

In the *Phaido*, Plato placed the source of the seas, lakes and fountains in Tartarus, the lower abyss, to which all the waters must return. Belon thought that the Mediterranean gushed from the bowels of the earth and, unlike some of his contemporaries, who held that it emerged beneath the Straits of Gibraltar, he agreed with Pliny that it sprang up beneath the Black Sea 'whither, once it has risen, it never returns again . . . but flows out through the Straits of Gibraltar . . . since otherwise it would drown all the surrounding countries'. Kircher resurrected part of this fable when he had the

9 16th-century alchemist's laboratory, after Breughel the Elder

10 Paracelsus, by Jan van Scorel

Mediterranean escape towards the North and South Poles. None of these men suspected the profound changes the earth had undergone in the course of its evolution. Some, like Scaliger, held that the initial model given by the Creator on the third day of Genesis had remained unchanged save for such local upheavals as earthquakes (Avicenna) and landslides, or by very gradual erosion.

Water was thought to have two opposite effects: pluvial, fluvial and marine erosion of the continents; and fluvio-marine deposition. Like Herodotos and Aristotle, Leonardo da Vinci argued that the land had risen up through the recession of the oceans, and Palissy remarked on the fluctuations of the coast line near Charente, where the 'ocean waxes and wanes'. In addition, it was held that new islands rose up vertically in mid-ocean, through submarine eruptions or flames and debris disgorged by the Great Abyss. This had been the view of Pliny, who was now ably seconded by Libert Froment. Thus, orogenesis was explained in terms of actualism and oceanic cataclysm. The best example of the latter was the Noachian Flood, a catastrophe which, according to Cardan, explained not only the different sizes of the various continents but also the presence on mountains of 'shells from the ocean, long since petrified'.

Palissy, who, as a good Huguenot, did not doubt the literal truth of the Bible, objected to this claim and explained that, far from resulting from the overflowing of the oceans, the Flood had been produced by 'forty days of rain from the fountains of the great deep and the windows of heaven'. He also explained that the 'lapidified' shells, which he himself had gathered near Paris and in the sands of Vallois and Soissons, and in the Ardennes, were simply 'fishes from the fountain of the great deep'. Mattioli, Calzolari and others ascribed the origin of these fossils to other legendary or occult causes. Belemnites (*lyncurium*) were commonly mistaken for the petrified urine of the lynx or for darts thrown by thunderbolts. True, some large fossil fragments whose skeletal nature was beyond doubt might have been the remains of Biblical giants, but all the rest was lumped together under the convenient heading of *ludibria naturae*.

It was Leonardo da Vinci, Cesalpino, Boccaccio, Fracastoro-Alessandro Alessandri and Gesner who first resurrected the long-forgotten and correct Greek theory of the nature of fossils. Palissy identified the shells he had collected in Parisian quarries as 'fishes' covered with pyramidal shells (*Cerithium?*) that 'had become petrified at the same time as the nearby stones had congealed'.

Bolder spirits even tried to attribute these fossils to extant animal species. Thus Fabio Colonna averred that glossopetres, far from being the petrified tongues of serpents, were in fact the teeth of sharks. Palissy accused Belon, who did not commit himself as to the nature of belemnites and nummulites, and Rondelet, the father of ichthyology, of neglecting or misunderstanding the nature of fossilized 'fishes'. According to Palissy, fossilized and extant sea urchins were of a kind, and he identified petrified cockles and mussels with living coastal species. Taking his morphological analysis even further, Palissy described aetites (silicified Cretaceous sponges) as 'lapidified fruit', a mistake which was to persist until the 18th century.

Rhea: the Earth and the Mineral Kingdom

There were great differences of opinion on the respective limits of the three kingdoms of nature, whose profuse productions were far too readily confused. Thus, organic secretions (pearls), pathological deposits (bezoars) and even unknown animals were classified as minerals. Caesius described corals as stones, and Encelius considered them congealed plants (*fruitex marinus*). Encelius also called zoophytes —an intermediate creature—*neque animal neque fruitex; illi commixta est natura animalis et plantae*, and Caesius described incense and camphor as solidified juices, and amber as the bituminous product of hidden fountains, 'congealed by the cold water of the ocean and cast on the shore by the waves'. According to Belon, it is unwise to 'trust in the vulgar names of things if they do not agree with the descriptions of the ancients'. Unfortunately, these ancient descriptions were a collection of the most disparate terms taken from the Greek, the Latin (Rabelais learned his mineralogy from Pliny), the Hebrew and the Arabic (particularly from Avicenna's *Canon* and the writings of the alchemists). All of them found their way into the medieval *Lapidaries* and the *Summae* of Isidore of Seville, Albert the Great, Vincent of Beauvais, *etc.* Thus, Hebrew terms (sard from *sared* = red), Arabic terms (*tinkar* = tincal or borax; *quadmyia* = cadmium; *talq* = talcum), Persian terms (*burah*, or *burag*, in Arabic = borax; *lazuward* = lazulite) existed side by side with Greek and Latin terms, based on legend (*aetite*); geographical terms (*Lapis*, *Assius*, *Armenius*, *Arabicus*, *Thebacius*, *Aethiopicus*, *Cimolia*, *Lemnos*, *Samos* and *Chios* earths); morphology (*chelonites*, *botryites*); and colours (*galactite*, *ophite*, *echite*). Even the Ethiopian language contributed the term *basalt*. It is easy to get lost in this confusion of terms. For instance, Agricola and Pliny probably referred to quite distinct substances when they spoke of 'basalt'.

Classification presented an equally difficult problem. Since it was no longer thought sufficient to list the minerals in the alphabetical order of their Latin names, Aristotle's and Theophrastos' method was brought back to honour. Fossils, presumed to be of telluric origin, were distinguished from metals which, being fusible, were thought to be of aqueous origin. Pliny distinguished between metals, earths, common stones and precious stones, and so did Encelius.

Agricola distinguished between *fossilia* and *metallica*. According to him, *fossilia* could be amorphous, friable and diffuse (earths); compact and concentrated (veins, nodules), or 'congealed' and more or less transparent (hyaline minerals, precious stones). In addition, there were the sulphurs and the salts.

(1) *Earths*. According to Palissy, earths are substances which 'cannot be exhaled or sublimed by the action of fire'. They included—apart from such common things as sand, chalk and clay—Fuller's earth, used in cleaning cloth; Lemnian earth or aphragide, which was an antidote; the astringent earths of Samos and Chio; the soft earth of Cimolia; and ampelite, which was used as a cosmetic and a poison against vine-weevils.

(2) *Rocks*. Rocks (Encelius' *saxa*) were either stratified (schists), sandy (Encelius' *Sandstein*), compact and occasionally polyhedral (Agricola's basalt columns), or vitreous (silex, *saxum cornutum*, Encelius' *Hornstein*).

(3) *Veins and seams*. According to Agricola, the presence of crystalline and amorphous minerals in veins and seams was due to the filling up of crevasses caused by the upsurge of mountains, by erosion, or, as Pliny and Theophrastos had suggested, by hot and dry exhalations.

The role of water in the formation of rocks was inferred by the Greeks and by Agricola from the existence of enhydrites, which Belon called 'weeping-stones'. Palissy, too, spoke of 'congealing waters which precipitate and harden the substances dissolved in them into rock crystals and other transparent stones, much as water congeals into ice'.

Encelius observed that rock crystals contain prisms with three or six faces; Palissy distinguished rectangles, pyramids, pentagons, hexagons and heptagons. In the Ardennes, he saw marcasite sparkling 'like so many scintillating dice', and in Montmartre he observed gypsum (selenite) split up into laminae 'as thin as sheets of paper . . . and as clear as glass'. Still, neither he nor anyone else even dreamt of classifying crystals by their geometric properties.

(4) *Salts*. As we shall have further occasion to remark, the properties of salts were exceedingly difficult to distinguish and to define. Thus sodium chloride had always been known to exist in two forms: 'natural' salt found in the sea and 'artificial' salt obtained from the Polish mines, from Salzburg and Stassfurt, which Agricola and Palissy described at length.

The term 'nitre', which the classical writers had used indiscriminately and which Pliny applied to saline exudations consisting chiefly of sodium carbonate, was used by Agricola and Aldrovandi to describe potassium nitrate, or saltpetre. Belon transferred this name from nitre to sodium carbonate, of which he had observed efflorescences in the Near East. Like the Greeks and the Romans, Agricola continued to confuse nitre with borax (Avicenna's *tinkar* or *chrysocolla auctorum*).

(5) *Precious stones.* Though gems were widely discussed, they proved most difficult to identify. Their occult virtues were praised in verse by Marbode in the 11th century, and Gilles Corozet followed suit in his *Blasons domestiques* (1539), Jean de la Taille in his *Blason des pierres précieuses* (1572), and Rémy Belleau in his *Amours et nouveaux eschanges des pierres précieuses* (1576). Campanella assured his readers that corals lose their colour when they are placed on the skin of feverish patients, and Belleau claimed that turquoise begins to look sad and cold at the onset of a disease.

(6) *Metals and metallogenesis.* We have already discussed the alleged role of the stars in the formation of metals. Alchemists associated gold with the sun, silver with the moon, white lead (tin) with Jupiter, black lead (lead) with Saturn, copper with Venus, iron with Mars and quicksilver with Mercury.

When these distinctions proved inadequate, Paracelsus and Duchesne divided metals into two classes: 'perfect' metals (gold and silver), and 'imperfect' metals (iron, copper, lead, tin), to which Palissy added antimony as the 'origin of lead and iron'. Imperfect metals were said to be adulterated with characteristic proportions of sulphur and quicksilver, but could be made 'perfect' again by the removal of the sulphur in them.

J. Aubert objected that no metals could be imperfect, since every substance has its own entelechy and is perfect in itself. Since they are designed by God, no one has the power to change natural substances in any way.

These scholastic arguments convinced neither Duchesne nor Agricola who, however, remained sceptical about the possibility of turning imperfect metals into gold. Most scholars held that only Aristotle's constituent elements were immutable; all other substances were not. They tended to explain the elements on mechanical principles by the interaction of the plenum and the void, movement and rest, and the four qualities (hot, cold, dry and moist). Aristotle had argued that metals are engendered in the ground by dry or humid exhalations. Albert the Great denied the cold principle, but was otherwise in agreement with the master. J. Aubert held that the immediate cause of metals was the combination of heat and cold, for the subterranean heat releases metallic vapours which the cold concentrates into veins.

Similar ideas were used to explain a wide range of physical and chemical phenomena. All nature was one and, as Leibniz was to say later, 'the generation of minerals can be explained by chemistry'. Surely the hidden forces of nature, which cause vapours to turn into metals, divining-rods to detect subterranean springs, magnetic needles to point to the north, iron to attract iron and rubbed jet and amber to attract chaff, might equally well cause one substance to be changed into another!

THE LESSONS OF PRACTICAL EXPERIENCE

Technical Literature

The working of quarries and mines became the subject of a host of technical and especially metallurgical books. In Italy, Vannoccio Biringuccio published a *De la pirotechnica* (1540); in Spain, Perez de Varga wrote a *De re metallica* (1569) and Villa Feina a book on the same subject (1572); in Germany, there appeared the alchemical writings of Libavius, Weiner, Mathesius, Encelius (*De re metallica*, 1551) and Lazarus Ercker (1573), all of which discussed the art of assaying metals and the chemical analysis of minerals. But the most famous of all was Agricola's *De re metallica*, a down-to-earth treatise which dealt with the detection and measurement of metallic seams (Agricola advocated detection by magnetic needles but was sceptical about the alleged virtues of divining-rods). More specialized than Gesner's and Aldrovandi's encyclopedic works, all these books, though still written in Latin, were addressed to practical men and not to theorists. Books written in the vernacular for the humble prospector also appeared, including Ulrich van Kalbe's *Augsburg Bergbüchlein* (1505). A German translation of Agricola's *De re metallica* was published in Basle in 1557. Palissy reported the results of his mining and pottery experiences in French.

Agriculture

As famines, wars and droughts continued to threaten the livelihood of the masses, agricultural reformers like Olivier de Serres, Ch. Estienne and J. Liébault studied the suitability of different soils for different crops, and methods of increasing the harvest. Since the practice of dressing with lime was not yet known, Palissy and Olivier de Serres advocated marling.

Architecture and Decoration

As inflammable wooden houses were gradually replaced by stone dwellings, a new Paris rose up made of plaster and limestone. Granite appeared in the great Breton monasteries, white stone in the elegant castles on the banks of the Loire, phonolite in the sombre churches and mansions of the Auvergne. The quarries were hard-pressed to produce enough freestone, millstone, tiles, bricks, slates, plaster and lime, as the never-ending demand for these materials was increased even further by the reconstruction of town walls damaged by war.

With increasing wealth there arose a need for greater comfort and architectural elegance. Marble was needed for the columns of porticoes and for the plinths of statues; skilfully blended enameller's earths were used by the Della Robbias for fashioning white medallions of infants against the deep blue of the ceiling, and by Palissy for his rustic figurines. The walls were supported with sumptuous revetments. Sideboards glittered with gilded tankards and cut glass, which gentlemen rivalled in collecting as an aristocratic hobby.

Metallurgy

To pay for all this luxury, the mining of precious metals had to be intensified. In about 1554, silver-mining was resumed at Pontgibaud (near Lyons) and gold-washers frequented the river sands in ever-greater numbers. Still the yields in Europe proved rather poor when compared with the Portuguese and Spanish harvest abroad. In 1545, the first silver ingots left the Potosí mines in Bolivia for Cadiz, and the *conquistadores* rifled the golden treasure of Mexico and Peru. Legend caused many an adventurer to go in search of the fabulous city of Eldorado, and to perish on the way.

The preparation of 'industrial metals' will be discussed in the next chapter, so that we can restrict our remarks to the most important advances in iron metallurgy. The simple forges of Gallic, Roman and medieval smithies were improved by the addition of movable furnaces which, like their forerunners, produced porous iron by the direct method. In the 16th century, the addition of flux to the ore led to the production of a malleable cast iron that could be hammered and refined in the forge. Bellows and hammer alike were driven by water power.

Wood was still the main source of fuel. Coal, called *carbo lapideus* (by Agricola and Encelius) and *lithanthrax* (by Encelius), was only used here and there, for instance in Newcastle and Liège. In France, coal was said to poison the drinking water and to cause diseases. However, a notarial deed mentions the leasing of coal-mining rights in Le Creusot in 1507. In 1548, Henri II approved the mining of coal by La Roque-Roberval. In 1562, coal-mining began to spread from the Loire region, where it first started, as far afield as Lyons and Forez. Laws governing the mining of coal were first promulgated in a special royal edict of 1597.

CHAPTER 2

Chemistry

THE MEDIEVAL HERITAGE

THE WRITINGS OF THE ALCHEMISTS fascinate historians not so much because of their contents as because of their picturesque language. Early chemistry was mystical and so full of confused ideas and allegorical terminology that it is extremely difficult to discover the real chemical knowledge of the times.

Though no historian of chemistry can afford to ignore the many myths that 15th- and 16th-century chemistry was heir to, and which were transmitted right down to the 18th century, he must also be able to sift the wheat from the chaff. If he does so, he will find that in the middle of the 15th century exact chemical knowledge was not much greater than it had been in the Middle Ages—chemistry had stagnated in the interval.

PRACTICAL CONTRIBUTIONS

Despite the widespread view to the contrary, technicians rather than alchemists laid the foundations of modern chemistry. However far back we delve into time, we shall find no period in which some aspects at least of practical chemistry were not part of everyday life. The first chemical reaction produced by man was the oxidation, the second the reduction, of metallic oxides. A number of organic reactions were also known and exploited early in man's history: the fermentation of milk and vegetable juices and the preparation of vinegar.

Long before history began to be recorded, therefore, man was familiar with elementary chemical techniques and had begun to apply them to an ever-wider range of phenomena. Fermentation was used for the preparation of new foods and beverages; putrefaction for skinning and tanning animal hides and later for retting flax and for producing the oldest-known chemical compound, sal-ammoniac. Early organic techniques were used mainly to obtain vegetable essences and dyes, which had previously been obtained from mineral pigments. Neanderthal man is known to have dug up lumps of manganese oxide and to have scraped them for their colour. Archaeologists have also discovered skeletons dyed red by Aurignacian or Magdalenian man. While artists used these colours to decorate caves, craftsmen soon afterwards used them for dyeing cloth. As the textile industry spread throughout the inhabited world, man learned to isolate coloured earths, in other words he invented the first processes for separating the constituents of natural substances. He also began to import chemical substances; alum, for instance, was one of the earliest objects of international commerce. Possibly it was the trafficking in mineral and vegetable dyes which did more than anything else to spread chemical knowledge among different people.

The use of fire in metallurgy and pottery led to further studies of the composition of minerals and earths. These materials were generally so close at hand that their commercial value was negligible. Tin and mercury, which were found in special regions, were the first minerals to be traded; they were joined later by antimony and arsenic sulphides.

Metallic sulphides were, in fact, the best-known of all mineral compounds, so much so that chemistry before the 15th century might be called the chemistry of the sulphides.

The Diffusion of Chemical Knowledge

Metallic sulphides, oxides and sulphates, and a few carbonates, chlorides and nitrates, were the only chemical substances studied by the early chemists. Craftsmen had established a body of traditional knowledge based upon them which they handed down to their heirs, first by word of mouth and later—probably at the beginning of the Christian era—on paper. These texts, which grew more voluminous as new compilers and translators added to them, reached the Western world at the beginning of the 14th century. Most were technical treatises on dyeing or on gilding, and nearly all were steeped in the esoteric jargon of the day. However, secret language was used only to describe the author's 'great recipes'; common methods of dyeing and tanning were usually presented in simple terms.

Special alchemical signs were not common until the 15th century, and even in the 16th century were in general use only by chemists writing in Latin. The Greek method of describing minerals by means of the signs of the zodiac, which had been discarded by the Arabs, made a gradual come-back in 13th- and 14th-century Latin manuscripts.

The Role of the Alchemists

The needs of dyers and smiths alone would not have led to the accumulation of an impressive body of chemical knowledge, for their work was based on only a limited number of procedures. True, the use of mordants drew attention to the properties of alums and vitriols, and hence paved the way for the preparation of acids, but if knowledge of chemical substances and their reactions went further than that at the end of the Middle Ages, it was mainly because chemists pursued aims quite other than the production of dyes or metals. However, one must not exaggerate the role of their traditional dream of changing base metals into gold. In fact, the mystical philosophy and the search for the philosopher's stone seem to have developed at a time when traditional alchemy had already been outstripped, so that they played no role whatsoever in the development of chemistry as an exact science.

Gilders and Goldsmiths

Rather was it the gilders and goldsmiths who, putting alchemical recipes into practice, gave chemistry its next great impetus. Gold and silver had been coveted since earliest antiquity, and medieval writers had referred to their alloys by a host of names, recording the preparation of each one in various compilations. These recipes show clearly that the aim of the operations was not so much the transmutation of base metals into gold as the production of a golden lustre by means of copper, arsenic sulphide and a number of coloured oxides.

As early as the beginning of the Alexandrian period, goldsmiths and chemists were familiar with a number of methods of assaying alloys of gold, silver, copper and lead, using sulphur and various metallic sulphides. The first gilding procedures date from about the same period. In fact, the recipes consulted by Paracelsus and his contemporaries had all been written by the 6th century A.D. The substance mentioned most frequently was arsenic sulphide or orpiment (*auri pigmentum*), whose very name shows the main use to which it was put.

The Chemistry of Gilding

Because of the ease with which they could be prepared, and also because they led to end-products of the most varied appearance, arsenic and sulphur compounds took pride of place in gilding techniques. They were known by various names: orpiment, realgar, sandarac and saffron. Arsenic oxides were known in the 5th century, when the term 'arsenic' was applied to arsenious ('white arsenic') oxide obtained by roasting. Metallic arsenic was mistaken for a special kind of mercury.

Nor was this the only confusion between chemical elements, and it was a long time before many of them could be isolated and identified.

Thus, antimony was not recognized as such until the end of the 14th century, and though arsenic and mercury were known to be different 'types' of metal, arsenic continued to be described as mercury in order to stress certain common properties, in particular the lability of the sulphur and oxygen compounds of both. But despite this ambiguous terminology, 16th-century chemists rarely confused the two, knowing perfectly well which was referred to in a given context.

Mercury—the metal we call by that name today—also played an important role in the production of pigments. The Romans had known mercury in its free state or as cinnabar. Since cinnabar is simple to reduce, the preparation of metallic mercury became a remunerative industry. From the 5th century A.D. onwards, artificial cinnabar—also called vermilion—was prepared from mercury and sulphur. Though medieval writers used the names 'cinnabar' and 'minium' as generic terms for all red metallic sulphides and oxides, it is usually possible to tell when they were referring to cinnabar in particular.

Quite naturally, early chemists looked upon the transformation of mercury as the key to some of nature's mysteries. When cinnabar was heated the metal distilled out; conversely, cinnabar could be obtained by heating a mixture of sulphur and mercury. Since heat was able to impart opposite qualities to substances, it was clearly the great 'transmuter'. The producers of pigments, not the alchemists, were undoubtedly the first to make these discoveries.

The Illumination of Manuscripts

In the Middle Ages, illuminators searched far and wide for suitable colours and, particularly, for indelible blue and gold pigments.

Persian, and later Chinese, lapis-lazuli, a complex silicate containing sulphur, was not used in Europe as a source of ultramarine before the beginning of the 15th century. Illuminators used instead such silicates as 'Egyptian blue', which had been manufactured in Italy for nearly a thousand years, or smalt, a compound of silica and cobalt first mentioned by Cennino Cennini in the early 15th century, and found in Siena and Germany. Copper compounds proved another source of colour, and played a particularly large role in gilding recipes. Copper was usually obtained by heating copper salts in the presence of the unstable sulphides of other metals. In this and similar ways, golden tints could be produced which, far too often, served to deceive simple-minded customers.

In the loveliest miniatures, thin gold leaf was applied to parchment treated with gum or albumen. Recipes for preparing these and similar adhesives abound in medieval manuscripts and in 14th- and 15th-century texts, side by side with gilding recipes for the use of copyists, painters and goldsmiths. In most of them, tin foil coated with arsenic sulphide was substituted for gold, whence it was but a short step to deliberate fraud. Many alchemical practices go back to this very substitution.

Mineral and Vegetable Pigments

Natural and artificial blues and golds were not the only pigments used by illuminators, painters and dyers. Reds were obtained from various clays, from iron oxide, from sinople, from porphyry (mentioned by Cennini and Agricola and which came to be known as Van Dyke red) and from hematite, one of the oldest sources of red colour. Illuminators also used yellow ochre, a mixture of clay and iron oxide; burnt sienna, a mixture of clay and manganese dioxide; green malachite, a hydrous carbonate of copper; and green azure (mentioned by Cennini), a mixture of cobalt and copper, iron and zinc salts. St. John's white, so well known towards the end of the Middle Ages, was calcium carbonate, carefully purified and dried in the sun. A recipe in a Syriac manuscript for the preparation of white lead or 'ceruse' is identical with a method still in use: sheet lead was placed in pots with a little vinegar, each pot being packed in dung.

In addition, early dyers used a host of vegetable pigments. There were the many extracts from the bark of the walnut, elm and Brazil trees mentioned by Cennini, together with nut gall, and the resins of the pine, fir and cedar trees; red resin had been known for a thousand years as dragon's blood, and other materials included the gums of the cherry and almond trees, gum lac, saffron and indigo imported from the East, madder (which had been cultivated in Gaul since the 5th century) and pastel, which was grown in Picardy and Languedoc from the 12th century onwards.

The best blacks were prepared from carbon obtained by various processes: from lampblack for the preparation of inks, from the furnaces of glassmakers for painting, and from vine stalks for charcoal.

The Chemical Aristocrats: Metals

Since metallurgy is one of the oldest chemical industries, the vocabulary describing the ores, oxides and sulphides of metals was vast. Metals were undoubtedly the first chemical substances to be considered a class apart, and possibly other groups were first distinguished by comparison with them. It was thus that systems of chemical classification were originally born.

Metals have always been considered the noblest of all chemicals: the Greeks had associated their two 'perfect' metals (gold and silver) and their 'imperfect' metals (iron, mercury, tin, copper and lead) with the seven planets.

Although not yet clearly identified, zinc had been known for centuries in the form of cadmia and calamine. It was used chiefly in brass-making, and must have been known in the metallic form as well. However, it continued to be called 'false silver' until Paracelsus gave it its modern name.

Antimony, whose sulphide—stibine—was known to Hippocrates, and which had served as a cosmetic in ancient times, must also have been clearly distinguished at the beginning of the 16th century, since Basil Valentine, in a special paper, mentions the metal by name. Bismuth was identified at about the same time, and was described by Valentine and Agricola. However, these two metals were still being confused with lead and tin and with each other. Only in the second half of the 17th century were they classified as special semi-metals, together with zinc and—later—arsenic, which was not fully identified until the beginning of the 18th century.

The Chemistry of Salts

Long before all this knowledge was consolidated, all non-metals were treated as 'salts'. This vast and badly-defined class contained not only the compounds which we ourselves would call salts, for example ceruse, verdigris and the chlorides of sodium, potassium and calcium, but also the oxides and a great number of organic compounds. Some salts were given special names, such as alum, vitriol and borax.

The term 'borax' was often reserved for alkaline compounds. Common salt had been known since earliest antiquity in both its forms (sea-salt and rock-salt), and so had sodium carbonate and sodium sulphate (which were often lumped together as 'natron') and potassium nitrate or saltpetre, which was used in the manufacture of Gregorian fire in the 7th century. Potassium carbonate was obtained by washing wood ashes and sodium carbonate by washing the ashes of seaweeds. Sal-ammoniac was used in the preparation of calcium chloride from lime. Quicklime was used in the preparation of caustic potash. From 10th-century recipes we know that soap was prepared from oil and caustic alkali.

Borax (in the modern sense) was known, though the term itself was applied not only to alkaline salts but also to solutions used for pickling metals.

The Discovery of Acids

Alums and vitriols had for centuries been considered to hold a place half-way between salts and acids; the latter were not clearly identified until the 16th century. However, as they worked with natural sulphates, chemists began to suspect the existence of acids and to study ways of isolating them. This is the reason why they distinguished alums and vitriols from other salts, and why they considered them related to each other.

Nitric acid was prepared in the Middle Ages by the calcination of saltpetre, or by heating saltpetre with a vitriol; the distillation product, *aqua fortis*, was the first acid to be isolated since the discovery of vinegar. This method of preparing acids gave a first hint of the violence of the hidden forces stored in vitriols. The preparation of sulphuric acid (spirit or oil of vitriol) from 'Martian vitriol' (ferrous sulphate) seems to go back to between the 10th and 12th centuries, though it was only during the 15th and 16th centuries that the technique was first recorded. This consisted of the calcination of sulphates or the combustion of sulphur in the presence of water, or the oxidation of sulphides or of sulphur in the presence of nitrates.

Once sulphuric acid was known, it was only a question of time before hydrochloric acid was isolated. Both were described by Basil Valentine, though hydrochloric acid, called 'spirits of salts', must have been prepared (but not identified) much earlier by the calcination of common salt.

The Notion of 'Spirit'

In all pre-18th-century chemical texts, spirits were generally distinguished from solid substances like salts and metals, but while medieval authors applied the term to a limited number of apparently similar substances, their 15th- and 16th-century successors applied it to a far wider range, including mercury, sulphur and arsenic as well as sal-ammoniac and hydrochloric acid, the aromatic essences and that marvellous discovery of the Middle Ages: alcohol. Before becoming a 'spirit', at the end of the 16th century, alcohol had lived an independent existence as *aqua vitae* or the promoter of long life. The term 'alcohol' was later applied to very fine powders, and it was not until the beginning of the 19th century that it was used generally for the distilled products of the grape.

The number of spirits was particularly large since, as we saw, 'mercury', 'arsenic' and 'sulphur' were used to refer to a great variety of substances. These names referred not only to the material substances but also to the observable properties which they conferred. This broad usage was most marked in the 15th and 16th centuries, when the 'new' theory of matter involving spirits, the four elements and their corresponding qualities was at its height. Its influence was later responsible for the notorious phlogiston theory.

The Search for a Unified Doctrine

Modern authors tend to exaggerate the incoherence of early chemical theories. Misled by the esoteric terminology of 15th- and 16th-century writers, they are unable to recognize that the theories themselves were based on solid observations. The early chemists, no less than those of modern times, tried to construct a theory or a philosophy of matter on the known physical and chemical properties of those substances which they had learned to handle. They had perforce to express this theory in the only language they knew.

Towards the middle of the 15th century, this body of knowledge had already been sufficiently co-ordinated to lead to a rudimentary classification, which remained in vogue until the reform of chemical nomenclature at the end of the 18th century. The theory of matter was still based on the four elements: earth, air, fire and water, and on the four main qualities: hot, cold, wet and dry. These gave rise to the spirits by their various associations, and to the generation of the seven metals.

Medieval chemists and their successors developed this theory in different ways in order to arrive at a more satisfactory and more 'knowledgeable' explanation of the observed facts. The more dogmatically they proclaimed their various 'self-evident' truths, the more self-satisfied they felt. In fact, there was little to choose between them, and the theoretical disputes between 16th- and 17th-century chemists strike us as singularly senseless exercises in hair-splitting. When all is said and done, no new 'truths' had been discovered for three centuries—all chemists were agreed on the immutability of the 'elements' and 'qualities', even at a time when greater familiarity with chemical compounds ought to have shown them the error of their ways. The probable explanation is that theory and experiment were still completely dissociated. The discovery of new phenomena was left to disinterested amateurs, while 'serious' chemists studied terminology and systematics, satisfied that the body of theoretical knowledge was already as perfect as it could be.

In this way, the medieval tradition, based on classical precepts, was taken over hook, line and sinker, and this continued faith in outworn ideas shows better than anything else what obstacles Lavoisier had later to overcome.

THE CHEMICAL RENAISSANCE

The end of the 15th century saw an upsurge of chemical research in the wake of the sudden appearance of a large number of chemical and alchemical texts. Compilers had begun to step up their activities from about the 13th century, when Vincent of Beauvais, Albertus Magnus, Arnold of Villanova and Roger Bacon had shown them the way. Many less-known and anonymous writers also left copies and summaries of ancient manuscripts and lists of their own recipes.

Books had begun to reach a far wider audience than ever before, thanks mainly to the improved network of trade routes which now covered all Western Europe, joining it to Scandinavia, Eastern Europe and the Middle East. This growth of commercial activities was, in turn, the result of a marked increase in technical activities, particularly in the textile industry and dyeing, and also in mining and metallurgy.

Technical and Commercial Factors

The importance of dyeing to the general progress of practical chemistry remains undiminished even today. Until the end of the 18th century, it was the sole chemical industry of any great significance, not excepting the manufacture of explosives. The discovery of alum deposits in Italy led to a complete transformation of production methods in the 15th century. Whereas alum had previously been imported from Milan by the Venetians and the Genoese at great cost, it now became a fairly cheap product, and its consumption increased even in northern countries. The manufacture of the coveted Flemish cloth involved the use of dyes from Eastern and Southern Europe, and the emergence of a textile industry in Great Britain intensified the volume of this trade. When the Atlantic route was opened up, not only dyes but also the less valuable minerals and metals began to be carried by ship.

Side by side with the expansion of weaving, there was a minor upsurge of metallurgical activities. During the 12th and 13th centuries, metals mined in the Eastern Alps and in Sweden had reached Mediterranean cities by way of the Flanders and Champagne overland routes, or down the Rhine and the Danube, though the German Hansa had used ships to carry copper from the Harz Mountains and iron from Hungary and Sweden. Flemish and Genoese traders had imported tin from Cornwall, Frisians and Saxons had traded in English lead since the 10th century, and brass- and copperware from the Meuse valley had been traded throughout Europe, but it was only in the 15th century that metallurgy became really important. Mining in Bohemia and in the Tyrol was stepped up on an unprecedented scale. At the same time, Swedish iron, Swedish, Russian and Polish copper, English tin and various local metals of lesser commercial value were produced at a growing rate.

This renewal of metallurgy had a considerable influence on the progress of chemistry. Assaying became a highly-prized skill and minerals, metals and their compounds were studied more thoroughly.

This new activity is reflected in the spate of works on mining which appeared in the 16th century. Agricola's famous *De re metallica*, published in 1556, was reprinted time and again. Many other German authors also published technical works in which mining took pride of place. Similar texts were published in 16th-century Italy and Spain (*cf.* page 117).

As a result, chemists were forced to re-examine their theories on the generation of metal, and it was on their results that Paracelsus and his successors were to build their own system.

The Personality and Doctrine of Paracelsus

Philippus Aureolus Theophrastus Bombast von Hohenheim, better known as Paracelsus (1493–1541), was the most illustrious chemist of his day, and even if his achievements have been exaggerated by his disciples, we must grant that he had a crucial influence on chemical thought and research for more than a century. Because he was steeped in the medieval tradition, Paracelsus' many attempts to rid himself of established dogmas were doomed to failure from the start.

His father was Professor at the School of Mines in Carinthia and, like him, Paracelsus gathered much of his chemical and mineralogical knowledge by working underground. He also studied medicine, travelling from university to university and acquiring a great love for foreign places. In the course of his travels, he sought out the company of alchemists, astrologers, caballists and members of secret societies, from whom he learned a number of useful recipes and secrets, and whose language and approach he adopted to the detriment of the clarity of his thought.

Having been appointed Professor of Medicine at Basle in 1526, he launched a virulent attack on the dogmas of scholastic medicine and gained great renown by effecting 'miraculous' cures through recipes containing opium and a number of mineral compounds. He died under rather obscure circumstances while still in his forties. Most of his writings were published posthumously.

Though his scepticism of accepted doctrines led him to direct experiments, neither the times nor his own mystical approach lent themselves to the development of a truly experimental method. All the same, by enjoining his pupils to ignore traditional writings and to observe nature instead, he launched chemistry on a path it has never abandoned since. The historical interest of his doctrine is that he founded it on the direct study of metals and mineral compounds, made for the dual purpose of justifying his theory and of introducing it into medical practice.

To effect his first objective, Paracelsus began the long series of researches which culminated in the work of Lavoisier, and hence affected the development of chemistry for two centuries. His mar-

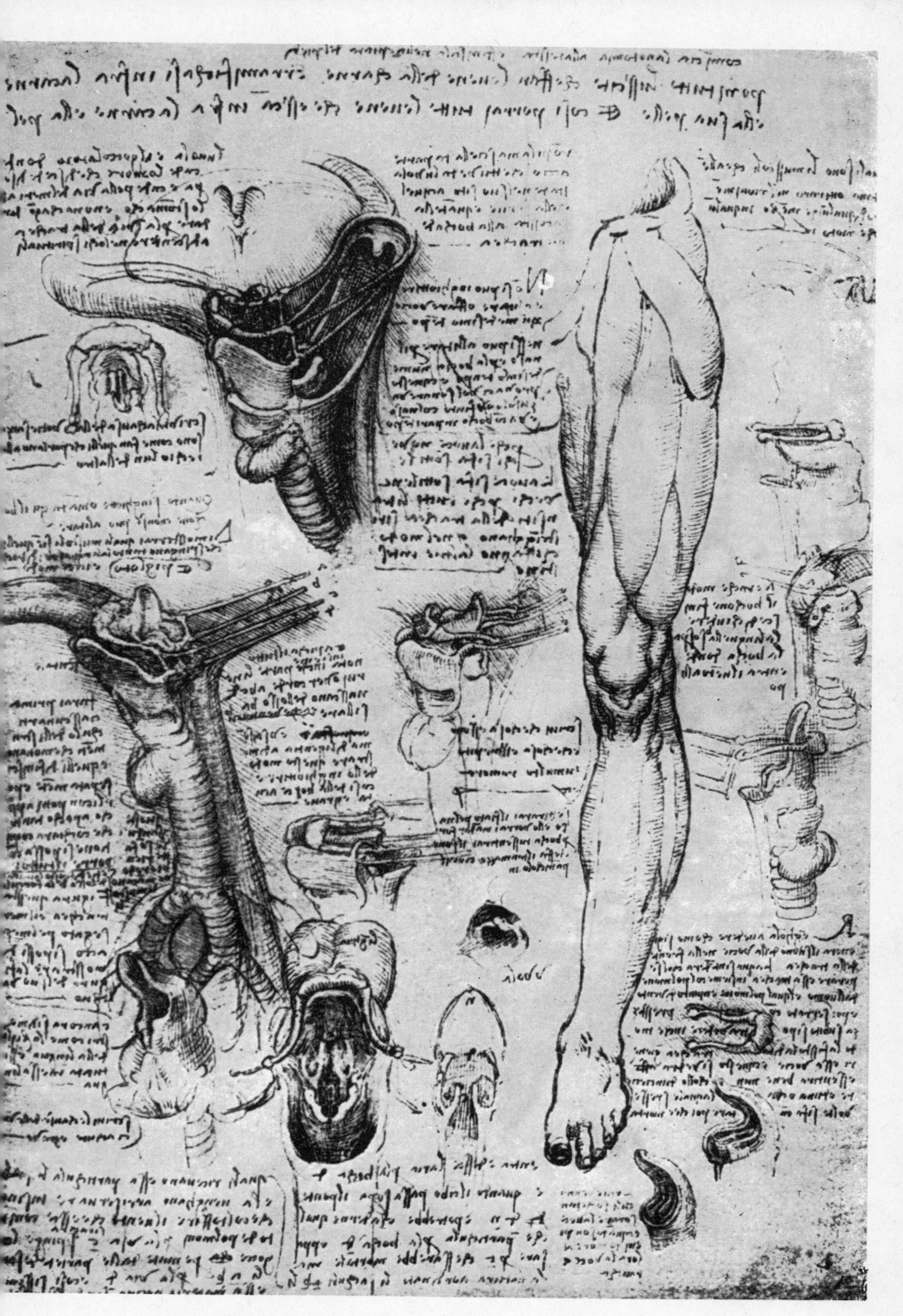

11 Anatomical drawings, from Leonardo's notebooks

12. Dissection. School of Michelangelo

riage of medicine to mineralogy was no less fruitful, for it wrested chemistry from the hands of the alchemists. Moreover, chemistry became a remunerative activity, attracting new talent. In short, Paracelsus was the first of the long line of physicians and mineralogists who laid the foundations of 18th-century chemical science.

The Natural Perfectibility of Metals

Paracelsus believed in the perfectibility of metals, claiming that experiment had shown that all metals have a natural tendency to develop into gold, and to a lesser extent into silver. However, whereas medieval chemists and alchemists believed that this process could be accelerated artificially—and it was to the discovery of a suitable method that they bent all their activities—Paracelsus held that the perfection of metals was the work of nature, which alone forged metals in the bowels of the earth with the help of cosmic and unknown forces. Men cannot affect this 'great work' in any way; all they can do is to sift the purified metal from its ore. Even to do this, they require much skill. Some of the separation techniques are so violent and others so delicate that only experts may use them. Moreover, if the cosmic forces are inclement, the proportion of pure metal in the ore may be so insignificant that it may elude even the experts.

In the fullness of time, the distinction between metals will disappear—all will have developed into gold. This is how Glauber put it in his commentary on Paracelsus:

> Nature's design is not for iron to remain iron, but for it to become perfected into gold: only the miner's impatience prevents it from reaching that state . . . instead of waiting for iron to attain the dignity of gold, he perforce uses it for his own purposes.

Since Paracelsus and his successors concentrated on gold and silver, they paid little attention to the other metals—tin, antimony, lead, copper and iron, in their order of 'perfection' or stability. Mercury was considered to be in a class apart.

The metals of these early chemists were not so much the real substances as their alleged ideal states. Since, in the crude state, all metals were thought to be mixtures of varying perfections, it was the chemist's chief task—by oxidation, solution, acidification, corrosion, sulphuration and the reduction of salts and alloys—to isolate the noble from the base.

The 16th- and 17th-century texts are full of recipes to effect this aim, couched in deliberately obscure terms. After a perfectly intelligible beginning, the authors usually resort to brief hints, implying that anyone with a modicum of skill and intelligence requires no further explanation. Those who went further than that were decried for betraying the noblest secrets of their craft, though few were bold enough to tell how pure gold could be obtained from, say, crude iron ore. At best, they showed how to concentrate traces of gold by what we would nowadays call fractional separation.

Paracelsus' immediate successors continued the attempts to transmute base into noble metals. Though doomed to failure, this work helped to acquaint chemists with a host of previously misunderstood phenomena, particularly with the oxidation of metals and the reduction of metallic oxides.

Chemical 'Principles'

Another consequence of the Paracelsian doctrine was the development of the notion of chemical 'principles'. Late 16th- and early 17th-century chemists held widely differing views on what Paracelsus had meant by his 'quintessence', and many came to look upon it as a sort of universal agent. Eighteenth-century chemists readily identified the quintessence with phlogiston.

Paracelsus himself had introduced the term to lend a measure of scientific respectability to his theories. While nominally rejecting the four basic elements and qualities simply because they were part of the scholastic heritage, he nevertheless held on to the underlying idea. Instead, he introduced 'principles' of his own, but his distinction between the old elements and qualities and the new principles was so subtle that it eluded his own disciples as much as it does the modern reader.

In addition to 'distant principles' (heat, cold, dryness, humidity), Paracelsus also introduced five 'immediate' principles, *viz.* mercury, sulphur, salt, phlegm and *caput mortuum* (the residue remaining after distillations). The first three were said to be fundamental or active principles, the two latter passive and not inherently incorruptible. In effect, experiment showed that phlegm and *caput mortuum* could be transformed by various common agents.

The first three immediate principles are not easy to define, though from the long discourses of Paracelsus and his commentators we gather that they are formed by the combination of distant principles in varying proportions. Mercury corresponds with predominantly humid compounds, sulphur with predominantly hot compounds, and salt with predominantly dry compounds. Apparently cold cannot predominate in any chemical substance, for there is no corresponding principle; the others could be combined in an almost infinite number of ways, for 'there are as many kinds of sulphur, mercury and salt as there are fruits'. Together with phlegm and *caput mortuum*, which are usually neglected by commentators, the first three immediate principles were said to account for all existing chemical substances.

The Quintessence

Paracelsus' theory of matter was completed by the quintessence, or fifth element.

> The quintessence [he explained] is a substance which may be derived from all nature's products endowed with life; which substance, being very subtle, must be purified to the most sovereign degree and cleansed by its separation from the impure and coarse elements holding it entwined; after which separation it rests incorruptible in its own nature.

Was the quintessence therefore a universal principle? Paracelsus called it 'the same as mercury', and spoke of the quintessence of all metals, except the basest.

> The essence of gold partakes of the humid nature of gold; the essence of Saturn [lead] draws cold and dryness from the earth; the essence of quicksilver is derived from the qualities of the air, being itself but a kind of rarefied and extremely subtle air within the bowels of the earth.

The Influence of Paracelsus

Clearly Paracelsus had simply re-introduced the four elements of the Greek philosophers in new guise, and his successors followed suit. This gives us some idea of the sum total of chemical theory for two and a half centuries. Paracelsus' original contribution was small, for what systematic improvements he introduced were mentioned by earlier writers. All he did was to consolidate old notions into what his contemporaries considered a coherent body of doctrine. The success of his theories was not so much due to his ideas as to his forceful personality.

The efficacy of his remedies, his contact with esoteric adepts of the occult sciences, his liking for drink, and his personal indiscretions made him a notorious character. The many attacks on him, during his life and long after his death, have done as much to establish his reputation as the eulogies of those admirers who defended him with blind passion. While later chemists eventually broke with his mystico-medical doctrine and with other alchemical and astrological notions, they continued to pay lip-service to Paracelsus in all their writings. No wonder, then, that chemistry remained largely Paracelsian until the coming of Lavoisier.

Though nowadays it is difficult to conceive that any author could have remained an almost undisputed oracle for more than two centuries, even at the end of the 18th century all scientists were really traditionalists. Even a hundred years later, when blind adherence to ancient doctrines was cast off in most other scientific disciplines, chemistry remained stubbornly immersed in the past. Modern doctrines were never allowed to oust the teachings of the ancients, but were simply superimposed upon them.

Basil Valentine

Though the name of Paracelsus can be met in all 16th- and 17th-century chemical texts, Paracelsus was by no means the only authority quoted in them. One of the most frequently cited of his contemporaries was Basil Valentine, the first chemist to publish a treatise on antimony (*The Triumphal Chariot of Antimony*). Little else is known of him, except that he was a 15th- or 16th-century Benedictine monk and the author of the *Twelve Keys of Philosophy* (published in Latin, French and German), and hence a mystical alchemist.

Bernard Palissy

Valentine may be contrasted with Bernard Palissy (1510?–1589), who, as a potter, learned to keep his eyes open in a way that would later be extolled as an example. At a time when chemists wrote nothing transcending the narrow dogmas of the day and preferred to shelter behind respected authority, Palissy dared to think for himself. He scorned such all-embracing notions as the elementary composition of matter, and if he mentioned them at all, it was only to profess his scepticism and to deny that the 'great work' of transmutation had ever been performed, or was ever likely to be. Instead, he concentrated on such clearly observable phenomena as the water-supply of fountains and the properties of salt, stones, clay and marl, giving proof of his common sense and unrivalled perspicacity. He published only two works, of which the chief was the *Discours admirables de la nature des eaux et fontaines tant naturelles qu'artificielles, des métaux, des sels & salines, des pierres, des terres, du feu & des emaux* ('Admirable discourses on the nature of waters and fountains, both natural and artificial, of metals, of salts & salt-pans, of stones, of earth, of fire & enamels'). It appeared in 1580 and contained the gist of the lectures by which he had proved his knowledge before a large public, and in which he had only spoken of what he knew through long practice.

This man, so reminiscent of Leonardo da Vinci, though perhaps somewhat less polished, made little impression on his contemporaries. To us, he seems a true representative of all those men who, by performing their tasks unostentatiously, contributed so much more to the development of modern chemistry than the most boastful theorists.

CHAPTER 3

Human Biology and Medicine

THE EMERGENCE AND TEACHING OF NEW CONCEPTS

The Metaphysical Origins of Diseases

The Biblical view that diseases are God's scourges was one of the leading themes of medieval painters. Up in the heavens towered God, worshipped by happy angels; in the centre was suffering and sinful mankind; below was the flaming mouth of hell with its devils and damned souls.

All three were spanned by God's hand, stretching right across the canvas. Calvin held that 'He warns us with comets' and Ambroise Paré looked upon monsters as the sign of His wrath. Heirs to the lesser deities of pagan tree, stone and water cults, the Christian saints were popularly held to have the gift of interceding on behalf of stricken mankind by healing those diseases which fell into their particular province. Meanwhile, satanic emissaries spread evil on earth. When pestilence laid Geneva waste, Calvin consigned fourteen sinners to the stake for having conjured up the plague by their incantations, and in 1577 the Senate of Toulouse condemned 400 wretches for having committed the crime of witchcraft. The lower depths, too, surged with evil spirits and devils, whose chief joy it was to incite men to sin. Since death is but the result of sin (Rom. 5: 12), it was clearly these devils who introduced sickness and death into the world. No wonder that the Reformation, which was quick to abolish the saints, left hell severely alone. Thus primitive marvels blended imperceptibly into Christian thaumaturgy, and popular legend continued to survive in the framework of scholastic science.

The Judaeo-Arabic Heritage and the Humanist Contribution

The core of medieval medicine was based on the Arab legacy: 'Aly ibn 'Abbās' translation of Isaac Judaeus, Constantine's translation of Hippocrates and Galen, the translations by Gerard of Cremona of Rhazes, Avicenna and Abulcasis, and Fernel's revisions of these works. Avicenna and Abulcasis were particularly popular. (A Hebrew edition of the surgical writings of Avicenna was published in Naples in 1491 and his complete works were published in 1527 by the Juntas.) But though the Arabic tradition was staunchly defended by Lorenz Fries (*Defensio medicorum principis Avicennae*, Strasbourg, 1530) and by B. Unger of Tubingen (*Apologetica epistola pro defensione Arabum medicorum*, 1533), Niccolò Leoniceno (*De Plinii et plurium aliorum in medicina erroribus*, 1492) attacked the errors of Avicenna, and Symphorien Champier objected strongly to 'the bad and deceitful writings of the Arab authors who have falsified the doctrines of the Greeks'. In fact, some of the original Greek manuscripts had meanwhile been rediscovered by the Crusaders and the humanists did their utmost to restore, amend and augment these rare treasures, drawing freely on Byzantine sources: Oribasios, Aëtios of Amida, Alexander of Tralles, Paul of Aegina, Demetrios Pepagomenos, Nicolas Myrepsos and John Actuarios.

Linacre's translation of Galen was corrected and revised by Guillaume Budé, his friend and teacher. In Paris, William Cop studied Greek under Erasmus, John Lascaris and Jerome Aléandre; while Guido Guidi and Louis Douret lectured on Hippocrates at the *Collège Royal*, and Jean de Gorris and J. Houllier at the Paris Medical School. Günther of Andernach taught Greek at Louvain.

It was to students of Greek that Giovanni Crestone and Pierre Gilles d'Albi addressed their Graeco-Latin lexicons in 1499 and 1532 respectively. In 1534, there appeared Otto Brunfels' *Onomasticon medicinae* which was soon superseded by H. Estienne's Graeco-Latin *Dictionarium medicum* (1564). Estienne was also the author of the *Thesaurus graecae linguae* (1572). Thus, as Lindroth has put it, Renaissance medicine was mainly a philological science. From then on, printing began to make up for the scarcity of manuscripts. Celsus was printed in Florence in 1478, long before Hippocrates and Galen. The presses of the Aldi in Venice, of J. Oporinus in Basle, of Trechsel, Rouillé, Gryphius and Tournes in Lyons, of Marnef in Poitiers, of Wechel and Estienne in Paris, of Plantin in Anvers poured forth those lovely editions, *amplissimis scholiis illustratae*, provided with tables of contents and indexes, which are still so delightful and profitable to read.

These works helped considerably to popularize the main classical texts, free of the errors introduced by Jewish copyists and shorn of what Guy Patin called the 'Arabesque dross' that had spoiled all scientific writings from the 13th to the 15th century. In 1531, while still a bachelor of medicine, Rabelais held forth on the teachings of the 'Man of Cos' before the assembled students of Montpellier, using an unpublished Greek manuscript he himself had discovered. Rabelais' own scientific work was published by his friend Sebastian

Gryphe (Gryphius) in 1532. It contained the *Aphorisms* of Hippocrates and four Galenic commentaries. In support of Manardi's call for a return to the original Greek sources, Rabelais prepared a new edition of the Italian's medical letters, writing a special preface to Volume II.

Those who were unable to follow the language of Homer could consult a host of Latin translations, and particularly Th. Gaza's and Leoniceno's renderings of Hippocrates' *Aphorisms* (Venice, 1493, and Ferrara, 1509). David of Pomi addressed his *Index . . . in singulis Hippocratis libris* (1591) to all those who wished to work their way through the Master's works, and at the end of the century there appeared the monumental Latin translation of Hippocrates (Wechel, Frankfurt, 1595) to which Anuce Foës had devoted his entire life. In Paris, Günther of Andernach published Paul of Aegina's *De re medica* in 1532, while Leoniceno's translation of Galen's *De motu musculorum* was published by Linacre in London.

Occasionally, either because of inconsistencies in the original text or else because of disagreements with other authorities, the master himself had to be corrected. Thus Andrès de Laguna tried to reconcile the views of Hippocrates and Galen in his *Epitome* (Lyons, 1553), which was revised by J. Peletier in the *De conciliatione locorum Galeni* (Paris, 1560). The resulting critiques of critiques and commentaries of commentaries were the worthy successors of the Jewish and Arabic glosses and of scholastic disputations.

In addition, the new translators felt impelled to adorn the rather dry dissertations of the Greeks with learned fancies of their own. Thus, Jean de Gorris and Jacques Grévin rendered Nicander's *Theriaca* in Latin verse. Latin and Graeco-Latin texts were soon followed by vernacular translations. While Paracelsus still caused a scandal in Basle when he began to lecture in German, his Spanish colleagues were encouraged to write and teach in their native tongue. In 1551, Bernardino Montaña de Monserrate published his *Libro de la anathomia del hombre* at Valladolid, and in 1555 Laguna published a Castilian translation of Dioscorides in Antwerp. An Italian version of Valverde's *Historia de la composicion del cuerpo humano* appeared in Rome in 1559.

French, too, came into its own, as Sébastien Colin and Jacques Grévin began to publish medical texts in that language. The oldest French edition of Hippocrates' *Aphorisms* was that of Jehan Brèche (Paris, 1550) which was frequently reprinted and became the basis of Jean Bomier's *Aforismes expliquez en vers françois* (Niort, 1596). Julien Béré spoke out strongly against this new trend in 1572, and though the Medical School approved Jean Canape's translation of Guy de Chauliac's *Surgery*, and tolerated French instruction in the training of barbers, it was opposed to the over-vulgarization of science. Thus it censured Ambroise Paré, the great barber who had dared to put on long robes to teach medicine in French quatrains.

Thanks to the presses of Linacre in England, of Baillou, Gorris, Joubert, Duret, Houillier and Champier in France, and of David de Pomi in Italy, the doctrines of Hippocrates and Galen were successfully resurrected in the West. Physicians everywhere became familiar with the humoral tetrad (blood, bile, atrabile, phlegm), the subsidiary doctrine of temperaments and dyscrasias and the nosological notion that peccant humours change from a state of crudity to one of coction during crises, when they are evacuated spontaneously under the action of *Natura medicatrix*, or else set up metastases in other parts of the organism. They began to prognosticate accordingly.

The Survival of Occultism

However, this apparently rational system was tinged with occult ideas of Alexandrian origin, which had first appeared in the writings of the Jewish physicians, and found a ready echo, through Paracelsus, among mystics everywhere. Cardan's thought was steeped in the reveries of Plotinus and, in France, Champier was not altogether immune from the doctrines of Marsile Ficin, and even Fernel was seduced into mystical speculation. Man's dependence on such universal forces as the airs, waters and places of Hippocrates, and also on astronomical and seasonal changes was generally recognized. Scholars had no objections to the popular tradition according to which phlebotomies, purges, surgical operations, baths and haircuts were most propitiously undertaken on days when the moon and sun were in the favourable positions, specified, for instance, in Jehan de l'Eptine's *Almanach* of 1534, or in Petries Brumesius' *Great and Perpetual Almanac* of 1554. In fact, Brumesius' dates were officially endorsed by order of the Bruges magistrates, and the famous phlebotomic calendars of German painters had the official support of the Churches. Brother Louis of Granada proclaimed that stellar influences were inscribed in the Book of Nature, and that the moon caused biological changes 'particularly when it is full, new, or eclipsed'. Calvin had similar views, for he argued that there is 'a covenant between the planets and the dispositions of the human body'. Hence, celestial phenomena were blamed for epidemics: Jacques Peletier (*De peste compendium*, 1563) attributed the plague to a conjunction of Saturn and Jupiter, and Jean de l'Espine propounded the view that the comet of 1553 had caused 'mortality in several places'. Individual complaints, too, were said to have celestial causes, on the assumption that every organ had its sidereal correspondent. The heart was said to be governed by the sun, the brain by the moon's orbit, the bile by Saturn which, being cold and dry, causes melancholia and avarice. The moon, being humid, governs the bodies of women. Venus calls to a life of ease, Mars to valour.

One of Paracelsus' pupils, Rhumalius, even blamed disequilibrium between mineral traces in the human body on the planets governing them—*similia similibus*!

In fact, it was believed that astral 'patrons' attach their visible signs to all terrestrial objects, and particularly to the palms of men—a subject on which Filippo Finella discoursed at length. Chiromancy, also known as the 'curious science', was at its height in the 15th and 16th centuries, when it was propounded by Bartolommeo della Rocca (*Chyromantiae . . . anastasis*, Bologna, 1504), John Indagine, or de Hayn (*Chiromancie*, 1592), the Dominican Patrice Tricasso da Ceresari (1534), Antonio Picciolo, Jean Taisnier and J. Rothmann. The palm was said to exhibit diagrams of the intellectual, astral and elementary forces governing the internal organs.

Further clues were provided by posture and facial expression, on which G. Grataroli of Bergamo based his *De praedictione morum naturarumque hominum cum ex inspectione partium corporis tum aliis modis* (Basle, 1554). The Neapolitan scholar G. B. Porta was another to suggest that physiognomy is a certain means of diagnosing symptoms.

Physiognomy, or the 'divinatory art', as it was also called, was a mixture of Persian notions handed on by the Arabs and of very ancient Chinese and Indian practices. Though astrological physiognomy was of Babylonian origin, its zoomorphic applications were inspired by Indian ideas. Rediscovered in the 13th century by Michael Scot, these fanciful speculations found their way into such 14th-century texts as the *Physiognomia* (*Anastasis*) of Bartolommeo della Rocca, the *Chiromancie et phisionomie* of Jean de Hayn and the *Metoposcopy* of Cardan, in which 'facial signatures' were said to reflect not only their owners' present, but also their past and future, condition.

Thus, Cardan was able to cast Christ's horoscope in retrospect, and Peletier predicted the future of his favourite heroes in the *De constitutione horoscopi*. Though the Pope of Rome and the Pope of Geneva condemned such practices in no uncertain terms, the nobility lent them a ready ear. Louise of Savoy made a habit of consulting Agrippa von Nettelsheim, an adept in black magic and divination, and the story of Nostradamus and Catherine of Medici is too well known to bear repetition. Though Erasmus jibed at those happy seers who have 'the heavens as their library and the stars for books', and though Rabelais was no less sparing in his ridicule of Agrippa, the cult of divination continued in full force.

SYMPTOMATOLOGY AND NOSOLOGY

Clinical Examinations

Medical teaching remained purely theoretical. The professor would simply read, comment on and discuss a given Hippocratic, Galenic or even modern text (Fernel had the great honour of being discussed in the schools during his lifetime). In order to translate their theories into practice, all future physicians were expected to serve under an established practitioner and to study his methods: inspection of the general constitution; inspection of the teguments and the mucous membranes (with the naked eye or with the *diopter* or the *speculum matrices*, later modified by P. Franco and A. Paré); palpation to diagnose algid and febrile states; determination of the rhythm, amplitude and approximate frequency of the pulse (the idea of actually timing the pulse had not yet occurred to anyone); and Hippocratic succession (auscultation had to await the coming of Laënnec). An even more important procedure was the examination of the humours: firstly of the colour and quality of the blood after phlebotomies, and secondly of the sputum, vomit and urine. Urinoscopy was, in fact, a solemn ritual, and in Anne of Brittany's *Book of Hours* St. Damien himself is shown holding the matual, or vessel containing the urine. Humoral inspections were thought to have the additional advantage that the patient himself need not be present at the examination—a chamber-pot sent by a messenger was all that was required.

The Nature of Morbid Phenomena

Though it was difficult not to get lost in the mass of 'fevers' and 'plagues' of the time, 15th- and 16th-century Hippocratic physicians managed to describe a number of morbid conditions correctly. Thus Baillou gave fairly accurate descriptions of whooping-cough and croup, while others began to disentangle the jumble of eruptive fevers. Baillou was also the first to isolate rubiola, which the Italians had already suspected to differ from scarlet fever (rosiana). The latter was described by Ingrassia of Naples in 1556 and defined more accurately by François Ulmeau and (in about 1578) by Jean Coytard of Poitiers, who called it 'purple epidemic fever'. Exanthematic typhus was well known to army surgeons under the names of *tabardillo* (Siege of Granada, 1479) and *febris pestilens* (Italian Wars, 1505–1550; the sieges of Meta, 1552; of Poitou, 1557; of Hungary, 1566; *etc.*). Finally, physicians were familiar with the sweating sickness which ravaged England in 1518, 1529 and 1551.

A renewal of nosology came in the wake of the great voyages of discovery, as explorers and traders began to open up the new territories. Prospero Alpino (*De medicina Ægyptorum*) made a special study of Eastern diseases. When Jean of Béthencourt reached the Indies he was greeted by Italian missionaries who treated their flock with European remedies. The Jesuit Matteo Ricci opened infirmaries in Cathay in the 16th century. During their visits to Indonesia, surgeons working for the East India Company opened their sea-chests, treating settlers and natives with remedies compounded in accordance with the rules, first of the *Amsterdamsche Apotheek* and, from 1746 onwards, with those of the *Bataviasche Apotheek*. The first of these men to be mentioned in any records was the surgeon Jacob Waterman, who disembarked at Banda in 1590.

Tropical diseases, elephantiasis and cholera were described in the letters of Filippo Sasetti, a merchant and scholar who died at Goa in 1588. Leprosy, which was still very common in the tropics, had receded so greatly in Europe that many lazar-houses had to be closed in the 16th and 17th centuries for lack of patients.

Forgotten since the Crusades, scurvy reappeared during 15th-century voyages. In 1498, it wrought havoc among Vasco da Gama's crew off Mozambique; in 1535 it killed Jacques Cartier's sailors off Canada. It decimated Drake's men in 1578 and Cavendish's in 1586.

The New World sent even worse scourges to the Old. Syphilis, which, as tradition has it, was brought back by Columbus' crew, was carried from Spain to Italy by the army of Gonsalvo di Cordova. The 'Neapolitan pox' became the 'French pox' when the army of Charles VIII brought it to France, whence it spread to the rest of Europe. Yaws, though possibly known to Arabic physicians, was not clearly identified until the 17th century.

Fortunately, the voyagers brought back not only diseases, but many remedies as well. Thus, the ancient Chinese technique of acupuncture was brought to Europe by Francisco Mendez Pinto, and new American drugs augmented not only the income of apothecaries and Jesuits, but also the disputes of the physicians.

THERAPY

Medical Therapy

Anti-epidemic measures were all too often purely empirical: quarantine, isolation, headlong flight. Quarantine and isolation (special costumes and warning clappers or bells) had proved their worth in a number of endemic diseases, and particularly in leprosy. But when it came to epidemics, apparently all one could do was hold fast to the old saying: *Abi cito et longe, et tarde redi*. Despite such common measures as the purification of the air by great fires and the isolation and protection of sanitary personnel (gravediggers, stretcher-bearers, plague-physicians and surgeons wore waterproof suits and masks soaked in aromatic oils), the plague, once started, invariably ran its full course. The causes being unknown, what remedies could, in fact, be opposed to them? Fracastoro, for one, tried to find a rational answer. Not only did he study typhus and the plague as scientifically as he could, but he foreshadowed Pasteur in claiming that the disease was produced by germs or *seminaria*, which attacked the humours through the respiratory system (*De contagione et contagiosis morbis*, Venice, 1546).

Hygiene began at the table. Gluttons were told in Cornaro's wise *Trattato della vita sobria* (Padua, 1558) to live frugally and well, while David de Pomi, the precursor of geriatrics, revealed the secrets of longevity in his *Enarratio brevis de senum affectibus praecavendis* (Venice, 1588).

* * *

Pharmaceutical knowledge was chiefly based on the classics (Günther of Andernach published a Latin translation of Galen's *De compositione medicamentorum* in 1533) and on the Arabs, as pharmacists continued to place their trust in the ancient *Antidotarium* of Nicolas Praepositus (Venice, 1471) or adopted the *Antidotarium* of Valerius Cordus (1546), together with the pharmacopoeias of Foës (1561), Nicolas Houel (1571), Sylvius (1542), L. Joubert (1579) and Bauderon (1588). The first pharmacopoeia to be published in the French language was Dusseau's *Enrichid ou manipul des miropoles* (1561). As for the regional pharmacopoeias, which were to abound in the next century, the only ones to appear at the time were those of Barcelona (1535) and of Augsburg (1564).

The common prescriptions of most *Consilia* (of which the best-known was Fernel's) sprang from the pathogenic theories of the day. They were based on the traditional tetrad: the four elements—water, air, earth and fire—or their associated elementary qualities (humidity, dryness, cold, heat) were said to correspond to the four humours (phlegm, bile, atrabile and blood) and hence to the four temperaments (phlegmatic, choleric, melancholic, sanguine). As a result, the remedies were largely allopathic (*contraria contrariis*) and designed to dispel humoral disturbances. Quantitative imbalance was treated with suppletive or depletive medicaments, the latter including vomitives, purgatives, enemas, diuretics, diaphoretics, expectorants, cuppings and phlebotomies. The choice of particular phlebotomic methods led to many bitter controversies, for instance between Brissot, who bled pleuritic patients on the infected side, and Denys, physician to the King of Portugal, who bled them on the opposite side. The argument was eventually brought before the University of Salamanca and later before the Emperor Charles V.

Qualitative dyscrasia was treated with remedies containing the opposite quality. Thus St. Anthony's fire was treated with 'cold herbs'. Another method was to eliminate the unknown but suspected cause, either artificially with vesicatories which, Ambroise Paré said, 'attract the superfluous humour', with setons equally successful in 'drawing up matter from below', or else with depurants, diaphoretics, *etc*.

A case in point was the sudorific and sialogogic treatment of syphilis with cinnabar fumigations, ointments, steam baths and Neapolitan balm. Apparently these methods were employed even in hell, where Epistemon claimed he had seen Pope Sixtus reduced to the sad state of 'pox-greaser'. In any case, they were so cruel and dangerous that Fracastoro and Lopez de Villalobos rejected them outright in favour of plant remedies from the New World: sarsaparilla, introduced into Europe in about 1530, China root, sassafras and, the most famous of all sudorifics, guaiacum or sacred wood, which was imported by J. Hernandez de Oviedo in 1509 and warmly recommended by A. M. Brasávola. Their Most Catholic Majesties, Ferdinand and Isabella, ordered every vessel returning to Europe to carry a load of this precious cargo at their cost.

These colonial remedies, which were popularized by Clusius and which were supplemented with Mexican jalap in 1550, and with ipecacuanha in 1607, were often combined with simples of local origin, traditional remedies that had proved their worth or else stood out by their occult 'signatures'. They were collected by an army of herbalists and rhizotomists, and cultivated in ever-growing number in the botanical gardens of various towns.

But the popularity of all these herbs notwithstanding, the effects of most were negligible. How fortunate that, by the side of scammony, rhubarb, cassia and senna, the poppy was also cultivated!

To the animal kingdom pharmacists were indebted for such unlikely ingredients as *album graecum* (the faeces of dogs fed on bones) or the faeces of wolves; European or foreign bezoars, including bufonites or toad-stones, which were supposed to be lodged in the heads of toads; the blood of young men; mummies; human crania; and heartbones of stags. All these were compounded into frightful electuaries, the most famous of which was *theriaca Andromachi* or Venice treacle. Galen compounded it of 74 ingredients, including the flesh of a viper, and his successors increased the number further still. In addition to these remedies, pharmacists developed a number of 'poison detectors' used at the tables of kings. These included strings of serpents' tongues (in reality sharks' teeth) and unicorn horns.

The mineral kingdom provided a cure for stomach complaints in Lemnian earth, and in 1520 Johann Lange of Heidelberg proposed to cure *morbus virgineus* with Martius' yellow. To the pearls prescribed by Nicholas and Avicenna, the author of the *Lumen apothecarium* added emeralds, hyacinths, sapphires, and powdered jasper mixed with unspun silk and ivory shavings, and so did Mesuë in his *Electuarium de gemmis*. All these exalted remedies were obviously intended for rich customers, who were also catered for by Roch le Bailif de la Rivière's *Traité de l'homme, de ses maladies, médecine et absolus remèdes ès teintures d'or, corail, et antimoine, magistère de perles, etc.*

Alchemy, too, made its medical contribution: *aqua vitae* which, by its incorruptibility, was said to preserve both the quick and the dead; the infernal stone; corrosive sublimate; red precipitate. Antimony became suspect after it had killed Basil Valentine and depopulated a monastery in Erfurt. Despite its defence by Paracelsus and later by Peletier and Louis de Launay, who was the author of a treatise on *The Faculties and Admirable Virtues of Antimony* (1564), Palissy, Jacques Grévin and the Parisian medical faculty were so opposed to its use that they appealed to Parliament. As a result apothecaries were instructed not to supply this drug except on medical prescription (1566). Though the Medical School expelled Dr. Le Paumier in 1579 for his support of the 'antimonial faction', it could not similarly silence either the Danish chemiatrist Peder Sörensen (Severinus) or the great champion of spagyric medicine, Duchesne *alias* Quercetanus.

Mercury fared better than antimony, for it fulfilled an urgent need in the 16th century. Giovanni da Vigo applied red precipitate to venereal ulcers and quicksilver was the main ingredient of the pills offered to Francis I by the Turkish admiral Barbarossa. Paracelsus did his utmost to broadcast the benefits of chemiatric medicine and metallotherapy, praising the marvellous virtues of potable gold and the life-prolonging properties of the philosopher's stone which procured miraculous longevity. This view was challenged by Jacques Aubert who showed in his *Institutiones physicae* that the use of the philosopher's stone ran counter to Aristotle's doctrine, and hence proved *chimiam esse vanam*. Thus he failed to appreciate Paracelsus' great merit in trying to replace the products of polypharmaceutical and Galenic empiricism with clearly defined chemical substances, and to preserve their 'quintessence' or active principle which was far too often destroyed or diluted by calcination, infusion and decoction. Foreshadowing modern homoeopathy, Paracelsus prescribed infinitesimal doses and, anticipating modern theories on lithiasis, he blamed calculi on chemical disequilibrium. Chemiatrists accordingly attempted to remove calculi (or 'tartar', as they called them) by dissolving them in appropriate chemicals, and Duchesne by removing the alleged excess of one of the three alchemical principles: mercury, sulphur or salt. Still, all these hermetic chemists lacked any deep understanding of chemical reactions or of quantitative techniques.

No wonder, then, that Paracelsus hid behind such mystic phrases as: 'All is in all, and all persists.' Faced with the mysterious powers of amber and magnets, he thought that similar emanations must also be produced by other substances. Thus the horn of the unicorn was said to detect poisons, and *armary ointment* and the *powder of sympathy* to cure injuries because of the inherent correspondence between the weapon and the wound.

Similar 'sympathies' were thought to exist between men and stones. Marbode, Albertus Magnus, Mondeville, Marsile Ficin, Mattioli and Cardan inherited the art of lapidary medicine from Dioscorides and Pliny: gems transmit the virtues of their associated planets, so that the symbol of a given mineral, like that of its planet, provides an effective amulet. Montaigne was presented by Peletier with 'a sliver of flat gold on which are engraved celestial figures against sunstroke . . . and headaches'. Then there were the many talismans whose 'secrets' Albertus Magnus praised volubly, together with the curative and protective amulets, including that discovered in 1505 on Christ's tomb and presented by the Pope to the Emperor Charles V 'for the cure of St. John's disease, St. Cornelius' disease, and to preserve a child from 82 misfortunes'.

Such, in short, was the modest state of medical therapy at a time when surgery, on the other hand, made very considerable advances.

Advances in Surgery

Surgery was developed particularly in Italy, where Tagliacozzi (1546–1599) became the (unrecognized) father of autoplastic surgery, and also in Germany, thanks mainly to the work of Fabricius Hildanus (Wilhelm Fabry, 1560–1634).

Surgery also progressed in France, despite the contempt in which the medical faculty held 'manual operators'. Rabelais invented, or re-invented, the *glossotomon* or *glossocomion* for setting fractured femurs, and a *syringotome* for operating on strangulated hernias. By far the greatest reformer of French surgery was Ambroise Paré, a man of the people, poorly educated but abounding in practical common sense and hence immune from the idle speculations of the learned. As a military surgeon, Paré greatly improved the method of locating and removing bullets, arguing that if the patient were restored to the approximate position in which he had been hit, the ball would be found in a straight line from where it had entered his body. He pleaded against the use of red-hot iron and boiling oil in the treatment of gunshot wounds, and re-introduced the use of the ligature to tie blood vessels (a technique described by Celsus, Paul of Aegina and Aetios of Amida). Paré also introduced methods for disarticulating the elbow and amputating the thigh. He, too, had his 'secrets', including the preparation of his famous salve (earthworms and puppies plunged into boiling oil), a bit of childish nonsense for which we may readily forgive him in view of his great achievements.

Another French surgeon worthy of mention was Pierre Franco of Turriers in Provence, an itinerant lithotomist with a singularly open mind. He initiated a great advance in herniotomy when he cured a double rupture without removing both testicles. He also improved the operation of perineal lithotomy by introducing the lateral operation and even foresaw the suprapubic operation of the future. He treated cataract by couching and improved the Caesarean section, thus sharing with Jacques Guillemot the honour of revolutionizing obstetrics.

HUMAN ANATOMY AND PHYSIOLOGY

The Study of the Human Body

When the various schools of physiological and anatomical thought were eventually driven to putting the classical authorities to the empirical test, they discovered to their dismay that the ancients had neither said nor foreseen everything, and that in some respects they had seen nothing at all.

All ancient religions had enjoined respect for the dead and Christianity continued this tradition. Even autopsies and embalmments were strictly regulated—as, for example, by the Bull issued by Pope Boniface VIII in 1299, which proscribed the boiling and stripping of flesh. Official dissections were rare and ceremonial rather than instructive, a physician holding forth before an assembly of students while a surgeon-barber wielded the scalpel.

Dissections were performed in Bologna from 1315 onwards, but not until 1407 in Paris, after which date official sanction was given for an annual maximum of three dissections.

In the 16th century, students became so dissatisfied with these regulations that they began to carry out clandestine autopsies. Braving prohibitions and public scandal, Vesalius removed corpses from the gibbet in Montfaucon, while F. Platter robbed a grave in Montpellier and, in spite of the stench, hid the body for some time before dissecting it.

Anatomical research made particularly brilliant strides in Italy, where great artists like Leonardo da Vinci and Michelangelo rivalled

13 Vesalius dissecting an arm, by van Calcar

14 The School of Apothecaries

or collaborated with the physicians. Eustachius (who was still concerned with 'saving' Galen), Ingrassia, Fallopius, Fabricius da Aquapendente and Variolus were all brilliant teachers of anatomy, whose pupils carried the new knowledge to most parts of Europe. A former pupil of Aldrovandi, the Frisian physician Volcher Coiter, became a teacher himself in about 1564, and studied the embryology of birds and man. In Paris, Günther of Andernach (1487–1574) taught a brilliant team of future anatomists, including Jacques Dubois (Sylvius), who earned fame by using intravascular injections to demonstrate the complex structure of the arterio-venous network; Rondelet (1507–1566); and Charles Estienne (1500–1564), the author of an important treatise on dissection which contained a clear description of the cranial nerves and distinguished the sympathetic from the pneumogastric. However, the greatest of all 16th-century anatomical works was Vesalius' *De humani corporis fabrica libri septem* (Basle, 1543). Vesalius (1514–1564) dared to claim—and to prove—that the infallible Galen had often erred because his dissections had been restricted to monkeys. This scandalous suggestion unleashed a series of violent attacks, led by Sylvius. But even Sylvius was forced to submit in the end, for the evidence against Galen was incontrovertible.

Physiology

According to the scholastic doctrine, physiological processes were governed by various spirits. *Animal spirits* (governing sensation) were said to be distilled in the *rete mirabile* of the cerebral ventricle; *vital spirits* (governing the circulation of the air and the blood) in the heart, and *natural spirits* in the liver. These spirits were also known respectively as the reasonable, sensitive and vegetative souls, and it was the last which, by its attractive, formative, digestive, retentive or expulsive powers, governed nutrition. To this triad of souls Aristotle had added an appetitive and a locomotive soul, arguing that life is movement initiated by the universal motor and perpetuated in the heart. This collection of philosophical entities was compounded into an Aristotelian-cum-Christian hotchpotch in Bigot's *Praeludium philosophiae christianiae* (Toulouse, 1549).

However, such abstractions were not to everyone's taste. Cesalpino refused to accept either the spirits of Galen or the souls of Aristotle, holding that one single and sovereign soul was seated in the heart, where it engendered animal heat and whence it distributed it to the rest of the body by the vessels.

However, Galen's views of the blood circulation remained unchallenged. Having given a perfect account of the foetal circulation, a description of the arterial canal which Fallopius rediscovered subsequently, and of the *foramen ovale* (the discovery of which has been wrongly attributed to Botalli), his mastery in at least this field seemed to be beyond all doubt. (No one suspected that, after birth, the *ductus arteriosus* begins to contract or that the foramen closes.) In Galen's scheme, the blood manufactured in the liver from chyle is carried by the *vena cava* into the right side of the heart, crosses the interventricular wall to pass into the left side of the heart whence, mixed with pneuma from the lung, it is taken by the aorta and the arteries to all parts of the body. Not even when Charles Estienne discovered the existence of venous valves (which were rediscovered independently by Fabricius da Aquapendente) was there any change in the general view of the blood circulation. Ibn al-Nafīs, who had spoken of the pulmonary circulation as early as the 13th century, remained a voice crying in the wilderness, and it was not until 1553 that an incidental phrase in Michael Servet's *Christianismi restitutio* foreshadowed the real facts. What 15th- and 16th-century physicians were mainly interested in was to discover how the respiratory air mixed with the blood constantly renews and distributes the vital spirits, the reflection of the divine spark. Not even Servet was fully convinced of the total impermeability of the interventricular wall. The discovery of the real nature of the blood circulation had to await the advent of Harvey.

MEDICAL INSTITUTIONS AND THE STATUS OF PHYSICIANS

The Physician's Place in the Social Hierarchy

Medicine had for too long been the prerogative of monks for the universities to forget its clerical associations. Though Bologna was, and remained, a federation of lay institutions, Louvain formally proclaimed its perpetual submission to the provost of the Chapter of St. Pierre as delegate of the Holy See.

In France, the University was the elder daughter of the Church: degrees were conferred in the name of the Church—in Paris by the Canon of Notre-Dame as episcopal delegate, and in Montpellier by the Bishop of Maguelone. Having dedicated his life to the teaching of his art, the newly-appointed physician was assured of a clerical benefice sufficient to keep him in reasonable comfort. In 1443, Pope Eugene IV created two canonical chairs of medicine in the Chapter of St. Pierre at Louvain. Appointed honorary canons by Urban V, the teachers at Montpellier wore the canonical over the professorial hood.

This association between medicine and the Church carried a

number of obligations and restrictions. First of all, doctors were expected to refrain from all surgical practices: *ecclesia abhorret ab sanguine*; and secondly, teachers of medicine were expected to remain celibate. Students, too, as associates of the clergy, were sworn to celibacy and it was not until 1598 that Cardinal d'Estouteville's 1542 reforms were implemented, and teachers were allowed to marry. But gradually, the Church began to lose its hold on medicine. In 1500, the Paris medical faculty counted no more than three priests among its twenty-one teachers. Noble or ennobled physicians, too, were the exception rather than the rule—the only ones to have left their mark were Scévola de Sainte-Marthe (Rabelais' 'Picrochole'), Louis de Bourges, Laurent Joubert, Symphorien Champier and Günther of Andernach. The ordinary medical practitioner belonged to the upper caste of the Third Estate. As a townsman, he left rural medicine to barber-surgeons, bone-setters and quacks, considering his profession vastly superior to their 'manual labour'.

From the Church, physicians had inherited a teaching monopoly, and though the *Collège Royal* in Paris had begun to encroach on clerical territory, university-trained French physicians remained in charge of the teaching of surgeons, their inferiors. As a result, there arose a great many cantankerous and futile disputes, during which the 'theorists', unfamiliar with surgical techniques, were mainly concerned with keeping the surgeons in their subordinate place. The physicians also tried to weaken their rivals by setting them against one another. Thus the long-robed surgeons' strivings for independence, organized in 1311 by Jehan Pitard, were thwarted by the defection of their short-robed colleagues. In 1575, all French surgeons alike were forced once again to submit to the tutelage of the physicians though recriminations and revolts continued as heretofore.

Times and Manners

Because of the educational and social organization of their institutions, doctors saw a great deal of the world. While apprentice surgeons were expected to tour their own country, prospective physicians visited distant universities with famous teachers or offering desirable degrees. This custom was a relic from the days when doctors used to travel from monastery to monastery, and when medieval universities were able to teach students from all corners of Europe in a common language—Latin. Much the same happened in the 16th century, when Orleans, Bourges, Poitiers, Toulouse and Montpellier welcomed a flood of foreigners. French students, in turn, usually completed their studies in Italy, the Netherlands or Germany. The Rhine lapped the walls of famous medical schools in Basle, Mainz, Strasbourg and Cologne. However, the call of learning was not the only reason for going abroad: fees varied, great teachers came and went, and epidemics often led to the temporary closing of a university.

Even when they had graduated, many physicians preferred travelling to the routine of local practice. A great number followed in the train of armies, princelings, cardinals and other dignitaries. Jewish physicians, particularly, came from distant places to enjoy the patronage of Popes Leo X, Clement VII and Paul III; Amatus Lusitanus attended to Pope Julius III and his sister; others, like Nostradamus, won the confidence of princes and kings. Christian physicians, too, answered the call of foreign sovereigns: the Italian G. Manardi was court physician to Ladislaus of Hungary from 1513 to 1519; Vesalius tended both the Emperor Charles V and Philip II of Spain. Rabelais followed in the train of John and William du Bellay; Pierre Belon served the Cardinal of Tournon; Scaliger accompanied the armies of Maximilian and of the King of France, before settling in Agen.

Then there were the many naval surgeons who took the treasures of their medicine chest to the East, or settled there for good. B. Carneiro founded a hospital in Macao in 1569, and medical missionaries brought European methods to Vietnam.

Apart from these trained physicians, there existed an army of strolling scientists, touring Europe in search of botanical specimens like Günther of Andernach and Lazare Peña, or going even farther afield like Belon, who accompanied the ambassadors of Francis I to Suleiman the Magnificent (1546–1549), or like Guilandino, Rauwolff or Alpino, who studied in the Near East.

CHAPTER 4

Zoology

THE MATERIAL SOURCES OF ZOOLOGY

Fashion and the Advance of Zoology

In zoology, the Renaissance took over a body of doctrine built up over the centuries. Hunting had ceased to be a matter of human survival, for most of man's enemies—with the exception of wolves and some plantigrades—had been eradicated, and had become a gentlemanly pastime, with special rites and a special literature. To the bow and arrow of yore, 16th-century sportsmen joined the arquebus and the pistolet; traps and snares gave way to ceremonial hunting, coursing and falconry.

Fishing rights, too, had passed into the hands of the gentry, except in coastal waters or on the high seas where fishermen continued to catch whales, herring and cod. Pools were increasingly stocked with freshwater fish, and pickling or smoking led to the accumulation of stocks, so that fishing became a business and supplies of fish ceased to depend on individual catches.

The end of the Hundred Years War was the signal for a return to the land. As money depreciated while rental incomes remained fixed, the gentry were reluctantly compelled to put their estates to more profitable use. Feudal castles lowered their walls and, at the end of the century, gave way to vast manors, half fortress, half farm, enclosing barns, sheepfolds, stables, chicken coops and dovecotes. The gentleman hunter had finally developed into a gentleman farmer.

Beyond the shadow of the keep there rose up luxurious residences set in sumptuous parklands. While elegant horses champed in the stables, rare birds and tame beasts displayed their plumes and furs in aviaries and menageries. King Henri II took his menagerie to St. Germain, Charles IX and Henri III brought theirs to the Louvre, and Henri IV to Vincennes. The Montmorencys opened their famous park at Chantilly. Zoologists profited greatly from this new fashion—Ambroise Paré, for instance, was able to dissect one of His Majesty's ostriches and to discourse on its strange anatomy.

Menageries and animal husbandry were not entirely devoid of dangers. Quite apart from the bites of wild or poisonous beasts, there was the recurrent threat of epidemics, of rabies and a host of other communicable diseases. Moreover, reliance on pickled meat increased the incidence of scurvy. Hence zoology may be said to have entered medicine through dietetics; some of the earliest remedies resulting from this union foreshadowed the methods of modern organotherapy.

The new fashion also helped man to win his age-old battle against the elements. Animal skins were transformed by skilful tanners and furriers into boots, harness, jerkins and costly furs. Silk, which had been imported exclusively from China, was increasingly produced at home as the mulberry tree was acclimatized, and sericulture became a European industry. Necklaces made of bears' teeth were discarded in favour of pearl or coral necklaces. Animals appeared increasingly as supporters on heraldic devices on the walls of castles, on banners, on furniture and on B. Palissy's famous figurines.

THE NEW INVENTORY OF THE ANIMAL KINGDOM

New Discoveries

Geographical exploration and discovery had extended man's knowledge of the animal kingdom very considerably. True, it was not nearly as great in the 15th and 16th centuries as it is in our own, with more than 30,000 vertebrates and some 575,000 invertebrates (including 500,000 species of insects), but it certainly went far beyond Aristotle's catalogue of 500. Olaus Magnus described the fauna of northern Europe (including the fabulous kraken); Siegmund von Herberstein studied the animals of Muscovy; Schwenckfeldt those of Silesia; Kentmann the birds on the banks of the Elbe; Turner the birds of England. Like Leo Africanus before them, Prospero Alpino, Gilles d'Albi, Belon and Thévet visited the Near East, where d'Albi observed the giraffe, the hippopotamus, the ichneumon and even the dugong.

Lourenço Diaz discovered the Guinea hornbill in 1477 and Pigafetta, who sailed with Magellan, spotted gigantic colonies of penguins in Patagonia. After the treaty of Tordesillas (1493), Spanish and Portuguese settlers began to open up new territories on their respective sides of the boundary meridian. They included such talented officials as Gonzalo Hernandez de Oviedo, missionaries like Lopez de Gomara and José de Acosta—'the Pliny of the New World'—physicians and surgeons like Garcia da Orta, Cristobal Acosto and Francisco Hernandez. It was these men to whom we owe the early botanical and zoological descriptions of the West and East Indies which were recorded in Seville by the physician Monardes (the first to describe *Myroxylon peruiferum* or Peru balm), and who, braving the elements, pirates, brigands, savages, wild beasts, snakes and crocodiles, built up a considerable body of new knowledge. Unfortunately, the collected works of F. Hernandez (17 volumes) were destroyed when the Escorial went up in flames in 1671, though some of his writings had been published in Mexico in 1615 and a summary of his discoveries in Rome in 1628.

As a result, the outmoded compilations of the past had to be revised drastically—a task which was tackled by Gesner, Aldrovandi and such minor polygraphers as Caius, Lonicer and Imperato. Wotton prepared a new and critical classification.

All of them, however, were careful not to challenge the existence of such revered beasts as, for instance, the unicorn, which is mentioned in the Holy Scriptures, and whose horn (in fact, that of the narwhal) was known to have marvellous virtues. Another fabulous animal admitted into the new faunas was the African basilisk, whose breath and eye were thought to be fatal. Its existence was confirmed by Aldrovandi who, however, doubted the authenticity of the seven-headed hydra displayed in Venice. It took a Rabelais to relegate to the 'Land of Satin' unicorns, harpies, seleucid and stymphalid birds, and satyrs—together with what were, in fact, a number of genuine species.

Language and Classification

The first problem the new classifiers had to solve was the inadequacy of their vocabulary and what new terms to introduce. Though Cornelius Agrippa and Giordano Bruno tried to construct an international scientific language with the ideas propounded in Raymond Lulle's *Ars generalis*, the anatomical vocabulary continued to be the heteroclite mixture of Greek, Latin, Graeco-Latin and Arab terms borrowed from Rhazes, Abulcasis and Avicenna. Schwenckfeld described vertebrates by joining Greek roots (*uropygium*) to Latin qualifiers (*incisurae*, *pinnae*, *pennae*, *etc.*), while other 16th-century naturalists borrowed their terms from popular etymologies.

Though the oldest-known catalogue of the animal kingdom (Gen. 2: 20), which, according to Rondelet, was obscure because of the 'confusion of languages in Babel', had mercifully been discarded, the new babblings were hardly very much more lucid or satisfactory, particularly since travellers and navigators had introduced the exotic syllables of Asiatic, Mexican, Caribbean and South American expressions. The result was the kind of heteroclite, amorphous, erroneous, misspelt and confused vocabulary which Gesner and Aldrovandi tried laboriously to compound into their polyglot catalogue.

EMPIRICAL METHODS OF CLASSIFICATION

1. *Alphabetic classification.* The simplest way of classifying animals was to list them in alphabetical order—a method adopted in the medieval *Summae* of Albertus Magnus and Bartholomew the Englishman, and copied by Gesner and Aldrovandi.[1]

2. *Empirical classification.* Others, like Paolo Giovio, based their classification on culinary considerations (freshwater fish, seawater fish), or on the degree of domestication (tame, ferine, sylvestrian). This was the method used, among others, by Buffon.

THE IDEAL CLASSIFICATION

These purely empirical methods were opposed by coherent *a priori* systems, alleged to reflect nature's own order.

1. *Animistic dynamism.* The most ancient of these systems was based on the order in which God had created animals on the fifth and sixth days of the Creation. The aesthetic view that nature tends towards perfection was first propounded by the Pythagoreans and by Plato. It was also the basis of Aristotle's theory of evolution (vegetative, sensitive and reasonable souls). At the bottom of the scale was the coral (which Campanella called a lapidified tree); next came the zoophytes (called *plantanimalia* by Theodore of Gaza). According to Aristotle and Pliny, zoophytes 'participate in two natures'; according to Belon they 'cannot be called either plants or animals'; and according to Rabelais (*Pantagruel*, Book III, 8) they must be classified as vegetables. A typical zoophyte was *Agnus scythicus*, found in Tartary, which was said to have a sheep's body and an umbilical stalk attaching it to the earth. At the very top of the scale were the higher animals whose blood 'rises from the feet to the head, like the sap in plants' (Cesalpino).

2. *Humoral classifications.* The humoral method of classifying the animal kingdom was largely inspired by Aristotle. At the bottom of the scale were the bloodless animals (*Exsanguia*); at the top were the red-blooded animals whose degree of vital heat determines their status in the scale, so that, according to Aristotle, man as the highest must also be the hottest.

3. *Generative classifications.* Other classifications were based on reproductive methods. All lower animals were said to be replenished by spontaneous generation. According to Jehan Massé, fleas are generated from 'superfluous humours', and José de Acosta argued that 'rats, frogs, bees and all other imperfect animals' are engendered

[1] Aldrovandi's classification is discussed in greater detail on pages 333–336.

by the earth. Paré relates that, in his vineyard at Meudon, he found a hollow stone containing 'a large living toad' which must have been generated by 'putrefied humidity'. By contrast, all perfect animals reflecting 'God's true order' were said to reproduce their kind sexually.

Viviparous animals, in particular, were said to perpetuate the 'perfection of forms', though the barnacle goose was thought to spring from the fruit of a tree (Aldrovandi) and though Pliny called the cuckoo the offspring of the sparrowhawk (whence Belon called it a bird of prey). Paré even spoke of the possibility of engendering composite animals by cross-breeding 'different fertile natures'. Still, these were exceptions, and the ladder of life was generally strait and narrow. Thus bats and ostriches were but two different stages in the gradual transition from flying to walking, and the unity of God's plan was emphasized in Belon's comparison between the skeletons of birds and man, and in Leonardo da Vinci's, Paré's and Coiter's comparative studies of birds, horses and monkeys. It is hard to tell whether these men were interested in comparative anatomy, as such, or whether they merely wished to prove the truth of the Aristotelian scheme; in any case, that scheme was later broken into four by Cuvier.

Apart from structural analogies, these men also introduced functional analogies (swimmers, creepers, runners, fliers) and ecological analogies (aquatic, subterranean, terrestrial and aerial faunas). As a result the term *Aquatilia*, for instance, was applied indiscriminately to fishes, molluscs, worms, ballans, frogs, whales, marine worms, sea-cows, hippopotami, water rats and beavers. Thus it came about that the Church voiced no objections to the eating of beaver-meat during Lent. Schwenckfeld lumped slugs and snakes together as reptiles; Lonicer combined fowls, magpies, wasps, bees, flies and even bats into birds of prey.

4. *Positive classifications*. These general categories were often subdivided according to concrete characteristics in a way that tended to remedy the worst faults. Thus Wotton and P. Belon made laudable attempts to return to Aristotle's anatomical and embryological criteria.

Some of the subdivisions were based on purely superficial phenomena (soft fishes, bony fishes, shell-fishes); others concentrated on only one characteristic (*e.g.* Emiliano's classification of ruminants by their horns), or on the distinction between cartilaginous and osseous skeletons, or else on the limbs (quadrupeds, solipeds, bisulcates, digitates, talonates, waders, palmipeds). The first serious anatomical investigation of a pachyderm since antiquity was that of Gilles d'Albi, who dissected a young elephant. The distinction between the common dolphin (*Delphinus delphis*, L.) and the porpoise (*Phocaena communis*, Less.) was first introduced by Belon, although fishermen had been capturing both species for generations. Even so, Belon continued to classify Pinnipeds and Cetacea among the fishes.

Nomenclature

In the face of the ever-growing number of newly-discovered facts, all classifications based on the ideal nature of the universe and the hidden connections between the visible and the invisible world had eventually to break down. Thus Gesner had to split his alphabetical classification to some extent into what Aristotle had called γένη (families or genera) and εἴδη (species).

Though the medieval quarrels on *universals* had by then abated, 16th-century zoologists, like Aristotle before them, failed to define genera and species by empirical criteria; if they occasionally associated two apparently distinct species into a common genus, it was by chance rather than design. Their terminology remained loose, heterogeneous and polymorphous, uni-, bi-, or trinomial, or occasionally qualified by such terms as *alter* or *altera*, *mas* or *fœmina*, *major* or *minor*, or else by the kind of descriptive phrases ridiculed by Rabelais in *Pantagruel*, Book III. In short, 16th-century nomenclature was anything but systematic, and it would be idle to claim Belon as a precursor of the modern binomial system.

ILLUSTRATED BESTIARIES

Art and Zoology

Artists made a considerable contribution to the popularization of scientific discoveries by their drawings (Albrecht Dürer and Leonardo da Vinci), by woodcuts (first used for printing fabrics in Basle in 1350), and by etchings (the first copper plates were probably made in Bourgogne in about 1450). The first woodcuts to illustrate a book appeared in Johann von Cube's *Gart der Gesundheit* (Mainz, 1485), and the first books illustrated with copper plates were printed in Germany and in the Netherlands.

While most were printed on special sheets, others were combined into complete albums, such as Belon's *Portraits d'oyseaux, animaux, serpens* (Paris, 1557); Adriaan Collaërt's *Avum vivae icones*; Gesner's *Icones animalium quadrupedum . . . et avium omnium* (Zurich, 1560); Lonicer's *Venatus et aucupium* (Frankfurt, 1582), and Coiter's *Humani corporis tabulae* (1573). Dürer and Holbein were acknowledged masters of ornamental capitals and vignettes; other great artists illustrated the figures in the text.

These men came from all the corners of Europe. Plantin of Anvers used A. Nicolai's plates (based on drawings by Van der Borcht) to illustrate Garcia da Orta's *Coloquios*, and Nicolai's plates were also incorporated into the first Parisian editions of Belon's *Observations* and Clusius' *Exoticorum libri*, in which many previously unknown animals were described. A. Bloemart's famous drawings of mammals and birds were engraved by B. Bolsverd; other remarkable plates were made by Collaert.

Some of the plates in Thévet's *Singularitez de la France antarctique* were made by C. L. Woeiriot of Lorraine, who also made the plates (based on P. Gourdet's drawings) for Belon's *De la nature des oyseaux*.

Illustrative art also flourished in Germany. The first drawing of a giraffe was made by Ehrhard Remich, who visited the Holy Land in the 15th century. Other animal painters were the two Hoefnagels, Jost Amman, who illustrated Jans Bocksperger's *Tierbuch*, and Albrecht Dürer, the most famous of whose drawings was of the rhinoceros presented to Leo X by Emmanuel of Portugal (1515). Hans Fred Manuel illustrated the German translation of Agricola's *De re metallica*.

In Switzerland, Gesner had his work illustrated by Jean Asper, Jean Thomas and Lucas Schroen. In Italy, Salviani employed Bernardus Aretinus for two years, together with many lesser artists, and Aldrovandi fetched the painters Cornelius Sivint from Frankfurt, Lorenzo Bernini from Florence, and the engravers C. Coriolanus and his nephew from Nuremberg. It was a refugee from Italy, Giorgio Reverdi, who drew the fishes in Rondelet's *Poissons*, while Belon took the figures illustrating the fishes of 'the Adriatic, Mediterranean, Aegean and Pontic Seas' from Plinio, a painter employed by Daniele Barbaro, the Venetian ambassador to London.

Not all these illustrations were of equal value. There were numerous anonymous 'master-plates' which kept cropping up in work after work, including Paré's *Monstres*. Others (*e.g.* of dolphins) reflected traditional misconceptions or onomastic and legendary associations (*e.g.* Lonicer's amphibians). Finally, there were some plates that were completely false.

Though Basque whalers could have taught him better, Johann von Cube continued to describe whales as sirens, and Gesner endowed them with formidable organs of defence. Belon mistook whalebone, which was used in the farthingales of fashionable ladies, for the eyelashes of whales. Cetaceans, which had been described as 'marine monsters with the faces of monks' by Albertus Magnus and Johann von Cube, were depicted in an illustration presented to Rondelet by Margaret of Navarre as combining the fabulous characteristics of artificial monsters, white-bellied seals, hooded seals and giant cephalopods.

Lonicer's vignettes of cetaceans were small and inaccurate; Rondelet's and Belon's generally poor but correct in detail; Salviani's 99 plates were elegant but superficial. Gesner's illustrations, too, were rather mediocre. Only when it came to human anatomy was there any real attempt to reflect reality—for instance, in those magnificent drawings of skeletons which van Calcar made for Vesalius and which have been wrongly attributed to Titian.

While the Old World fauna was described at length in Garcia da Orta's *Coloquios*, it was from the New World that Belon took his pictures of the armadillo and 'Brazilian hedgehog', and Clusius and many Spanish painters their various silhouettes.

As the art of illustration developed, traditional errors were gradually corrected by the painters' keen eyes. Hence, zoology owes much of its modern development to the fine arts.

CHAPTER 5

Botany

THE MAIN STAGES IN THE DEVELOPMENT of modern botany were the identification of an increasing number of plants in the 15th and 16th centuries, their classification according to artificial methods in the 17th century, the introduction of more natural methods in the 18th century and the study of the thorny problems of the origin of species and their evolution in the 19th century, which also saw the birth of such new disciplines as cryptogamy, plant physiology, plant pathology and plant ecology.

Botany awoke from its age-long slumber at the beginning of the Renaissance, with the rediscovery of the Greek and Latin authors and with the appearance of such works as Ermolao Barbaro's *Castigationes plinianae* (1492); R. Constantin's *Theophrasti de historia plantarum* (1584), Saracenus' translations of the works of Pliny (1598), and Mattioli's edition of Dioscorides' *Commentaries*, which was first published in 1554, republished with large woodcuts in 1565 and finally translated into numerous languages.[1] Another preoccupation of 16th-century botanists was the compilation of such great herbals as Gherardo Cibo's (kept in the Bibliotheca Angelica, Rome), which took the author from 1532 to 1540 to complete, or that of the Lyons surgeon Girault (1558), now kept in the Paris Museum. Other herbals which appeared at the time were based more directly on medieval recipes and included the *Herbarium* (J. de Dondis, 1485), the

[1] The Greek text of Theophrastos' *Historia plantarum* and *De causis plantarum* was included in Vol. IV of the first edition of Aristotle (Venice, 1497; republished in 1541). A Latin translation of the works of Theodore of Gaza was published in 1483 and ran through several editions. The main commentators were Ruel, Gesner, Cesalpino and Zalusanski.

Dioscorides' *Commentaries* were first printed in Latin in 1478 and in Greek in 1499. Six Greek editions, eight Latin editions (of which the most famous was Mattioli's), three Italian translations, three French translations, *etc.* were published before the end of the 16th century.

Pliny's *Historia naturalis*, which was first printed in 1469, had no less than eighteen printings in incunabular form (fifteen in Latin and three in Italian). Almost fifty Latin editions but relatively few translations of it appeared in the 16th century (French translation, 1562; English translation, 1601). On the other hand, very many commentaries on it were published in various languages.

Arbolayre (P. Caron, Paris, 1495), the *Grand Herbier en françois* (1545) and the *Herbolario vulgare* (Venice, 1537). All these works paved the way for new systems of classification based on the direct observation of plants.

Classification of Plants

One of the first to classify plants anew was Andrea Cesalpino (1590–1603), professor at Pisa and later physician to Pope Clement VIII. In his system, he paid particular attention to seed structure, to the presence or absence of fruits, to the number of loculi and, less happily, to the general appearance of the plants. It was thus that he distinguished between *arbores* and *fructices*, *suffructices* and *herbae*. This classification in the tradition of Theophrastos, which seemed convenient but was not based on natural characteristics, was to remain in vogue for more than two centuries, thus paralysing the efforts of all other systematizers. According to Haller, Cesalpino distinguished more than 1,500 different species of plants.

One of the most famous descriptive botanists of the time was Charles de l'Écluse, or Clusius (1526–1609). He was born at Arras and taught at Montpellier, where he was also secretary to Rondelet. Among his pupils were such famous botanists as Bauhin, de Lobel and Péna. Montpellier was, and still is, one of the most important centres of French botanical research. Clusius collected plants throughout Europe, was appointed Director of Gardens by the Emperor Maximilian II, and finally became a professor at Leyden. He published a large number of works, particularly the *Rariorum plantarum historia* (1601) in which he described and illustrated some 1,585 plants, classified as trees and shrubs, bulbs producing odorous, non-odorous and malodorous flowers, poisonous, narcotic, acrid and lactiferous plants, umbellifers, ferns, graminaceous and leguminous plants. Though Clusius' classification left much to be desired, his accurate descriptions were based on a keen sense of observation. He was the first to distinguish between edible, poisonous and pernicious mushrooms, and to cultivate the potato, which Zarate had introduced from Peru in 1555.

Caspar Bauhin (1560–1634) and his brother John (1541–1613) were born in Switzerland. John, who was taught by L. Fuchs, became physician to the Duke of Württemberg. At Montbéliard, he wrote two great works (published posthumously): the *Historia plantarum prodromus* (1619) and the *Historia universalis plantarum* (1650–1661), which was divided into 40 books, illustrated with 3,426 figures taken partly from Fuchs, and contained a description of 5,226 plants. The *Historia* was, in fact, a vast compilation of everything that had been written on plants since antiquity. John Bauhin, who was in touch with most botanists of his time, also published his correspondence with Gesner (1594).

Much more important still was the work of his brother Caspar. In the *Phytopinax* (1596), Caspar described 2,700 species of plants, including the potato, which he called *Solanum tuberosum*, a name it has kept ever since. But Caspar's fame rests not so much on that book as on the *Pinax theatri botanici*, the first work to describe plants by a Latin noun corresponding to what was later to be called the genus, and by two or three adjectives designating the species. Caspar Bauhin was therefore a forerunner of Linnaeus. In addition, he not only listed the names used by earlier authorities, but, unlike so many of his predecessors, he eschewed the alphabetical method of classification and considered natural relationships instead. Though his system was still imperfect, it marked a great advance over anything that had gone before. Finally, Caspar Bauhin wrote the *Prodromus theatri botanici* (1620), a work containing 600 plates of 6,000 recognizable plants, including many new species.

Matthias de l'Obel (Lobelius, 1538–1616) was the author of the *Stirpium adversaria nova*, a descriptive and ecological flora of the surroundings of Montpellier and of the Cévennes. In it, he made the first attempt to distinguish monocotyledons from dicotyledons among 1,200–1,300 species of grasses, orchids, pot-herbs, legumes, trees and shrubs, palms, and mosses. In 1576, Lobelius completed this work with his still more important *Plantarum seu stirpium historia*, illustrated with 1,486 figures, many of which had not been published before. Encouraged by Christopher Plantin, he published a new version of the work in 1581, together with an index in seven languages, an album of 2,491 figures, and a list of all previous references to the species described. The work was so brilliantly conceived that Linnaeus referred to it on many occasions. Unfortunately Lobelius was also one of the first systematizers to classify plants by the shape of their leaves, an arbitrary method that led to much confusion.

At about the same time, a set of 500 engraved plates was made from the drawings of Richer de Belleval (1564–1632), who used to wander among the plants of the Pyrenees, the Alps and the Cévennes. Unfortunately the plates were not printed until the 18th century, when Gilibert used some of them to illustrate his edition of Rozier and Clarette de la Tourette's *Démonstrations de botanique* (1789).

Like so many botanists of his period, J. Dalechamps (1513–1588) began his work by writing commentaries on Pliny. Practising medicine at Lyons, the environs of which are particularly rich in plants, he was able to build up a considerable herbarium. He also commissioned engravings of the many drawings he received from Lobelius, Clusius and other botanists, and published a *Historia generalis plantarum* illustrated with 2,731 woodcuts. These were presented without any semblance of order, and the same species was often described under two or three different headings. Another magnificently produced work was the *De natura stirpium libri tres* by Jean Ruel (1479–1537), Dean of the Paris Faculty of Medicine. This book, which appeared in 1536, was a veritable inventory of the botanical knowledge of the time.

Germany also produced several botanists of great renown. One of the earliest was Otto Brunfels, a Carthusian monk converted to Protestantism, who became a physician in Basle, where he published the *Herbarum vivae eicones*, illustrated with 283 excellent woodcuts (1530–1536). Jerome Bock or Tragus (1498–1544), a pupil of Brunfels, described 800 species of plants in his *New Kreütter Buch* (1539) and attempted to classify them into three groups: herbs and odoriferous plants, clovers or grasses, and trees or shrubs. He insisted on the distinction between individual species.

Leonhard Fuchs (1501–1566), physician at Munich, Ingolstadt and Tübingen, was the first to pay attention to botanical nomenclature. His *De historia stirpium* (Basle, 1542), which was often reprinted and translated into many languages, was provided with a small glossary of the main botanical terms then in use. Fuchs described 500 (mainly medicinal) plants, giving their names, shapes, sites, 'temperaments' and therapeutic virtues. Though he failed to arrange his plants in any kind of order, his woodcuts were so clear and elegant and the book so conveniently small that many laymen carried it about with them to study botany for themselves.

The great naturalist and physician Conrad Gesner (1515–1565) of Basle put his vast knowledge of plants into his *Opera botanica*, which was not published until 1751–1771. The 1,500 drawings which he assembled for this purpose, most of them original, were used to illustrate many later works. Gesner argued that plants are best classified by their flowers and fruits. He also had an early inkling of the notion of 'genus', for he showed how species with natural affinities could be grouped together. He described a great number of mountain plants, including *Eryngium* and *Rhododendron*, and was the first to attempt a complete description of the Alpine flora. He also published a plant catalogue in four languages.

Rembert Dodoens, or Dodonaeus (1518–1585), was born at Malines, and studied at Louvain and at a number of German and Italian universities. He was a keen collaborator with a number of botanists, and particularly with Clusius and Lobelius. Encouraged by Christopher Plantin, who may be called the Maecenas of early botanists, he published a Flemish *Herbal* in 1554, which Clusius translated into French and of which the *Stirpium historiae pemptades*

15 The treatment of syphilis in the 16th century

16 Rhinoceros, by Dürer; Sea-serpent, after Belon

sex sive libri XXX (1583), illustrated with 1,305 figures (mostly borrowed from other authors), became the definitive edition. Dodoens classified plants both by their external characteristics and also by the alphabetical order of their names.

Among works of lesser importance were Aldrovandi's *Dendrology*, the botanical textbooks of J. Duchoul and Adam Lonicer, and the *Eicones plantarum* (1519) of Bock's pupil, T. Tabernaemontanus, which described 5,800 species and contained 2,480 figures taken from unacknowledged sources. It was still being republished in 1687.

Not until the 17th century did the first truly systematic catalogues begin to appear. Few earlier works, other than those by botanist-explorers (see below), merit the name of 'flora'. We have already discussed Fuchs and Gesner, and need merely add that Gesner was responsible for publishing V. Cordus' (posthumous) study of the flora of Italy in 1561. The figures in it are clear but small and arranged without any method. Clusius began the study of the flora of Spain and Austria; Thalius published a catalogue of the forest plants of Thuringia, grouped into such natural families as *Lactuceae* and *Gramineae*—an exceptionally lucid classification for the times. F. L. Calzolari and J. and F. Pona studied the flora of Monte Baldo.

Structure and Function of Plants

Though it would be wrong to speak of 16th-century plant anatomy and plant physiology, Cesalpino may be said to have pointed the way towards these disciplines when, at the beginning of his *De plantis libri XVI* (1583), he wrote that plant life can be reduced to three functions: nutrition, growth and reproduction. Since plants, unlike animals, lack feeling and movement, the organization, although comparable, requires a less complicated apparatus. Like animals, plants have souls, located in the collar, *i.e.* the junction between the stem and the root, which is their heart. From it springs the root (comparable with the mouth or stomach) and the stem bearing the flowers (comparable to the foetal membranes). Plants may therefore be called animals standing on their heads; their sap ascends from the roots and descends from the branches to meet in the collar, much as the blood of animals is carried to and from the heart by the arteries and veins. Cesalpino observed that the collar corresponds to the *copulum* of seeds, which he used as a systematic criterion.

At about the same time, V. Cordus and G. da Orta gave an excellent description of the leaf-patterns of leguminous plants.

Sexuality of Plants

In 1605, J. Pontanus mentioned the existence of male and female palm trees—a new discovery that was to prove of great importance.

In 1522, P. Alpino became the first to fertilize dates artificially. In the same year A. Zaluzhansky, following Pliny, affirmed that every plant bore male or female reproductive organs, either jointly or separately. Cesalpino observed the existence of two types of pedicle in both garden mercury and hemp, one sterile, and the other fertile 'provided it was close enough to the first to take its fertilizing effluvium'. Anthers were first described by G. Manardi.

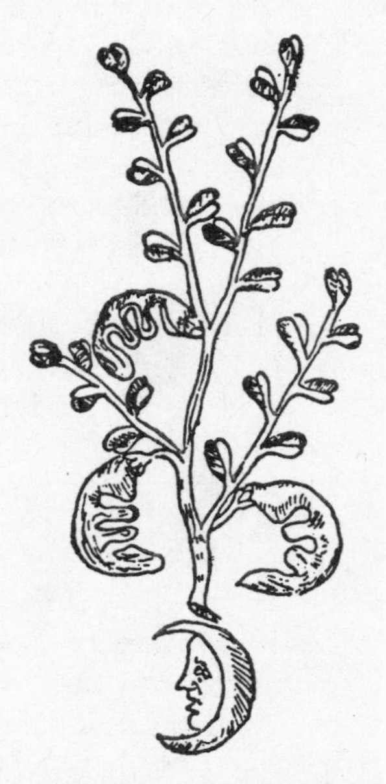

fig. 13 Leaves of Botrychium lunaria, according to J. B. Porta's 'Phytognomica' (1608).

Medical Botany

Interest in classical botany during the 16th century was mainly restricted to the medicinal properties of plants. The majority of classical botanists had, in effect, been physicians, concerned above all with the virtues of simples.

Paracelsus developed the strange doctrine of the 'signature' of plants, according to which plant organs resemble the diseases which they are destined to cure. Thus the 'yellow-blooded' celandine was an excellent remedy against jaundice; the cordiform leaves of the lilac a cure for heart diseases; and the lungwort, whose spotted leaves vaguely resemble the lobes of the lungs, a cure for chest conditions.

One of the most active defenders of this doctrine was Giambattista della Porta (1540?–1595), whose *Phytognomonica* (1588) discussed the similarities between leaves and the moon *(see fig. 13)*, between roots and human hair, and between flowers and insects. Though Porta's views were challenged, particularly by A. van der Spiegel (1606), a vast number of treatises on the doctrine of signatures continued to be published until the 18th century.

Many other works also dealt with plant remedies. Medieval recipes went into M. Sylvaticus' *Liber pandectarum medicinae* (1474), M. Platearius' *Liber de simplici medicina* (1497), and J. Serapion's *Liber aggregatus in medicinis simplicibus* (1473). The most important of the 'modern' treatises were the *Examen simplicium medicamentorum* by the Italian botanist Brasávola (1536), Jacques Dubois' (Sylvius') treatise on the preparation of simples (1542), Anguillara's *Simplici* (1561), and R. Constantin's treatise on the medicinal plants of Provence (1597). In Germany, Euricius Cordus studied plant synonymy (*Botanologicon*, 1534), while his son Valerius Cordus (1515–1544) gathered material for a flora of Germany and Italy, which, together with his commentaries on Dioscorides, was published by Gesner in 1561. Valerius Cordus also wrote a *Dispensatorium pharmacorum* (1546) which was translated into French (Lyons, 1578).

Botanical Gardens and Agriculture

The publication of numerous *Horti sanitatis* encouraged the systematic cultivation of medicinal plants in monastery and university gardens, where students would henceforth be able to study their properties on the spot. Such was the origin of the botanical gardens of Northern Italy, famed for its excellent climate. The oldest was founded by Gualterus near Venice (1533). In 1545, Buonafede opened another garden near Padua, a catalogue of which was published by Cortuso in 1601. Anguillara was appointed *ostensor simplicium* of the Pisa gardens in 1546, and Luca Ghini of the Bologna gardens in 1568. Holland and Germany soon followed suit: the Leyden botanical gardens were opened in 1577, and the Leipzig gardens in 1580. At Paris, N. Houel opened an apothecaries' garden in 1576, and R. de Belleval founded the Montpellier Botanical Garden in 1598. In 1533, the great humanist S. Chamier of Lyons supervised the publication of a *Hortus gallicus* and a *Campus elyseus galliae*. Charles Estienne, son of the famous printer Henry Estienne, published a number of works on horticulture which made him a worthy precursor of Olivier de Serres. He also collaborated with his son-in-law, Liébault, in publishing the *Agriculture et maison rustique* (1564). In 1540, P. Belon opened an *arboretum* in Touvoie (Sarthe), which was mentioned by Rabelais, who took a keen interest in the acclimatization of plants. Among the first French agronomists were Davy de Brossard, Mizauld and Londric.

In 1588, the German botanist Joachim Camerarius (1534–1598) published a plant catalogue of his Nuremberg garden. It contained excellent illustrations, particularly of the germination of the date and the American agave. Illustrations of unrivalled excellence were also found in the work of B. Besler (1561–1629), director of the St. Wildebald gardens. His catalogue was arranged by seasons and at least six engravers collaborated in making the 374 plates, illustrating more than a thousand flowers.

The English botanist William Turner (1515–1568) published a *New Herball* in 1568. In it he stressed the individuality of plant species which he, nevertheless, classified in the alphabetical order of their Latin names. The English have always taken a keen interest in horticulture. John Parkinson's *Paradisi in sole* ['Park-in-sun's'] *Paradisus terrestris* (1629) listed more than 7,000 plants suited to British conditions. His classification was based partly on medicinal properties and partly on habitat. The book is of great historical interest for it gives us a clear idea of the chief varieties of edible plants cultivated at the time. J. Gerard established an apothecaries' garden at Holborn and published its catalogue in 1597.

The First Botanist-Explorers

Columbus' discovery of America in 1492, and Vasco da Gama's discovery of the Cape of Good Hope and of the sea-route to the East Indies in 1497, ushered in the age of botanical voyages. In their search for new specimens early botanical 'pilgrims' thought nothing of braving the hazards of long and slow voyages, precipitous mountains, jungles and tropical diseases.

One of the first of these pioneers was Pierre Belon (1517–1564). He was born in Maine, near the city of Le Mans, and studied under Valerius Cordus of Wittenberg. With the help and protection of Cardinal Tournon he set out for the East, visiting Greece, Turkey, Asia Minor, the Mediterranean islands, Egypt and Palestine (1546–1549). In 1553, he published an account of his many singular discoveries. The work was republished in 1588 with beautiful woodcuts, and was later translated into Latin by Charles de l'Écluse. It contained the first European references to such exotic plants as *Platanus orientalis* and *Caucalis orientalis*. However, Belon was far more interested in the practical uses of plants than in correct terminology.

In his *Cosmographie du Levant* (1554), André Thévet (1503–1592) described his travels in Palestine and Asia Minor; a later expedition to South America became the subject of his *Les singularitez de la France antarctique* (1558). Having an open but somewhat woolly mind, he gave a rather uncritical account of everything he had found: weapons, pottery, plants, animals and minerals. He shares the credit of introducing tobacco to Europe with Jean Nicot (1530–1588) and G. Benzoni, who travelled in America from 1541 to 1560.

The German botanist L. Rauwolff left Europe for the Levant in 1573 and visited most Eastern countries disguised as a merchant. The first account of his travels was published in 1581. Part of his *Herbal* was incorporated into Gronovius' *Flora orientalis* (1775), which mentions coffee. The Italian botanist Prospero Alpino (1553–1617), soldier, physician and later professor at Padua, described some 50 Egyptian plants, including *Lycium* and the Senegal *Acacia*. He also discussed various Cretan plants in a book published by his son in 1627. M. Guilandino (Wieland), who visited Syria and Egypt, wrote on the Pliny papyrus and compared classical with modern systematic terminology. The Mediterranean islands were explored by J. Casabona, Keeper of the Botanical Garden in Florence, and by Anguillara, who showed that many common names of plants were modifications of their classical equivalents.

Forty years before the discovery of America the Venetian botanist Cá da Mosta visited the Canary Islands, Madeira and the west coast of Africa, where he discovered the baobab tree (rediscovered independently by Adanson) and *Dracoena draco* in 1455. Gonzalo Hernandez de Ovieda, a Spanish official in the New World, published a *Historia general y natural de las Indias* (1525–1535), in which he mentioned the guava and the avocado. Lopez de Gomara, a missionary from the Canaries, published a *Historia general* of his native islands (1553) which contains the earliest description of the cacao tree. Jean de Léri (1534–1611), who accompanied the Chevalier de Villegaignon on his travels through Brazil, published an account of their journey in 1598. He also described the 'trees, herbs, roots and exquisite fruits' of that country. The Spanish Jesuit B. Cobo (1582–1657) visited Peru and wrote an (unpublished) history of the Indies. His colleague Martin del Barco went to Paraguay in 1573, where he discovered the mimosa and the passion flower. N. Monardes published a remarkable study of the plants of the 'West Indies' (Seville, 1565–1574), which was translated into Latin by Charles de l'Écluse in 1574 and into French by A. Colin in 1602.[1]

Linschooten's account of his voyages to the East Indies (The Hague, 1599) contained descriptions of the mango tree and of a *Polyanthes tuberosa*. Garcia da Orta became chief physician to the Count of Redondo, Portuguese Viceroy of the Indies, in 1534. His *Coloquios dos simples e drogas* (1563) was translated into Latin and into French. Cristobal Acosta, a Portuguese Jesuit, spent much of his life in the East Indies, and his own *Drogas* (1578) was based largely on da Orta's. The brothers Poli, Venetian merchants who travelled in

[1] See also Part IV: Science in Colonial America (page 614).

Central Asia, Mongolia and China, described the spice tree, the coconut, the banana, and the 'apple of Paradise'.

In short, 15th- and 16th-century botanists had begun to observe plants in their natural habitat and to describe them correctly. Moreover, by teaching the Old World about the flora of the New, botanist-explorers helped considerably to pave the way towards the modern method of plant classification.[1]

[1] My very special thanks are due to Professor Eichhorn (Sorbonne) who was kind enough to revise the text and also to P. E. Pillet, Professor of Plant Physiology at the University of Lausanne, who made a great number of valuable suggestions.

CONCLUSION

Intellectual Developments and the Reformation

THE 16TH CENTURY is one of the most difficult periods in history for, as E. Callot has very justly remarked, every judgment on it is open to challenge. Nor is it easy to speak of the individual contributions of different nationalities in an age where science was taught by itinerant teachers to itinerant students. What country, for instance, had the greatest share in the education of Vesalius, who was born in Brussels, studied at Louvain, became an imperial army surgeon, a professor at Padua, Bologna and Pisa, and finally court physician to Charles V and to Philip II?

Clearly, intellectual activity flourished best where commercial crossroads met to produce a keen exchange of ideas. One such area was the Mediterranean basin, one of the oldest melting-pots of different traditions; another was the route across the Rhône and Rhine rivers, with Lyons, the international and commercial banking centre, as the intellectual relay station between the south and the north. Lyons became a haven of literature, of medical science and botany, and so did the Rhineland, that other staging-house of European thought. As Germany became parcelled out into 400 small states, new capitals rose up to become new intellectual centres.

What role did the religious schism play in the development of science? A. de Candolle has suggested that Protestant scientists were more given to the direct study of nature than to the abstract speculations in Graeco-Roman rationalism; J. Pelseneer believes that Paracelsian doctrines sorted far better with Germanic pantheism than with Catholic monotheism.

In truth, though one cannot dismiss the effects of national psychology and religious beliefs on scientific thought, the intellectual scene cannot be distinguished by these effects alone. A fervent Catholic like Belon was as great a physicist as Rondelet, one of the leading Protestants at Montpellier; Pierre Gilles, a protégé of Cardinal d'Armagnac, was as great an observer of nature as Paré or Palissy, both of whom were Huguenots.

It must, however, be granted that the Reformation, from its very beginnings, found an echo in the hearts of many intellectuals, who resented Catholic attempts to subordinate science to Church dogma, or were disgusted with the scandalous conduct of many leading Churchmen. A number of scientists were involved in the political and religious upheavals which shook all Europe, with personal results that differed from country to country.

In Spain, a country that had barely shaken off the yoke of the Moors and the Arabs, and which was still divided into the old kingdoms (Aragon, Castile, *etc.*) and privileged cities (*fueros*), political cohesion could be assured only through religious unity. Hence, the Holy Office had to fight the return of Judaeo-Islamic ideas with the utmost ruthlessness, and an edict of Philip II (1559) prohibited the departure of students to countries where they might be polluted with subversive or foreign ideas. In the circumstances, it was a miracle that the University of Salamanca had the courage to introduce not only the anatomical innovations of Vesalius, but even the far more compromising ideas of Copernican astronomy. Later, when it was spared by the religious wars, the Iberian peninsula could afford to open its arms to the humanist ideas of J. Luis Vives, inscribe over the portals of its medical school the name of Andreas Laguna, tackle the immense labour of classifying the natural resources of America, and begin the great work of intellectual colonization: the establishment of universities at Lima (San Marcos, 1551), Mexico (1550) and Cuzco (1598). (The short-lived University of San Domingo was founded as early as 1538.)

Spain found that some of her satellites were far less compliant than others. Thus the University of Louvain, which demanded guarantees of orthodoxy from its students and teachers, and forbade its students to visit foreign colleges or to read imported works, was impotent to stem the intellectual and Protestant trends fermented by the Prince of Orange. After the secession of the Netherlands, William the Silent erected the intellectual bastion of Leyden as a Protestant answer to Louvain. Belgian scientists braved the storms as best they could, but the greatest of them were forced to seek fame abroad. Though Vesalius dedicated his *Epitome* to Prince Philip, son of the Emperor Charles, it was at Basle that he had his great work printed. Dodoens fled to Holland, and an ancestor of the Bernoulli family left Antwerp for Frankfurt, whence his descendants emigrated to Basle. The Portuguese physician Roderigo da Castro judged it prudent to decamp from Antwerp to Hamburg in 1594. Another Portuguese, Lopez Garcia, imprudently returned to his own country and was burned at the stake as a heretic in 1572. Garcia da Orta left Europe for Goa, where he wrote his *Coloquios*. But the Holy Office had a long arm, and though it was too slow to catch the miscreant while he was still alive, it burned his remains with great ceremony.

Rome under the Borgias witnessed a return to laxer manners, but other Princes of the Church proved far less tolerant. Paul III created the Inquisition in 1542, and Paul IV introduced the Index in 1557. The intransigence of the Church increased with each meeting of the Council of Trent (1545–1563). Aldrovandi was apprehended by the henchmen of the Holy Office (1549) and deported from Padua to Rome, where he found favour in the eyes of Julius III. Because of the repressive anti-Jewish measures of Paul III and later of Paul IV, the author of the infamous Bull *Cum nimis absurdum* (1555), Amatus Lusitanus had to flee from Ancona to Ragusa, then an Ottoman city. In 1600, the Holy Office consigned Giordano Bruno to the stake and later prepared its case against Galileo (1633). Even so, Italian science, and particularly Italian mathematics and botany, continued to flourish. Colombo and Berengario da Cari taught at the University of Bologna; Vesalius wrote his *Fabrica* at the University of Padua; Eustachi lent fame to the University of Pisa, which, like the Universities of Pavia and Rome, did much to further the study of anatomy. Italy, though divided and regularly ravaged by opposing armies, nevertheless remained the mother of the arts, the mainspring of European learning and the inspiration of scholars at home and abroad.

In Germany, Charles V was impotent to stem the rising Protestant flood. Though he put down the Hussite revolt in Prague, he lost ground everywhere else. The expropriation of Church lands provided funds for the support of such Lutheran colleges as the University of Marburg, which Philip, Landgrave of Hesse, founded in 1527, and where Euricius Cordus taught botany. In the imperial city of Strasbourg, some of the canons' stipends were diverted to the professors of the University. Melanchthon's proposed syllabus for the old University of Wittenberg included the study of Pliny. Everywhere science gained ground in the wake of heresy. Meanwhile, although the Diet of Augsburg had granted equal rights to Catholics and Protestants, Duke Ulrich of Württemberg and his counsellor, Grynaeus, expelled all Catholic students from Tübingen, which they turned into one of the intellectual bulwarks of Lutheran Germany. Conversely, the itinerant botanist Rauwolff of Augsburg returned home in 1576, only to be driven out as a Protestant. In 1599, Kepler was forced to quit his post at the University of Graz for the same reason, though he was later allowed to rejoin Tycho Brahe in Prague.

The Inquisition raged as far afield as the University of Cracow in Poland, where Alexander Zuchta, a pupil of Paracelsus, was found guilty of heresy, stripped of his hood and possessions and then driven into exile. Unbridled intolerance flourished in Calvin's Geneva as well. Calvin banished the physician Jérôme Bolsec, with whose medical doctrines he disagreed, and, in 1533, burned Michael Servet for having committed a theological error. In 1559, when the University of Geneva opened under the iron dictatorship of Theodore de Bèze, natural science was labelled *diabolica scientia* and its teaching was proscribed. Calvin denounced science as nothing but 'impudent curiosity and impertinence'.

England, which had become the centre of humanism with such illustrious men as Thomas Linacre, Thomas More and John Colet, was particularly exposed to the repercussions of the Reformation. The execution of Thomas More (1535), the development of Protestant thought under Edward VI, the massacres of Mary Tudor and the intolerance of the triumphant Anglican Church all caused upheavals. Nevertheless, English science made a brilliant new start at the beginning of the 17th century under Gilbert, Bacon and Harvey.

In France, about to be united under a central sovereign, reformers and counter-reformers were constantly at one another's throats. Spain had the Inquisition—Paris had the Sorbonne. Heretical views (the definition of which varied as royal opinions changed) were suppressed with the utmost vigour. The physician Jean Bauhin had to flee the stake to Basle in 1541, and in 1543 all teachers at the University of Paris were forced to submit a written declaration of their orthodoxy.

Things became worse when the conflict passed from the religious to the political sphere, with various factions fighting for influence over the throne. Pamphlets and edicts were followed by executions, and finally by the eight Wars of Religion. Deprived of their doctorates (1562 and 1567), J. Le Paumier and Jacques Grévin went into exile, and in 1571 Jacques Aubert was forced to seek asylum in Lausanne. Only the personal intervention of Charles IX saved his leading surgeon, Ambroise Paré, from being massacred like Pierre Ramus on St. Bartholomew's Night (24th August 1572). Bernard Palissy died in the Bastille in 1589. The 'War of the Three Henrys' (1585–1589) produced fresh devastation, and the Edict of Nantes (1598) brought no more than transitory relief.

However, whether it persecuted or was persecuted itself, Protestantism contributed to scientific progress, albeit indirectly. Thus the incessant accusations and counter-accusations and the constant flow of refugees from Catholic countries to Protestant countries, and *vice versa*, led to an increase of intellectual contacts. Beyond that, neither Catholics nor Protestants could permanently confine the *libido sciendi* behind sectarian boundaries. G. Bigot was allowed to teach at Tübingen in about 1535; Belon, a fanatical anti-Huguenot, nevertheless profited from the open invitation which the University of Wittenberg had extended to all foreign students. At Wittenberg, he studied under the botanist Valerius Cordus, and even had discussions with Luther in 1540. French universities, equally anxious to enrol students, also tolerated dissenters (at least during political lulls); Montpellier welcomed Felix Platter of Basle and many of his compatriots, with the only proviso that they avoid causing public scandals.

In the 17th century Father Mersenne was to act as a link between numerous scholars from different countries, but enlightened sovereigns and scholars had already begun to keep in touch with such men as Gesner and Aldrovandi. From Naples, Ferrante Imperato corresponded with Aldrovandi, Bauhin, Clusius and Mattioli; from Zurich, Gesner wrote to Rondelet, Belon, Thévet and Platter. A new community of science had risen up above the political struggles and the confessional disputes. Thus, while battles continued, while cities were being besieged, and schools, churches and homes were being laid waste and pillaged by mercenaries, European thought soared to unprecedented heights.

Though it wedded intellectual progress to pitiless destruction, the Renaissance may be called a great age, the age in which modern science was born and in which great cultural advances were made in spite of oppressive religious and secular wars—bitter struggles from which the great treasures of Italy and the cathedrals of France and Belgium seem to have escaped only by a miracle.

BIBLIOGRAPHY

General History

For an overall historical survey, see:

H. HAUSER and A. RENAUDET, *Les débuts de l'âge moderne* 3rd ed., Paris, 1946.

H. HAUSER, *La prépondérance espagnole (1559–1660)*, 3rd ed., Paris, 1948.

R. MOUSNIER, *Les XVIe et XVIIe siècles* (*ib.*, Vol. IV), Paris, 1954.

E. PERROY, *Le moyen âge* (Vol. III of *L'Histoire des Civilisations*), Paris, 1955.

Detailed bibliographies are given in the 'Clio' collection, particularly Vols. V and VI:

J. CALMETTE, *L'Élaboration du monde moderne* (Vol. V), 3rd ed., Paris, 1949.

H. SÉE, A. RÉBILLON and E. PRÉCLIN, *Le XVIe siècle* (Vol. VI), Paris, 1950.

See also:

L. FEBVRE, *Le problème de l'incroyance au XVIe siècle: la religion de Rabelais*, Paris, 1947.

L. FEBVRE and H. J. MARTIN, *L'apparition du livre*, Paris, 1958.

E. GARIN, *Il Rinascimento. Significati e limiti*, Florence, 1953.

J. W. THOMPSON *et al.*, *The Civilization of the Renaissance*, Chicago, 1929.

General Bibliography

J. C. POGGENDORFF, *Biographisch-literarisches Handwörterbuch*, 7 vols., Leipzig, 1863–1962.

F. RUSSO, *Histoire des sciences et des techniques: bibliographie*, Paris, 1954; cyclostyled suppl., 1955.

G. SARTON, *Horus, a Guide to the History of Science and Civilization*, Waltham, Mass., 1952.

The periodic bibliographies published in the *Bulletin signalétique du C.N.R.S.*, in *Isis*, and in the *Proceedings* of leading scientific societies.

Studies on General Science

P. A. CAP, *La science et les savants au XVIe siècle*, Tours, 1867.

N. DAUMAS *et al.*, *Histoire de la science*, Paris, 1957.

P. DELAUNAY, *La médecine et l'Église.*

S. D'IRSAY, *Histoire des Universités*, Paris, 1935.

R. W. T. GUNTHER, *Early Science in Oxford*, 14 vols., Oxford, 1920–1945.

A. R. HALL, *The Scientific Revolution, 1500–1800*, London, 1954.

A. C. KLEBS, 'Incunabula scientifica et medica' in *Osiris*, IV, 1938, pp. 1–359.

A. LEFRANC, *Histoire du Collège de France*, Paris, 1893.
Le Collège de France (1530–1930), Paris, 1932.

A. MIELI, R. PAPP and J. BABINI, *Panorama general de historia de la ciencia*, Vols. III–VI, Buenos Aires, 1950–1952.

J. PELSENEER, 'La Réforme et l'origine de la science moderne' in *Revue de l'Univ. de Bruxelles*, 1954.
'Les persécutions contre les savants en Belgique' in *Le Flambeau*, 1954.

G. SARTON, *The Appreciation of Ancient and Medieval Science during the Renaissance*, Univ. of Pennsylvania Press, 1955.
Six Wings, Men of Science in the Renaissance, Indiana Univ. Press, 1957.

E. NEWTON HARVEY, *A History of Luminescence from the Earliest Times until 1900*, Philadelphia, 1957.

A. M. SCHMIDT, *La poésie scientifique en France au XVIe siècle*, Paris, 1938.
L. THORNDIKE, *History of Magic and Experimental Science*, Vols. IV–VI, New York, 1934–1941.
A. WOLF, *A History of Science, Technology and Philosophy in the 16th and 17th Centuries*, 2nd ed., London, 1950.
R. TATON, *Reason and Chance in Scientific Discovery*, London, 1957.
H. T. PLEDGE, *Science since 1500*, London, 1946.

Mathematics

M. CHASLES, *Aperçu historique sur le développement des méthodes en géometrie*, 2nd ed., Paris, 1875.
A. G. KÄSTNER, *Geschichte der Mathematik*, 4 vols., Göttingen, 1796–1800.
J. E. MONTUCLA, *Histoire des mathématiques*, 2nd ed., 4 vols., Paris, 1799–1802.
Among more recent works:
O. BECKER and J. E. HOFMANN, *Geschichte der Mathematik*, Bonn, 1951.
E. BORTOLOTTI, *Studi sulla storia delle matematiche in Italia*, 2 vols., Bologna, 1928–1944.
P. BOUTROUX, *Principes de l'analyse mathématique*, 2 vols., Paris, 1914–1919.
A. VON BRAUNMÜHL, *Vorlesungen über die Geschichte der Trigonometrie*, 2 vols., Leipzig, 1900–1903.
F. CAJORI, *History of Mathematical Notations*, 2 vols., Chicago, 1928.
M. CANTOR, *Vorlesungen über die Geschichte der Mathematik*, Vol. II, 3rd ed., Leipzig, 1907.
J. L. COOLIDGE, *The Mathematics of the Great Amateurs*, Oxford, 1949.
G. LORIA, *Storia delle matematiche*, 2nd ed., Milan, 1950.
D. E. SMITH, *Rara Arithmetica*, Boston, 1908–1939.
History of Mathematics, 2 vols., Boston, 1923–1925.
J. TROPFKE, *Geschichte der Elementarmathematik*, Vols. I–IV, 3rd ed., Berlin, 1930–1939; Vols. V–VII, 2nd ed., Berlin, 1921–1924.
H. G. ZEUTHEN, *Geschichte der Mathematik im XVI. und XVII. Jahrhundert*, Leipzig, 1903.
A. HOOPER, *Makers of Mathematics*, New York, 1948.

Astronomy

J. BERTRAND, *Les fondateurs de l'astronomie moderne*, 5th ed., Paris, 1875.
J. B. DELAMBRE, *Histoire de l'astronomie au Moyen Âge*, Paris, 1818.
J. L. DREYER, *Tycho Brahe*, Edinburgh, 1890.
History of Astronomy from Thales to Kepler, 2nd ed., New York, 1954.
A. KOYRÉ, *From the Closed World to the Infinite Universe*, Baltimore, 1957.
T. S. KUHN, *The Copernican Revolution*, Harvard Univ. Press, 1957.

E. ZINNER, *Geschichte der Sternkunde*, 2nd ed., Berlin, 1943.
Entstehung und Ausbreitung der Copernicanischen Lehre, Erlangen, 1943.

Physics and Mechanics

E. GERLAND and F. TRAUMÜLLER, *Geschichte der physikalischen Experimentierkunst*, Leipzig, 1899.
K. LASSWITZ, *Geschichte der Atomistik*, 2 vols., Leipzig, 1890.
J. C. POGGENDORFF, *Geschichte der Physik*, Leipzig, 1879.
F. ROSENBERGER, *Geschichte der Physik*, 3 vols., Brunswick, 1882–1890.
Among more recent works:
E. J. DIJKSTERHUIS, *The Mechanization of the World Picture*, Oxford, 1961.
R. DUGAS, *History of Mechanics*, London, 1957.
Mechanics in the Seventeenth Century. From the Scholastic Antecedents to Classical Thought, Neuchâtel, 1958.
P. DUHEM, *Les origines de la statique*, 2 vols., Paris, 1907.
Le mouvement absolu et le mouvement relatif, Montligeon, 1907.
Études sur Léonard de Vinci, 3 vols., Paris, 1906–1913.
E. JOUGUET, *Lectures de mécanique*, 2 vols., Paris, 1924.
E. MACH, *Science of Mechanics*, London, 1893.
L. OLSCHKI, *Geschichte der neusprachlichen wissenschaftlichen Litteratur*, 3 vols., Halle, 1919–1927.
For Leonardo da Vinci see:
R. MARCOLONGO, *Memorie sulla geometria e la meccanica*, Naples, 1937.
G. SEAILLES, *Léonard de Vinci, l'artiste et le savant*, Paris, 1892.
G. UCELLI, *Scritti di meccanica*, Milan, 1940.
Léonard de Vinci et l'expérience scientifique au XVIe siècle, Paris, 1951.

Chemistry and Alchemy

M. BERTHELOT, *La chimie au Moyen Âge*, 3 vols., Paris, 1893.
M. P. CROSLAND, *Historical Studies in the Language of Chemistry*, London, 1962.
M. DELACRE, *Histoire de la chimie*, Paris, 1920.
D. I. DUVEEN, *Bibliotheca alchemica et chemica*, London, 1949.
J. FERGUSON, *Bibliotheca chimica*, 2 vols., Glasgow, 1906.
H. E. FIERZ-DAVID, *Die Entwicklungsgeschichte der Chemie*, 2nd ed., Basle, 1953.
E. J. HOLMYARD, *Makers of Chemistry*, Oxford, 1931.
Alchemy, London, 1957.
W. M. LEICESTER and H. S. KLICKSTEIN, *A Source Book in the History of Chemistry*, New York, 1952.
E. O. VON LIPPMANN, *Entstehung und Ausbreitung der Alchemie*, 2 vols., Berlin, 1921–1931.
H. M. PACHTER, *Paracelsus. Magic into Science*, New York, 1951.

Geology

F. D. ADAMS, *The Birth and Development of the Geological Sciences*, 2nd ed., New York, 1954.

E. DE MARGERIE, *Critique et géologie, Contribution a l'histoire des sciences de la terre*, 4 vols., Paris, 1943–1948.

E. DUPUY, *Bernard Palissy*, 2nd ed., Paris, 1902.

A. GEIKIE, *The Founders of Geology*, London, 1890.

G. VON GROTH, *Entwicklungsgeschichte der mineralogischen Wissenschaften*, Berlin, 1926.

K. F. MATHER and S. L. MASON, *A Source Book in Geology*, New York, 1939.

S. MEUSNIER, *L'évolution des théories géologiques*, Paris, 1911.

K. A. VON ZITTEL, *History of Geology and Paleontology to the End of the Nineteenth Century*, London, 1901.

See also the English translations of: KALB's *Bergbüchlein* (A. G. SISCO and C. S. SMITH, New York, 1949); AGRICOLA's *De re metallica* (H. C. HOOVER, London, 1912); and L. ERCKER's *Treatise* (A. G. SISCO and C. S. SMITH, Chicago, 1951).

Biology

E. B. ALMQUIST, *Grosse Biologen*, Munich, 1931.

F. BOURLIÈRE, *Éléments d'un guide bibliographique du naturaliste.*

E. CALLOT, *La renaissance des sciences de la vie au XVIe siècle*, Paris, 1950.

W. A. LOCY, *Biology and its Makers*, 3rd ed., London, 1915.

E. NORDENSKIÖLD, *The History of Biology*, New York, 1928.

E. RÁDL, *History of Biological Theories*, New York, 1930.

C. SINGER, *History of Biology*, New York, 1950.

Anatomy and Physiology

L. CHOULANT, *History and Bibliography of Anatomical Illustrations*, Chicago, 1920.

F. J. COLE, *History of Comparative Anatomy*, London, 1944.

H. CUSHING, *A Bio-bibliography of Vesalius*, New York, 1943.

J. F. FULTON, *Selected Readings in the History of Physiology*, Springfield, 1930.

J. NEEDHAM, *A History of Embryology*, Cambridge, 1934.

C. D. O'MALLEY and J. B. DE C. M. SAUNDERS, *Leonardo on the Human Body*, New York, 1952.

K. E. ROTHSCHUH, *Geschichte der Physiologie*, Berlin, 1953.

C. SINGER, *The Evolution of Anatomy*, New York, 1926.

C. SINGER and C. RABIN, *A Prelude to Modern Science*, Cambridge, 1946.

Zoology

J. ANKER, *Bird Books and Bird Art*, Copenhagen, 1938.
M. BOUBIER, *L'évolution d'ornithologie*, Paris, 1925.
J. V. CARUS, *Geschichte der Zoologie*, Munich, 1872.
P. DELAUNAY, *Pierre Belon, naturaliste*, Le Mans, 1926.
J. H. GURNEY, *Early Annals of Ornithology*, London, 1921.
T. S. HALL, *A Source Book in Animal Biology*, New York, 1951.
G. LOISEL, *Histoire des ménageries*, 3 vols., Paris, 1912.

Botany

A. ARBER, *Herbals . . .*, 2nd ed., Cambridge, 1937.
W. BLUNT, *The Art of Botanic Illustration*, London, 1951.
A. DAVY DE VIRVILLE *et al.*, *Histoire de la botanique en France*, Paris, 1954.
C. S. GAGER, *Botanical Gardens in the World*, New York, 1937.
E. L. GREENE, *Landmarks of Botanical History*, Washington, 1909.
F. W. T. HUNGER, *Charles de l'Écluse*, The Hague, 1927.
L. LEGRE, *La botanique en Provence au XVIe siècle*, 5 vols., Paris, 1899–1904.
M. MÖBIUS, *Geschichte der Botanik*, Jena, 1937.
C. NISSEN, *Die botanische Buchillustration*, 2 vols., Stuttgart, 1951.
H. S. REED, *Short History of Plant Science*, Waltham, Mass., 1942.
F. J. G. VON SACHS, *History of Botany 1530–1860*, Oxford, 1890.

Medicine

F. H. GARRISON and L. T. MORTON, *A Medical Bibliography*, London, 1943.
J. F. FULTON, *The Great Medical Bibliographers*, Philadelphia, 1951.
W. OSLER, *Incunabula Medica*, Oxford, 1923.
E. C. KELLY, *Encyclopedia of Medical Sources*, Baltimore, 1948.
C. V. DAREMBERG, *Histoire des sciences médicales*, 2 vols., Paris, 1870.
A. CASTIGLIONI, *History of Medicine*, 2nd ed., New York, 1947.
H. E. SIGERIST, *Great Doctors . . .*, London, 1933.
F. H. GARRISON, *Introduction to the History of Medicine*, 4th ed., Philadelphia, 1929.
R. DUMESNIL *et al.*, *Les médecins célèbres*, Paris, 1947.
P. M. M. LAIGNEL-LAVASTINE (ed.), *Histoire générale de la médecine . . .*, 3 vols., Paris, 1936–1949.
P. DIEPGEN, *Geschichte der Medizin*, Vol. I, Berlin, 1949.
A. PAZZINI, *Storia della medicina*, 2 vols., Milan, 1947.

P. DELAUNAY, *La vie médicale aux XVIe, XVIIe et XVIIIe siècles*, Paris, 1935.

E. WICKERSHEIMER, *La médecine et les médecins en France à l'époque de la Renaissance*, Paris, 1905.

G. BARRAUD, *L'humanisme et la médecine au XVIe siècle*, Paris, 1942.

A. CASTIGLIONI, *The Renaissance of Medicine in Italy*, Baltimore, 1935.

G. ZILBOORG, *The Medical Man and the Witch during the Renaissance*, Baltimore, 1935.

A. PECKER and H. ROULLAND, *L'accouchement au cours des siècles*, Paris, 1958.

E. R. LONG, *A History of Pathology*, Baltimore, 1928.

H. GRAHAM, *The Story of Surgery*, New York, 1939.

M. BOUVET, *Histoire de la pharmacie en France*, Paris, 1937.

J. GRIER, *A History of Pharmacy*, London, 1937.

P. DELAUNAY, *Ambroise Paré, naturaliste*, Laval, 1926.

J. DOE, *Bibliography of Paré's Works*, Chicago, 1937.

K. SUDHOFF, *Paracelsus*, Leipzig, 1936.

PARACELSUS, *Four Treatises* (ed. H. SIGERIST), Baltimore, 1941.

PART II

The 17th Century

WHEREAS THE RENAISSANCE marked a return to classical concepts, the 17th century set science on entirely new foundations.

To begin with, algebra, number theory, probability theory, projective geometry and the infinitesimal calculus were given so great an impetus that the very scope of mathematics was radically changed. The new, unlike the old, mathematics could be successfully applied to theoretical physics—first of all to dynamics, which Galileo and Newton turned into an autonomous discipline, then to celestial mechanics where Kepler and Newton revolutionized the Copernican system, and finally to optics, which was gradually transformed into a mathematical science. At the same time, there were tremendous advances on the experimental front, thanks mainly to the invention of the telescope and the microscope, to the discovery of the geometrical laws of optics and to the more accurate interpretation of magnetic and electrical phenomena, while more gradual advances in acoustics, chemistry and thermodynamics prepared the ground for the advances to be made in the 18th century.

In biology, though taxonomy marked time, there were such great contributions as the discovery of the circulation of the blood and the foundation of microscopic anatomy, genetics and plant physiology. All these new departures had direct repercussions on the progress of medicine. Finally, as the medieval and clerical prejudices in its path were gradually swept away, geology became a true science.

Hand in hand with these developments went a profound change in the spirit and method of science. By destroying a sterile tradition, Gilbert, Galileo, Bacon, Kepler, Harvey, Huygens, Malebranche, Newton and Leibniz became the founders of modern science. True, not all their bold speculations proved equally fruitful, and some of their worst errors had to be painfully corrected by their successors, but, on balance, no one can deny that by their original and incisive methods they opened up vast new horizons and gave scientific research a crucial impetus.

The 17th-Century Scientific Revolution

WHEN HISTORIANS CALL the 17th century the cradle of modern science, they do not mean that Descartes or even Newton were 'modern' scientists like Bohr or Einstein. Thus, we could not possibly understand these men or their work if we looked upon them as our intellectual contemporaries.

For example, it was not until the 18th century that the notion of mass made its first appearance; the 17th century was unfamiliar with such concepts as calories and living cells; magnetism and electricity were still in their infancy, and so was geology. Descartes held that thunder was the result of a chemical explosion, and that mountain springs were fed by the oceans. The heliocentric doctrine remained purely speculative until Newton supported it with decisive arguments, and the doctrine that man is a machine made biology a hotchpotch of ill-digested notions.

OLD IDEAS IN NEW GUISE

Scholasticism survived in Descartes' contention that the physical world can be inferred from God's existence, in the many sterile disputes between the iatromechanists and the iatrochemists and in the quarrels about the *vis viva*. In short, if we set out with the misconception that 17th-century scientists were truly 'modern', the discovery of their many errors and shortcomings may cause us to dismiss them as so many impostors.

But this would be to do them a grave injustice, for, as Butterfield has rightly argued, our own pundits would possibly do no better had they to lay the very foundations of science, as the 17th-century scientists did in their day. An age which made such impressive contributions as Kepler's laws, Galileo's mechanics, Harvey's discovery of the circulation of the blood, Descartes' geometry, Steno's geology, Newton's astronomy and Leeuwenhoek's microscopy may be forgiven some of its errors, the more so since, to make its discoveries, it had first to overthrow established ideas of science and scientific research that had held sway ever since Aristotle.

THE SCIENTIFIC REVOLUTION OF 1620

Developments in 1620 did for science what Greek thought did for Western civilization as a whole. It was in that year that qualitative physics was ousted by quantitative physics; the hierarchical cosmos by an 'unbounded' universe without privileged centres and occasionally without a teleological purpose; and the world of direct perception by the world of mathematical concepts based on the telescopic and microscopic study of phenomena.

The greatest merit of 17th-century scientists, therefore, is not that they *saw more things* than their predecessors, but that they regarded the world with *new eyes*. It is only in that sense that the 17th century is rightly called a 'modern' age.

THE ORGANIZATION OF SCIENCE

The new science grew up on the fringe of official science and was often opposed by it. Like their precursors, 17th-century scientists wisely veiled their work in secrecy, for the Church continued to be a powerful enemy and the man in the street indifferent. Bacon complained that all science was addressed to men of letters and metaphysicians, and it was not until a hundred years later that more popular works began to appear in any number.

As J. Pelseneer has shown, the true scientist, like the true artist, works in isolation. A case in point is Roberval, who kept many of his most important discoveries to himself. Descartes, though the author of many elegant phrases in praise of scientific co-operation as a duty to posterity, also wrote a eulogy of the lone scientist: 'It is true, indeed, as regards the experiments which may conduce to this end [the discovery of new truths] that one man is not equal to the task of making them all, but yet he can advantageously avail himself, in this work, of no hands but his own' (*Discourse on Method*, Part VI). No wonder that Descartes kept changing his address so frequently—he was jealously guarding his own privacy, and so did most of his contemporaries. Newton was notorious for his reticence and had to be bullied by Halley into the publication of the *Principia*.

When scientists did begin to exchange views, it was largely due to public challenges. The practice of challenging one's rivals to public debates was a relic of the scholastic disputes—and a certain way of making one's name. On the other hand, the custom of addressing the public at large by treatises printed in the vernacular was quite novel. Galileo's *Dialogo* appeared in 1632, Descartes' *Discourse* in 1637 and Newton's *Opticks* in 1704, and the public was not slow in responding to them.

The Italian Example

In 16th-century Italy, the rising merchant class began to rival the princes of State and Church in patronizing scientific research. Such traditionally independent cities as Padua, Pisa and Florence went out of their way to attract scientists of renown. Modern science, like modern art, sprang from Italy, so much so that most early 17th-century French scientists spoke and wrote Italian in addition to Latin. In 1603, Prince Federico Cesi helped to found one of the first scientific academies, the *Accademia dei Lincei*, in Rome. One of its leading members was Galileo. Fifty years later, Ferdinand II, Grand Duke of Tuscany, founded the Florentine *Accademia del Cimento* ('Experimental Academy'), which included such men as Viviani, Borelli, Redi and Steno.

The life of Galileo (1564–1642) is an example of the dangers and rewards attending the new science. Though protected by the Grand Duke of Tuscany, who appointed him Professor of Mathematics at Pisa and later implored him to leave for Florence, where his talents would be better appreciated, Galileo was powerless when the Church opened its case against him in 1633 and exiled him to Arcetri where he wrote his *Discorsi*.

Flanders and Holland

Flanders and Holland, which were as prosperous as Italy, were also in the vanguard of scientific progress. Thus, Descartes was persuaded to devote himself to scientific research by the Dutch physicist Isaac Beeckman, who was recently resurrected from long obscurity by C. De Waard. At Bruges, and later in Holland, Simon Stevin (1548–1620), mathematician and dyke engineer, proved the great practical worth of physics and aroused keen interest in science shorn of speculation and placed in the service of man. Antony von Leeuwenhoek of Delft (1632–1723), a cloth merchant by trade and the holder of important municipal and commercial offices, never left his workbench for a university. Men like Descartes, who flocked to Holland and Flanders, did so to take advantage of the liberty of thought and expression which these advanced provinces enjoyed.

No less significant in the spread of science was the contribution of such great printers as the Elseveers, to whom Galileo in distant Italy entrusted the publication of his *Discorsi*, or as Jean Maire, who published Descartes' *Discourse on Method*. A leading magistrate, Constantijn Huygens, placed his intelligence and influence at the service of Descartes and Mersenne. Mersenne was quick to appreciate the genius of Constantijn's son, Christiaan Huygens (1629–1695), who was later to bridge the gap between Galileo and Newton.

Christiaan Huygens spent most of his working life in France (1665–1681), was given a pension by Louis XIV and was elected a member of the *Académie des Sciences*.

FRANCE

In France, the formation of scientific societies was encouraged by two noblemen: Peiresc, Counsellor to the Provence *Parlement*, and Mazarin, who engaged the enterprising Gabriel Naudé to reform his magnificent library, and to whom many great scientists dedicated their works. Though many eminent men worked in the provinces—Peiresc in Aix-en-Provence, Fermat in Toulouse, Étienne Pascal in Clermont-Ferrand and later at Rouen—the centralization of science had begun, and it was in Paris that French science reached its greatest heights.

In Paris, as in the provinces, science owed little to the universities, which remained steeped in scholastic doctrines. It was the *Collège Royal* which opened its doors to Gassendi and Roberval. The brothers Dupuy organized a group of free-thinking scientists, but the greatest advocate of liberal science was Marin Mersenne (1588–1648), a Minimite Father who devoted his life to that end. In 1634, he wrote that 'the sciences have sworn inviolable friendship to one another', and called on specialists from every branch to compare their respective discoveries and to work together. His own contribution was to keep scientists informed of the work of their colleagues by conducting a vast correspondence, ranging as far afield as Constantinople and Transylvania, and by his publication of such works as the *Mechanics of Galileo* and the *New Thoughts of Galileo*. In 1635, he helped the Dupuy group to realize a common dream—the foundation of the *Academia Parisiensis*, in which scientists from all branches could meet together. Just as the *Académie Française* was born from Conrart's famous *Salon*, so Colbert's inauguration of the *Académie des Sciences* in 1666 was the official endorsement of Mersenne's efforts. The first issue of the *Journal des Savants* appeared in 1665. It was responsible for introducing Descartes' vortices as a topic of discussion in polite society.

It is hard to conceive of two men whose ideas were more opposed to each other than those of Descartes and Pascal. While Descartes (1596–1650) was, above all, a theorist, anxious to found a new science on deductive principles as rigorous as Aristotle's, Pascal (1623–1662) despised all principles as mere anticipations of the real facts. His views, which were shared by Roberval (1602–1675) and most other scientists, led to the first pragmatist—or even positivist—formulation of science by Mersenne and Malebranche (1638–1715).

ENGLAND

Seventeenth-century science may be said to have begun with the appearance of Gilbert's *De magnete* in 1600. Court physician first to Queen Elizabeth and later to James I, William Gilbert (1540–1603) wrote a host of scientific papers which were published posthumously by his brother as the *De mundo nostro sublunari philosophia nova* (1651). Though much better known than Gilbert, Francis Bacon (1561–1626) was a far lesser scientist. In particular, he failed to appreciate that the new science must be based on mathematics. Nevertheless, writing as a philosopher, he was able to show how inadequate all the old theories really were. While Lord Chancellor of England and later, during his enforced retirement, he did his utmost to destroy the common opinion that scientists were mere artisans. Two years before the publication of Bacon's *Novum organum* (1620), William Harvey (1578–1658) was appointed physician to the court of James I. His *Exercitatio anatomica de motu cordis et sanguinis in animalibus* was to upset all the previous ideas on the circulation of the blood.

Bacon advocated the necessity of a keener exchange of intellectual views and his call did not go unheard. It led first of all to the formation of a Baconian circle at Cambridge and later to its extension to London, thanks largely to Theodore Haak, a German who had settled in England. Another group, formed at Oxford, was joined by Robert Boyle (1627–1691), the great gentleman-scientist. The Royal Society was founded on 28th November 1660, at Gresham College. Though the famous *Philosophical Transactions* began to appear in 1665, it was not until the 18th century that they became the official organ of the Royal Society. But from the beginning, they were instrumental in spreading the new discoveries and ideas not only throughout England, but to all Europe as well.

It was in England, also, that the new science reached its greatest heights with the work of Isaac Newton (1642–1727) and of Robert Hooke (1635–1703). Newton, who was born a few months after Galileo's death, was responsible for steering Galileo's fragile science towards the great synthesis for which he is famous. Elected to Parliament in 1703, President of the Royal Society from 1703 until his death, Newton was one of those rare men who saw their genius appreciated and admired in their own lifetime.

CENTRAL EUROPE

In Central Europe, science had to wage a much harder struggle against the prevailing intellectual climate. On 29th December 1646, Princess Elizabeth, writing to Descartes from Berlin, complained of the scarcity of scholars there. The reason was, she went on to say, 'that all the people here are poor so that no one studies or reflects except to gain his livelihood'. In the prevailing political turmoil every scientist took his chances where he could find them; Tycho Brahe at Hveen and later in Prague; Father Magni in Warsaw; Hevelius in Danzig; Steno in Italy. Everything depended on the attitude of the reigning monarch: the scientific 'conversion' of Sweden did not survive the reign of Queen Christina; Johannes Kepler (1571–1630) was driven from Graz for his Protestant views, was welcomed (though badly paid) in Prague and elsewhere, was suspected in Linz, had to defend his mother against accusations of witchcraft and to chase after subsidies that never materialized. His life shows better than anything else what obstacles the unfortunate scientists of his day had to overcome.

Later, things began to change for the better. When Gottfried Wilhelm Leibniz (1646–1716), a man of universal genius, a great traveller, and a political and diplomatic adviser, was appointed Keeper of the Hanover Library, he not only found sufficient intellectual sustenance to feed his prodigious erudition, but was able to use his great influence to spread the light of knowledge abroad. In 1700, he founded the Berlin Academy of Science, and in 1682 he became one of the first contributors to the *Acta eruditorum*, published in Leipzig, a journal that rendered incomparable services to science.

From the Repository to the Laboratory

The rise of these academies and scientific journals was accompanied by a new craze—the acquisition of individual collections, or 'cabinets' as they were called. While most of them were repositories filled with all sorts of junk, others were organized with far greater discrimination. The Dupuy circle met regularly in the 'cabinet' of their two founders; Father Mersenne owned a 'cabinet' made up chiefly of physical instruments; Father Kircher's 'cabinet' in Rome contained fossils, driftwood, rhinoceros teeth and horns, *etc.*; Barberini's and Aldrovandi's 'cabinets' were stuffed with dragons.

It would be wrong to take too critical a view of all these strange activities. Freed at last from scholastic speculation, these men were merely trying to look at every aspect of the world with new eyes. Travellers, while continuing to take an interest in foreign manners and customs and bringing back all manner of historical and legendary souvenirs, also inspected the salt-pans, the mines, the caves, and took notes on the weather and on local remedies. They had not yet learned to distinguish between interesting specimens and bric-à-brac, and it was not until the late 17th century that their ideas began to crystallize, that botanical gardens were set up in great numbers, and that amateurs began to bring some order into astronomical observations. Father Humbert mentions the existence of no less than 23 observatories in Paris between 1610 and 1667, and the end of the century coincided with the opening of the first two 'official' observatories, those of Paris and Greenwich.

'NATURE IS WRITTEN IN MATHEMATICAL LANGUAGE'

This phrase, which appeared in Galileo's *Saggiatore* (1623), expressed a singularly revolutionary idea. By a stroke of the pen, Galileo had abolished the *natura* of the ancients, with its substances, forms and qualities. Nature had become the sum total of quantitative phenomena, and the very purpose of scientific research was henceforth completely changed.

The Mathematical Basis of Science

Revolutionary though Galileo's formulation was, it was based on rather shaky foundations. For when he wrote, ten years before the appearance of his *Dialogo*, that nature is written in mathematical language, he had nothing to go by except ancient speculations on the lengths of vibrating strings, Kepler's inaccurate law of refraction, Archimedes' principle, and since 1609, Kepler's laws of planetary motion, which, as we know, Galileo treated with scepticism. In any case, it was a long step from the establishment of isolated numerical relationships to the radical formulation of the *Saggiatore*. Descartes took a similar leap into the dark when, long before he had made any experiments, he contended that all certain knowledge must be based on the 'firm and solid' foundations of mathematics. But Galileo and Descartes were merely expressing the views of their fellow scientists. 'It is a hard task', Kepler declared in the preface to his *Astronomia nova* (1609), 'to write mathematical and above all astronomical books, for few can understand them. . . . I myself, who am considered a mathematician, become tired when reading my own work.' And yet he, too, devoted himself to the task of placing science on mathematical foundations.

The New Pythagorism

In effect, it was mathematics itself which stood in need of development, for it had stood still since Greek antiquity. 'How many mathematicians are there', Kepler asked, 'who have taken the pains to read the whole of Apollonios' *Conics*?' And yet it was books like these, together with Cardan's and Vieta's new contributions, by which alone 17th-century mathematicians, each in his own way, were able to score the successes they did.

Since very few quantitative laws had been established, because mathematics itself was in urgent need of repair, and since great scientists had not yet learned the art of working with numbers, their desire to 'write nature in mathematical language' expressed, not so much a real need, as a confession of faith—a stupendous *a priori* assertion. Before the facts could be fitted into the framework of mathematics, the framework itself had first to be erected. Kepler, Galileo and Descartes did little at first but take up the great Pythagorean and Platonic dream of mathematical perfection—so much so that Kepler was led astray into his doctrine of the harmony of the spheres. Though they gradually turned this vague dream into a reality, there is no doubt that their scientific intentions were running well ahead of the known facts.

THE NEW CONCEPT OF SCIENCE

It appeared very soon that it was not enough merely to revise ancient notions, but that an entirely new natural philosophy had to be built up. In fact, the quantitative physics of the future would have practically nothing in common with the qualitative physics of the past.

The new philosophy defined its aims with great prudence. Mersenne, for instance, emphasized that his attempt to give a mathematical account of acoustic phenomena must not be read as a rejection of mental phenomena, for sound is not only vibration of the air but also an effect on a sense organ. Was his prudence merely dictated by a fear of offending established opinion? A more likely explanation is that his appreciation of the complexity of reality, his legitimate recognition that the quantitative expression of phenomena is an abstraction—however fruitful—and not a substitute for sensation, had survived as a fortunate relic of his scholastic training.

Be that as it may, 17th-century science sought the objects of its research no longer among perceptual qualities but among measurable quantities.

Physical Phenomena

Previously, science (ἐπιστήμη) had been considered the study of *being* (τὸ ὄν) and not of phenomena, which, as contingent aspects of *being*, were dismissed as matters of personal opinion (δόξα). Now the emphasis was changed: being, as such, was largely ignored, and scientists concentrated on the study of phenomena, now defined as measurable sense data.

At the same time, 17th-century scientists did away with the old distinction between science as the contemplation of the eternal verities, and art, or the empirical manipulation of appearances.

Whereas it had been argued that art 'imitates' nature but can never grasp it, and that laboratory experiments cannot possibly reflect 'natural' reality, the new philosophers proceeded to prove the contrary. This astonishing transformation can be followed step by step from the work of Bacon to that of the 18th-century scientists.

True, Bacon, the scientist, remained an epistemologist of the old school, but Bacon, the philosopher, was quick to grasp the new status of science: scientific theories must be verified by the hitherto despised 'art' of manipulating natural phenomena. Henceforth, the slogan was no longer 'knowledge is contemplation' but 'knowledge is the power of creation'.

The New Scientists

Bacon, Galileo (the disciple of the 'divine Archimedes'), Descartes (to whom all artificial things were natural), Mersenne and many others like them caused the almost forcible entry of 'laboratory scientists' into what had been the exclusive preserve of students of 'essences'. As a result, metaphysical principles ceased to be the sole explanations of phenomena, and mechanical models—previously despised—came to be considered as the very crux of the new science, and nature herself as a gigantic machine.

Thus Descartes believed that the human body is a machine whose movements are directed by the soul, much as a fountain is played by a fountain-master, or organ-pipes by an organist. Gilbert studied magnetism and terrestrial electricity with spherical magnets called *terrelae* (small worlds); Descartes used an aeolipile to study the motions of vapours; Fournier constructed a special tower with cleverly designed outlets for the same purpose.

Mechanism

Such, in brief, were the origins of mechanistic physics, and hence (by extrapolation) of mechanistic biology and mechanistic physiology (Hobbes), all of which claimed to copy nature by 'art' and hence to deserve the name of 'science'. Except for Descartes, 17th-century mechanists were singularly undogmatic. Thus Mersenne spoke for most of his contemporaries when he said that, though science reconstructs the image of things, the things themselves have their own nature. In other words, early mechanistic science did not claim to be an all-embracing philosophy, but welcomed pragmatists like Mersenne, Gassendi and Roberval, mystics like Pascal and metaphysicians like Descartes and Newton. Malebranche summed up this tolerant approach very well when he wrote: 'Let us leave to metaphysics the study of the efficient causes of things; science must be content with studying their laws.'

The Re-introduction of Values

However, as the new philosophy of nature got into its stride, it increasingly claimed that it alone had the right to be called 'scientific'. From Bacon to the 18th century, the study—and the manipulation—of phenomena gradually ousted metaphysics from science, so that metaphysical views came to be dismissed as personal opinions of little value. This was a tremendous step when one considers the original meaning of the terms 'physics' and 'metaphysics'. Roberval was probably the first true agnostic in the modern sense of the word.

The Remoulding of Men's Minds

Science had changed its meaning, simply because intellectual attitudes had changed. 'Experience shows clearly', Malebranche wrote, 'that it is impossible to convince a Cartesian with Aristotelian arguments, or a Peripatetic with Cartesian principles.' And Galileo wrote that, though the new science had demolished immutable 'natures', and with them 'the refuge and Prytaneum' in which philosophers had hitherto dwelt (*Dialogo*, 1632), the 'new science' would prosper only if 'men's minds are first made over'. They must accept that all life is motion, following the established cycle of generation and corruption; all the rest is useless, despicable and dead. The same idea can be found in Gilbert's *De magnete*, a work which appeared symbolically in 1600, at the dawn of the century, and of which Galileo spoke with 'praise and envy'. Attacking the Aristotelian claim that nature seeks rest, Gilbert wrote that 'all generation springs from motion, without which nature herself would fall asleep. . . . Aristotle's world would seem to be a monstrous creation, in which all things are perfect, vigorous, animate, while the earth alone, luckless small fraction, is imperfect, dead, inanimate and subject to decay.'[1]

The 'changing of minds' therefore implied a prior changing of hearts—the courage to leave the haven of incorruptible beings for the real world of corruptible 'phenomena'. According to Galileo, Gilbert was the great initiator of the conversion, the man who led the fight against that 'pusillanimity of the mind which is content with repetition and spurns all innovations'. Gilbert himself called magnetic science a 'new style of philosophizing', which he dedicated 'not to lettered clowns, grammatists, sophists, spouters, but to you alone, true philosophers, ingenious minds, who not only in books but in things themselves look for knowledge'.

[1] Gilbert, *De magnete* (London, 1600), Book V, chapter 12, page 309. These were the very words which Galileo was to use in his *Dialogo* (*Opere*, Vol. VII, pp. 82–83).

TOWARDS AN UNBOUNDED UNIVERSE

In many fields, however, and in cosmology in particular, this change of attitude was preceded by advances in mathematical techniques.

The orderly, finite, incorruptible and hierarchical cosmos of the ancients had first begun to crack in Cusanus' *De docta ignorantia* (1440). But when Cusanus challenged geocentrism, when Copernicus introduced heliocentrism, and when Bruno propounded the idea of an infinite Universe, they were simply putting forward *a priori* theories about infinity and motion, and not systems based on empirical research. Their destruction of the celestial spheres was no more than a stopgap.

The Universe as a System of Forces

This is how things stood at the beginning of the 17th century, before dynamics came into their own and before phenomena began to be studied for their own sake. It was then that *a priori* speculations were first held up to the mirror of reality. Thus Gilbert, who agreed with Copernicus that the earth rotates on its axis, was the first to seek the *physical* cause of that rotation. He found it in the earth's magnetism—the only error with which Galileo could reproach him. With its two magnetic poles, Gilbert's earth was the physical centre of a system of forces and his model represented an immense advance on that of Copernican kinematics.

Kepler, the real founder of scientific heliocentrism, also described the sun and the planets as magnets. Going much further than Gilbert, he was able to construct a 'solar system' moved by attractive and magnetic forces whose actions he was able to explain exactly. To do so, he was forced—after many scruples and a great deal of labour—to break once and for all with the ancient doctrine of circular motion. His achievement, therefore, was not only that he calculated better than his predecessors, but that he was able to discard a time-hallowed dogma. Though Kepler's space remained bounded by the sphere of fixed stars, and hence was finite, it was no longer the qualitative space of 'natural places'. All 'places' had become equal—another instance of how advances in technique can lead to new visions.

The Corruptible Universe

In 1609, Kepler still held that the fixed stars beyond the solar system were immutable; one year later, astronomical telescopes revealed the existence of spots in the sun and mountains on the moon. Galileo's Simplicio, one of the *dramatis personae* of his *Dialogo*, refused point blank to accept such scandalous findings, for they not only deprived the stars of their incorruptibility but suggested that the earth was a planet like all the others. These and similar objections were overruled by Galileo, not only because they were invalid but also because the new discoveries went a long way towards helping to 'phenomenalize' the stellar world.

Though Galileo's astronomical ideas were no improvement on Kepler's, and though he was wrong not to adopt Kepler's view that the planets describe elliptical orbits (so great was the appeal of circular motion even to a mind as original as his), he had the great merit of restoring freedom to the Universe. True, he did not call the Universe infinite in so many words—he must have been warned by Bruno's terrible fate—but he did say that the idea of a finite world had no other foundation than man's stubborn anthropocentrism. His world, like that of Descartes, was therefore 'indefinite' and, in any case, not encumbered with the sphere of fixed stars, which Kepler had retained.

Correlation of Celestial and Terrestrial Physics

However, Galileo's greatest claim to glory rests on his contribution to dynamics and on his courage before his persecutors. For the new dynamics not only proved the fallacy of the geocentric idea, but also showed that Tycho Brahe's distinction between the earth and the planets was wrong. On the other hand, Galileo still denied that the earth exerts a tangential force on falling bodies, and so did Borelli, the first to introduce centrifugal forces into celestial mechanics. Hence Galileo and his disciples failed to appreciate the advantages of regarding the earth as a planet. Only with Newton were the heavens and the earth subjected to the *same forces*. The unification of terrestrial and celestial physics was therefore the work of an entire century, and even then it took a Newton to do away with the *psychological* obstacles to it.

Propulsion or Attraction

Gilbert, Kepler and Newton introduced the concept of *attraction* (first conceived as a magnetic force) in opposition to the old view that falling bodies are *propelled* by the desire to rejoin their natural places. Attraction was denied by Descartes (and by Malebranche), who dismissed the *vis attractiva* as just another occult virtue. According to him, falling bodies are propelled by mechanical vortices. This quarrel was only one aspect of the battle between mechanists and dynamists, to which we shall return.

The History of the Earth

On the other hand, Descartes, more than anyone else, defended the thesis that the earth and the planets have identical 'natures'. Sunspots convinced him that the sun, and hence all the stars, have a history; that the earth is a star which has grown cool; and that all stars obey the same laws. Athanasius Kircher incorporated these ideas into his eccentric but valuable *Mundus subterraneus* (1664–1665), which can be considered the first modern work on geology.

For geology to be born, tremendous obstacles had first to be surmounted—the chief of which was the common belief that subterranean phenomena could be explained by supraterrestrial events (*e.g.* meteors). Moreover, the earth, as one of the basic 'elements' and hence as a simple 'principle', was generally thought to require neither observation nor analysis. Galileo had to devote many pages of his *Dialogo* to persuading Simplicio that the earth is not a simple element but an assembly of very complex bodies. Here, again, men's eyes refused to see until their minds were changed. Steno's geological work was still full of Cartesian notions, and it was only when the new scientific precepts were generally adopted that the great geological contribution of Bernard Palissy was finally rescued from oblivion.

In short, the Universe could only shed its bounds after innumerable observations and incessant calculations had rendered these bounds unacceptable to the intellect.

BEYOND PERCEPTION

Whereas qualitative physics equated reality with direct perception, the new mechanical philosophy concentrated on the reality of thought (Brunschvicg).

However, it is a far cry from mathematical formulations to the concrete facts. Early 17th-century attempts to build a bridge between the two with the resurrected atomic doctrine of Epicuros and Lucretius or with Cartesian vortices proved utterly abortive.

The 'new physics' was not only new, but over-enthusiastic as well. With the notable exception of Mersenne, most scientists extrapolated with deceptive ease—we need only recall their lengthy discussions about the trajectory of bodies 'falling to the centre of the earth'; Galileo's cavalier dismissal of many justified criticisms, or Descartes' deductive proof of the existence of a world in which everything is as clear and certain as in Aristotle's. No doubt, their lack of restraint had its advantages, for had they grasped the real difficulties they would have given up in despair. In any case, while they eschewed Aristotelian reality, their own was often the reality of very imperfect machines. It was only in 1650 that the new approach became refined and that science began to gain in prudence and maturity.

The Study of Details

The gap between the universe of the senses and the universe of thought began to be closed when mathematicians introduced infinitesimal considerations into physics. Thus Galileo, who had studied Cavalieri's work on indivisibles, argued that the surfaces and volumes of solid bodies are made up of an infinity of finite atoms. In this way he was able to join perception to reality in a manner that could be grasped, if not by the intellect itself, at least by mathematics.

With the invention of the infinitesimal calculus, scientists were also able to probe into realms that had previously been veiled by such *a priori* systems as the Greek atomic doctrine or Descartes' vortices.

All Leibniz's work, and particularly his principle of indiscernibles, reflected his deep concern with the observation of fine detail and his appreciation of the complexity of reality. Descartes had failed to take this complexity into account, so much so that Leibniz was able to say of his great rival that 'presenting as proven what are very uncertain matters, he misleads the easygoing reader by his dictatorial brevity' (*Animadversiones*).

Malebranche, too, was aware that Descartes' 'World' was too good to be true, and that the real world is infinitely more complicated than any man-made machine, or even the great cosmic machine of Descartes' imagination. 'Nature is never abstract; real levers and wheels are not the lines and circles of mathematics. . . . The assumption, for instance, that the planets describe perfect circles and ellipses is utterly false.' When Kepler broke with the magic of the circle and claimed that the planets move in elliptical orbits, he not only destroyed an old-established myth, but proved his concern for detail. Malebranche realized that even the elliptical orbits were not perfect, and Newton explained why, in fact, they could not be so.

The new science had begun by teaching Simplicio that there was no good reason for calling the earth an element. In time, it came to be realized that many of the other 'elements' were equally unnecessary and that a great deal of further analysis was needed. Thus began the era of precise observations: the optical experiments of Malebranche and Newton, the accurate measurement of the meridian (1671) and of variations in gravity (1673), the geological observations of Leibniz, *etc.* Science prepared at last to dispense with its time-worn crutches.

The Microscope

In this intellectual climate it seems strange that the work of Leeuwenhoek, who did more than anyone else to bring the 'world beyond perception' within man's grasp, should have been ignored as much as it was. True, Robert Hooke invited him to contribute to the *Philo-*

sophical Transactions, but Leeuwenhoek's informed attacks on the theory of spontaneous generation fell on deaf ears, and his important discovery of spermatozoa did little but reawaken the quarrel between the preformationists and the epigenesists. Though La Bruyère realized that Leeuwenhoek and Swammerdam had at last brought some sense into the age-old speculations on the nature of cheese-mites, professional scientists—apart from Hooke and Leibniz—seem to have utterly misunderstood the general scope of microscopy. One reason for this is that Leeuwenhoek, though a brilliant autodidact, was often unfamiliar with the wider problems of science.

But there were other reasons, as well. As Bacon has said, concrete observation demands a long apprenticeship. It also demands boldness, but the kind of empirical approach which reigned after Descartes' death had lost all vestiges of that. At the beginning of the century, the new images revealed by the telescope had posed the great metaphysical problem of explaining the sudden emergence of previously non-existing objects. Galileo himself had the utmost difficulty in correlating these new objects, conjured up as they were from the void, with the objects of direct perception, previously the only legitimate 'beings'. Though this problem was no longer posed in astronomy after 1650, the elevation of infinitely small entities to the rank of sense data continued to be opposed in theoretical physics and mathematics. When Leeuwenhoek had to admit that he had never *seen* atoms, the theorists gave him a wide berth. 'Man', says C. Dobell, 'had all the necessary data and also—as ever—a convenient hypothesis; but, as history has shown, his knowledge and his ideas usually arrive too early.'

MECHANISM AND DYNAMISM

The new physicists were most anxious to describe nature as a gigantic machine, devoid of souls and virtues and even of life. Their boldest extrapolation by far was the theory of animal-machines. All these theories, however far-fetched, had the advantage of freeing physics from its bondage to animist ideas and of founding a mechanistic biology that would render very useful service in the future.

In the 17th century, no one questioned the new mechanistic philosophy as such, but there were many bitter quarrels about the elements with which the mechanical universe was constructed.

Cartesian Geometrism

Descartes' mechanical philosophy was held in particularly high esteem. According to Descartes, the Universe is constructed on geometrical lines, and matter is to be identified with extension. His ignorance of the notion of mass, and hence of density—which Boyle was the first to dispel—led him to his basic definition: 'Neither weight, nor duration, nor colour, *etc.* serve to define the nature of bodies, but only their extension' (*Principia* II, 4).

Only because there is motion are there phenomena and a world. God has endowed the world with a constant quantity of motion—Descartes' famous error. Descartes had great difficulty in specifying where this motion resides and how it is transmitted, for, as a reaction against traditional physics but also because of his highly individual approach, he was utterly averse to the idea that bodies are moved by forces (*virtutes*).

Descartes took the relativity of motion, which had been postulated by Galileo, to extreme conclusions. He not only exaggerated the principle to explain how the earth could remain at rest in its enveloping vortex, but used it to effect the 'extenuation' of all phenomena.

Because of his identification of matter with extension, Descartes denied the existence of both vacuums—which imply 'extension without extension', and atoms—which imply 'indivisible extension.'

Descartes explained the workings of the 'cosmic machine' by recourse to divine immutability, but failed to give explicit definitions of the terms he employed. Even his fundamental concept 'motion' was nothing more than the transport of a body from contact with those in its vicinity to contact with others. Moreover, by contending that a body at rest or in motion has a certain 'force' to resist any change, Descartes turned the world into an 'immense game of billiards' (R. Dugas). Descartes' basic geometrism—however fruitful—was his 'original sin' (A. Koyré). He was, in fact, a Platonist in disguise, as his picture of God the Great Geometer suggests. God had designed a perfect plan, and then impressed translational motion on the cogs of His machine in such a way that motion is communicated from one cog to the next after 'residing' as little as possible in each. Faced with reality, Descartes was sometimes forced to use subterfuges, but it is his main scheme by which his contemporaries best knew him. Thus, though Malebranche adopted occasionalism, he felt no need to break with Cartesianism; it was only when Leibniz and Newton introduced *forces* that the Cartesian structure became completely undermined.

The Return of Forces

Just as life had to be restored to the animal-machines, so forces had to be re-introduced into physics. Slowly the concepts of rest and motion, obscured by Descartes, began to be seen in a new light. The study of the former led to the formulation of the concept of mass and to a methodical study of elastic phenomena: Descartes' absolutely rigid bodies ceased to exist; bodies resist and transmit motion because they act as 'springs'. As for motion itself, Huygens was the first to disprove the third Cartesian law: not motion, but the *living force*—or what Leibniz called the *vis motrix*—is conserved. Physics was on the way to discarding Cartesian impact kinetics for dynamics.

But what, in fact, were forces? So great had been Descartes' influence that his successors, though compelled to introduce them, felt a great reluctance to define them.

Leibniz

There was, moreover, an obvious risk in all such definitions: the resurrection of the semi-mystical *virtutes* of ancient physics. Leibniz, for one, succumbed to this temptation—if not in his physics at least in his philosophy. The guiding thought of his entire system was his theory of 'small perceptions', the philosophical counterpart of the infinitesimal calculus, and Leibniz's substitute for the Cartesian impacts. Unfortunately that theory was psychological and not physical. According to Leibniz, conscious perception is at the top of an infinite scale, beginning with unconscious perception, as the infinitesimally small unit of consciousness. A similar scale ranges from material forces to spiritual forces. All physical and psychological forces are spontaneous, conscious and directed towards the future. Forces invariably produce 'changes' in the scholastic sense of the term, *i.e.* changes with qualitative and purposive results. Galileo and Descartes had challenged this view when they denied all but local motion in physics. According to Leibniz, change represents 'diversity in uniformity' and 'is none other than what we call perception'. Leibniz, who reproached Descartes with having robbed animals of their souls, now discovered a soul in all bodies, whose *forma substantialis* he resurrected: 'I discovered that their nature is force, and that they must therefore be likened to sentiment and appetite; hence we must think of substantial forms much as we think of the soul.'

Material and spiritual forces entered jointly into the 'pre-established harmony', by which Leibniz reintroduced finality into science. Though his real discoveries stamp him one of the greatest scientists of all time, Leibniz's philosophy threatened to compromise the integrity of the new physics. But physics had learned to stand on its own feet, so that all Leibniz managed to do was to cast doubt on the existence of those forces which he so ardently advocated.

Newton's Dynamics

Newton proved far more prudent than his rival. To re-introduce forces into post-Cartesian physics, he kept strictly to the facts—the magnetic phenomena already discussed by Gilbert and Galileo, the phenomena of electric attraction and repulsion which Otto von Guericke had done so much to elucidate, and finally the centrifugal and gravitational effects, by which he himself had brought celestial phenomena within the grasp of terrestrial physics. Like Galileo and Huygens, Newton was an atomist: real bodies are not indifferent to one another like the geometrical bodies of Descartes, for the 'smallest particles of matter' act upon one another 'by the attractions of gravity, magnetism, electricity and by other attractive forces unknown to us' (*Opticks*, Query 31).

So great was the Cartesian influence that this statement was sufficient to produce a storm. Leibniz himself attacked the *vis attractiva*, and flung at Newton his *Antibarbarus physicus* in which he objected to the resurrection of 'scholastic qualities and chimerical forces'. Huygens, although a dynamist himself, rejected both Leibniz's vague forces and Newton's *vis attractiva*, which he called an absurdity. Malebranche exclaimed that scientists 'make themselves ridiculous if they have to adduce attractive notions and faculties in order to explain how it comes about that chariots follow the horses by which they are drawn'.

Newton himself was clearly embarrassed by having to work with such unfamiliar concepts. As a true scientist of his time he had to speak of forces, but he was hesitant about affirming their 'reality'. Like his Cartesian adversaries he denied that two bodies could act on each other at a distance. The attraction and repulsion of bodies must have external causes, but it is not the physicist's task to explain them.

Thus, in the passage from the *Opticks* which we have just quoted, he goes on to say: 'How these Attractions may be perform'd I do not here consider. What I call Attraction may be perform'd by Impulse or by some other Means unknown to me. I use that Word here to signify only in general any Force by which Bodies tend towards one another, *whatsoever be the Cause*.' At the beginning of his *Principia*, Newton wrote that he considers forces mathematically and not physically (Book I, Def. VIII), but in the *General Scholium* (Book III), he was compelled to admit their physical 'reality', for no true physics could be constructed without them: 'And to us it is enough that Gravity does really exist [*quod gravitas revera existat*] and act according to the Laws which we have explained, and abundantly serves to account for all the Motions of the celestial Bodies, and of our Sea.' In other words, attractive forces are 'realities' inasmuch as they serve to explain the phenomena; they are not 'causes' in the metaphysical sense of the term, but are necessary principles in Descartes' sense.

These forces, whose nature, or rather *cause*, eludes physics, combine to form the ordered whole which is the world. Like Leibniz, Newton was thus able to re-establish the finality of nature, to discover God, the Creator, in natural philosophy, and to dismiss the Cartesian doctrine as rank atheism. By hesitating to attribute reality to those forces on which the practical experimenter must rely, Newton may well have tried, albeit unsuccessfully, to draw a Kantian distinction between empirical realism and transcendental idealism. What is true beyond all doubt is that Newton, as a deeply religious man, saw a close link between physics and metaphysics.

Malebranche and Scientific Positivism

Malebranche went much further in putting physics on an autonomous basis. Though he realized full well that Descartes' impact physics and laws of motion were in urgent need of revision, and that the *vis viva* had to be readmitted into science, he nevertheless remained a staunch Cartesian, refusing to join physics to such 'metaphysical' concepts as forces and general causes. Now Newton had claimed that he simply admitted attraction because it exists and that he was unconcerned with its causes, but in fact he had assumed the causes implicitly and was bound to arrive at the theological view of the *General Scholium*. Malebranche's own, far more radical, formulation, 'Laws alone are effective and active, while bodies cannot act', was the statement of a scientific positivist and, above all, of an empirical realist. Causes may be left to metaphysicians; the scientist asks for laws, and for laws alone.

As Meyerson has shown, Malebranche's search for laws was, in fact, a search for the Newtonian 'reality'. Nevertheless, Malebranche's 'occasionalism' presented the 17th century with a 'modern' scientific outlook. Applied to the body-soul problem, it led to the theory of psycho-somatic parallelism. In general science, it led to the synthesis of various disciplines, each of which, though applied to a series of special phenomena, was said to be related to the others, since all combine in nature to make a 'coherent whole'. In physics, it was the solutions suggested by Malebranche which enabled 18th-century scholars to assuage, at least for a time, the quarrel between the mechanists and the dynamists.

* * *

The 17th century began with the Baconian dream of science and with Gilbert's *De magnete*, and culminated with Newton's *Principia* in 1684 and his *Opticks* in 1704. Between the *De magnete* and the *Opticks* came the contributions of Galileo and Descartes, without which science might have stood still. Descartes' work was grandiose but overoptimistic, and there is an astonishing gulf between his *Dioptrique* (1637), in which light was a pencil simply because the ideal world is constructed on straight lines, and Newton's *Opticks*, in which the phenomena were described step by step with the help of observations and experiments. These observations and experiments were organized —and first of all in Newton's *Principia*—by means of 'definitions' whose rigid and clear formulations bore witness to the fact that the mathematical Platonism of Galileo and Descartes would never again be forgotten. Less obviously, biology also took tremendous strides between Aldrovandi and John Ray. Practical science, encouraged and guided by the advances in theoretical physics, began to speak the language of positivism. The path had been cleared; the rest was only a matter of time.

MATHEMATICS AND PHYSICS

CHAPTER 1

From Symbolic Algebra to Infinitesimal Calculus

IN THE 17TH CENTURY, mathematics had particularly close links with natural philosophy, for great analysts like Fermat and Descartes also took a keen interest in astronomy, mechanics or optics. Conversely, men like Galileo or Kepler, who were not concerned with pure mathematics as such, nevertheless played a leading role in its development. For instance, Galileo's astronomical discoveries of 1610 drew the attention of scientists to mathematical optics, and particularly to Kepler's *Ad vitellionum paralipomena* (1604) and *Dioptrics* (1611). As a result, there was a revival of interest in conic sections which greatly influenced the work of Descartes and others.

Though we have devoted a special chapter to pure mathematics, the reader would do well to remember that our procedure has been artificial. We must stress again that science forms a whole whose various facets cannot really be isolated.

THE DEVELOPMENT OF TRIGONOMETRY AND ALGEBRA

TRIGONOMETRY

Trigonometry has very close links with astronomy and with optics. In 1579, Franciscus Vieta (1540–1603), then a privy councillor, published his remarkable *Canon mathematicus* which took eight years to print. It contained tables of the trigonometrical functions together with a theoretical section, the *F. Vietaei universalium inspectionum ad canonem mathematicum liber singularis*.

In this lucid book Vieta introduced the rudiments of his future algebraic notation, and stressed the superiority of decimal over sexagesimal fractions.

His tables were based on the multiplication and division of arcs, two operations in which Vieta excelled. He was not the first or the only mathematician to use this method—his rivals included Jost Bürgi (1552–1632) and Adriaan Van Roomen (1561–1615), who, in 1593, set the mathematicians of his day the following problem:

If the first term of a proportion is to the second as 1 (1) is to 45 (1) −3795 (3) +95634 (5) −1138500 (7) −7811375 (9) + . . . +945 (41) −45 (43) +1 (45), and if the second term be given, find the first.

Example: If the given term is R. bin. 2+R. bin. 2+R. bin. 2+R.2, the solution is R. bin. 2−R. bin. 2−R. bin. 2+R. bin. 2+R. bin. 2 +R.3. . . .

In modern notation (Van Roomen was using Stevin's), the problem was to solve the equation $x^{45}-45x^{43}+945x^{41}\ldots 45x=a$.

Here $$a=\sqrt{2+\sqrt{2+\sqrt{2+\sqrt{2}}}}$$

and $$x=\sqrt{2-\sqrt{2-\sqrt{2+\sqrt{2+\sqrt{2+\sqrt{3}}}}}}.$$

Vieta immediately found the general solution (for $a\leqslant 2$): '*ut legi ut solvi*'. Van Roomen's problem might also have been put: If, in a circle of radius 1, the chord of an arc is given, find the chord of its 45th part.

The brilliant response of the 'Prince of Amateurs' (Fermat) to this achievement caused a considerable stir in the scientific world.

The case of $a>2$ was later solved by Fermat in a letter to Christiaan Huygens. Fermat used the example of the cubic equation, which Vieta (and later Albert Girard) had solved by angular trisection and the insertion of two geometrical means.

As a counter-challenge, Vieta defied Van Roomen to construct a circle touching three given circles. Vieta's own solution was later generalized by Fermat, who applied it to the case of spheres, and by Pascal, who applied it to conics. Van Roomen's solution, which Vieta rejected as not being 'plane', was used by Newton for rule-and-compass constructions.

Another problem studied by 17th-century mathematicians, and also associated with the calculation of trigonometrical tables, was the evaluation of π, or the quadrature of the circle. Among the many optimists who tackled the problem without adequate theoretical training was Joseph Scaliger (1540–1609), whom Van Roomen and Vieta felt impelled to reprimand. Simon du Chesne, or van der Eycke, a civil engineer from Dôle, also committed elementary errors which were exposed by Adriaan Anthonitz (1543?–1607)—the father of Adriaan Metius (1571–1635)—and by Ludolph van Ceulen (1540–1610).

Vieta calculated π to ten correct decimal places. Ludolph began his own calculations in 1586, using Archimedes' method and a decimal notation. From Ludolph's first results Adriaan Anthonitz was able to show that $3\frac{15}{106} > \pi > 3\frac{17}{120}$, whence Metius deduced the excellent approximation $\pi = \frac{355}{113}$.

Van Roomen calculated π to 15 correct decimal places in 1593, and Ludolph van Ceulen to 20 in 1596. In 1615, van Ceulen's widow published his approximation correct to 32 decimal places.

In 1593, Vieta was the first to introduce infinitesimal considerations into the problem. He showed that the ratio of a square to its circumscribed circle $\left(\frac{2}{\pi}\right)$ can be expressed by the infinite product

$$\sqrt{\tfrac{1}{2}} \cdot \sqrt{\left(\tfrac{1}{2}+\tfrac{1}{2}\sqrt{\tfrac{1}{2}}\right)} \cdot \sqrt{\left\{\tfrac{1}{2}+\tfrac{1}{2}\sqrt{\left(\tfrac{1}{2}+\tfrac{1}{2}\sqrt{\tfrac{1}{2}}\right)}\right\}} \ldots$$

The Archimedean method of squaring the circle came to an end with Snell and with Huygens' *De circuli magnitudine inventa* (1654). Vieta's method marked the beginning of a new era.

In spherical trigonometry, Vieta proved the so-called Napier analogies and used the polar triangle. Willebrord Snell (or Snellius) (1580–1626), who, with Descartes, discovered the law of refraction, used that triangle to even better advantage.

Meanwhile, a study of Witelo's optics led Harriot, Briggs, Albert Girard and Cavalieri to the study of the area of spherical triangles, which Witelo had suggested as a means of measuring solid angles. Though all these men—preceded by an anonymous 13th-century commentator, possibly Regiomontanus—were familiar with the idea of spherical excess, it was Cavalieri who gave a near-perfect proof that the sum of the angles of a spherical triangle is greater than 180° and less than 540°.

Literal Algebra

As a keen student of classical geometry, Vieta tried to return to the analytical methods of the ancient geometers. The recent discovery of the works of Diophantos and Pappos (first edition, 1588) helped to crystallize his own ideas. He demonstrated the basic isomorphism of the numerical algebra of Diophantos, Cardan, Tartaglia, Bombelli and Stifel on the one hand, and the geometrical analysis underlying the synthetic arguments of Euclid, Archimedes and—above all—of Apollonios on the other.

To express this isomorphism he invented 'specious logistic', *i.e.* the art of calculating with symbols, or species, representing geometrical and arithmetical magnitudes.

His logistics were subdivided into three fundamental branches: *Zetetics*, or the art of investigating problems by means of suitable symbols and equations; *Poristics*, or the art of transforming and discussing these equations; and *Exegetics*, or the art of solving equations either by geometrical constructions or by numerical calculations.

Vieta thus became the founder of modern mathematical analysis, which uses these very principles. Though his work was a little too advanced and esoteric for most of his contemporaries, it nevertheless had a tremendous revitalizing effect on early 17th-century mathematics.

Vieta invariably expressed unknown quantities by Latin vowels, and known quantities by Latin consonants, and indicated their respective dimensions.

Thus, he would write $x^3 - 3bx^2 + (3b^2 + d)x = c + db + b^3$, as

$$\left.\begin{array}{l} \text{E cubus} \\ -\text{B in E quadr. ter.} \\ \left.\begin{array}{l} +\text{B quadrato ter.} \\ +\text{D plano} \end{array}\right\} \text{in E} \end{array}\right\} \text{aequabitur} \left\{\begin{array}{l} \text{Z solido} \\ +\text{D plano in B} \\ +\text{B cubo} \end{array}\right.$$

Among his most influential writings were the *Zetetica* (1593), which treated Diophantine problems by his method of 'specious logistic'; the *De numerosa potestatum purarum atque adfectarum ad exegesin resolutione* (1600) which presented the first systematic method of solving equations numerically; the *De aequationum recognitione et emendatione* (1615), a fundamental work on the theory of algebraical equations; and finally the *In artem analyticam isagoge* (1591), a short general survey of his analytical methods.

In 1646, when van Schooten published a near-complete edition of Vieta's works, Vieta's ideas were already applied so widely that the new publication proved to be of purely historical interest.

Vieta's importance is best appreciated by comparing the results of his pupils Fermat and Roberval with those of Cavalieri and Torricelli. Though the two latter had at least the same geometrical skill and the same general knowledge as the two former, they were often left far behind, even by Beaugrand, one of Vieta's lesser disciples.

The Theory of Algebraic Equations

The work of 16th-century algebraists, and especially of the Italian school, had prepared the way for the 17th-century theory of algebraic equations. We lack space to discuss each individual contribution to this theory, and must therefore restrict our discussion to only the leading figures. Harriot (1560–1621) simplified Vieta's notation by introducing greater homogeneity and by replacing Latin capitals with small letters. He also introduced greater clarity in the way he expressed the relationship between roots and their coefficients.

In 1629, Albert Girard (1595–1632) made these relationships the very basis of his own theory. In order to establish generality he accepted negative, and even imaginary, solutions in a vaguer but wider sense than Bombelli had done in 1572. Girard also established that an *n*th degree equation has *n* roots.

In 1637, Descartes presented his own theory of algebraic equations in his *Geometry*, which he published as an appendix to the *Discourse on Method*. His ideas, though very similar to those of Harriot and Girard, were nevertheless original, for the book was a survey of Descartes' personal discoveries, some of which went back to 1620.

Descartes used an algebraic notation which, by and large, was the same as our own: the last (small) letters of the alphabet were reserved for unknowns and combined with the exponential notation of Stevin, Bombelli and Chuquet. The equality sign, $\propto$, was also introduced.

Descartes summarized the basic principles of the new algebra on the following lines:

(1) In every equation, the unknown quantity can have as many roots as it has dimensions . . . for if, say, we assume $x=2$, *i.e.*, $x-2=0$, and also $x-3=0$, and multiply the two equations, we obtain $x^2-5x+6=0$, or $x^2=5x-6$.

Often, however, some of these roots are false, or less than nothing; for instance, when x represents a 'deficiency' of 5, *i.e.* when $x+5=0$.

(2) It follows that every equation having more than one root can be divided by a binomial expression consisting of the unknown quantity less the value of any of its true roots or plus the value of any of its false roots. In this way, its dimensions can be suitably reduced.

(3) We can also determine the possible number of true and false roots in any equation: there can be as many true roots as there are changes of plus and minus signs, and as many false roots as there are successive pairs of plus or minus signs.

(4) It is easy to transform a given equation so that all its false roots become true roots or conversely, for example, by changing all the plus or minus signs in the second, fourth, sixth, or other even places. . . . In order to increase or reduce the [unknown] value of the roots of an equation by a known quantity, all we have to do is to replace the unknown term throughout the equation with another term increased or reduced by that quantity.

(5) This method of changing the value of unknown roots has two advantages. The first is that we can always eliminate the right side of an equation. . . .

(6) . . . The second is that, by increasing the value of the true roots by a quantity greater than any of the false roots, we can always turn all false into true roots, provided only that there are no successive pairs of plus or minus signs, and that the known quantity of the third term is greater than the square of half the second term. . . .

(7) Moreover, without knowing the value of the true roots of an equation, we can multiply or divide them by any known quantity

whatsoever . . . which may help us to turn fractions or surds into rational numbers. . . .

(8) In addition, not all true and false roots are real. Some may be imaginary, *i.e.* correspond to no quantity. Thus, though we can imagine three roots in $x^3-6x^2+13x-10=0$, there is only one real root, *i.e.* 2. As for the other two, no matter by how much we increase, reduce, or multiply them, we can never make them anything but imaginary.

Descartes finally showed (9) how to obtain the rational roots of an equation with rational coefficients.

The *Geometry* goes on to discuss the construction of roots by means of the intersection of two curves and gives Descartes' rule for the solution of biquadratic equations by considering the left-hand side as the product of two quadratic trinomials.

In his admirable summary of the state of the theory of equations in 1637, Descartes did not rely upon proofs but gave numerous examples instead. Not all the findings were Descartes' own. Thus (1) was first discussed by Albert Girard; (2) was known to Cardan and his successors; (4), (5), (6) and (7) were developed by Vieta; and (9) was mentioned by Jacques Peletier. Only (3), the 'rule of Descartes', though vaguely known to Cardan, was a personal contribution by the great philosopher. The discussion of imaginary roots in (8)—another of Girard's ideas—shows clearly how little was really known about them.

Descartes' principles were later developed, particularly by van Schooten's disciples and by Newton, who used them to establish 'Newton's identities', as they came to be called. These were certain relations between the sums of powers of all the roots of a polynomial equation and its coefficients. (The case of the first four powers was studied by Girard.)

As we saw, Vieta considered the solution of equations an integral part of his analysis. Descartes, the pure theorist and lover of absolute truth, did not bother about Vieta's approximate method of solving numerical equations. He therefore left it to his English disciples, Harriot and Oughtred (1574–1660), to develop what became the basis of Newton's method of approximation.

The Birth of Analytical Geometry

On the other hand, Descartes applied Vieta's analysis to geometrical problems, thus founding analytical geometry (the actual term was coined in the early 19th century) with Fermat, but independently of him.

Though both mathematicians applied specious logistic to the analysis of loci, and particularly of the loci of the conics of Apollonios and Pappos, they differed considerably in the way in which they translated the earlier methods into a new language. Fermat, as always, remained faithful to Vieta's notation, whereas Descartes invented a notation of his own, which fully reflected his identification of numerical algebra with geometry.

Fermat was born in Beaumont-de-Lomagne in 1601. He studied law, was appointed a magistrate in 1631, and died at Castres on 12th January 1665, at the end of a very quiet life. Like his immediate predecessors, he studied the work of the great Alexandrian mathematicians and tried to reconstruct Apollonios' plane loci. His first results, published when he was twenty-eight, were written in the style of the Greeks, but by the time his characteristically short *Ad locos planos et solidos isagoge* appeared (in 1636 at the latest), he had developed a style of his own which, coupled with Vieta's notation, was to become that of modern analytical geometry.

Had this discovery preceded my much earlier reconstruction of the *Plane Loci*, I should have been able to present the theorems with far greater elegance; nevertheless I have no regrets. . . . Science has, in fact, a concern not to deprive posterity of the work of yet unformed spirits, showing how, from simple and crude beginnings, it gathers strength and improves with new inventions. Indeed, there is much to be learned from the contemplation of the spirit's progress and the spontaneous development of art.

His rival, Descartes, was led to his own method by a strange combination of external pressures and by deep meditation. Thanks to a precocious liking for mechanical contrivances he had made a number of inventions, including a special 'compass' for drawing what he would later call 'geometrical curves', and by which he tried to go beyond Vieta's rule-and-compass constructions. At the same time, his passion for optics caused him to look at conic sections more closely and hence to discover the laws of refraction (*c.* 1625). In this field, he was greatly influenced by Kepler.

In addition, a study of Pappos (either directly or through Clavius) suggested the idea that higher equations could be solved by geometrical means. This brought him close to Vieta's geometrical exegetics or to what came to be called the 'effection of equations'. Everyone tried his hand at it. In about 1629, Descartes produced his elegant solutions of the cubic and quartic equations by the intersection of a parabola and a circle; in 1636 or 1637, Fermat scored a brilliant success when he discussed effection in a special appendix of his *Ad locos*. Roberval (1602–1675), who kept even closer to Vieta, treated the problem by considering the case of the conchoid of Nicomedes.

The problem of effecting equations continued to interest mathematicians up to the time of, and including, Newton. One of its most brilliant exponents was René de Sluze (1622–1685), but Newton was to show that it was too rough a method to serve as anything but a preliminary step of separating the roots of an equation.

In about 1635, Golius set Descartes the famous 'problem of Pappos', known as the 'locus with three, four or five lines'. Descartes solved it in three weeks, proving the excellence of his method and arriving at the precise definition that the curves involved are those in which the co-ordinates x and y are related by the equation $P(x, y) = 0$. Descartes noted that it was possible to construct each point of these curves for any value of x by a finite series of 'effections' of algebraic equations of increasingly higher degree. Such constructions are generally impossible for mechanical, or what Leibniz called 'transcendental', curves, which therefore fall outside the field of analytical geometry.

Henceforth, the work begun in 1637 was clearly mapped out. We shall be returning to some of its other aspects, for they had an important effect on the development of other branches of modern mathematics.

MISCELLANEOUS ADVANCES

Diophantine Analysis

We have already stressed Diophantos' considerable influence on algebraists from Bombelli to Vieta, whose *Zetetics* followed the analytical tradition of the Alexandrian master. In 1621, Bachet de Méziriac published the first Graeco-Latin edition of Pappos' *Arithmetic* with a comprehensive commentary. By then the analytical principles involved were already well known either from Xylander's Latin edition (1575), or from Bombelli's, Stevin's, Girard's and Clavius' commentaries.

The fashion for exercises in Diophantine analysis without any particular end in view persisted throughout the 17th century. The acknowledged expert in the field was Fermat. His comments on Diophantos, written in the margin of his copy of the Bachet edition, were discovered by his son Samuel, who incorporated them into his republication of the work in 1670. A summary of Fermat's method was also published by Father de Billy. Though Diophantine analysis is little used nowadays, it enabled 17th-century algebraists to exercise their intellect and to refine their methods. Its influence on the Bernoulli brothers and hence on infinitesimal calculus was considerable.

Fermat and Number Theory

What was far more important was that Fermat's reflections on Diophantine analysis led him, between 1636 and 1643, to the creation of number theory. His main discoveries were:

(1) The method of infinite descent, a purely arithmetical technique of limited scope which, however, stood Fermat and his successors in very good stead.

(2) Fermat's 'little' theorem: if p is a prime, $a^p \equiv a \pmod{p}$.

(3) Propositions of the kind:

Every integral number is the sum of at most four square, three triangular, or five pentagonal numbers, *etc.*

Every prime number of the type $4n+1$ is the sum of two squares.

No number of the type $3n-1$ is of the type a^2+3b^2.

The area of any right triangle whose sides are integral numbers cannot be expressed as a square.

(4) Fermat's 'great' theorem: the equation $x^n+y^n=z^n$ (where n is an integer greater than 2) has no rational solution.

(5) The Pell-Fermat theorem: the equation $Nx^2+1=y^2$ has an integral solution.

Fermat lacked proofs of a number of his theorems, particularly of his 'great' theorem, which has not been proved to this day.

While Diophantine analysis, which required nothing but patience and skill, was a great favourite with Fermat's contemporaries and immediate successors, his far more demanding number theory had no followers until Euler and Lagrange. In the interval, what results there were were few and meagre.

Desargues and Projective Geometry

At about the time that Fermat was developing his analytical ideas, another equally original mathematician, G. Desargues (1591–1661), concentrated his attention on pure geometry.

While such great scholars as Gregory de St. Vincent, Cavalieri and Mydorge (1585–1647) were studying conics by Apollonian methods, with important though somewhat fragmentary results, Desargues developed a completely new technique: projective geometry. Of his two small book, the most important was the *Brouillon project d'une atteinte aux evenemens des rencontres du cône avec un plan* ('Proposed Rough Draft of an Attempt upon the Intersection of a Cone and a Plane', 1639). It was written in French, without any Greek or Latin technical terms, and was therefore dismissed as a popular work. As a result, Desargues had only a few disciples: the engraver Bosse—who developed and popularized the technical applications of Desargues' ideas—Blaise Pascal and Philippe de La Hire. The complete text of the book was not published until 1951.

Pascal, who acknowledged his debt to Desargues openly, discovered the theorem which came to be known as Pascal's on the inscription of hexagons in a conic, and made it the basis of a complete theory of conics. The only one of his papers on this subject to have been preserved is the short *Essay pour les Coniques* (1640). Philippe de La Hire (1640–1718), a much more prolific but far less original writer, was an 'official' scientist and one of the earliest members of the *Académie des Sciences*. His father, the painter Laurent de La Hire, was a personal friend of Desargues.

It is impossible here to go fully into Desargues' contribution, which included such concepts as a point placed at the extremity of an infinite straight line; a beam of parallel straight lines meeting at an infinitely distant point; parallel planes meeting at an infinitely distant line; the involution of sets of points (and the resulting 'Desargues' Theorem'); and finally his theorem on homologous triangles.

The simultaneous development of analytical geometry, in which La Hire played some part, and of infinitesimal analysis, caused Desargues' work to fall into temporary oblivion, from which it was not rescued until the pupils of Monge once again focused attention upon it, thus helping it to assume its rightful place in mathematics.

Napier and Logarithms

We must now go back in time to discuss a most important discovery which sprang from the trigonometrical work of astronomers but had far-reaching repercussions on pure mathematics and on all other branches of science—the discovery of logarithms. In his desire to simplify trigonometrical calculations, John Napier of Merchiston (1550–1617), a Scottish baron, took up the old idea of the correspondence between arithmetical and geometrical progressions:

> The Logarithme of any sine is a number very neerely expressing the line, which increased equally in the meane time, whiles the line of the whole sine decreased proportionaly into that sine, both motions being equal-timed, and at the beginning equally swift. (*Mirifici logarithmorum canonis descriptio* . . ., 1614.)

This definition calls for a number of comments. To begin with, logarithms were thought to express a *logos*, or *ratio*. We know that from the Greek mathematicians to the 18th century the theory of ratios was, in some respects, couched in what we might call 'logarithmic language'. If, for instance, r^1 is the ratio A : B, and r^2 the ratio B : C, the ratio A : C was not called the product but the *sum* of r^1 and r^2. Thus, from the case of the equalities $\frac{a}{1} = \frac{a^2}{a} = \frac{a^3}{a^2} = \frac{a^4}{a^3}$, it was argued that the ratios $\frac{a^2}{1}$, $\frac{a^3}{1}$, $\frac{a^4}{1}$ were respectively twice, three times, and four times the initial ratio, $\frac{a}{1}$. Expressions of this type were still so common in the 17th century that Newton used them in his *Principia*. Desargues, among others, introduced this terminology into many geometrical proofs, which completely elude the modern reader unless he bears the above comments in mind.

Napier based his logarithms on sines because he was concerned with the practical aims of first simplifying trigonometrical computations and then applying them to astronomy. Though his logarithms were expressed as numbers, they were in fact close approximations of the length of a continuous magnitude, *viz.* a line. The line itself was considered a 'function' of the sine—though the word 'function' is perhaps a misnomer and was, in any case, coined later by Leibniz. It was introduced by way of a differential equation, the first to appear in the history of mathematics. If R is the radius of the circle, or the whole sine (*sinus totus*), x the sine, and y its logarithm in Napier's sense, then $y=0$ for $x=R$ and $dy=-(R/x)dx$.

This formula expresses the relationship between Napier's own logarithms and our 'Naperian logarithms' (a term first introduced by Lacroix), *viz.*: $y=R \log (R/x)$.

Though it may be doubted whether Napier was the inventor of the *concept* of logarithms, it is certain that his keen awareness of the concept of continuity, involving great knowledge of mathematics, and his brilliant idea of introducing that continuity through motion and hence of giving a differential definition of logarithms, make him one of the most important mathematicians of the early 17th century.

The differential definition led to the fundamental law that sines decreasing in geometrical progressions from R have logarithms increasing in arithmetical progression from zero, and Napier was not afraid to admit negative logarithms when most mathematicians dismissed all but positive magnitudes. Significantly, at the very time that Napier was developing his theory of logarithms, Galileo used similar arguments to show that the velocity of falling bodies could not vary with the distance they had travelled, for, in that case, their fall would have to be instantaneous. At the request of Gassendi, Fermat perfected this argument in 1642.

Long before that, Napier had established a table of logarithms by a series of ingenious interpolations, with $R=10^7$.

Since these early logarithms proved rather clumsy, Henry Briggs, after consulting Napier, established new tables in which $\log 1=0$ and $\log 10=1$. When his *Arithmetica Logarithmica* appeared in 1624, it contained the logarithms of the numbers 1–20,000 and 90,000–100,000, to fourteen decimal places.

These tables, which filled an urgent need of computators, and especially of astronomers, were received with great enthusiasm. From 1614, when the *Mirifici logarithmorum canones descriptio* first appeared, until 1631, more than 20 versions based on it were printed. Among them was Bürgi's *Arithmetische und Geometrische Progress-Tabulen*, which may be called a primitive table of antilogarithms. Though they were not published until 1620, they were compiled between 1603 and 1611, and hence independently of Napier's work.

Other workers in the field included John Speidell, Kepler, Edmund Gunter—the inventor of the logarithmic 'line of numbers' known as Gunter's scale, a forerunner of the slide rule—Vlacq and Denis Henrion, who published the first French work on logarithms in 1626.

Combinatorial Analysis and Probability

Another new contribution to mathematics was combinatorial analysis, in which Fermat distinguished himself once again by developing, before 1636, the 'figured number formula' which we now write as:

$$C^p = \frac{n(n-1)\ldots(n-p+1)}{p!}$$

In his short work on the 'Arithmetical Triangle' (1654), Pascal proved this formula by complete induction, a method previously used by Archimedes, Maurolico and Bachet de Méziriac, and which was later developed by Jacques Bernoulli.

In the same context we must also mention the work on magic squares, an analytical pastime 'modernized' mainly by Bachet (1612 and 1624) and by Fermat (1630), who once again displayed his astonishing virtuosity. Frénicle de Bessy (1605?–1675) also distinguished himself both in this field and in number theory.

Probability theory, which had its forerunners in Pacioli, Cardan and Galileo, took its first firm steps in 1654 in the course of an exchange of letters between Blaise Pascal, then 31 years old, and Fermat. The two correspondents treated the theory as part of combinational analysis, in which Fermat outshone his young rival. Huygens, who was told of the letters, became interested in the subject himself and, in 1657, published the first treatise on probability theory, the *De ratiociniis in ludo aleae*.

THE BIRTH OF INFINITESIMAL CALCULUS

If we were asked to give a brief list of the main mathematical discoveries of the 17th century, we should begin with Vieta's specious logistic and its two extensions: the theory of algebraic equations and analytical geometry, and end with infinitesimal analysis with its two (originally distinct) branches: differential and integral calculus. To the history of infinitesimal analysis we shall now turn our attention.

Fermat: Maxima and Tangents

By 1630, at the latest, Fermat had developed a method of determining the maxima and minima of algebraic functions. Though he was led to this great discovery by his reading of Pappos, it was only because he was a disciple of Vieta that he was able to exploit it to the full.

Most historians agree with Montucla that Fermat based his method on a principle expounded by Kepler in the *Stereometria doliorum*, namely, that a function varies imperceptibly near its maximum or minimum. In fact, Fermat's principle was based on the realization that a function has the *same value* on either side of its maximum or minimum.

Take the polynomial $P(x)$ and let a approach the maximum. Then $P(a+e)=P(a)$, *i.e.* we have an equation in e with roots O and e, the maximum value of x lying between a and $(a+e)$. By simplification, we obtain the equation $Q(a+e)=O$. As a tends towards the required maximum e tends towards O. Hence, maxima and minima can be determined by the equation $Q(a, O)=O$.

In applying the same method to the determination of tangents, Fermat made use of the fact that, near its point of contact, the tangent must lie outside the curve. Let a 'geometric' curve have the equation $P(x, y)=O$, where P is a polynomial. The tangent at a point M defined by the co-ordinates x_o, y_o, cuts the axis at the point x_o-s, s being the sub-tangent. The tangent is therefore defined by the co-ordinates $x, y=\frac{y_o}{s}(x-x_o+s)$.

Applying this value of y at $P(x, y)$ we obtain a new polynomial in x. Now, since the tangent remains outside the curve in the neighbourhood of M, this polynomial, which vanishes for $x=x_o$, will have a constant sign in that neighbourhood. Hence its maximum or minimum must coincide with x_o. Expressing this fact by Fermat's method, we obtain the equation of the sub-tangent s.

This is how Fermat himself discussed the tangent to the parabola in 1637, by a method he had perfected in 1632 *(fig. 14)*:

Let the parabola BDN have the diameter [axis] DC, and let it be required to draw a tangent at any point B on the curve, which meets the axis produced in E. Take any point O on BE and draw the ordinates OI and BC. Since the point OI lies outside the parabola, $\frac{CD}{ID} > \frac{BC^2}{OI^2}$. But

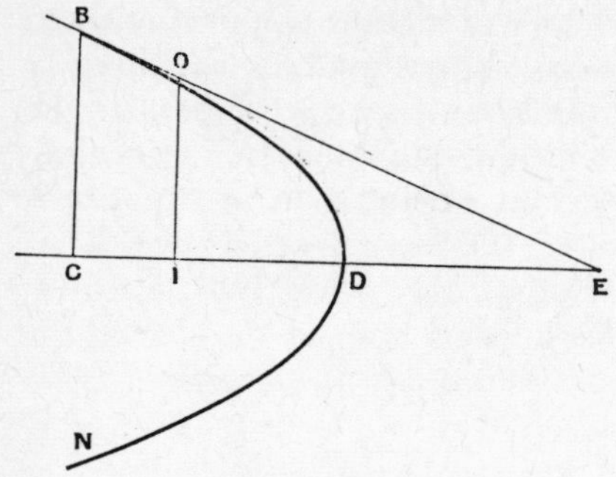

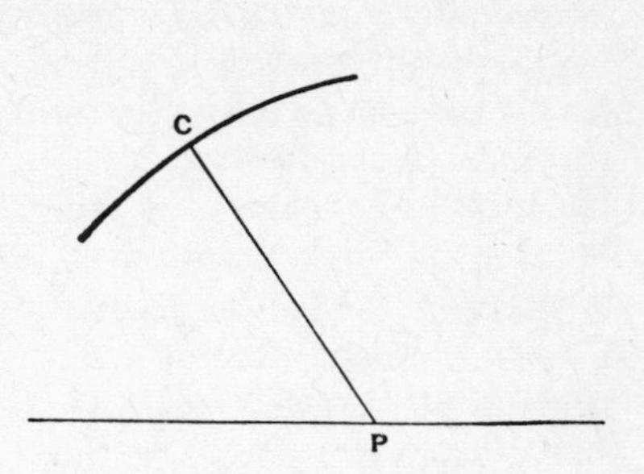

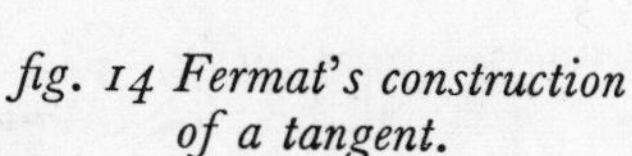

fig. 14 Fermat's construction of a tangent.

fig. 15 Descartes' construction of a normal.

by similar triangles $\frac{BC^2}{OI^2} = \frac{CE^2}{IE^2}$. Hence $\frac{CD}{ID} > \frac{CE^2}{IE^2}$. Now the point B being given, the ordinate BC is known, and so is the point C, and hence the length CD. Denoting CD by d, CE by a, and CI by e, we have:

$$\frac{d}{d-e} > \frac{a^2}{(a-e)^2}$$

or

$$a^2d - 2ade + de^2 > a^2d - a^2e$$

or

$$de^2 + a^2e > 2ade$$

or

$$de + a^2 > 2ad.$$

Now if O move into coincidence with B, these will become equal; e will vanish, and therefore de also. Hence $a^2 = 2ad$, or $a = 2d$. Hence we have proved that CE$=$2CD, which, indeed, it is.

Descartes was led to the problem of constructing tangents, or rather normals, to geometrical curves by his optical studies.

Long after discovering the laws of refraction, but in any case before 1636, he tried to find a curve having two given points A and B such that all light rays emerging from A and refracted by the curve would pass through B.

By an unexplained method he then discovered his 'ovals', the first curves to be defined parametrically. In his *Geometry*, he suggested that the normals to geometric curves could be constructed in the following way:

Let the normal PC to the ellipse $F(x, y) = O$ cut the x axis at C. A circle described with centre P and radius PC would, in general, cut the ellipse in two points. If PC is the normal, these two points coincide, and the roots of the above equation will be equal.

The problem is therefore reduced to one of pure algebra, and can be solved by Descartes' own method of indeterminate coefficients.

Because Descartes' and Fermat's methods were purely geometrical they had a limited application. Both mathematicians tried to remedy this failing in characteristic ways, Fermat's being greatly superior to his rival's. Descartes, in fact, discussed the matter only once, when dealing with the tangents to his 'roulette' or cycloid. By substituting a polygon for the generating circle, he was able to determine the instantaneous centre of rotation of the curve and the property of the normal passing through that centre.

Fermat argued that it should be possible to express the ordinates of curves by means of the ordinates of the tangents, and arcs of curves by means of the corresponding lengths of the given tangents. In 1660, he was able to give a partial proof of this claim and hence to construct tangents to the many transcendental curves which he had begun to study in 1638.

One of the problems he had studied at that time was the following *(fig. 16)*: Let there be any number of curves BE, BD, BF, BA, given in position, and let another curve BM be drawn so that its projection MC is the mean proportional between the sum of BA, BF, BD, BE and the sum of their projections AC, FC, DC, EC. Find the tangent to MB at a given point.

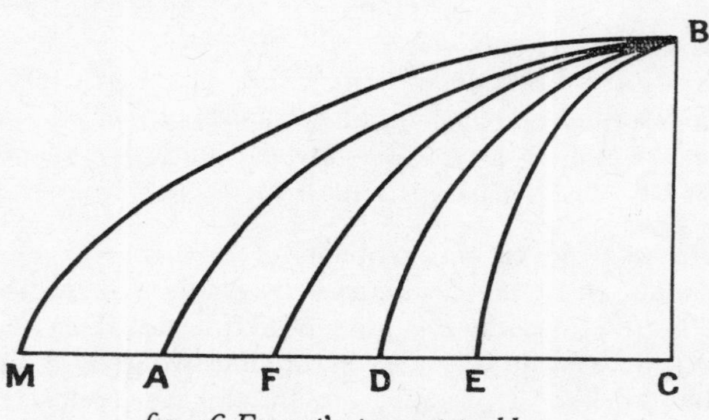

fig. 16 Fermat's tangent problem.

Should you require the other curves in my example to be a circle, a parabola, a hyperbola, and an ellipse, I agree on condition only that you believe that I can equally well apply the solution to any number of curves of whatsoever type, and this without any asymmetry (or expressions containing radicals), which strikes me as being marvellous.

While Descartes and Fermat treated the problem of tangents, and hence of 'mechanical' curves, by purely algebraic methods, Roberval used a kinematic approach. Admittedly he, too, used algebra when investigating the existence of the roots of quartic equations by an analysis of the tangents to the conchoid of Nicomedes, but in his main study (*c.* 1638) he regarded the direction of the tangent as the direction of motion of the point which describes the curve. According to him, this point partakes of two motions, the relative velocity of which depends on the nature of the curve. His method may be likened to the modern procedure which, in the case of curves defined by parametric expressions of x and y, treats the tangent as the line of support of the vector of the co-ordinates x^1 and y^1.

The methods of Fermat and Descartes, which, when all is said and done, are identical in principle, were systematized by the next generation of mathematicians, including van Schooten's pupils Hudde and Huygens, and Sluze, who, though he claimed to be a direct disciple of Vieta, had, in fact, been influenced by Galilean ideas through Ricci. Another, though somewhat later, mathematician to be influenced by Ricci was Barrow, Newton's brilliant teacher and a forerunner of Leibniz.

Indivisibles

The beginnings of integral calculus go back to Euclid and above all to Archimedes, whose works were closely studied in the late 16th century. Lucca Valerio, the author of a book dealing with centres of gravity (1604), was one of the first to appreciate the great importance of Archimedes. Cavalieri (1598–1647), an indirect disciple of Galileo, has often been called the 'father of integral calculus'. In fact, while his famous *Geometria indivisibilibus continuorum nova quadam ratione promota* (1635) had a decisive influence on the next generation of mathematicians, he had many contemporaries who expressed much the same ideas.

Thus when Cavalieri presented his 'indivisible geometry' in 1629, he had been preceded by Kepler who, in his *Nova stereometria doliorum vinarium* (1615), had compared a curve to a polygon with an infinite number of sides, thus giving a fairly precise definition of indivisibles. Moreover, in 1625, Gregory de St. Vincent (1584–1667) had developed an excellent technique of his own, based on the classical method of exhaustion. Unfortunately, the loss of most of his papers during the fire of Prague prevented his publishing the *Opus geometricum quadraturae circuli et sectionum coni* before 1647. Misjudged in his time, he has remained so to this day, partly because of his extreme rigour and laboured explanations, and partly because of his mistaken attempts to square the circle. Even so, Leibniz numbered him, together with Cavalieri and Pascal, among his direct predecessors.

In France, Descartes, Fermat and Roberval, using methods of literal algebra, managed to square the parabola $y=ax^n$, and later

(Fermat and Roberval) the more general parabola $y^p = ax^n$. They also cubed paraboloids of revolution and determined their centres of gravity. The last of these problems was not tackled by Cavalieri until after 1640, partly at the request of Jean de Beaugrand and partly in order to refute Guldin (1577–1643), the Austrian Jesuit who is remembered for his famous theorem: 'If any plane figure revolve about an external axis in its plane, the volume of the solid so generated is equal to the product of the area of the figure and the distance travelled by the centre of gravity of the figure.' Though this theorem had been propounded much earlier by Pappos, the Greek text was not rediscovered until long after Guldin.

All the methods of the authors we have quoted went back to the Archimedean tradition, which they must have reconstructed for themselves, since Archimedes' *Letter to Eratosthenes*, in which he revealed his analytical method, was not rediscovered until the beginning of the 20th century. Each of them believed himself to have gone beyond Archimedes—hence their endless priority claims and accusations of plagiarism, a crime of which all, except perhaps Beaugrand, were completely innocent.

Fermat was a great believer in concise synthetic proofs, but since his genius kept leaping from one discovery to the next, he was often too hard pressed for time to offer more than the results of his analysis without any further explanation.

Historians have failed to pay sufficient tribute to the remarkable contribution of Cavalieri and to the depth of his views. He argued, for instance, that the determination of an area is equivalent to finding the sum of all the parallel lines of which it is made up. Again, his concept of similarity which he expounded in the first book of his *Geometria indivisibilis continuorum* . . . was much more general than Euclid's. Nevertheless, his attempt to generalize geometry was a failure, at least from the theoretical point of view, for he was forced to introduce unnecessary postulates of his own in addition to those of the Greek geometers. In fact, he failed to follow the precepts laid down by Roberval and popularized by Pascal in 1659:

> Everything that can be proved by the laws of indivisibles can also be proved by the method of the Ancients, for the two do not differ except in terminology; which cannot confuse reasonable persons once they have been clearly informed of the matter. Hence I shall not be adding to their perplexity when, in what follows, I use the language of indivisibles and speak of the *sum of lines* or the *sum of planes*, or when, for instance, I consider the diameter of a semicircle divided into an indefinite number of parts equal to the points Z from which the ordinates ZN are drawn, or again when I speak of the *sum of ordinates*, a term which may strike those as

ungeometrical who do not understand the doctrine of indivisibles and who consider it a sin against geometry to describe a plane by an infinite number of lines. This springs from their lack of knowledge, for this [last] term refers simply to the sum of an indefinite number of rectangles, each contained by an ordinate and a small portion of the diameter. Their sum is unquestionably a plane that does not differ from the area of a semicircle except by a quantity smaller than any given quantity.

This quotation may strike one as an excellent elementary definition of the definite integral and of the limit. In fact, it was a simple summary of the ancient method of exhaustion, translated into the language of indivisibles. Under the influence of Leibniz these lucid notions were to disappear in the course of the 18th century—part of the ransom that had to be paid for Leibniz's tremendous contribution to integral calculus. In the 19th century, Cauchy, in particular, led the way back to Archimedean concepts.

The Most Important New Results

By the method of direct integration, or by what he called the 'method of indivisibles', Cavalieri was able to prove that (in modern notation):

$$\int_0^a x^m dx = \frac{1}{m+1} a^{m+1}$$

He arrived at this result in 1629 but did not publish it until 1635, first for $m=1$ and 2, and later for $m=3$ and 4, and then by complete induction, for $m=$any positive integer.

In 1635, Fermat gave a rigorous proof of this generalization and extended it before 1638 (at the latest) to all positive fractional powers. In his own words, he had succeeded in squaring the general parabola: $y^p a^m = b^p x^m$. Roberval obtained similar results. In 1643, Torricelli, who was an expert manipulator of 'curved indivisibles', discovered the volume of the 'sharp conoid' generated by the rotation of a hyperbola about its asymptote. Spurred on by a controversy with Roberval, he managed to extend his results and to square the general hyperbola $x^n y^p = a^n b^p$.

Wallis was introduced to the subject by his reading of the works of Torricelli and Cavalieri. In his *Arithmetica infinitorum* (1656) he obtained the quadrature of curves by incomplete induction, using numerical calculations. He was one of the first to free infinitesimal analysis from its reliance on spatial models.

The problem of the cycloid, *i.e.* the plane locus of a point fixed on the circumference of a circle as the circle rolls upon a straight line, is related to the preceding problems but introduces trigonometrical functions. It was apparently first posed by Mersenne to Roberval, who managed to square an arc of that curve in 1637, using a very simple and ingenious method. On that occasion, Roberval invented the sine-curve, which he called the 'roulette companion'. When Fermat, Descartes and, later, Torricelli learned of Roberval's success, they produced their own contributions: Descartes found the tangent to the cycloid by considering the instantaneous centre of rotation, as did Fermat by using his general method, and Roberval by his kinematic method—which, in fact, he invented for this specific purpose. Viviani followed suit a little later, using a method similar to Torricelli's.

Both Roberval and Torricelli calculated the volume generated by the rotation of the arc about the base and, in 1644, Torricelli even believed (wrongly) that he had determined the volume generated by the rotation of the arc about the axis and the exact position of the centre of gravity of the 'plate' generated by the semi-arc. He published his results without proof.

Roberval discovered the error, challenged his rival and, in 1645, after having studied the question for two years, published the correct result. To do so, he had been forced to develop the method of integration. His own methods were perfected by Pascal who, using the pseudonym of Dettonville, had challenged all mathematicians to solve the cycloid problem.

The problem of the general quadrature of parabolas had therefore been solved by the middle of the 17th century, but not the problem of squaring the circle, though the cycloid solution involved the squaring of such functions as $x^m \sin^n x$, where n and m are simple positive integers.

Torricelli, Roberval, Fermat and Wallis also managed to square hyperbolas, *i.e.* they integrated functions of the type x^{-r}, where r is a positive rational number. Only the quadrature of the ordinary hyperbola, that of Apollonios, in which $r=1$, continued to resist their methods. Though Roberval came very close to relating this problem to the new theory of logarithms, he published no papers on the subject. Hence it was left to Gregory de St. Vincent to establish this connection, albeit implicitly, in 1647, when he showed that abscissae in geometric progression correspond to areas in arithmetical progression. The merit of making this identification explicit fell to his pupil Sarasa.

Meanwhile, the calculus of indivisibles was being applied to other fields: to the determination of centres of gravity and to the rectification of arcs of curves.

The Paris school, which, spurred on by Mersenne, was applying the hypothesis of convergent gravitational lines to the study of inclined planes, discovered a spiral curve, our logarithmic spiral, and established its main properties. Descartes, who kept in touch with the work of the school, showed that this mechanical curve was of finite length.

Moreover, by studying Archimedes' treatment of the parabola and of the spiral $\rho=\alpha\omega$, Cavalieri and de St. Vincent discovered (well before 1630) that the two had many similarities. In 1642 or 1643, Roberval proved the equality of the arcs of the two curves. Soon afterwards Torricelli obtained the same results, which he extended to parabolas and spirals in general. He thus rediscovered the logarithmic spiral (which he called the 'geometric spiral'), and established its 'remarkable' properties.

However, the most important advances in the rectification of curves were still to be made and we shall return to them below.

Roberval's Quadratrices

Before we do so, however, we must mention a very simple and yet far-reaching discovery of Roberval, which enabled him to establish a fundamental connection between the determination of tangents and the computation of areas. This discovery clearly proved the superiority of his conception of indivisibles over that of Cavalieri.

In about 1645, Roberval was struck by the following fact:

> Let AC be a convex curve with axis $x'\mathrm{A}x$ [*fig. 17*]. At any point M in AC draw the tangent MT to meet the axis in T. Draw TN perpendicular to the axis and let it meet MN, drawn parallel to the axis, at N. Let AΓ be the locus of N. Then the areas lying (1) between the curve AC, the ordinate M*m* and the segment of the axis A*m*, and (2) between the curve AC, the parallel NM and the curve AΓ are equal.

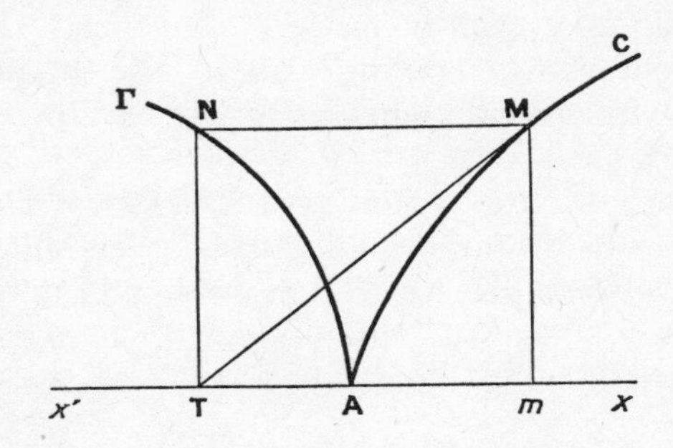

fig. 17 Roberval's quadratrix.

He informed Torricelli, who immediately discovered a proof of his own, which he used to good effect in his attempts to square hyperbolas. In fact, Roberval's 'quadratrices' proved an invaluable aid to integration. Torricelli's friend Ricci prized Roberval's discovery very highly; it was used to great advantage by James Gregory, and it allowed Leibniz to share one of his earliest successes with Gregory: the discovery of the series $\frac{\pi}{4} = 1 - \frac{1}{3} + \frac{1}{5} \ldots$

The Inverse of the Tangent Problem

Before we examine the contribution of the generation immediately preceding Leibniz and Newton—Wallis, Barrow, Pascal, Huygens and Gregory—we must still look at another great problem in infinitesimal analysis: the inverse of the tangent problem, *i.e.* the determination of a curve from its tangential properties. A problem of this kind had been posed in 1604 in Kepler's *Ad Vitellionem paralipomena.* In it, Kepler was looking for the *anaclastic* curve, which is the curve refracting parallel rays and bringing them to a focus. Having none but Witelo's rudimentary tables, Kepler realized that he could do little more than make a qualitative study of the tangents to the curve, determining the nature of its curvature and proving that it had an asymptote. That is as far as he could go, for though the curve resembled Apollonios' hyperbola, he was unable to identify the two. (Napier's definition and construction of logarithms involved a problem of the same order.)

Subsequent attempts to solve this problem included the (unspecified) analysis which led Descartes to his ovals, and the analysis which led the Parisian mathematicians to their logarithmic spiral.

In 1635, Fermat tackled the determination of the centres of gravity of parabolas and paraboloids of revolution in much the same way. In 1638, Debeaune proposed a problem whose solution involved the construction of a curve from its tangential property. This curve was a logarithmic curve with oblique axes. The manner in which Descartes dealt with the problem was highly reminiscent of Kepler's treatment of the anaclastic.

Roberval's transformation, moreover, had shown that the calculation of the areas of a number of curves (parabolas, hyperbolas, logarithmic curves) was related to the problem of determining their tangents.

John Wallis

We come now to the contribution of the next generation. John Wallis (1616–1703), a self-confessed autodidact, began to pick up his mathematical knowledge at the age of 30 from his reading of Oughtred, Harriot, Cavalieri and Torricelli. He showed great skill in his treatment of number problems, even though he based his methods on incomplete induction. Fermat had this to say about it:

The said Mr. Wallis sets out a series of quantities in arithmetical progression beginning with 0 (which represents the point) and then determines the ratio of the sum of the said quantities to the sum of terms equal to the greatest of the given quantities.

In order to determine this ratio, he takes the sums of various quantities of numbers commencing with the least and compares the ratios with each other and so deduces a general proposition.

This method can be used if the proof of the proposition is hidden and if, before the investigation is begun, the approximate truth is ascertained; but one must guard against placing one's trust in it too blindly and treat it with caution, for though one could apply the method and find that it holds for a number of particular instances, it might nevertheless be false and lack universality. . . .

Though Fermat's comment was quite sound, mathematicians had little else to go by before Huygens and Newton had made their contributions. Even they would occasionally adopt expedient methods before justifying them theoretically.

In any case, Wallis did well to draw attention to the great usefulness of approximations based on infinite series. Thus, in his work on systematic decimal and sexagesimal fractions, he was able to show that, unlike rational ratios, irrational ratios do not lead to periodic fractions. He gave his famous value of $\frac{4}{\pi}$ in the form of an infinite approximation, while his friend Lord Brouncker expressed the same value by making use of continued fractions. Continued fractions, an invention of Bombelli, had been treated systematically at the beginning of the 17th century by Cataldi, professor of mathematics at Bologna. Wallis was the first to associate them systematically with decimal fractions, and Schwenter (1585–1636) the first to use them for practical calculations (1627). Huygens used continued fractions when working on the construction of his planetary clock, but this part of his work was not published until 1713, after his death.

Convergent Series

However, the most important contribution of Wallis's school was the introduction of convergent series.

That term was first used analytically by James Gregory (1638–1675) in his *Vera circuli et hyperbolae quadratura* (1667), though in a slightly different sense from ours. Gregory applied it to the series of values obtained when a sector of a circle is rectified alternately 'by excess' and by 'falling short', each successive pair of values being contained in the preceding. The word 'convergent' itself was taken from optics (James Gregory was also an optician).

'True' convergent series (which Gregory himself was to study later) were first used in 1650 by Mengoli (1626–1686), then professor of mathematics at Bologna. Though his work became known in England in about 1670, he seems to have had little influence on English mathematicians.

Nicolas Mercator (Kauffman) (1620–1687) was the first to use the new technique to really good effect. In his *Logarithmotechnia* (London, 1668) he rectified the hyperbola by expressing $\frac{1}{1+x}$ as a geometrical series and then integrating it, term by term, according to Wallis's method. In the same year, Wallis himself solved this problem in much the same way. He published the results in 1670.

The new method proved so successful that, within a few years, James Gregory, Newton and Leibniz had all become masters in it. The palm must go to Newton, who expanded $\frac{1}{1+x}$ by the binomial theorem he had discovered. In 1676, long after the actual discovery, he revealed that he had also discovered the expansions of arc sine x, arc versine x, sine x, cos x, *etc.*, and similar series for the arcs of ellipses and even for segments and arcs of Dinostratos' quadratrix.

Huygens

Unlike Wallis, Christiaan Huygens (1629–1695) had a sound mathematical education, not only in the methods of the ancient Greeks, but in those of Vieta and Descartes as well. His teacher, van Schooten, was in fact the publisher of these two great mathematicians and the pupil of the latter. Here, we shall merely discuss Huygens' purely mathematical contribution, however artificial this approach may be.

Huygens combined a considerable gift of invention with a highly developed feeling for mathematical aesthetics. His love of elegance and rigour were such that he would publish nothing tainted with the slightest flaw. As a result, his publications were invariably held back for many years, so that his original contributions must be discovered from his correspondence. His most famous treatise, the *Horologium oscillatorium* (Paris, 1673), which describes his pendulum experiments during some twenty years, is a model interpretation of experimental evidence.

In the practical task of adapting the pendulum to the regulation of clocks, Huygens soon discovered that its oscillations were not as isochronous as Galileo had believed. To correct the resulting errors, he invented a method of automatically reducing the length of the pendulum as the amplitude of the oscillation increased. This he did by making the suspending thread wrap itself alternately about two symmetrical jaws. So far, the problem was a purely mechanical one.

But Huygens the mathematician was not satisfied until he had given a mathematical analysis of his experimental results. The actual steps he took to do so were quite different from the procedure he described in 1673. He began by investigating the case where the bob describes an arc of a circle. In the course of direct integration (indivisibles), involving what came to be known as elliptical functions, Huygens replaced the arc with a superosculating parabola (a curve discussed by Gregory de St. Vincent in 1647, though the term itself was coined by Leibniz's followers).

In this way, he was led to the integral $\int_0^h \frac{dz}{\sqrt{z(h-z)}}$

Huygens knew this integral from Roberval's transformation, but it was only because of his familiarity with Cartesian methods that he was able to express the case of perfect isochronism with it. However, the problem of finding what curve of the bob this integration represents still remained.

In 1658, Pascal (Dettonville) challenged all mathematicians to solve the problem of the 'roulette'. Its solution was also the solution of Huygens' problem: the required curve was the cycloid.

The Cycloid

We are thus brought back to what was probably the most important curve studied in the 17th century. Pascal's investigations of it exploited infinitesimal analysis to the full. When Wren (1632–1723), rebuilder of London after the Great Fire, managed to rectify the arc of the simple cycloid, Pascal immediately showed that the arcs of the other two species of cycloid could be reduced to arcs of ellipses.

The renewal of interest in the rectification of arcs of curves led to a number of remarkable advances. Almost simultaneously, but quite independently of one another, Wallis's pupil W. Neil (1637–1670), the Dutch mathematician van Heuralt (1633–1660), and Fermat managed to rectify the semicubic parabola $ay^2=x^3$. Fermat published two special papers on the subject; the first appeared in the works of his friend Laloubère (1600–1664), and dealt with arcs of curves, while the second (which was published by his son in 1679) discussed methods of integration. Both papers were far superior to anything Pascal had contributed. Fermat's method of direct integration, which he invented rather late in life, was probably a development of Roberval's proof (1643) of Torricelli's theorems on the 'sharp conoid'. The papers also described Fermat's analytical method of transforming integrals.

Evolutes and Involutes

However, we must return to Huygens and his pendulum studies. Having just discovered the isochronous curve, Huygens began to investigate how the length of the thread could be regulated so that the pendulum may describe a 'roulette'. Since the thread itself remains normal to the trajectory of the bob, he was led to a study of evolutes and involutes, on which he founded and developed a new theory. He determined the evolutes of conics, and showed that the evolute of any geometrical curve is an algebraically rectifiable curve, and that the evolute of the cycloid is another cycloid.

Newton

Two men, Newton and Leibniz, were to re-examine all the work of their predecessors, and fuse it into a tremendous synthesis. Newton, like Huygens, had a solid academic training, for his teacher was the great Isaac Barrow (1630–1677), a man of wide learning and the author of the *Lectiones mathematicae*, a profound study of basic scientific precepts, and of the *Lectiones geometricae* (1670), which stressed the connection between the 'inverse of the tangent problem' and the quadratures of curves. Barrow had a tremendous influence on Newton, and, in particular, he kindled his enthusiasm for Greek science. In addition, Newton developed a taste for contemporary mathematics, and especially for Descartes, whose *Geometry* he developed in the *Arithmetica universalis* (1707).

Newton's studies of third-order curves, inspired by Fermat's critique of Descartes' classification, helped to develop the methods of analytical geometry and illustrated their full scope. Newton's fundamental work, *Philosophiae naturalis principia mathematica* ('The Mathematical Principles of Natural Philosophy'), generally known as the *Principia*, passed in review the geometrical contributions of all the greatest mathematicians, past and present.

It was about 1655 that Newton first conceived the idea of his 'calculus of fluxions' and discovered the binomial theorem, but neither was published until very much later. The calculus was first expounded in the *Principia*, in 1687, and later in the *De analysi per æquationes numero terminorum infinitas* (written in 1669 and published in 1711), the *Method of Fluxions and Infinite Series* (written in Latin in 1671, but translated by John Collins and first printed in English in 1736), and the *Tractatus de quadratura curvarum* (written in about 1676 but published in 1707 as an appendix to the *Opticks*).

In the *Tractatus*, Newton declared:

> I do not consider mathematical Quantities as constituted of Parts, however small, but as being described by continuous Motion. Lines are

described and engendered, not by the Apposition of their Parts, but by the continuous Motion of Points; Surfaces by the Motion of Lines; Solids by the Motion of Surfaces; Angles by the Rotation of Sides; Time by a continuous Flux; and so on. . . . Considering then the Quantities increasing in equal Time are greater or smaller according as they increase with a greater or smaller Velocity, I have sought a Method to determine Quantities by the Velocities of the Motions or Increments which engender them. Calling Fluxions the Velocities of these Motions or Increments, and Fluents the Quantities engendered by them, I happened in about 1665 or 1666 on the Method of Fluxions which I shall use in the Quadrature of Curves.

Calling x the quantity under consideration, or the *fluent*, Newton represented its *fluxion* by $\dot{x}$; if the independent variable—time, in Newton's scheme—has the infinitely small *moment*, or increment, o, he expressed the moment of x by $\dot{x}$o. Hence Newton's fluxions were no more and no less than our derivative. The fluxion of a fluxion was represented by $\ddot{x}$, *etc.*

The magnitude whose fluxion is x was called $\boxed{x}$, x', or $[x]$.

The notation of the method of fluxions was based on the search of the fluxion of a product. Thus Newton deduced (*Princ.* Bk. II, Lemma II) that the fluxion of $A^mB^nC^p$ is:

$$maA^{m-1}B^nC^p + nbA^mB^{n-1} + pcA^mB^nC^{p-1}$$

where a, b and c are the fluxions of A, B and C, and m, n and p any fractions or integers.

Though Newton's ideas were similar to Leibniz's, his approach was perhaps a little less rigorous and more effective. This is how Newton presented what he called his 'method of first and last ratios' in Book I of the *Principia*:

Lemma I: Quantities and the ratios of quantities, which in any finite time converge continually to equality, and before the end of that time approach nearer the one to the other than by any given difference, become ultimately equal.

If you deny it, suppose them to be ultimately unequal, and let D be their ultimate difference. Therefore they cannot approach nearer to equality than by that given difference D; which is against the supposition.

Lemma II: If in any figure A*ac*E (*fig. 18*) terminated by the right lines A*a*, AE, and the curve *ac*E, there be inscribed any number of parallelograms A*b*, B*c*, C*d*, *etc.* comprehended under equal bases AB, BC, CD, *etc.*, and the sides B*b*, C*c*, D*d*, *etc.*, parallel to one side A*a* of the figure; and the parallelograms *a*K*bl*, *b*L*cm*, *c*M*dn* are completed; then if the breadth of those parallelograms be supposed to be diminished, and their number to

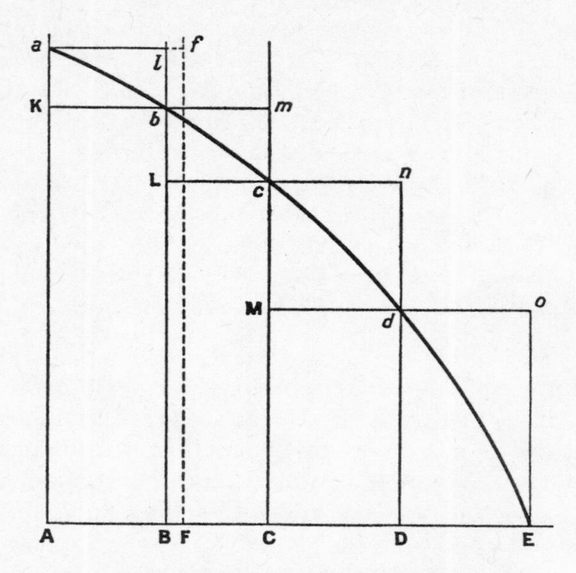

fig. 18 Figure accompanying Lemma II of Newton's 'Principia'.

be augmented *in infinitum*, I say that the ultimate ratios which the inscribed figure AK*b*L*c*M*d*D, the circumscribed figure A*albmcndo*E and the curvilinear figure A*abcd*E will have to one another, are ratios of equality.

For the difference of the inscribed and circumscribed figures is the sum of the parallelograms K*l*, L*m*, M*n*, D*o*; that is (from the equality of all their bases), the rectangle under one of their bases K*b* and the sum of their altitudes A*a*, that is, the rectangle AB*la*. But this rectangle, because its breadth AB is supposed diminished *in infinitum*, becomes less than any given space. And therefore (by *Lemma I*) the figures inscribed and circumscribed become ultimately equal one to the other; and much more will the intermediate curvilinear figure be ultimately equal to either. Q.E.D.

Lemma III: The same ultimate ratios are also ratios of equality, when the breadths AB, BC, DC, *etc.* of the parallelograms are unequal, and are all diminished *in infinitum*.

For suppose AF equal to the greatest breadth, and complete the parallelogram FA*af*. This parallelogram will be greater than the difference of the inscribed and circumscribed figures; but, because its breadth AF is diminished *in infinitum*, it will become less than any given rectangle. Q. E. D. [There follow four corollaries.]

Lemma IV: If in two figures A*ac*E, P*pr*T [*fig. 19*] you inscribe (as before) two ranks of parallelograms, an equal number in each rank, and, when their breadths are diminished *in infinitum*, the ultimate ratios of the parallelograms in one figure to those in the other, each to each respectively,

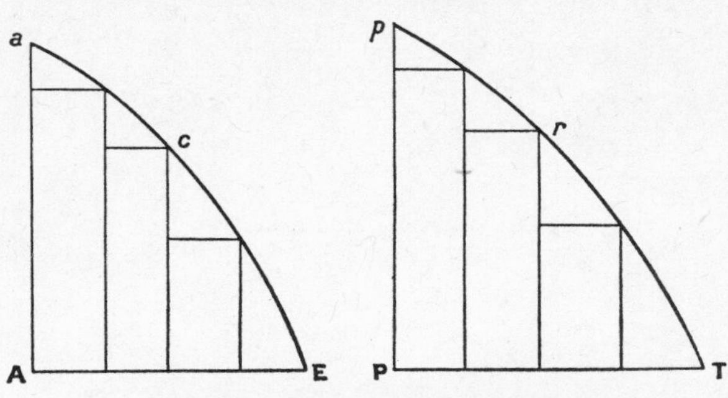

fig. 19 Figure accompanying Lemma IV of Newton's 'Principia'.

are the same; I say, that those two figures A*ac*E, P*pr*T, are to one another in the same ratio.

For as the parallelograms in the one are severally to the parallelograms in the other, so (by composition) is the sum of all in the one to the sum of all in the other, and so is the one figure to the other; because (by *Lemma III*) the former figure to the former sum, and the latter figure to the latter sum are both in the ratio of equality. Q.E.D.

Lemma V: In similar figures, all sorts of homologous sides, whether curvilinear or rectilinear, are proportional; and the areas are in the duplicate ratio of the homologous sides. (No proof.)

Lemma VI: If any arc ACB given in position is subtended by its chord AB, and in any point A, in the middle of the continued curvature, is touched by a right line AD, produced both ways; then if the points A and B approach one another and meet, I say the angle BAD, contained between the chord and the tangent, will be diminished *in infinitum*, and ultimately will vanish.

For if that angle does not vanish, the arc ACB will contain with the tangent AD an angle equal to a rectilinear angle, and therefore the curvature at the point A will not be continued, which is against the supposition.

Lemma VII: The same things being supposed, I say that the ultimate ratio of the arc, chord, and tangent, any one to any other, is the ratio of equality.

For while the point B [*fig. 20*] approaches towards the point A, consider always AB and AD as produced to the remote points *b* and *d*, and parallel to the secant BD draw *bd*: and let the arc A*cb* be always similar to the arc ACB. Then, supposing the points A and B to coincide, the angle *d*A*b* will vanish, by the preceding *lemma*; and therefore the right lines A*b*, A*d* (which are always finite) and the intermediate arc A*cb*, will coincide, and become equal among themselves. Wherefore the right lines AB, AD, and the intermediate arc ACB (which are always proportional to the former) will vanish, and ultimately acquire the ratio of equality. Q.E.D.

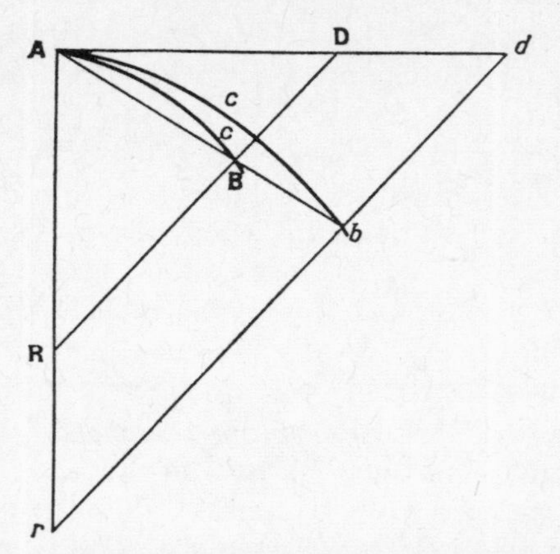

fig. 20 Figure accompanying Lemma VII of Newton's 'Principia'.

These brief examples were offered by Newton as substitutes for the clumsy methods of antiquity and for Cavalieri's method of indivisibles, which he called 'too ungeometrical and too far-fetched'.

Nevertheless when, for instance, he had to determine the force of attraction of a sphere on a particle, Newton, too, calculated the definite integral by direct summation. He even used a terminology resembling Cavalieri's, and justified his doing so in his lemmas. Though these lapses have been considered so many blots in Newton's great copybook, Chasles has argued convincingly (*Aperçu historique*) that, in some cases, the direct geometrical method has many advantages over the analytical approach. Were it not for these 'lapses' we should not be able to salute Newton as the precursor of vector analysis and of differential geometry.

Leibniz

We shall allow Leibniz to introduce himself, by quoting from a letter which he wrote to Jacques Bernoulli in April 1703:

> When I came to Paris in 1672, I was a self-taught and rather inexperienced geometer, lacking patience to run through all the long and wearying demonstrations. As a child, I had studied the elementary algebra of one Lancius, and later that of Clavius; as for that of Descartes, it struck me as being too difficult. I was seized by what seems now to have been a great deal of impudent confidence. I had the temerity to delve into such profound books as Cavalieri's *Geometry* and Léotaud's *Elements of Curves*, which I found by chance in Nuremberg. I tried to run before I could even walk. I had barely begun to read Roman History. I then made a geometrical calculation in which I expressed variables by quadrilaterals

and cubes, unaware that Vieta and Descartes had already dealt with this question, and much better. Despite my superb ignorance of mathematics, I continued to concentrate on the study of history and law. Meanwhile, mathematics continued to be an agreeable distraction; I was fascinated by the workings of machines, and I tried to invent new ones. It was at this time that I discovered my arithmetical machine, and that Huygens, who must have judged me more capable than I really was, brought me a new edition of the *Pendulum*. This was my introduction to deeper geometrical studies. During our meetings, he convinced me that my ideas on centres of gravity were inaccurate; he explained the notion in a few words, adding that Dettonville [Pascal] had dealt with this question admirably. As I was the most docile of men, and as, with the help of only a few words from the lips of a great man, I had often absorbed the objects of innumerable reflections, I quickly followed the advice of this great mathematician, particularly since I readily appreciated his greatness. I blushed at my ignorance of the matter, and anxious to take up the serious study of geometry, I asked Buot for the work of Dettonville and of Gregory de St. Vincent, which was kept in the Royal Library. Without delay, I studied these works—these gems invented by Vincent and perfected by Pascal. I was delighted by their sums and sums of sums, by the resulting solids, and by their demonstrations. All of it gave me more pleasure than work. It was at this point that I chanced upon one of Dettonville's simple demonstrations. How great was my astonishment, when I realized that his eyes must have been closed as if by fate: for I saw at once that his theorem could be applied to all curves and not only to those whose perpendiculars meet in a common centre.

I quickly called on Huygens, whom I had not seen since, and told him that, having followed his advice, I had already discovered something that Pascal did not know, and then expounded my general theorem on the rectification of curves. He was taken by surprise and told me that mine was the very theorem on which he had based his own constructions to determine the areas of parabolic, elliptical, and hyperbolic conoids. Roberval and Boulliau, he added, had been unable to discover it. After praising my progress . . . he advised me to consult Descartes and Sluze, who taught the method of local equations which, he added, was extremely useful. I therefore examined Descartes' *Geometry* and also Sluze's, entering geometry, as it were, by the back door. Stimulated by my progress and by the new treasures to which my eyes were being opened, I wrote a few hundred pages of my own in the same year, dividing my work into two parts: assignable and unassignable. 'Assignable', I called everything that I could derive from the work of Cavalieri, Guldin, Torricelli, Gregory de St. Vincent, and Pascal on sums of sums, transpositions . . . truncated cylinders . . .; 'unassignable' I called what I obtained by the use of the triangle that I would henceforth call *characteristic*; from it I deduced many related facts. Huygens and Wallis were the first to appreciate their importance. A little later, James Gregory's *Geometry* fell into my hands; I recognized the same method (although obscured by his archaic proofs). Finally, I read Barrow and discovered a summary of most of my theorems. I was greatly excited, for I saw that this game could be played even by a novice, provided he had been introduced to the correct notions. I also saw that many complex things had been left unexplained, and that a new method of calculation was needed to account for them. It was then that I presented my arithmetical quadrature and similar matters, which were received with enthusiasm by both French and English mathematicians. But I did not judge this work worthy of being published. As it is, I have had enough troubles with it. . . . You know what happened later, and my letters, published by the English themselves, will bear me out.

In so far as Leibniz may be called the pupil of anyone, he was firstly the pupil of Huygens, who guided his first steps, and secondly, by his reading, of Cavalieri, Gregory de St. Vincent, Descartes, Sluze, Gregory and Barrow. The only author whom he had not studied directly was Fermat, but then Huygens, who was as familiar with Fermat's work as with that of Descartes and Galileo, must have bridged that gap in Leibniz's mathematical education.

Leibniz was the first to define the principles of the differential calculus, to create an excellent notation (Huygens had invented a notation for first-order infinitesimals but did not publish it), and to identify the 'inverse of the tangent problem' with the problem of integration. In that way he founded the differential and integral calculus.

Leibniz presented his ideas on the subject in two papers: the *Nova methodus pro maximis et minimis itemque tangentibus, quae nec fractas nec irrationales quantitates moratur, et singulare pro illis calculi genus* (*Acta eruditorum*, 1684) and the *De geometria recondita et analysi indivisibilium atque infinitorum* (*Acta eruditorum*, 1686).

The first paper described the method of differentiating all sorts of rational, irrational, integral or fractional quantities. Leibniz applied it to solving Fermat's problem of the path of a light ray between two different media, and showed that Debeaune's curve reduces to a logarithmic curve. In the second paper, he presented the fundamental rules of the integral calculus.

His papers show that he had perfected his notation and principles as early as 1675. In a letter to the Abbé Conti, he wrote:

Though I was still a novice in these matters, I quickly discovered my general method by arbitrary series, whereupon I was led to my calculus of differences, in which what observations I had made in my youth on the differences of series of numbers helped greatly to open my eyes. For it is not by fluxions of lines but by differences in numbers that I arrived at my method, considering, as I did, that when these differences are applied to continuously increasing magnitudes, they vanish with respect to them, whereas they subsist in numbers (because numbers increase or decrease by jumps). And I believe that this approach is the more analytical of the two, since the geometrical calculation of differences, which is identical with the method of fluxions, is but a special case of the analytical calculus of differences in general.

More telling still was Leibniz's reply, in December 1694, to Jean Bernoulli, who had just informed him that he had discovered what amounted to Taylor's series, by a method close to our integration by parts:

$$\text{In } dz = nz - \frac{1}{1.2}zz\frac{dn}{dz} + \frac{1}{1.2.3}z^3\frac{ddn}{dz^2} - \frac{1}{1.2.3.4}z^4\frac{dddn}{dz^3}, \text{ etc.}$$

In his reply Leibniz said that a study of Pascal inclined him to the following solution:

> Let the decreasing series be: *a, b, c, d, etc.*
> its first 'differences': *e, f, g, h, etc.*
> its second 'differences': *l, m, n, o, etc.*
> its third 'differences': *p, q, r, s, etc.*
> its fourth 'differences': *t, u, v, x, etc.*
> its fifth 'differences': *β, γ, δ, θ, etc.*

$a = e + f + g + h$, *etc.* $= 1l + 2m + 3n + 4o$, *etc.* $= 1p + 3q + 6r + 10s$, *etc.* $= 1t + 4u + 10v = 20x$, *etc.*

On the other hand, $e = e$; $f = 1e - 1l$; $g = 1e - 2l + 1p$; $h = 1e - 3l + 3p - 1t$, and so on.

Applying these values to $a = e + f + g + h$, we obtain:

$$\begin{aligned} a = {} & 1e \\ & 1e - 1l \\ & 1e - 2l + 1p \\ & 1e - 3l + 3p - 1t \\ & 1e - 4l + 6p - 4t + 1\beta, \text{ etc.} \end{aligned}$$

Now in the differential calculus, put $a = y$, and $e, l, p, t, \beta = dy, ddy, d^3y, d^4y, d^5y$, *etc.*

For unity, put dx, and also $1 + 1 + 1 + 1 \ldots = x$; $1 + 2 + 3 + 4 \ldots = \int x$; $1 + 3 + 6 + 10 \ldots = \int\int x$, *etc.*

We have: $y = dy.x - ddy\int x + d^3y\int\int x - d^4y\int\int\int x$, *etc.*

But $\int x = \frac{1}{1.2}xx$; $\int\int x = \frac{1}{1.2.3}x^3$; $\int\int\int x = \frac{1}{1.2.3.4}x^4$, *etc.*

Whence, restoring homogeneity:

$$y = \frac{1}{1}x\frac{dy}{dx} - \frac{1}{1.2}xx\frac{ddy}{dx^2} + \frac{1}{1.2.3}x^3\frac{d^3y}{dx^3} \text{ etc.}$$

To emphasize how clear-cut was Leibniz's conception of the differential calculus, we shall quote from the *Analyse des infiniment petits* (1696) of the Marquis de l'Hôpital. In it the Marquis expounded the principle of Leibniz's calculus as he had been taught by Jean Bernoulli in 1691.

Definition I. We call *variable* those quantities which increase or decrease continuously; conversely *constant* quantities are those which remain unchanged while the variables change. In a parabola, the applicates [ordinates] and segments [abscissae] are variable while the perimeter is constant.

Definition II. The infinitely small portion by which a variable quantity increases or diminishes continuously, will be called the difference.

Let a curve AMB *(fig. 21)* with axis AP have the applicate *pm* infinitely close to the applicate PM. Draw MR parallel to AP, and draw the chords AM and A*m*. With centre A and radius AM draw an arc to cut A*m* in S. Then P*p* will be the difference of AP; R*m* the difference of PM; S*m* the difference of AM; and the arc M*m* the difference of the arc AM. Similarly, the triangle MA*m* with arc M*m* as its base, will be the difference of the segment AM, and the area AP*p*M the difference of the mixtilinear area AMP.

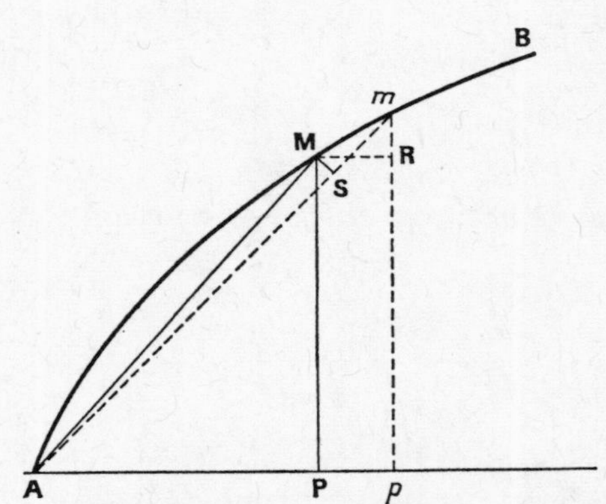

fig. 21 Figure illustrating Definition 2 of de l'Hôpital's 'Analyse des infiniment petits'.

Corollary I. It is evident that the difference of a constant quantity must be zero—or (which amounts to the same thing) that constant quantities have no differences.

Advertisement. In what follows we shall use the letter or characteristic d to express the difference of a variable quantity which we shall express by a single letter. To avoid confusion, the letter d will have no other meaning in the following calculations. If, for instance, we call x, y, z the variable lines AP, PM, AM, and u, s, t the arc AM, the mixtilinear area AMP and the segment AM, then dx will represent the value of Pp, dy the value of Rm, dz the value of Sm, du the value of the arc Mm, ds the value of the area MPpm, and dt the value of the mixtilinear triangle MAm.

I. *Requirement or supposition.* It is assumed that two quantities differing by only an infinitely small quantity may be treated as being identical, or (and this amounts to the same thing) that a quantity increased or decreased by another quantity infinitely smaller than itself may be considered to have remained unchanged. Thus Ap is supposed to be equal to AP, pm to PM, ApM to APM, MPpm to MPpR, the sector AMm to the triangle AMS, the angle pAm to the angle PAM, *etc.*

II. *Requirement or supposition.* It is assumed that a curve can be considered as the sum of an infinite number of infinitely small lines, or (which amounts to the same thing) as a polygon with an infinite number of infinitely small sides, which, by the angles between them, determine the curvature. Thus we assume that, since the curve Mm and the arc MS are so small that they can be considered as straight lines, the figure mSM may be called a triangle.

The reader will be struck by the geometrical aspects of these early definitions. Leibniz and Jean Bernoulli had not yet introduced the abstract concept of a function. When they did so, they performed one of their greatest feats, which is far too often forgotten.

The reader will also note the ease with which de l'Hôpital was able to present his suppositions. Leibniz's predecessors had paved the way to the threshold, but had hesitated when it came to crossing it. Leibniz took the last step and justified it by the very success of his new method.

He was the first to express the difference of the sum, the product, and the quotient of two finite quantities. In the case of the product, he put: $(x+dx)\ (y+dy)-xy=ydx+xdy+dxdy$. The last term can be discarded, because, as de l'Hôpital explained, '$dxdy$ is infinitely small with respect to the other terms'.

To differentiate the quotient $x:y=z$, Leibniz put $x=yz$, whence he obtained $dx=zdy+ydz$; $dz=\dfrac{dx-zdy}{y}=\dfrac{ydx-xdy}{y^2}$. Similarly, he differentiated x^m for any m.

Though the new notation stopped short at this point, it enabled Leibniz to find the equation of the tangent, to determine maxima and minima, and to deal with inflections, evolutes, caustics and envelopes. Once again, we see how deeply steeped the beginnings of differential calculus were in geometry.

De l'Hôpital defined the higher derivative as follows:

The infinitely small portion whose variable has a continuously increasing or decreasing difference is called the *difference of the difference* of that variable, or its *second difference.*

From the start, Leibniz identified the 'inverse of the tangent problem' with that of quadrature or integration. The tangent problem itself had led him to the study of the 'characteristic triangle', whose three sides were the difference dx of the abscissa, the difference dy of the ordinate, and the difference ds of the arc. The converse problem was to obtain the actual functions from these differences—in other words to integrate the latter.

Thus Leibniz wrote:

This method, or this *calculus differentialis*, enables one not only to obtain differences but also to obtain sums, which are the reciprocals of these differences, much as ordinary calculations enable one not only to obtain powers but also the roots which are the reciprocals of these powers.

De l'Hôpital said much the same:

Lemma. In any number of quantities a, b, c, d, e, *etc.*, whether finite or infinite, whether lines, areas, or solids, the sum $a-b+b-c+c-d+d-e$, *etc.*, of all their differences is equal to the difference between the greatest, a, and the smallest, e, or simply to the greatest, for the smallest is zero. Which is obvious. (*Analyse des infiniment petits*, Article 96.)

Now this kind of *summation* is, in fact, identical with the evaluation of areas and volumes by the old method of indivisibles. However, a new approach crystallized in about 1690 when Jacques Bernoulli introduced the expression 'integral calculus' to emphasize that its main object was to discover the whole from the differences, or from its parts. This was tantamount to stressing the inverse of the tangent problem at the expense of the quadrature problem. Moreover, Leibniz considered differentiation as the more primitive operation of the two, one that was always possible, whereas integration was not:

. . . Just as it is not always possible to obtain the rational magnitudes of common arithmetic by the extraction of roots, so it is not always possible to obtain the ordinary or algebraic magnitudes of common analysis from the sums of quadratures.

Gradually, integration became what G. Bouligand has called a 'synoptic method'. Integrals could be read off from lists of differentials whenever algebraic transformations based on Diophantine analysis allowed one to do so. Where they did not, the function was broken down into a series that could be integrated term by term. It was in this way that the method of direct summation was gradually ousted in the 18th century, and that the integral came to assume its modern connotation. Paradoxically enough, Leibniz's notation $\int f(x)dx$ survived the change even though it stemmed clearly from the old approach.

To sum up the contribution of Leibniz and his school, we may say that they made skilful use of a new algorithm, exploiting its possibilities to the full. Though their method itself proved very fruitful, the foundations on which it was built required radical reconstruction. The leading members of the school were its founder Leibniz, Jacques and Jean Bernoulli, and Guillaume de l'Hôpital. Leibniz's proselytizing spirit, the fame of his *Acta eruditorum*, the inventiveness of the brothers Bernoulli, and the elegant prose of de l'Hôpital—all had a profound influence on the development of mathematical thought.

* * *

Of the two co-inventors of modern infinitesimal analysis, both of whom drew freely on the knowledge of their predecessors, Newton paid greater regard to strict logic. Even so, it was Leibniz's notation (dx, ddx, d^3x, *etc.*), and not Newton's, that was to be adopted by modern mathematicians.

Though Leibniz introduced the notation $\int f(x)dx$, an expression stemming from the old methods of summation and indivisibles, nevertheless, as his use of the word 'integral' suggests, he, too, was concerned with finding functions from their known differentials, just as Newton tried to find the fluent $[x]$ from its fluxion x.

As both mathematicians gradually broke with geometrical models, they opened up a new era in mathematics. Few other inventions have proved so useful as their calculus, which, freed of its bondage to geometry, became the basis and dominant factor of all analyses before Monge.

Newton also used his method of fluxions to solve a number of physico-mathematical and astronomical problems. Leibniz and the Bernoullis concentrated on the inverse tangent problem and used it to develop a method of solving differential equations.

This takes us into the 18th century, which the two great rivals opened with as great a show of brilliance as they had closed the 17th, rightly called the 'great'.

CHAPTER 2

The Birth of a New Science: Mechanics

AT THE DAWN OF THE 17TH CENTURY, mechanics became the object of remarkable studies which were to turn it, in the course of the next two centuries, into an exact science. The 'new' science was created by Galileo, who was mainly concerned with the law of falling bodies and the motion of projectiles. His manner of posing and solving the problems involved proved crucial to the emergence of a methodology which, though truly scientific, had hardly thrown off the shackles of scholasticism. The 'new' science still had to state its axioms, concepts and principles, and to define its general laws, before it could attempt to apply them to systems of points or masses, and hence to the motion of celestial bodies. That was the task of the 17th and 18th centuries, and so immense was it that we can do no more than sketch its main outlines.[1]

GALILEO'S INFLUENCE

We shall begin with an examination of Galileo's chief contribution to mechanics.

Galileo's early works, and particularly his *De motu*, which was written in Pisa between 1589 and 1591, were steeped in the misconceptions of his day.[2] Thus he argued that, just as iron returns to its natural state of coldness once the source of heat is removed, and just as a bell loses its *qualitas sonora* as the external disturbance of its 'natural silence' ceases to act upon it, so motion is an impressed virtue that vanishes as the moving body recedes from its motor. In other words, he took over the qualities and poor analogies of Peri-

[1] René Dugas, the author of the two chapters devoted to 17th- and 18th-century mechanics, died before he had a chance to round off his text. This task fell to P. Costabel, who has also added a number of additional paragraphs, particularly on the work of Galileo and Pascal.

[2] See A. Koyré's analysis of F. Bonamico's *De motu libri X.* (Bonamico was professor of philosophy at Pisa at the time that Galileo was a student there.)

patetic physics. But far from lessening his achievements, these early beginnings merely enhance them, since, in order to overcome ancient prejudices, Galileo had to shed practically everything he had been taught, and to rebuild physics on entirely new foundations.

His *Dialogue on the Two Main Systems of the World*—the systems of Ptolemy and Copernicus—published in Florence in 1632 marked the end of a long and arduous intellectual struggle. Written in the vernacular so as to reach the widest possible public, and in the form of a dialogue between three characters who have since become classical—Simplicio the conservative, Salviato the ardent radical, and Sagredo the cultured and moderate arbiter between the two—this work purported to retrace the very steps Galileo himself had followed. Even so, it does not reveal all the devious paths taken by a great intellect in search of the truth, or the full resources which Galileo must have brought to bear on his studies.

Falling Bodies

Simplicio spoke for the schoolmen when he affirmed that 'everyone knows' that the cause of the fall of bodies is gravity. To this Salviato replied:

> You err, Simplicio, for you should rather have said that everyone knows that this cause is *called* gravity. Now, I am not asking you for the names but for the very essence of this matter. Apart from the name given to it, which has become familiar by usage, we know no more about the virtue causing a stone to drop than we do about the virtue tending to keep a projectile aloft or about the virtue which guides the moon on its orbit. . . .

Did Galileo already suspect that these apparently unrelated phenomena were governed by one and the same set of laws—the laws which Newton was to establish? We cannot tell; all we can say with certainty is that he appreciated the sterility of a method based on nothing but nomenclature.

Simplicio, like everyone else, assumed that a ball thrown into a hole drilled through the centre of the earth would be pulled towards the centre by a 'natural and intrinsic' principle. Once there, it would continue to move by itself.

> 'But', Salviati asked, 'would not the motion beyond the centre be an ascending motion and hence, according to your claims, violent and unnatural? On what other principle would you have it depend if not on that which caused the ball to fall towards the centre, and which you have called intrinsic and natural?'

In other words, Galileo realized that the distinction between 'gravity' and 'levity' was fallacious, and that the fall of heavy bodies and the rise of projectiles were governed by an identical law. The oscillation of the pendulum, on which he had reflected at length, had furthermore shown him that the upward motion is simply the downward motion in reverse. Moreover, in his *De motu* he refuted the Aristotelian thesis that there could be no vacuum, claiming that it is precisely in the vacuum that the true nature of gravity and motion can be most clearly discerned. Finally, in 1604, in his famous letter to Paolo Scarpi, he propounded a law which was not fully understood for a century: that the distances travelled in equal times are related to each other as the consecutive odd numbers starting from unity. Though he explained later (in his *Discorsi e dimostrazioni matematiche intorno a due nove scienze attenanti alla mecanica ed i movimenti locali*, published in Leyden, 1638) that he had deduced this law 'after he had repeated his observation a hundred times', it would be truer to say that the experiments merely *suggested* the law, and that he himself had the great wit to attribute what discrepancies there must have been between the 'ideal' law and the experimental results to air resistance.

His approach to the problem of gravity was so novel that it may be called a scientific revolution. Aristotle had known that falling bodies travel with ever-increasing speed, but he had offered a causal and qualitative explanation: they do so *because* they must reach their natural places in the quickest possible time. Galileo suspected the Aristotelian distinctions between natural and unnatural motions, and also eschewed the search for obscure and inaccessible causes. He *observed* the accelerated motion of falling bodies and asked himself *how* that motion would be expressed by a simple mathematical law. He then assumed the classical law of distances, $S = \text{constant} \times t^2$. Hence his outlook differed radically from Aristotle's.

At first, Galileo believed that the velocity was related to the height of the fall, which failed to bear out his law of distances. After many false starts, he was eventually able to eliminate the worst errors and to arrive at the correct solution: the velocity varies as the time.

The Motion of Projectiles

While 16th-century schoolmen had tried in vain to solve the problem of the motion of projectiles, Galileo succeeded by means of a remarkable analysis involving the principle of inertia, the concept of compound motions and the isolation of effects from their causes.

The problem is treated in the *Discorsi*, where Galileo asserts that a moving body thrown on a horizontal plane, without any obstacle, will remain in uniform motion indefinitely if the plane extends to infinity. But if this plane is limited, and when the moving body, which is under the influence of gravity, passes the end of the plane, 'it will add to the first uniform and indestructible motion the downward propensity which it has because of gravity'. Hence there arises a motion composed of the horizontal motion and the naturally accelerated motion of descent. Galileo goes on to demonstrate that, animated by compound motion, the projectile describes a parabola. The ensuing discussion between the three characters in the dialogue is of considerable interest. Sagredo remarks that this argument supposes that the two motions combined in this way 'neither alter, confuse, nor hinder each other', and Salviati observes that air resistance can alter the trajectory of such very rapid projectiles as cannon-balls.

We might mention, incidentally, that the principle of the independence of compound motions helped to overcome one of the chief objections to Copernicanism, *viz.* that a rotating earth must leave birds and clouds 'behind' in the sky. Galileo's answer was that all bodies floating near the earth are carried along by the earth's motion as well as their own.

Galileo had established the principle of compound motions so well that future mathematicians could adopt it without fundamental revision. His principle of inertia, however, stood on rather shaky foundations. Since Galileo assumed that every body had a 'natural inclination to take itself to the centre of the Earth', he was forced to introduce the artifice of the horizontal plane, on which its downward propensity is eliminated. On it, the body is 'indifferent to motion or to rest and does not of itself show any tendency to move in any direction, or any resistance to being set into motion'. Because of this *indifference*, any moving body will continue to move uniformly.

Galileo's solution helped to crystallize a fundamental principle and involved a most fruitful formulation: the motion of projectiles is the 'marvellous' combination of the two most simple motions, namely, a uniform horizontal and a naturally accelerated falling motion. But precisely because Galileo had introduced uniform motion by an artifice intended to eliminate the action of gravity, he was unable to arrive at the principle of inertia by which every body preserves its state of rest or uniform motion unless it is compelled to change that state by forces impressed upon it.

The Oscillation of the Pendulum

Tradition has it that Galileo discovered the isochronism of the pendulum in 1583, while looking at a swinging lamp in the Cathedral of Pisa. In the *Dialogo*, where he discussed this matter, he argued that the period of vibration varies with the length of the thread ('the smaller the circle, the less the time taken'). The true law, that the square of the period varies with the length of the thread, was first mentioned in 1637 in his correspondence, and later in the

Discorsi. In 1641, one year before his death, Galileo tried to use the pendulum for the regulation of clocks.

These facts are very important. Because he drew attention to the connection of the problem of oscillation, not only with the major problem of time-keeping, but also with the law of gravitation, Galileo prepared the way for the concept of kinetic energy.

In the *Discorsi*, Galileo observes that if the length of the simple pendulum is shortened at the moment when it passes the vertical, the bob would nevertheless ascend to its previous level. This, he argues, is an illustration and a consequence of the 'obvious' proposition that 'the velocities acquired by a body in falling on differently inclined planes are equal'. 'Obvious' though it was, this hypothesis was not established until Huygens demonstrated that a falling body acquires a velocity which can make it rise again to its original height. From his hypothesis, and the $v^2 = ks$ law, it was but a short step to expressing motion in terms of energy. Though Galileo failed to take it himself, he was the first to suggest it.

Resistance of Materials and Hydrostatics

Galileo's contribution to the mechanics of continuous media, another 'new science' which he founded, was rather mediocre because, ignoring elasticity, he was forced to introduce principles (rigid beams, inelastic strings) which reduced the problem to one of pure statics. His conversations with craftsmen had led him to investigate the cohesion of solids, which he attributed to two causes: resistance to the formation of vacuums between their several parts (whence the difficulty of separating two polished surfaces in contact) and the presence of a viscous substance binding these parts together.

Like his contemporaries, Galileo believed in the *horror vacui*, and made it an essential part of his hydrostatics, and particularly of his theory of pumps. However, when he learned that a newly-constructed pump could not lift water higher than eighteen Italian ells, though its aspiration tube was much longer, he concluded that eighteen ells must be the limit to Nature's abhorrence of the vacuum.

Discussing the syphon, Galileo remarked that a small mass of water contained in a narrow vessel could balance a large mass of water contained in a wide vessel, because a small lowering of the second entails a great increase in the height of the first. In this, Galileo was guided by a tradition that went back to Leonardo da Vinci and Benedetti, but it is interesting to note that here, as in his work on the resistance of materials, Galileo made use of the principle of virtual velocities, according to which equilibrium is established whenever the respective products of the masses and the velocities which *would* prevail in the absence of equilibrium are equal.

17 Descartes (attributed to Frans Hals)

18 The Academies of Science and Fine Arts, by Sébastien Leclerc

Though his contribution to the mechanics of continuous media was therefore rather meagre, though he did little more than gather the scanty data of an empirical tradition, and though he even adopted inaccurate conclusions (*e.g.* that a string suspended from two nails describes a parabola), Galileo nevertheless deserves credit for having entered the new field with the eye of a mathematician and for the skill with which he 'geometrized' practical problems. In that respect, too, he was a true pioneer of modern theoretical mechanics.

The Work of Torricelli

In 1644 one of Galileo's pupils, Torricelli, published a treatise on the motion of heavy bodies, in which he developed and systematized the dynamics of the *Discorsi*. By the principle bearing his name, he proved that bodies falling from equal heights on differently inclined planes travel with equal velocity: two bodies connected together cannot move spontaneously unless their common centre of gravity descends. (In the generalized form which Huygens was to give it, this simple principle proved extremely fruitful.) Torricelli's name is also associated not only with the famous barometer experiment, but also with the first quantitative law of hydrodynamics, namely that the flow of a liquid through an orifice is proportional to the square root of the height of the liquid. He discovered this law by analogy with the law of falling bodies.

Father Marin Mersenne

By his French translation of Galileo's *Mechanics* (Paris, 1634), Father Mersenne did much to acquaint European scholars with the new science. He also helped to popularize the ideas of other mathematicians, and his voluminous correspondence reads like an international review of mechanics. But though he was a great popularizer of the ideas of others, Mersenne managed to preserve his independence, so that while greatly admiring Galileo and Descartes, he never took sides in their disputes.

Sceptical about the rational basis of Galileo's theory of the fall of heavy bodies, Mersenne devoted much energy to its experimental verification. In particular, he had the brilliant idea of timing the fall on inclined planes by means of a pendulum. It was in the course of these experiments that Mersenne discovered the $T \propto \sqrt{l}$ law directly, unlike Galileo who discovered it after many trials and errors.

Mersenne fared much less happily when he tried to repeat Gassendi's experiments on the rotation of the plane of oscillation of the pendulum, or rather, he was misled by Gassendi's explanation that this rotation was caused by tides, when he tried to observe what does not, in fact, exist.

GASSENDI

In 1624, Gassendi began his teaching career by denouncing the errors of the schoolmen and their slavish adherence to Aristotle. But soon his prudence prevailed and he began to 'look to his security and to bow to circumstances'. Even so, he felt free to defend Epicurus and to follow the path of reason.

In formal opposition to Descartes, Gassendi regarded space as merely a container of 'beings'. His space was immense, immobile, incorporeal and necessary. Time, too, was unlimited, incorporeal and uncreated, and passed even in the absence of all motion. Holding these views, Gassendi was clearly a precursor of the Cambridge school and hence, indirectly, of Newton.

He also postulated the existence of primary matter, common to all bodies, and divisible into solid and impenetrable atoms, whose diversity of form explained the diversity of natural bodies. Atoms have weight, and hence the faculty of motion.

Gassendi defined motion as a simple translation from one place to the next, *i.e.* as something that could not occur in the solid world of Descartes. Atoms are the first cause of motion, so that matter is endowed with activity, much as Leibniz's substance.

On the principle of gravity, Gassendi differed from Galileo, arguing that gravity is not an inherent property of bodies, but is bestowed upon them by the attraction of the earth. This attraction is transmitted by a chain of particles between the body and the earth, according to a model suggested by Kepler.

In mechanics, Gassendi attempted to refute an old objection to the moving-earth hypothesis by an experiment based on Galileo's *Discorsi*. In 1640, he dropped a stone from the top of the mast of a moving ship: the stone landed at the foot of the mast as Galileo had predicted, and not in the ship's wake as the Peripatetics believed. Gassendi explained that though the stone describes a parabola in space, the horizontal component of its parabolic motion cannot be observed on board ship. He thus stated what may be called a principle of relativity.

For Gassendi all motions were violent inasmuch as they invariably resulted from an external motor; the fall of heavy bodies was no exception. Contrary to the belief of the schoolmen, he held that violent motions can be perpetual, provided only that they are uniform. This brought him to the principle of inertia: a stone placed in 'imaginary space', far beyond the visible world and hence unaffected by the action of the earth, would remain at rest indefinitely. If any cause whatsoever were to disturb its rest, the stone would be set into uniform and infinite motion. Thus Gassendi's principle of inertia entailed unimpeded motion through empty space, devoid of all forces. Let us add that, though Gassendi was a Copernican, his lectures to the *Collège Royal* (1617) gave an unbiased explanation of the three prevailing systems of the world.

DESCARTES

We come now to Descartes, a man whose work was to dominate science even after the appearance of Newton's *Principia*. In what follows we shall distinguish between Descartes' mechanics, *i.e.* the concrete problems which he himself investigated, and Cartesian mechanics, *i.e.* his system of the world—a distinction which he himself introduced for fear of having to share Galileo's fate.

It must be said at the outset that Descartes' mechanics added little to positive science. On the other hand, his mechanical philosophy did much to renew science by its simplicity and by its appeal to the visual imagination. It also ousted all those occult qualities on which the schoolmen had thrived.

Descartes and Beeckman

In 1618, a public challenge to scientists to solve a mathematical problem brought Descartes, then stationed at Breda, into contact with Isaac Beeckman, who became his teacher. Their subsequent collaboration is fully recorded in Beeckman's diary (published by Cornelis de Waard).

Though Beeckman was an atomist, he filled his space with a 'subtle matter', by which he explained the fall of heavy bodies, the action of the magnet and some aspects of the vacuum.

Beeckman believed in the conservation of motion: once set into motion, a body continues on its path unless it is halted by an external obstacle. Not only rectilinear but also circular motion, such as the diurnal and annual motions of the earth, are preserved in this way. Beeckman was clearly a convinced Copernican.

Beeckman devoted much time to the verification of his hypothesis that bodies, including corpuscles of light, fall through the air with a limited velocity. He also studied the impact of bodies, and the laws he propounded resemble those of Descartes. But unlike Descartes', most of Beeckman's laws, which applied exclusively to inelastic bodies, were experimentally correct.

Beeckman and Descartes made a joint study of the fall of heavy bodies and obtained an exact law before Galileo did. Oddly enough, Descartes forgot this result and hence committed grave errors. In general, Descartes pretended to have ignored Beeckman's teaching, suggesting that he had created his own system *ex nihilo*, by following only the lights of his own reason. As a result, he often ignored truths that he could ill afford to neglect.

Cartesian Mechanics

In 1634, Descartes first came across Galileo's *Dialogue on the Two Main Systems of the World.* He read it in thirty hours and never ceased criticizing it afterwards, particularly its explanation of tidal phenomena. However, he called Galileo's concept of motion 'excellent philosophy', and praised its independence of orthodox opinion.

In statics, Descartes used the entire weight of his great authority to substitute—as Stevin had done before him—what we now call the principle of virtual work for the virtual velocities of the schoolmen. In a letter to Constantin Huygens, dated 5th October 1637, he wrote:

> The invention of all simple machines (with the help of which a very heavy weight can be raised by a small force) is based on but a single principle, which is that the same force which can lift a weight of, say, a hundred pounds to a height of two feet, can also lift one of two hundred pounds to a height of one foot, or one of four hundred pounds to a height of half a foot, and so on, however this may be applied.
>
> And this principle cannot fail to be accepted if it is agreed that the effect must always be proportional to the action which is needed to produce it. . . .

This force, he added, 'invariably has two dimensions', for it is compounded of the weight and the height.

Descartes was, moreover, the first to notice the *differential* character of this fundamental principle of statics. Thus he wrote:

> The relative weight of every body must be measured by the *start* of the movement which the power that supports it can produce rather than by the height to which it can rise after it has fallen down. Note that I say 'start to fall' and not simply 'fall' because it is the start of the fall that must be taken care of.

Static force, in Descartes' sense, is therefore expressed by the product of weight and height, while *momento* in Galileo's sense is expressed by the product of weight and velocity. Thus Descartes argued that Galileo's writings on the lever and the balance explain the *quod ita fit*, but not the *cur ita fit*. (Letter to Mersenne, 15th November 1638.)

After reading Galileo's *Discorsi*, Descartes sent a number of severe criticisms to Mersenne under the seal of secrecy (11th October 1638). At that stage, Descartes had begun to judge everything by his own principles. The truths of positive science no longer interested him unless they could be fitted into his own mechanistic framework.

As a consequence, he rejected all the hypotheses on which Galileo's theory of the fall of heavy bodies was based:

> Everything he [Galileo] has to say about the velocity of bodies falling in a vacuum, *etc.*, is built without foundations; for he ought first to have determined what really is weight; had he known the truth he would have realized that it [the weight] vanishes in the vacuum [*sic*].[1]

Descartes nevertheless admitted that Galileo 'philosophized' much better than the 'common herd', and that he 'examined physical substances with mathematical reasons', which was the 'only means of arriving at the truth and of abandoning the errors of the schoolmen'.

He was right to reproach Galileo with having calculated the trajectories in his artillery tables on the assumption that air resistance can be ignored.

Descartes, for his part, made a detailed study of impact problems. He was quick to appreciate all the difficulties involved. Unable to solve them, he offered a number of *a priori* rules in his *Principles*, which Huygens later corrected.

In 1644, Roberval published his treatise on Aristarchos in which, without formally siding with any one of the three astronomical hypotheses, he showed his clear preference for the Copernican system. He also propounded a theory of universal attraction inspired by Pythagorean notions. For this he earned the scorn of Descartes:

> To propound this kind [of attraction] one must not only suppose that each part of the universe is animated, and animated, moreover, by numerous and diverse Souls, which do not hinder one another, but also that these Souls are so intelligent and divine as to be able to know what occurs in places very far removed from them, without any messenger to inform them. . . . (Letter to Mersenne, 20th April 1646.)

This dismissal of attraction was one of the reasons why the Cartesians received Newton's system with so much reserve.

We cannot go into all the details of the discussion between Descartes and Roberval on the determination of the *centre of agitation*, *i.e.* the search for a solid that would have the same period of oscillation as a pendulum of given length. This problem was very difficult to resolve with the inaccurate chronometers of the time, and neither Descartes nor Roberval managed to find a complete answer. The problem was later re-examined by Huygens using an entirely different approach. Though Roberval is said to have gained the upper hand over his opponent in this argument, it must be stressed that Descartes,

[1] In other words, Descartes denied the existence of the vacuum, and considered gravity the result of the impact of bodies on the subtle matter filling all space.

far from losing all along the line, realized the importance of gravity much more clearly than Roberval.

Descartes' System of the World

Descartes, however, influenced his contemporaries not so much by his solution of concrete scientific problems as by offering them a *complete system* of the world. In it he tried to scrap every vestige of the scholastic doctrine and to replace qualities and substantial forms with a universal mechanism in which all phenomena could be explained by only three concepts, namely extension, figurability and motion.

In this reduction of the number of permissible concepts lies the profound originality, the justification and the usefulness of Descartes' system. By suggesting that all phenomena in the sensible world can be explained mechanically, Descartes provided scientific research with a powerful lever.

He first elaborated this new system in his *Le Monde*, which he prepared for publication in July 1633. However, Galileo's fate decided him not to rush into print with it, and the book did not in fact appear until 1664, long after its author's death. In the meantime, Descartes decided to publish his *Principia philosophiae* (1644), a far more learned work, and it was from that work that the world first learned about his mechanical philosophy.

According to Descartes, all matter is extension, and thus lacks any special qualities or attributes. Matter fills all space—there is no vacuum and there are no atoms, and the world is an unbounded *plenum*. All motion is relative and must be defined by reference to a fixed point. Rest is of the same nature as motion; the two are truly symmetrical and neither can be created or destroyed:

> God in His omnipotence has created matter together with the motion and the rest of its parts, and with His day-to-day acts He keeps as much motion and rest in the Universe now as He put there when He created it. . . .

Descartes' first law of motion was a kind of principle of inertia: a body does not change its state of motion (or rest) unless it meets another body; once in motion, all bodies continue to move.

The second law states that all parts of matter tend to move along *straight lines* unless they meet other parts of matter.

The third law was formulated by way of seven rules for the impact of bodies. All but the first, which defined the impact of two equal bodies moving with equal velocity, were experimentally incorrect.

This failure ought not to surprise us, for it was only after a great deal of experimental research that mathematicians were led to combine Descartes' guiding idea, the conservation of the quantity of motion, with a coefficient of restitution, varying from 0 in the case of inelastic bodies to 1 in the case of perfectly elastic bodies.

Let us add that Descartes explained the cohesion of the parts of elastic bodies by assuming that they are at rest with respect to one another. This was a typical paradox of Cartesian logic.

With the aid of his concepts and laws, Descartes propounded the 'admirable structure of this visible world' in his *Le Monde*. Anxious to placate the Church, he promised:

> I shall be much more careful than Copernicus not to attribute any motion to the earth, and I shall attempt to make my arguments truer than Tycho's.

He went on to explain that, though the parts of the sun are agitated like the parts of every flame, the sun nevertheless remains at rest. Matter in the heavens is liquid, and so is the matter of the sun and of the fixed stars. The earth is at rest with respect to its enveloping *vortex*, which carries it along:

> Having removed any possible scruples about the motion of the earth, we conclude that the celestial matter containing the planets revolves incessantly in a vortex with the sun as its centre . . . and that all the planets (among which we shall now number the earth) are kept suspended between the same parts of this celestial matter. For only in that way can we gain a simple understanding of all the things that can be observed.

When, at the beginning, God divided all matter of which He created the visible world into equal parts, He could not have made them round since tightly packed round particles necessarily leave a vacuum between them, and God intended no vacuum. Matter became rounded gradually, and as it did so the empty spaces became filled with 'fine dust', rubbed off from the corners of the original particles.

Descartes' physical universe was made up of three main elements: fine dust in rapid motion, rather coarser spherical particles apt for motion, and, finally, very coarse, irregular and sluggish particles.

According to Descartes' theory, the sun and the fixed stars are the centres of immense vortices formed of the first element; the sky of the second; the earth, the planets and the comets of the third.

These vortices touch one another at their poles in such a way as not to interfere with their respective rotations. Particles of the first element flow incessantly from the point of the vortex furthest from the poles, to the poles themselves.

Third-element particles are shaped like screws and hence are able to 'turn' into the spaces left between the second-element particles.

When they float to the surface of a given star, they congregate into spots, as froth rises to the surface when a liquid is brought to the boil. Occasionally an entire vortex may be destroyed by its neighbour, whereupon its central star becomes a comet or a planet. This risk is not run by 'spotless' vortices. With the aid of this model, Descartes then tried to explain the motion of planets and comets, the tails of comets, tidal phenomena, *etc.*

Descartes expounded his views on gravity in his *Principia philosophiae* (which also dealt with many physical and biological topics that have no bearing on the system of the world). The space round the earth is not empty, for otherwise bodies at the surface would be flung into the heavens by the earth's rotation (Descartes had no qualms in adopting this scholastic argument).

Since the earth cannot turn by itself, it must be pulled along by the celestial matter by which it is surrounded. Now, that matter, because of its excessive mobility, tends to withdraw from the centre and hence becomes much lighter than the earth.

Celestial matter cannot push terrestrial matter downwards except by filling the gap it has left behind. If a body's pores contain less celestial matter than the surrounding air, the excess matter in the air will drive it towards the centre of the earth, 'thus endowing it with the quality which we call gravity'.

There is no point in dwelling at length on all the serious flaws of the Cartesian model, with its many far-fetched and oddly-shaped elements. This model, which Descartes considered tantamount to a mathematical demonstration, was in fact no more than the kind of qualitative sketch for which he attacked the schoolmen. What quantitative laws it contained—*e.g.* the rules for the impact of bodies—were experimentally incorrect. Even so, his model was based on admirably simple premises and did much to stress the need for a clearer representation of physical phenomena.

PASCAL'S HYDROSTATICS

The Weight of Air and the 'Horror Vacui'

It took the great authority and rigour of Pascal and the force of his dialectical arguments to destroy the doctrine of the *horror vacui*, once and for all. He also proved irrefutably that air has weight, a fact suspected by many of his predecessors, including Nicholas of Cusa, but challenged by others. Cardan seems to have been the first to weigh air, concluding that it is fifty times lighter than water.

In 1630, Jean Rey, a French physician, attributed the increase of weight of calcined tin to its absorption of air.

Isaac Beeckman believed in both the weight of air and the existence of a vacuum. Baliani suggested the same view to Galileo, who, as we saw, assumed that the *horror vacui* had an upper limit, and who established the weight of air at half the real value. Father Mersenne, applying the laws of scholastic dynamics, found the density of air to be roughly one-ninetieth that of water.

In 1646, P. Petit repeated Torricelli's experiment before Pascal in Rouen and published a model account of it, in which he recorded every single practical detail. Pascal repeated this and similar experiments publicly, and challenged his adversaries to refute him. In his *Expériences nouvelles touchant le vuide* (1647), he did not yet pronounce against the absurd doctrine of nature's abhorrence of the vacuum, but merely affirmed that 'the force of this abhorrence is limited . . . to about 31 feet'.

The Great Experiment

On 15th November 1647, Pascal asked his brother-in-law, Florin Périer, a judge at Clermont, to carry out a 'crucial' experiment, *i.e.* to 'repeat the ordinary vacuum experiment on one and the same day in one and the same tube with the same quicksilver, at the foot and at the summit of a mountain at least five or six hundred fathoms high'. Should the height of the mercury column prove to be lower at the top than at the foot of the mountain, it must follow that the mercury is supported by the pressure of the air alone.

The experiment, performed on 19th September 1648, showed a difference in mercury level of 3 inches and 1½ lines[1] between the bottom and the top of the Puy de Dôme. Subsequently Father de La Mare recorded a difference of 2 lines between measurements at the bottom and at the top of the tower of Notre Dame de Clermont and Pascal himself obtained a comparable result when he repeated the experiment on the tower of St. Jacques in Paris.

The success of what he later called his *great experiment* allowed Pascal not only to defeat the adversaries of the vacuum, but also to vindicate the methods of scientific positivism, and to declare that 'nature has no abhorrence of the vacuum, and makes no effort to avoid it; all the effects that have been attributed to it are due to the weight and pressure of air'. Only because they were ignorant of the true causes had his predecessors invented the imaginary *horror vacui*. Nor was this 'the only case in which men, too weak to find real causes, have used their subtlety to introduce imaginary causes which they describe by specious names that satisfy the eyes but not the mind'.

Earlier, Mersenne had devised a host of experimental projects to

[1] A line is the twelfth part of an inch.

prove the weight of air. Descartes and Beeckman also believed that air has weight. In a letter to Mersenne, dated 13th December 1647, Descartes claimed that it was he who had proposed to Pascal 'to find out by experiment whether quicksilver rises to the same height on top as it does at the bottom of a mountain'. He repeated this claim in a letter to Carcavi, dated 11th June 1649.

Modern scholars have devoted a great deal of ink to the respective priority of Pascal, Descartes and Mersenne. In fact, the 'great discovery' was the combined achievement of the synthetic though narrow approach of Descartes, the experimental versatility of Mersenne, and the positivism of Pascal. For a long time the great experiment had been 'in the air', and Pascal himself said that 'a universal hope had made it famous even before it appeared'. Even so, it was due to Pascal that the actual experiment was carried out.

The Barometer and the Compressibility of Gases

Pascal was also responsible for the shape of early syphon barometers. (The name 'barometer' was coined later, in Mariotte's *Essai sur la nature de l'air*, 1676.) On the other hand, the use of 'Torricelli's tube' for meteorological predictions was the work, not of Pascal, but of Otto von Guericke (1602–1686), whose spectacular instrument (a float moving the arms of a small figure as the atmospheric pressure fluctuated) is described in his *Experimenta nova Magdeburgica de vacuo spatio*, written in 1663 and published in 1672.

Otto von Guericke proved the weight and elasticity of air independently of Torricelli and Pascal. His practical interests then drove him into different fields. In 1632, he turned his attention to the construction of an instrument that could extract all the water from a vessel and thus produce a vacuum in it. When he failed, he repeated the experiment with an air-filled vessel and thus invented the pneumatic pump and the famous Magdeburg hemispheres, which he demonstrated before the Diet of Ratisbon in 1654. Robert Boyle (1627–1691) and Robert Hooke (1635–1703) improved the pump mechanism by driving the piston rod with a rack and pinion instead of the simple lever of the earlier models. Thus they were able to perfect von Guericke's experiments and, in particular, to confirm that a bell cannot be heard in an evacuated vessel (*New Experiments Physico-mechanicall*, 1660). Von Guericke himself was the first to use a manometer to measure the degree of evacuation inside a vessel.

Further improvements of the pump mechanisms by Huygens, Denis Papin and other less well-known physicists included two- or three-way taps, double-cylinder pumps, *etc.*, all of which helped to increase the efficiency of pumps. However, since none of these improvements introduced any new principles, it is true to say that

Pascal and Otto von Guericke were alone responsible for refuting the objections of the *horror vacui* school. These objections were, moreover, beneficial to science since it is because of them that Boyle investigated the elasticity and compressibility of air (1661). Boyle himself failed to appreciate the full importance of his quantitative results, and left it to Towneley to propound the law which became known as Boyle's Law, that the volume of a gas varies inversely as the pressure, the temperature remaining constant. The experimental verification of this law (which may, in fact, have been discovered by Hooke) led to a number of further improvements in the construction of compression pumps and manometers, but also aroused a great deal of criticism. Thus Jacques Bernoulli pointed out in 1683 that, below a certain volume, the air molecules are packed so tightly together that they cannot be compressed any further. Mariotte, who accepted the law and verified it for himself in 1679, affirmed the existence of yet another limit, namely that gases cannot be rarefied below $\frac{1}{4,000}$ of their normal concentration, but this was refuted by Amontons in 1702.

Hydrostatics and Pascal's Method

Admirable though it was, Archimedes' principle ignored the pressures obtaining in the interior of a fluid. Hence it had fallen to Simon Stevin, who related Archimedes' principle to the impossibility of perpetual motion, to analyse the pressure of fluids in equilibrium, and even to determine the resultant of the pressures on an inclined boundary wall.

Pascal dealt with these and similar problems in his two *Treatises on the Equilibrium of Liquids and the Heaviness of the Mass of Air*, published in 1663 but prepared between 1651 and 1654. These two treatises may be called Pascal's crowning glory.

As Leon Brunschwicg and Pierre Boutroux have stressed, Pascal 'looked upon pump and barometer experiments not as points of departure for new hypotheses, but as consequences of general principles, which he applied to the equilibrium of liquids before he extended them to atmospheric pressure effects'.

Following Descartes, Pascal related hydrostatics to the principle of virtual work. Then, using Torricelli's principle without acknowledgment, he managed to explain the equilibrium of pistons in hydraulic machines: 'I consider it a principle that a body never moves because of its weight unless its centre of gravity descends.' He then applied this principle to the two pistons 'considered as one and the same body'. Similarly, he held that liquids are in equilibrium because 'a vessel filled with water is a mechanical machine for multiplying forces'.

From hydraulics, Pascal passed to the weight of air, which 'no one continues to deny'. He calculated the weight of the total volume of air in the world, and challenged the Aristotelians—who, moreover, took up the challenge—to explain, by means of the *horror vacui*, all the effects which he could explain by the weight of air.

We know from his *Pensées* that Pascal rejected Descartes' mechanical philosophy:

Descartes. We must say summarily: 'This is made by figure and motion', for it is true. But to say what these are, and to compose the machine, is ridiculous. For it is useless, uncertain and painful. And were it true, we do not think that all philosophy is worth one hour of pain.

To write against those who made too profound a study of science: Descartes.

I cannot forgive Descartes. In all his philosophy he would have been quite willing to dispense with God. But he had to make Him give a fillip to set the world in motion; beyond this, he has no further need of God.

Descartes useless and uncertain.

In other words, Pascal felt that Descartes' speculations were so many unproven hypotheses.

Modern science would tend to side with Descartes, at least in principle. Physical theory starts from experiment and returns to it to test hypotheses. But in the interval it is free to consider any *unobservables* and abstract elements useful to its analysis.

THE CARTESIAN SCHOOL

Descartes believed that he had clarified and formulated the principles of physics permanently if not definitively. Thus, in the Letter-Preface to the French edition of his *Principia philosophiae*, he told his successors that little remained to be done beyond verifying them:

I know full well that it may take many centuries before all the truths that can be deduced from these principles may have been so derived, since most of them depend on individual experiments which will not be encountered by chance, but must be sought after with care and expense, by men of high intelligence.

Cartesian physics was first taught at Utrecht and Leyden, and the first Cartesian professor, Reneri, followed closely in Descartes' footsteps. Trouble began with Regius, whose *Fundamenta physices* (Amsterdam, 1646) was disowned by Descartes. Not only did Regius mutilate Descartes' metaphysics but he brought back scholastic doctrines with all their forms, mutations and qualities.

Clerselier, the publisher of Descartes' correspondence in three volumes (1657, 1659 and 1666), helped to resurrect Descartes' quarrel with Fermat on the laws of reflection and refraction.

Rohault

By far the greatest Cartesian was Jacques Rohault, whose *Treatise on Physics* (1671) was to reign supreme for almost sixty years, and was still being read at Cambridge in Newton's day.

Rohault attacked not only pure empiricism but also exclusive reliance on reason, and distinguished between three categories of experiment: those which are based purely on observation; those which are performed deliberately but without any knowledge of the possible result; and, finally, those whose outcome can be anticipated by reason. Though the last are the most noble and the most useful to physicists, the two less exalted categories must nevertheless not be despised.

Rohault was a pure Cartesian in his views of extension and the impossibility of the vacuum. He supported the principle of inertia with arguments based on both Galileo and Descartes. His laws of non-elastic impact were simpler and more accurate than those of Descartes; his hydrostatics was very similar to Pascal's, but his interpretation of the barometer experiment was purely Cartesian—he argued that a 'true substance' is found above the mercury column in the barometer tube.

Rohault cited microscopic observations and especially the fine structure of small insects as evidence in favour of the Cartesian *inobservables*. He refused 'to fall into the error of those who ridicule everything that has no bearing on their crude ideas, and who are deaf to any explanations about the existence of subtle matter, whose agitation and smallness enable it to penetrate all things'.

Rohault's cosmogony was based on Descartes' three elements, though his model of the Universe was much simpler than Descartes'. He also made a detailed study of surface-tension phenomena, so that Leibniz could say: 'The small tubes of M. Rohault are the only Cartesian discoveries which merit that name.' Florin Périer paid similar tribute to Rohault in his preface to the posthumous works of Pascal.

Rohault's elegant and lucid *Treatise* served the Cartesian cause so well that it became a serious obstacle to further progress in mechanics.

Pierre-Sylvain Régis was another famous Cartesian whose philosophical activity had great scientific repercussions. A great scholar and an excellent popularizer, Régis managed to combine the Cartesian doctrine with the latest experimental findings, and hence to uphold it against widespread opposition from the Church and the universities.

Malebranche

Malebranche was the most rigid Cartesian of his day, though even he had to admit that Descartes was not altogether infallible. Thus he said that 'one must not believe everything Descartes writes unless it is supported by evidence'.

Malebranche denied Descartes' identification of rest with motion. According to him, rest is nothing but 'pure privation', and hence independent of God's positive volition. Motion, on the other hand, implies an 'effective agent' and springs from God.

Denying that rest is the sole cause of the cohesion of rigid bodies, Malebranche argued that they must be compressed by the subtle matter surrounding them. He also explained elasticity and fluidity in similar terms. Hence there was some resemblance between his views and the early views of Leibniz.

In his discussion of impact phenomena, Malebranche had a decided advantage over Descartes: he could consult Huygens, Wallis, Wren, and Mariotte, and hence was able to use accurate laws where Descartes had relied on *a priori* principles. However, Malebranche tried to interpret these laws in the Cartesian manner:

> 'It seems clear to me', he wrote in the *Recherche de la Vérité*, 'that every body, taken by itself, is infinitely soft, since rest lacks the force to resist motion, so that any part of a body that is more agitated than its neighbour must become separated from it. Hence hard bodies are hard only because they are compressed by the invisible matter surrounding them. . . .'

Outdoing Descartes, Malebranche increased the number of vortices *ad infinitum*. According to him, not only the planets and satellites, but all matter flows along in vortices, each following a special course. As a result, vortices impinge on one another and their consequent adjustment is the cause of the cohesion of bodies.

> I could, with reason, consider the diameters of small vortices as being millions of millions times smaller than those of the large ones; in short, I could call them infinitely small, which would increase their centrifugal force to infinity.

Small vortices explain the effects of thunder, cannon powder, fire and chemical reactions.

Finally, Malebranche treated gravity as a hydrostatic phenomenon, centred in the ether.

HUYGENS

Huygens was first acquainted with science by his father, a man of great learning and a close friend and admirer of Descartes. This is how Huygens described his early initiation into Cartesian physics:

M. Descartes had seen fit to present his conjectures and fictions as so many truths. Hence many readers of his *Principles of Philosophy* fare much like those who mistake pleasant romances for true histories. The novel appearance of his small particles and his vortices caused a great deal of pleasure. When I read the *Principles* for the first time, I felt everything was well with the world, and that any difficulties I encountered were due to my inability to grasp his thought. I was only 15 or 16 years old. But having since discovered many obviously false and highly improbable matters in it [the *Principles*], I was driven back to my own preoccupations.

The Laws of Impact

It was in 1652 that Huygens first began to doubt the validity of Descartes' impact laws. When van Schooten, a rigid Cartesian, counselled him to reserve his judgment, Huygens replied on 29th October 1654: 'If all Descartes' laws except the first are not false, I can only say that I cannot distinguish truth from falsehood.' Three years later, on 2nd November 1657, he wrote to van Schooten saying that: 'I have found certain rules [on the impact of bodies], and nothing has given me greater pleasure than to find them borne out by experiment.'

In 1666, the Royal Society set certain of its members, including Huygens, Wallis and Wren, the problem of investigating the laws of impact.

Wallis supplied the exact laws of inelastic impact and Wren those of elastic impact, but neither provided any real proof. Huygens' much profounder study of elastic impact was based on the principle of inertia, the principle of the relativity of motion, and the hypothesis that two equal bodies moving with equal but opposite velocities will, after impact, rebound with velocities that are, apart from the sign, the same.

According to Huygens' principle of relativity, the result of an impact is the same in a system at rest as it is in one that is in rectilinear and uniform motion with respect to the first system. Thanks to this principle, Huygens could justify the following proposition:

If a body is at rest and an equal body collides with it, after the impact the second body will be at rest and the first will have acquired the velocity that the other had before the impact.

As for the more general problem of the impact of two unequal bodies, Huygens, like Wren, was unable to solve it at first. The solution finally appeared in 1700, in his posthumous *De motu corporum ex percussione* (1700).

Mariotte was another mechanist to discuss impact theory. However, his *Traité de la percussion ou choc des corps* (1673) added little to the work of his predecessors and was, moreover, less lucid than most. He discarded Wallis's *perfectly hard* bodies and concentrated exclusively on *elastically flexible*, *i.e.* perfectly elastic bodies and on *inelastically flexible*, *i.e.* perfectly soft bodies. Mariotte realized that it is the quantity of matter in a body, and not its weight, which determines its quantity of motion and hence its impact. Mariotte also investigated centres of percussion.

Centrifugal Force and Gravity

Let us now return to Huygens and to his important discovery of the laws of *centrifugal force*. Huygens was apparently set on this path by his reading of Galileo and Descartes and also by his practical attempts to construct a cycloidal clock.

The results (13 propositions) first appeared in an appendix to the *Horologium oscillatorium* (1673), though Huygens had written a special treatise on the subject, the *De vi centrifuga*, as early as 1659. However, the earlier work was not published until 1703, after Huygens' death.

To study the centrifugal tendency (*conatus*) of a body attached to a wheel, Huygens used an artifice whose object was to introduce a movable reference system. He assumed that a man, holding a ball of lead by a thread, is tied to a wheel. Purely geometrical considerations then showed that if he releases the ball at the point A of the wheel, the ball flies off at a tangent, tending away from the point A (which keeps revolving with the wheel) so that the successive distances between them are as the square numbers 1, 4, 9, 16, ... 'The *conatus* of a sphere attached to a revolving wheel is therefore the same as if the sphere tended to advance along the radius with a uniformly accelerated motion.' Hence Huygens obtained the quantitative laws governing the *vis centrifuga*, a force which he considered to be as real a force as gravity.

In Search of a Conservation Principle

'A long time ago, when I was still almost a child,' Huygens wrote in his *Horologium oscillatorium*, 'the very wise Mersenne suggested to me and to many others the investigation of centres of oscillation or agitation.' Huygens completely solved the problem by generalizing Torricelli's principle. In other words, he assumed that the centre of gravity of a simple system cannot rise to a greater height than that

19 Galileo, by J. Sustermans

ICONISMUS XI
Cap. 23 Lib.
Fig. I.
A
B
H
Fig. IV.
Fig. V.
Fig. II.
D
Fig. III

from which it started. He also assumed that, in all cases of elastic impact, the *living force* (Leibniz's *vis viva*) is conserved. These dynamic considerations, which were much simpler than Descartes' and Roberval's explanations, enabled Huygens, after investigations of increasingly complicated systems, to give a quite general solution of the problem as early as 1664. However, he failed to convince a great many of his contemporaries, and was engaged in violent polemics on the subject with the Abbé Catelan, Jacques Bernoulli and the Marquis de l'Hôpital.

Huygens, who claimed that all his mechanical studies served to 'corroborate and to extend Galileo', applied the principles of inertia and of the composition of motions to the fall of bodies and to rectilinear uniform motion in any direction. He contended that each of these motions can be considered separately and that one does not disturb the other.

Theory of the Pendulum

With the help of these laws, Huygens began to study the cycloidal pendulum. He knew that Mersenne had been right to argue against Galileo that the isochronism of a circular pendulum is limited to small oscillations. To determine the period of these small oscillations by infinitesimal geometry, Huygens treated the arc described by the pendulum as an oscillating parabola at the lowest point of the curve.

But this result failed to satisfy him both as a geometer and a clockmaker. He was looking for a pendulum that would be isochronous no matter what the amplitude. Further analysis led him to the cycloid with a vertical axis, whose summit is placed below, and hence to the cycloidal pendulum. Having proved its isochronism by a dozen propositions, he constructed a cycloidal clock (1657).

The Relativity of Motion

Throughout his life Huygens remained a Cartesian in that he adopted the relativity of motion. At first he contrasted uniform and rectilinear motion (which he called *straight*) with circular motion: 'Whereas straight motion is relative, circular motion has a characteristic κριτήριον of its own.' This 'criterion' was evidently the tension of strings under the centrifugal force of revolving bodies attached to them.

However, when he had read Newton's *Principia*, he reacted so violently that he adopted a more strictly Cartesian view:

> One can in no wise conceive of the true and natural motion of a body as differing from its [state of] rest. . . . In circular motion as in free and straight motion, there is nothing except relativity.

Huygens was the main link between Galileo and Newton, and the first scientist to have discarded every show of scholastic prejudice. The most scrupulous of observers, Huygens never forgot that experiment must be governed by reason—*experientia ac ratione* was the hallmark of all his work.

THE ENGLISH SCHOOL FROM DESCARTES TO NEWTON

Though Cartesian views had percolated to England by about 1650, most English scientists preferred to take a more materialistic and empirical view of nature.

Thus Hobbes was a pure empiricist who argued that Descartes' God was not a suitable subject for philosophical speculation. He also believed that life is nothing but the motion of the limbs. Perception is due to the conflict of two kinds of *conatus*, of which one, the external, springs from the object, while the other springs from man himself. Their impact produces a jarring of the nervous system.

Space is a purely imaginary concept; the corresponding reality is *extension*—the essential characteristic of all bodies.

In nature there is motion but there is no time; time is a simple illusion based on memory and anticipation.

Motion cannot be spontaneous: no body can pass from rest to motion without an external agent.

Like Descartes, Hobbes denied the existence of the vacuum.

On the other hand, Henry More, a Cambridge Platonist, asserted the reality and eternity of spiritual substances. Unlike Descartes, whom he nevertheless called the greatest philosopher of the age, he refused to identify matter with extension, but held that God Himself had endowed matter with a 'spirit of nature'.

More postulated the existence of absolute, homogeneous and immutable space as the necessary condition of motion. Absolute space is a spiritual substance, which, like God, has the following attributes: One, simple, immobile, eternal, perfect, independent, existing, self-sufficient, incorruptible, necessary, immense, uncreated, infinite, boundless, omnipresent, incorporeal, all-pervading, all-embracing, essential, actual, and purely real.

With Robert Boyle we come to a more realistic approach. Acknowledging both Descartes and Gassendi as his teachers, and unconcerned about their quarrel, Boyle was an atomist, and based his corpuscular physics on Cartesian principles. He assumed the existence of two different types of æther: one transmitting Cartesian mechanical effects, and the other transmitting Gilbertian magnetic effects.

Boyle was not satisfied with efficient causes alone, and argued that experimental science cannot provide us with a true explanation of phenomena; that explanations can be found only in God, the intelligent Author of all things.

In short, though English science offered nothing on which Newton could base his mechanics, his metaphysics had been clearly mapped out for him.

NEWTON

Newton's great work, the *Philosophiae naturalis principia mathematica* (1687), which was to introduce dynamics into cosmology, was the happy issue of his extraordinary powers of abstraction. It begins with definitions and axioms or 'laws' of motion covering the whole of mechanical science.

Newton introduced the notion of 'mass' or 'quantity of matter' into mechanics, thus ridding it of non-mathematical qualities. However, he reserved the right to retain the æther hypothesis in all cases that could not be reduced to problems of mass.

He defined the 'quantity of motion' as the product of mass and velocity, the *vis insita*, or innate force of matter, as proportional to the mass, and the *vis impressa*, or impressed force, as an action exerted upon a body in order to change its state, either of rest or of uniform motion in a straight line.

The *vis impressa* can be produced by impact, by pressure, or by the *vis centripeta*, by which bodies are drawn or impelled towards a point as to a centre. Unlike the innate and impressed forces, the centripetal force is an action at a distance.

Newton also distinguished between the absolute quantity, the accelerative quantity, and the motive quantity of the centripetal force. Only the motive quantity is involved in the fundamental law of motion.

In his treatment of time, space and motion, Newton invariably distinguished absolute from relative, real from apparent, and mathematical from common quantities. His absolutes—time and space—were those of Henry More and Isaac Barrow, respectively.

By the side of absolute time, Newton introduced relative (common) time, and by the side of absolute space, relative space, which is of the same nature as absolute space but may differ from it 'by number'.

Newton considered motion as the translation of a body from one place to the next. It is absolute if the respective places are absolute, relative if the places are relative.

To arrive at *true and absolute* motion, Newton considered the relative motion of a body in a relative place which itself is in relative motion with respect to another place, and so on until an *immobile place* is reached, which is the reference point of absolute motions.

Thus *apparent motions* are differences between true motions, the causes and effects of true motions are forces—hence forces are absolutes.

In fact, Newton adopted an absolute reference system whose axes were centred on the sun and pointed towards two fixed stars. In this system, the absolute circular motion is the *true* motion, a conclusion which, as we have seen, was rejected by Huygens.

Newton's first law of motion is the law of inertia: Every body perseveres in its state of rest, or of uniform motion in a straight line, unless it is compelled to change that state by forces impressed on it.

The second law states that the rate of change of linear momentum is proportional to the force applied, and takes place in the straight line in which that force acts. (If m is the mass, $\vec{v}$ the velocity, $\vec{F}$ the force, and t the time, then $d(m\vec{v}) = \vec{F}dt$.)

The third law states that an action is always opposed by an equal reaction, or the mutual actions of two bodies are always equal and act in opposite directions. Since this law is trivial in the case of contiguous action, Newton extended it to the case of actions at a distance.

Newton acknowledged his debt to Galileo for the first two laws of motion, and to Wren, Wallis, Huygens and Mariotte for the third. He himself made laborious experiments on the impact of two pendulums to verify the third law, and also studied the impact of imperfectly elastic bodies, where the ratio of the relative velocities before and after impact is no longer unity, but a smaller ratio depending on the materials (Newton's coefficient of restitution).

Newton's Explanation of the Motion of the Planets

With the help of these concepts and laws, Newton was able to present, in his *Principia*, a host of brilliant geometrical demonstrations in which he used his 'method of fluxions' to great advantage.

We cannot possibly give a detailed analysis of Newton's masterpiece, and must therefore make do with only a brief summary. In Book I, Newton proved quite generally that the motion of a material point subject to a material force is contained in a plane and follows Kepler's law of areas (the radius vector sweeps through equal areas in equal times). In particular, if the point describes an ellipse, and if the centre of the material force is situated in a focus of that ellipse, the force is inversely proportional to the square of the distance between the point and the centre.

For the first time, the motion of celestial bodies had been shown to follow the ordinary laws of dynamics.

Book I also contained Newton's theorems on the mutual attraction of spheres, which enable one to treat a spherical body made up of concentric and homogeneous layers as a material point.

In Book II, Newton examined whether the force of resistance opposing the relative motion of a body is proportional to the relative velocity or the square of the relative velocity. He based his laws of fluid friction on the second hypothesis, and then tried to find the least resistant solid of revolution with a view to applying it to shipbuilding. He also studied the velocity of wave propagation, thus anticipating Laplace. He distinguished clearly between perfectly incompressible fluids, viscous fluids (giving a precise definition of viscosity) and compressible fluids. Finally, he made a close study of the ballistic curve, and proved in a remarkably simple way that it must have an asymptote, no matter to what power of the velocity the resistance is proportional.

In Book III, Newton developed his system of the world. It begins (at least in all editions from 1713 onwards) with the *Regulae philosophandi*, goes on to discuss the *Phaenomenae* (astronomical observations), states the relevant propositions, and ends with a *Scholium Generale* presenting Newton's religious views, and propounding his famous assertion: 'I do not frame hypotheses' (*hypotheses non fingo*). In the body of this book, Newton attributes the motions of satellites about a central planet and of planets about the sun to universal attraction, and shows how the theory of attraction helps one to deduce the ratios between the masses of the planets and the mass of the earth. He then gave the density of the earth as between 5 and 6 (the modern value is 5.5), and evaluated the masses of the sun and of planets with satellites, and the flattening of the earth ($\frac{1}{230}$ as against the modern value of $\frac{1}{297}$). He was the first to give a mathematical explanation of the precession of the equinoxes, to study variations in gravitational acceleration with latitude, to explain the main variations of the moon's motion in terms of solar attraction, and to place tidal theory on solid foundations. Finally, he showed that the trajectory of comets can be explained by solar attraction and how their periodic appearances can be predicted. All in all, Newton's contribution to celestial mechanics was prodigious and marked the greatest advance ever made by a single man.

Newton's Scientific Philosophy

Let us return briefly to Newton's *Regulae philosophandi* with which Book III opens. The first two rules simply state that we are to admit no more causes than such as are sufficient to explain the appearance of natural things, and that the same effects must be explained, as far as possible, by the same causes.

The third rule states that those qualities which are found to belong to all bodies within reach of experiment are to be esteemed the universal qualities of all bodies whatsoever. It is by Rule III that Newton felt justified in inferring, by induction from terrestrial, lunar and solar gravitation, the existence of *universal* gravitation, without, moreover, having to turn gravitation into an inherent quality of matter (by reason of its variability with distance).

Rule IV states that propositions collected by general induction from phenomena can always be challenged with new experiments, though not with contrary hypotheses. This rule was Newton's answer to the critics of his colour theory and to Cartesian objections to his cosmological system.

In much the same spirit, Newton declared in the General Scholium which concludes the *Principia* (from the second edition onwards):

> Hitherto we have explained the Phaenomena of the Heavens and our Sea by the Power of Gravity, but have not yet assigned the Cause of this Power. . . . But hitherto I have not been able to discover the Cause of those Properties of Gravity from Phaenomena, and *I frame no Hypotheses*; for whatever is not deduced from the Phaenomena is to be called an Hypothesis, and Hypotheses, whether metaphysical or physical, whether of occult Qualities or mechanical, have no Place in experimental Philosophy. In this Philosophy, particular Propositions are inferred from the Phaenomena, and afterwards rendered general by Induction.

Despite this profession of positivist faith, Newton sinned against his own tenets when, for instance, he argued in the *Principia* that the vapour exhaled by the tail of comets is scattered through the whole heavens and attracted to the planets by its gravity and mixed with their atmosphere. As the sea is needed to exhale vapours with which to water the earth, comets are needed 'that, from their exhalations and vapours condensed, the wastes of the planetary fluids spent upon vegetation and putrefaction, and converted into dry earth, may be continually supplied and made up'.

In fact, Newton's claim that he framed no hypotheses was chiefly a tactical manœuvre to ward off the long-winded objections of his opponents, whom he told that he would listen only to solid experimental facts couched in mathematical language.

As E. A. Burtt has stressed in his *Metaphysical Foundations of Modern Physical Science*, this approach forced Newton to construct a harsh, cold, colourless, silent and dead Universe of quantities and mathematically precise motions, and to attribute a very minor role to the world of immediate perception.

To explain the triumph of Newton's mathematical physics, many historians have ignored the intuitive basis on which it was originally built. By stripping the Newtonian absolutes of their metaphysical and theological contents, by eliminating the final causes with which Newton endowed the optical and gravitational æthers, by passing in silence over the role which he assigned to attraction as an active principle, and by shrugging off his idea of instantaneous actions bridging vast spaces, they have reduced the complexity of Newton's thought to absurd simplicity.

In fact, Newton was a great visionary who, throughout his life, brought his lively and bold imagination to bear on hypotheses of all kinds. Newton, the author of the *Principia* who listened to nothing but mathematical certainties, was opposed by the Newton of the *Opticks*, who illustrated his creative thought with a host of scintillating images.[1]

Newton's mechanics were joined to profound religious beliefs that were the more important in that his theological disciples far outnumbered his scientific followers. His world was presided over by an omniscient and omnipresent God, whom man can come to know only 'by the most excellent contrivances of things and final causes'. Human understanding is but the infinitesimal reflection of God's, and, in the *Opticks*, Newton turned infinite space into a *sensorium* in which God perceives and understands all things at once. He also held that the harmony of the Universe stems from God's deliberate choice, and not from chance. No natural cause could have sufficed to establish it.

Newton *v.* Descartes

Newton felt so keen an antipathy to Descartes' mechanical philosophy that he was opposed to it on principle. Thus he proved that Kepler's third law does not hold if the planets are, in fact, carried round in vortices—on the assumption that successive vortical layers obey the laws governing viscous fluids.

Newton attached much importance to this proof, declaring in the General Scholium at the end of Book II of the *Principia*:

> Hence it is manifest that the Planets are not carried round in Vortices . . . the Hypothesis of Vortices is utterly irreconcilable with astronomical Phaenomena, and rather serves to perplex than explain the heavenly Motions. How these Motions are performed in free Spaces without Vortices, may be understood by the first Book; and I shall now more fully treat of it in the following Book.

[1] For a fuller account, see R. Dugas, *La mécanique au XVIIe siècle* (Neuchâtel and Paris, 1954); see also A. Koyré, *From the Closed World to the Infinite Universe* (Baltimore, 1957).

Elsewhere (*Opticks*, Query 28) Newton gave a general proof of the impossibility of motion in Descartes' dense universe:

> And therefore to make way for the regular and lasting Motions of the Planets and Comets, it's necessary to empty the Heavens of all Matter except perhaps some very thin Vapours, Steams, or Effluvia arising from the Atmospheres of the Earth, Planets, and Comets, and from such exceedingly rare æthereal Medium as we described above. A dense Fluid can be of no use for explaining the Phaenomena of Nature, the Motions of the Planets, and Comets, being better explain'd without it. It serves only to disturb and retard the Motions of those great Bodies, and make the Frame of Nature languish: and in the Pores of Bodies it serves only to stop the vibrating Motions of their Parts wherein their Heat and Activity consists. And as it is of no use, and hinders the Operations of Nature and makes her languish, so there is no Evidence for its Existence, and therefore it ought to be rejected.

Newton also opposed Descartes' view of the conservation of motion. In this refutation he committed the (deliberate?) error of adding the motions arithmetically—as Descartes himself had done—instead of vectorially. This is his conclusion:

> Seeing therefore the Variety of Motion which we find in the World is always decreasing, there is a necessity of conserving and recruiting it by *active Principles*, such as are the Cause of Gravity by which Planets and Comets keep their Motions in their Orbs, and Bodies acquire great Motion in falling; and the Cause of Fermentation by which the Heart and Blood of Animals are kept in perpetual Motion and Heat; the inward Parts of the Earth are constantly warm'd and in some Places grow very hot; Bodies burn and shine, Mountains take Fire, the Caverns of the Earth are blown up, and the Sun continues violently hot and lucid, and warms all Things by his Light. For we meet with very little Motion in the World, besides what is owing to these active Principles. And if it were not for these Principles, the Bodies of the Earth, Planets, Comets, Sun, and all Things in them, would grow cold and freeze, and become inactive Masses; and all Putrefaction, Generation, Vegetation, and Life would cease, and the Planets and Comets would not remain in their Orbs. (*Opticks*, Query 31.)

However fallacious much of Descartes' mechanics, and however solid Newton's own, there is no denying that this kind of imagery is a step back from the Cartesian statement of the conservation of motion. Moreover, by his constant use of active principles Newton simply ignored dynamics.

In fairness to Newton, we must state that he seems to have changed his views later. Thus he came to admit that, once created, the Universe might run on without any further intervention by God.

Unable to ignore the Cartesian condemnation of his occult qualities, Newton contended that attractions, as he understood them, were 'manifest qualities':

> These [active] Principles [*e.g.* gravity] I consider not as occult Qualities, suppos'd to result from the specifick Forms of Things, but as general Laws of Nature, by which the Things themselves are form'd; their Truth appearing to us by Phaenomena, though their Causes be not yet discover'd. For these [Principles] are Manifest Qualities and their Causes only are occult. (*Opticks*, Query 31.)

Writing to Bentley, his first religious disciple, Newton warned him against turning gravity into a scholastic quality.

> You sometimes speak of gravity as essential and inherent to matter. Pray, do not ascribe that notion to me; for the cause of gravity is what I do not pretend to know, and therefore would take more time to consider of it.

European Reaction to Newton

When Newtonian science went out into the Cartesian world it was given a cool reception. Fontenelle had just popularized Descartes' vortices in his charming *Entretiens sur la pluralité des mondes* and, in any case, few scholars could follow Newton's synthetic arguments. The *Journal des Savants* analysed Newton's *Principia*, and, while paying tribute to the theoretical perfection of his mechanics, considered them devoid of any physical value because 'they do not fulfil the necessary requirement of rendering the universe intelligible'.

Newton's greatest sin in the eyes of the Cartesians was that he had substituted attractions for direct actions, thus re-introducing the kind of qualities that had been condemned a century before.

So eminent a scientist as Huygens expressed his clear preference for Descartes' vortices as against Newton's attractions and absolutes. Though the *Principia* later convinced him of the validity of Kepler's laws and hence of the impossibility of Cartesian vortices, he still felt the need to repair rather than scrap the mechanical philosophy. Thus he wrote in his notes:

> Vortices destroyed by Newton. Replace with vortices in spherical motion.
>
> Correct the idea of vortices.
>
> Vortices necessary, else the earth would escape from the sun; but very distant from one another and not touching like those of M. des Cartes.

These ideas were developed in Huygens' *Discours sur la cause de la pesanteur*, an appendix to his *Traité de la lumière* (Leyden, 1690). In it, Huygens presented a mechanical model of gravity, and regretted that he had allowed Newton to forestall him simply because 'I failed to extend the quantitative laws of the *vis centrifuga* to the moon and the sun.'

Leibniz explained the motion of the planets as due to a combination of swirling fluids, centrifugal forces, and attractions. Huygens was able to show him that he could easily dispense with the fluids and that the inverse square law coupled to the centrifugal force would suffice to explain Kepler's ellipses.

LEIBNIZ

Leibniz's first contribution to mechanics was his *Theoria motus abstracti* (1671), which was based on Hobbes's conception of the *conatus*. In it, Leibniz presented the paradox that a *conatus*, however feeble, has the property of reaching infinite distances and of acting on any obstacle, however great.

In the *Theoria motus concreti* or *Hypothesis physica nova*, Leibniz tried to solve this paradox by turning the æther into the medium of gravity, of the motions of the solar system, and of elasticity, and into a universal property of all physical bodies.

In a letter to Arnauld, dated 28th November 1686, Leibniz launched a well-prepared attack on the Cartesian law of the conservation of motion, claiming that the *vis motrix* cannot be measured by the product of the 'body' and its velocity, but only by its possible effects, for instance by the height to which it can raise a heavy body.

With this letter to Arnauld, Leibniz inaugurated the quarrel of 'living forces' which lasted for more than thirty years, in which both sides concentrated on impact phenomena.

As against the Cartesians, Leibniz and his followers maintained that it is not the sum of the quantities of motion but the sum of living forces that is conserved during impact. This quarrel was largely a splitting of hairs, since both parties adopted the same laws of impact. Both were equally wrong: the Cartesians should have considered the direction of motion and the Leibnizians should have limited the conservation of living forces to the case of perfectly elastic bodies.

Leibniz also introduced the term 'motive action', which he intended to substitute for 'quantity of motion'. In uniform motion, the motive action is expressed by the product mvs of the mass, velocity and distance. Leibniz turned the action into an absolute, and its conservation into a law of nature. He also distinguished between the *formal effect* ms of that action, and the vigour or velocity, v, with which this formal effect is produced.

But Leibniz's main claim to fame in mechanics is his use of the differential and integral calculus as a bridge between dynamics and statics; he considered the living force the result of an infinity of continuous impressions by dead or static forces. This formulation afforded Leibniz a number of metaphysical satisfactions: the introduction of an 'absolute', *i.e.* the *vis viva* (which, in fact, was only a remarkable kinematic invariant), the justification of the principle of continuity, and finally the perfect balance between total cause and total effect.

Leibniz's mechanics therefore turned motion into the underlying reality of all actions and all continuous substances.

Leibniz denied the existence of the vacuum with purely metaphysical and theological arguments, and the existence of atoms in the name of the principle of continuity. He also rejected the Cartesian concept of extension, arguing that extension, being no more than a simple attribute expressing a present state, cannot be the cause of any action or of any change. The correct definition of substance must embrace past, present and future all at once. Finally, Leibniz attacked the Newtonian absolutes, and defended the relativity of all motions, and hence the equivalence of all astronomical hypotheses.

Survey of 17th-century Achievements

It would be idle to try fitting the complex contributions of the founders of mechanics into a mould. The greatest of them, not content with attacking the schoolmen, fought against one another with as much bitterness if not with more. Mechanics in the 17th century was still in search of its basic principles and methods, hence it was a long time before its solid acquisitions could be isolated from its metaphysical speculations. We have dwelt at length on the latter because there is a tendency to ignore them altogether and hence to simplify the march of scientific thought. We have also tried to show how, against this metaphysical background, mechanics began to define its concepts, develop its vocabulary and perfect its mathematical analysis, by which apparently dissimilar phenomena, that had puzzled scientists for ages, could now be shown to obey the same laws. Following different paths, Huygens, Leibniz and Newton bequeathed to the 18th century the intelligible and rational science of mechanics on which Galileo had set his sights. All that remained to be done was to organize the new findings and to put them to use.

CHAPTER 3

The Golden Age of Observational Astronomy

IN THE 17TH CENTURY, astronomy made astonishing advances. From the wealth of observations recorded by Tycho Brahe, Kepler framed laws of remarkable simplicity, while Galileo began to observe the sky with the refracting telescope. All three therefore helped to prepare the great Newtonian synthesis. The 17th century was also the golden age of amateur observers who, using the simplest instruments, made some surprising discoveries about the universe.

The bold views of Copernicus were confirmed, and what vestiges of scholastic astronomy had survived were thrown out once and for all. The telescope was increasingly used not only for observing stars, but also for *measuring* astronomical, geographical, geological and navigational phenomena. Newton's mathematical genius was quick to seize on all this new-found knowledge and to synthesize it into a universal law.

The importance and depth of this new trend can also be seen in the daily lives of the astronomers. At the beginning of the 17th century, Kepler was forced to earn his livelihood by dabbling in almanacs and, less honourably, in astrological predictions, but by the end of the century the status of astronomers had greatly improved. In 1675, Charles II appointed England's first official astronomer or 'Astronomical Observator' (a title later changed to 'King's Astronomer' and then to 'Astronomer Royal'), with a salary of £100 a year. The duty of his office was 'forthwith to apply himself with the most exact care and diligence to the rectifying of the tables of the motions of the heavens, and the places of the fixed stars, so as to find out the so much desired longitude of places for the perfecting the art of navigation'. It was in the newly-built Observatory of Paris that Colbert decided to house the new *Académie des Sciences*. Almost every day, astronomical advances made a fresh impact on social life. Two public events may serve to mark the beginning and end of the phase in astronomical history we are about to discuss: in 1610, Galileo invited the Doge of Venice to observe the satellites of Jupiter from the top of the Campanile of St. Mark's, and in 1671, Louis XIV paid a state visit to the Observatory of Paris. Astronomy had become an integral part of world history.

THE REVOLUTION OF ASTRONOMY

The Successors of Tycho Brahe

Though Tycho Brahe died at the turn of the century (in 1601), the harvest of his remarkable observations was not reaped until the 17th century. Thus Kepler was able to give a far better interpretation of Tycho's results than Tycho himself could have done. It was the work of Kepler and Galileo which provided incontrovertible proof of the correctness of the Copernican system.

Kepler

Johannes Kepler was born in Weilderstadt, Württemberg, on 27th December 1571, and studied astronomy at Tübingen. It was here that Mästlin acquainted him with the doctrine of Copernicus. In 1594, he was appointed 'Provincial Mathematician' of Styria, and soon afterwards published his first great work, the *Prodromus dissertationum cosmographicarum continens mysterium cosmographicum* (Tübingen, 1596). Though it was not on a par with his later writings, this book contained Kepler's first great discovery.

In the first chapter, Kepler explained his reasons for abandoning the Ptolemaic in favour of the Copernican system, showing, for instance, that the Ptolemaic epicycles of the outer planets would subtend exactly the same angle when seen from the earth as the Copernican orbit of the earth would when seen from a point on a given outer planet. This explains why the epicycle of Jupiter is much smaller than that of Mars, and that of Saturn smaller still, though their deferents are much larger than that of Mars. The Ptolemaic systems could assign no cause for this fact, nor explain why the period of the inner planets on their deferents was equal to that of the sun, and that the sun and the moon never became retrograde. All these phenomena were, however, given a simple explanation by the doctrine of Copernicus, and that is why Kepler, despite his close contact with Tycho, remained a convinced Copernican throughout his life.

The *Prodromus* also propounded an ingenious idea which, although incorrect, throws some light on Kepler's own preoccupations. In dealing with the problem of the relative distances of the planets, he argued that the five intervals between the six planetary spheres of Copernicus could be filled with five regular polyhedra, so that the sphere of Saturn is circumscribed to a cube in which the sphere of

Jupiter is inscribed, the latter is circumscribed to the tetrahedron, in which the sphere of Mars is inscribed. There follows the dodecahedron, the sphere of the earth, the icosahedron, the sphere of Venus, the octahedron, and the sphere of Mercury. Kepler was so enamoured of this strange scheme that he repeated it with slight modifications even in the second edition of the *Prodromus*, which appeared in 1625, after the promulgation of his third law. Clearly, therefore, the search for geometrical perfection was the underlying motive of all his work.

As we have said, it was in the *Prodromus* that Kepler published his great discovery that the planes of the planetary orbits pass through the sun. Lacking accurate tables, and still influenced by Ptolemaic notions, Copernicus had wrongly drawn these planes through the centre of the terrestrial orbit, with the result that he was faced with inexplicable changes in the eccentricity of the inner planets. Kepler showed that this anomaly disappears when the planes are drawn through the sun, which exerts a stronger attraction on the planets nearest to it. Kepler's conception also explained why the orbital planes have a constant inclination to the ecliptic. Thus, this early work of the then 25-year-old astronomer was of the utmost importance.

Driven from Styria by religious persecution, Kepler was forced to seek asylum in Prague, where he joined Tycho Brahe, then Imperial Mathematician, in February 1600. Tycho died too soon after this meeting for their disagreement on the Copernican system to have come to a head. Thus Kepler came into possession of the material with which he was able to implement his great dream of 'geometrizing' the universe, and established the relationship between the radii of the planetary orbits and their eccentricities and periods. Moreover, he took over Tycho's job of Imperial Mathematician, and though this forced him to cast horoscopes he neither minded nor allowed his real work to suffer from this activity.

In 1604, Kepler published his *Ad Vitellionem paralipomena, quibus astronomiae pars optica traditur . . .*, in which he gave a definition of light rays, explained the reflection of light, and showed that atmospheric refraction deflects the light of all the stars.

At the same time he continued with his purely astronomical work. Analysing Tycho Brahe's observations of Mars, he found an error of 8′ between the observed position of the planet and the position calculated from the theory of eccentrics (deferents) and epicycles. The error could not be imputed to Tycho, whom Kepler knew to have been a scrupulous observer, but to a false view of the terrestrial orbit. Kepler therefore searched Tycho's records for observations of Mars at various intervals, each of 687 days, *i.e.* the period of the planet's revolution about the sun. He then used the Sun-Mars axis as a fixed line to which successive positions of the earth could be referred. From these observations, he was able to conclude that the earth has a circular orbit (a very good approximation, since the sun is, in fact, only 0.018 radii from the centre of the earth's orbit or practically half Tycho's value).

Kepler argued that the sun exerts a tangential force (*anima motrix*) on the earth's orbit (he was unfamiliar with the principle of inertia), and that this force, and hence the earth's velocity, is inversely proportional to the distance SE *(fig. 22)* of the sun from the earth. We know now that this is not the case, and that the velocity of the earth is, in fact, proportional to the distance between the sun and the tangent to the trajectory (SH). However, Kepler was misled by having verified his hypothesis in only the particular cases when the earth is at perihelion or aphelion.

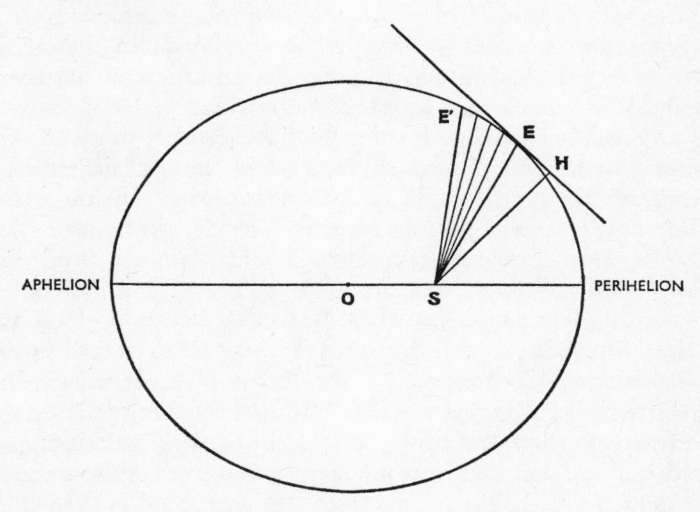

fig. 22 Kepler's proof of the law of areas.

By chance, he compensated this error with another: the time taken by the earth to cover an infinitely small arc of its orbit is proportional to the length of the radius vector SE. Now, lacking the resources of integral calculus, Kepler replaced the sum of all the vector radii between SE and SE′ with the area of the sector ESE′ swept out by the planet. This was a providential error since it enabled him to formulate his great law that the radius of the terrestrial orbit sweeps out equal areas in equal times. All his observations confirmed this hypothesis, so that having revised Tycho's orbit of Mars, he immediately applied it to that planet as well. Kepler's so-called second law was therefore the first in chronological order.

Further studies of Mars showed that, though the circular theory holds when the planet is at perihelion or aphelion, it breaks down when Mars occupies other parts of its orbit. Hence Kepler was forced to abandon the circular hypothesis and to conclude 'that the orbit of Mars is not a circle but an oval figure', with the sun in one of its foci.

We might point out in passing that Kepler's simplifying hypotheses could not be refuted in his day. On the one hand, Tycho's observations, however excellent, were correct to within only one minute, so that observational errors masked any irregularities due to perturbations; on the other hand, Kepler, though familiar with conic sections, lacked the resources of the differential calculus, which alone would have helped him to arrive at the correct solution. In this connection, Einstein made the following comment: 'Kepler's work demonstrates that knowledge cannot be derived from experiment alone; true knowledge implies the comparison between what the mind has conceived and what it observes.'

In any case, by 1605 Kepler had become convinced that the planetary orbits must be elliptical, and he published the final wording of his first two laws four years later in the *Astronomia nova* αἰτιολογητος *seu physica coelestis, tradita commentariis de motibus stellae Martis. Ex observationibus G. V. Tychonis Brahe* (August 1609).

It was only later, on 15th May 1618, that he announced his third law, that the squares of the times taken by two planets to describe their orbits are proportional to the cubes of their mean distances from the sun. Kepler's love of the 'harmony of the world' had at last borne fruit. At the same time, he completed the work of Copernicus and rid it of ancient conceptions, so that despite Kepler's many confused ideas his three laws played an indispensable role in the Newtonian synthesis.

Nor was Kepler a pure theorist, for until his death, and despite all personal difficulties, he was also a keen observer. Spurred on by Galileo, he studied the comets of 1618 and recognized their 'celestial' nature (many astronomers continued to describe them as meteors). He also observed sunspots. In 1627, at the court of Rudolph II in Ulm, where he had been forced to seek refuge, he published his *Tabulae Rudolphinae*, the first planetary tables to be computed on the basis of his three laws. In 1629, these tables, dedicated to John Napier, whose logarithms had greatly facilitated Kepler's calculations, enabled Kepler to predict the transit of Mercury across the sun's disk on 7th November 1631, and those of Venus on 4th December 1639 and 6th June 1671. For a whole century these tables remained the basis of all astronomical computations.

21 Johannes Kepler; portrait by an unknown artist

22 Galilean telescopes

GALILEO

Galileo was born in Pisa in 1564 and taught mathematics, first at the University of Pisa and later at Padua. He became a Copernican in 1597, but his fame as an astronomer—until then he was considered a great mathematician—dates from his observations of the nova of 1604 in the constellation of Ophiuchus. The absence of any observable parallax convinced Galileo that the nova was a distant star, and that Aristotle's belief in the immutability of the heavens was therefore false. When he expressed these views publicly—as he invariably did with all his findings—he aroused the life-long enmity of all the opponents of modern science.

In June 1609, Galileo learned that a refracting telescope had been presented to Count Maurice of Flanders. He immediately constructed one of his own and turned it towards the sky. The great emotion he felt when at last he beheld 'nature's splendid marvels' can best be appreciated from a perusal of his letter, and from the very title of the work in which he described them: *Sidereus nuncius, magna longeque admirabilia spectacula pandens, suspiciendaque proponens unicuique, praesertim vero philosophis atque astronomis, que a Galileo Galileo* . . . (Venice, March 1610).

The book begins with a list of all the mountains whose bright peaks protrude above the moon's terminator. From the respective radii of the earth and the moon, Galileo inferred that these peaks are four times higher than mountains on earth. He went on to discuss the possible existence of a lunar atmosphere and, comparing the light of the moon with earthlight (the 'ashy light' visible as 'the old moon in the new moon's arms'), he concluded that the earth reflects light like the other planets.

On a special page, Galileo mapped all the unknown stars he had discovered in Orion (listing 80 in Orion's belt where formerly no more than 9 had been observed with the naked eye), and in the Pleiades (where he discovered 36 stars in a cluster). He was correct in describing the Milky Way as a tightly packed system of stars and not a nebulosity reflecting the light of the sun or moon, nor a meteor (Aristotle's view).

Finally, and above all, the *Sidereus nuncius* mentioned the discovery of the satellites of Jupiter. On 7th January 1610, Galileo observed three new bodies in the neighbourhood of Jupiter, but mistook them for fixed stars. On the following day he found that the bodies had shifted their relative positions (the book gives clear illustrations of his various observations); on 11th January he saw only two bodies; on 14th January he saw four. He was now convinced that these bodies could not be fixed stars, but were satellites revolving about Jupiter. Unable to distinguish them all, he could determine only the period of revolution of the fourth, which stands out most clearly. Even so, he had delivered a further blow to the anti-Copernicans, who had scoffed at a system in which all the planets revolve about the sun excepting only the moon, which for some inexplicable reason did not. No wonder that Galileo rushed into print to publish his additional proof of the validity of the Copernican doctrine—a proof, moreover, which required no complicated calculations and which could be seen and understood by all.

Of course, not everybody agreed with him. One objection was that the satellites were no more than distortions produced by faulty telescope lenses; another that it was stupid to propound the existence of bodies that had escaped the keen minds of Ptolemy and Aristotle.

Having read the *Sidereus nuncius*, Kepler sent Galileo a letter, *Dissertatio cum nuncio sidereo*, in which he, too, expressed his doubts about the existence of the satellites. Since the earth, which was second to the sun in nobility, had but one satellite, how could Jupiter possibly boast four? However, when Galileo presented him with a telescope, Kepler was able to observe the satellites for himself (September 1610), and to acknowledge his error in the *Narratio de observatis a se quatuor Jovis satellitibus erronibus*. Thanks to him, a second edition of the *Sidereus nuncius* was published in Germany within the year.

Before we make a detailed analysis of 17th-century astronomical discoveries, we must dwell on the year 1610, which represents a turning-point in astronomical history. Until then, theoretical speculations had masked the essentially experimental nature of that science. Galileo's modest telescope may be called the symbol of a new approach. Handled by ignorant or clumsy men, any instrument, however perfect, is bound to lead to poor results, but if the observer understands its scope and limitations, if he does not concentrate on observations at the cost of mathematics, he can open up vast new horizons. Henceforth, all astronomical progress would spring from a dialogue between theoretical speculation and technical progress: observational discoveries, no matter how fortuitous, would support theoretical research and prevent its straying from reality, while theoretical studies of the new results would call for ever better instruments which, in turn, would lead to further discoveries. Bailly had this to say about Kepler:

Men must perforce study nature bit by bit. When they have seen enough, they withdraw into themselves. They have gathered the facts, but lack the connecting links; but those links exist and can therefore be discovered. Those who know how, take up a pencil and draw up a plan; one of these was Kepler. All that was needed after him, was to apply the plan, devised by the imagination, to the great model, nature, by further observations. (*Histoire de l'astronomie ancienne*, 1779.)

Assessment of Galileo's Contribution

Galileo's most fruitful contributions to astronomy date from 1610 to 1619. In April 1611, one year after his discovery of Jupiter's satellites, he was able to distinguish between them and hence to observe their individual motions. He then determined their approximate periods of revolution, an operation so delicate that Kepler had judged it impossible. It must be stressed that Galileo was not influenced in his measurements by Kepler's first two laws, for he refused to rely upon anything but his own observations.

Galileo computed a table of the mean periods of the four satellites, which ranged from less than two days for the innermost to just under seventeen days for the most distant, in order to predict their future eclipses. However, he realized that to determine these periods accurately he would have to spread his observations over at least the sidereal period of Jupiter; only when the planet had returned to a previously observed position could the conjunctions of its satellites be measured with any precision. Now, Galileo's observation covered no more than the brief span of 1610 to 1619, and he had worked with a very inadequate instrument. To the tube of one of his telescopes he had attached a graduated scale, which he watched with his left eye while he looked through the glass with his right. Nevertheless, despite the poor experimental conditions, he was able not only to determine the orbits of the satellites but to refer them to the heliocentric system, thus eliminating all irregularities arising from Jupiter's motion with respect to the earth.

When the Stadholder of the Dutch republic offered a prize of 25,000 florins for a method of determining a ship's position at sea, Galileo felt that Jupiter's satellites might provide the answer: the simultaneous observation of a given configuration by two observers at different stations would give the measure of the terrestrial longitude. Encouraged by Galileo, Father Renieri, professor at the University of Pisa, worked at this problem until his death. It was only in 1668 that Cassini was able to publish his famous *Ephemerides bononienses mediceorum siderum* and hence to solve the problem in the way his two great predecessors had suggested.

While on the subject of longitude, we might mention that, in 1611, N. C. Fabri de Peiresc, a former pupil of Galileo and a Member of the Parliament of Provence, suggested the same method of measuring longitudes quite independently of his teacher. (Jupiter's satellites were first observed in Aix-en-Provence on 24th November 1610 by Joseph Gaultier; it was while looking for them on the following night that Peiresc discovered the Great Nebula in Orion.) Peiresc sent his assistant, Lombard, first to Malta and later to Syria, to put the new method of finding longitude to the test. Though the results were disappointing, Peiresc persisted and organized a network of observers to watch the eclipse of the moon on 28th August 1638. As a result, errors of the order of 600 miles were eliminated from maps of the eastern Mediterranean.

Galileo himself had meanwhile stipulated the necessary conditions for solving the longitude problem successfully: more accurate tables, better telescopes, a method of taking accurate measurements at sea, and, finally, accurate clocks. All these requirements were to be met before the end of the 17th century.

Galileo's interest in Jupiter's satellites did not cause him to neglect the rest of the sky. However, his observation of Saturn proved most unrewarding: 'I have observed the highest planet and I have found it triple', he wrote. A little later, he found it 'simple'—his telescope was too poor to resolve Saturn's rings, which look different when seen at different angles.

On the other hand, Galileo made clear observations of the phases of Venus, which provided him with fresh evidence in favour of the Copernican system. In this connection, he wrote to one of his friends, Father Benedetto Castelli:

> What marvellous consequences spring from my observations! But you make me laugh when you think that they will dissipate all the clouds, and cause all dissensions to cease. The proof has long since been brought for every least detail. Our adversaries would have been persuaded if they could have been. But they prefer to persist in their deceptions. . . .

His observations of the moon showed Galileo not only that our satellite always turns the same hemisphere towards us, but also that its motion is subject to the anomaly which we now call libration. Hevelius, and later Cassini, were to study this phenomenon more closely; Galileo himself was wrong in attributing it exclusively to the parallactic effect resulting from the observer's variable position on a moving earth.

In 1610 and again in 1612, Galileo observed spots on the sun's disk. In this, he was anticipated by Fabricius (who published a pamphlet on the subject in 1611), and possibly by Father Scheiner, a Jesuit teacher of mathematics at Ingolstadt, who claimed that he had observed the spots in 1611. In any case, this is how Galileo himself spoke of the spots in 1612:

> I believe that these new discoveries will toll the knell of pseudo-philosophy; signs of it have already appeared in the sun and the moon.

I expect to hear great proclamations by the Peripatetics, who believe in the immutability of the heavens, but I do not know how they can save and preserve it. (Letter to F. Cesi, May 1612.)

The Last of the Anti-Copernicans

Though Galileo's discoveries, coming as they did after Kepler's first two laws, left little doubt about the validity of the Copernican system, the anti-Copernicans continued to put up a very tough resistance. Pope Paul V condemned as erroneous and impious all opinions which placed the sun in the centre of the universe. In reply to him and his other opponents, Galileo published the *Il Saggiatore* (1623), a masterpiece of polemical writing, and the *Dialogo* (1632), in which he listed his chief arguments against Aristotle and presented his own oversimplified system (Galileo continued to disregard Kepler's laws). By turning mechanics into the indispensable complement of the Copernican system, Galileo prepared the way for the Newtonian synthesis, though he himself never suspected that the motions of planets and projectiles were governed by identical laws.

Because the *Dialogo* was written in popular style and hence was accessible to a wide public, it came under the scrutiny of the Holy Office, which had not bothered about Kepler's more abstruse writings. On 22nd June 1632, after a trial lasting twenty days, a tribunal of seven cardinals declared:

To maintain that the sun is immobile and occupies the centre of the world, is an absurd proposition, false in philosophy, and heretical inasmuch as it is contrary to the witness of Scripture. It is equally absurd and false in philosophy to contend that the earth is not the immobile centre of the world; and this proposition, considered theologically, is no less erroneous in faith.

Galileo was forced to sign a recantation, and was thereupon banished to Arcetri. There he lost his sight, and died on 8th January 1642.

Though a detailed examination of the motives and effects of his trial falls outside the scope of this work, the trial itself illustrates one of the grave problems with which 17th-century scientists had to contend: they were allowed to pursue their great work of discovery, provided only that they kept the results to themselves. Thus, Galileo's persecutors hounded him not so much for his own views as for openly proclaiming the views he had inherited from his great predecessors.

The anti-Copernicans were given a brief new lease of life. The *Astronomia danica* by Longomontanus, a pupil of Tycho and a defender of his system, appeared in 1640. Even among the Copernicans themselves, there were some who refused to adopt Kepler's laws. Philip

Lansberg based his planetary tables on the theory of epicycles and Ismaël Boulliau (*Astronomia philolaica*, Paris, 1645) replaced the second law with a complicated system aimed at restoring uniform motion. But these were so many death-rattles, and it fell to the Copernicans to make all the great discoveries of the future.

THE RISE OF OBSERVATIONAL ASTRONOMY

Contributions by Amateurs

As soon as Galileo's discoveries were made known by the prompt publication of his *Sidereus nuncius*, an army of amateurs rushed to equip themselves with telescopes. As a result of their observations the sky began to be mapped as never before. We shall mention only the most important of their discoveries, beginning with lunar topography.

The first map of the moon was prepared by Peiresc, aided by Gassendi, and was engraved by Claude Mellan (1636). There followed the lunar maps of Langrenus (Spain, 1645), Hevelius (Danzig, 1647), and of Riccioli and Grimaldi (Italy, 1650). Hevelius also discovered the libration of the moon in longitude (1657) and Grimaldi was the first to give orographic details. All these men paved the way for Domenico Cassini, whose engraved chart of the moon, more than two feet in diameter, was completed in 1679 and remained unequalled until the end of the 18th century.

Stellar phenomena were rather neglected, largely because the primitive telescopes proved unequal to the task. True, Peiresc discovered the Great Nebula in Orion in 1611, and Simon Mayer (or Marius) (1570–1624), a court astronomer to the Elector of Brandenburg, was the first to observe the faint 'nebula' in Andromeda, but progress was so slow that the next discovery—the star cluster in Hercules—was not made until 1715 (by Halley). It seems that chance alone was responsible for all these early discoveries, whose true significance could, in any case, not have been understood at the time.

In 1596, Fabricius observed the variable luminosity of the brightest star in Cetus, which Hevelius later named Mira Ceti. In 1652, Boulliau measured its period of 333 days.

Hevelius also discovered the existence of solar faculae—further evidence that the sun is neither immobile nor immutable—and began the compilation of a star catalogue in which he named a small constellation of stars in the Milky Way 'Sobieski's Shield' (a name used to this day) in honour of his protector, John III Sobieski. Finally, Hevelius published the first book exclusively devoted to comets, the *Cometographia* (1668), in which he proved, from their parallaxes, that the comets of 1662 and 1664 could not have been meteors, but that they travelled in parabolic or near-parabolic orbits about the sun.

Meanwhile, other astronomers concentrated on the planets. The Italian Jesuit Niccolo Zucchi observed spots on Mars and belts on Jupiter in 1640. (Fontana may have made similar observations in 1636.) Previously, Peiresc had been the first to observe Mercury in broad daylight, claiming that it reflected the light of Venus.

There was much interest in verifying Kepler's prediction that Mercury would cross the sun's disk in 1641. The event took place and was observed by Gassendi. P. Humbert had this to say of the observation:

> In truth, Gassendi discovered nothing . . . he merely confirmed [previous] discoveries. But in all his observations, he showed a keen mind, a concern for accuracy, and a care for elegance, which set him well above his contemporaries. (*L'œuvre astronomique de Gassendi*, Paris, 1936.)

Gassendi observed the transit by projecting the sun's image on a screen, and calculated that it lasted for five hours precisely.

Subsequent transit observations were not nearly as accurate as Gassendi's. In 1639, Horrocks observed the transit of Venus from a point near Liverpool. This young astronomer, who died so tragically at the age of 21, was also the first to apply Kepler's laws to the motion of the moon and to give an elegant explanation of the inequality in the moon's longitude by assuming a libratory motion of the apsides and a variable eccentricity. Hevelius in Danzig, and Huygens in London observed the transit of Mercury on 3rd May 1661.

This rapid sketch shows how many and varied were the observations made during this remarkable period. They were, however, of limited value and there was no one of the calibre of Kepler or Galileo to fit them into a coherent framework. The next great step sprang from the construction of better instruments by an accomplished scientist—Huygens.

Huygens

Huygens' interest in optical problems had convinced him that further advances in astronomy would have to await technical improvements. He accordingly constructed a new telescope in 1655. In 1659, he wrote:

> All telescopes equipped with none but convex lenses have a spot, at a distance from the eye approximately twice as great as [the diameter of] the convex eyepiece, such that an object, however fine and small, placed in it, can be seen distinctly and in very clear outline, hiding from sight,

according to its lateral dimensions, part of any luminous object, for example the moon, observed with the telescope. . . .

In other words, though Kepler had advised the use of converging eyepieces as early as 1611, it took nearly fifty years before his suggestion was implemented. Better lens-making techniques, and especially the technique of making lenses with any desired curvature, soon enabled Huygens to add to Galileo's discoveries. Though his contribution was not nearly as important as the *Sidereus nuncius*, it marked a new departure in observational astronomy.

Huygens' first discovery was Titan (1665), the largest of Saturn's satellites. Including the moon and Galileo's four Jovian satellites, there were now six known satellites—as many as there were solar planets. Huygens attached great importance to this coincidence, arguing that there could not possibly be more satellites than there were planets. This *a priori* notion hampered his further research, and he left it to J. D. Cassini, working with telescopes that were no better than his own, to discover Iapetus in 1671, and Rhea in 1672. (In March 1684, Cassini discovered two further satellites of Saturn: Tethys and Dione.)

But Huygens' brilliant observational ability was fully proved in 1656, when he solved the riddle of Galileo's 'triple planet' and correctly described Saturn's ring. This had disappeared in 1665, and Huygens was able to follow its gradual reappearance. He published his discovery in his *De Saturni luna observatio nova* (1656), though in the form of the following anagram: AAAAAAA CCCCC D EEEEE G H IIIIIII LLLL MM NNNNNNNNN OOOO PP Q RR S TTTTT UUUUU. He restored the letters to their correct positions in his *Systema Saturnium* (1659), when they read: ANNULO CINGITUR, TENUI, PLANO, NUSQUAM COHÆRENTE, AD ECLIPTICAM INCLINATO ('It is girdled by a slender, flat ring, everywhere distinct from its surface, and inclined to the ecliptic').

Huygens also predicted the disappearance of the ring in July–August 1671 (it actually disappeared in May) and gave the correct explanation. When the position of the planet in its orbit is such that the plane of the ring passes through the sun, only the edge of the ring is exposed to the sun's rays; as a result, the illuminated surface is too small to be detected by the eye.

The importance of this discovery and of its correct interpretation cannot be stressed too much: no similar object had been discovered before, nor has any been discovered since. Nevertheless, Huygens himself remarked:

Had earlier observers used larger telescopes with better lenses, there is no doubt that instead of seeing three round objects, they would have seen the very same thing which, as I have said, I saw in 1655, and again on the 13th October of the following year. (*Systema Saturnium*, 1659.)

Huygens' emphasis on the close connection between advances in instrumental technique and the progress of science, as such, may strike us as trivial. However, in Huygens' day the idea was truly revolutionary. It bore further fruit on 16th June 1657, when Huygens published his work on the pendulum clock, for this instrument was to play a paramount role in precise transit measurements.

At the time that Louis XIV established the *Académie des Sciences* and the Paris Observatory, Colbert invited Huygens to Paris, where he met Picard, Auzout and Cassini. After the revocation of the Edict of Nantes, he was forced to return to Holland. With the help of his brother, he devoted the rest of his life to the construction of optical instruments.

The Telescope as a Measuring Instrument

Long after the invention of the telescope, the alidad—a graduated sector provided with simple sights—remained the sole instrument for measuring angular separations. It was probably Jean Baptiste Morin (1585–1656) who first used a graduated arc in conjunction with a telescope. But since his telescope lacked cross-wires ('spider lines') the results he obtained were inaccurate.

In December 1666, Adrien Auzout (1622–1691) showed how a micrometer screw can be applied to movable cross-wires (over a fixed scale) so as to measure the distance between two points accurately. In the following year, he published his *Manière exacte pour prendre le diamètre des planètes, la distance entre les petites étoiles, la distance des lieux, etc.* A paper on the subject, which he sent to the Royal Society in London on 28th December 1666, unleashed a bitter priority quarrel: on 4th April 1667, Towneley claimed that from 1638 to 1648 Crabtree had measured the stars in the Pleiades with a micrometer instrument developed by William Gascoigne (1619–1644). Quite possibly, the work of Gascoigne and Crabtree, like Horrocks's observations of the transit of Venus, had failed to attract attention when they were made because England was then shaken by grave political upheavals and had little time for other matters. In any case, it was in 1666 that the kind of instrument described by Adrien Auzout came into general use.[1]

Soon afterwards, Jean Picard (1620–1682), one of France's most brilliant astronomers, mounted a telescope provided with cross-wires

[1] For further details of this priority quarrel, see Danjon and Couder, *Lunettes et télescopes*, pp. 627–629. *Cf.* also Henri Renan, 'Le nouveau micromètre enregistreur du Cercle méridien du Jardin de l'Observatoire de Paris' (*Annals of the Paris Observatory*, Vol. XXVI).

on a quadrant of radius 1.03 metres, and used it for measuring meridian arcs by Snellius' method of triangulation. He measured thirteen triangles between Sourdon (near Amiens) and Malvoisine (near Paris), and found that 1° 23′ 55″ of the arc corresponds to a distance of 78,850 fathoms, *i.e.* 1°=57,060 fathoms. This figure was later adopted by Newton.

It was now only a matter of time before a full transit instrument could be assembled and Picard was the first to appreciate its tremendous advantages. Ahead of his time, he attempted to measure the parallax of α Lyrae, but failed. Since Jean Hecker's planetary tables had been calculated only as far as 1689, Picard proposed, in 1679, to publish annual tables of his own. He himself computed ephemerides for the first five years and Lefèvre continued the work until 1706, presenting a new book to the Sovereign at the beginning of every year. Picard did not live to see the completion of the first transit instrument in the Observatory of Paris: the mural arc mounted in the western tower by Philippe de la Hire. From then on, the great advances in astronomy may be ascribed to the organization of large observatories.

The Great Observatories

The Royal Observatory of Paris was founded by Louis XIV in 1667. In order to compare local observations and measurements with those of Tycho Brahe, Picard was soon afterwards despatched to Denmark and charged to take new measurements of the position of Uraniborg, Tycho's famous retreat. He discovered that Tycho's measurement of the meridian must be corrected by 18′. The reason was that 'the Pole star has variations which Tycho overlooked and which I have observed for the last ten years' (1672). In other words, Picard had hit upon aberration (see pp. 441–442). Finally, and this was by no means the least result of his trip—Picard returned to Paris in the company of young Römer, who was one day to become famous. Picard, Auzout, Huygens and Römer formed the nucleus of the great astronomical school of Paris. The only name missing is that of Cassini, who was to be their leader.

Jean Dominique Cassini was born in the County of Nice in 1625, and succeeded Cavalieri as professor of mathematics at the University of Bologna. In 1669, he was summoned by Louis XIV to join the staff of the new *Académie des Sciences*. We have already mentioned his discovery of four of Saturn's satellites, and in 1666 he had discovered the rotation of Mars (giving 24 hours 40 minutes instead of 24 hours 37 minutes). In 1675 he discovered the narrow dark band dividing the ring of Saturn into two concentric rings and called 'Cassini's division' to this day.

He established accurate tables of the periods of Jupiter's satellites, which he asked Römer to check. In doing so, Römer was greatly surprised to observe a systematic retardation or advance of the eclipses of these satellites, depending on whether Jupiter was in conunction or in opposition. Römer gave a correct interpretation of this phenomenon: the total discrepancy (which he took to be 22 minutes instead of the modern value of 16 minutes) represents twice the time that light takes to travel from the sun to the earth. Römer's paper on the velocity of light was written on 22nd November 1675, a date which is commemorated on a plaque in the Paris Observatory.

As we saw earlier, the Greenwich Observatory was founded for the very special purpose of fixing longitudes for 'perfecting the art of navigation'. This emphasis also determined the choice of its original site: Greenwick Park overlooking the mouth of the Thames. John Flamsteed (1646–1720), the first Astronomer Royal, proposed to begin the work by establishing a star catalogue in which Tycho's results would be corrected by means of a transit instrument, and then to improve the existing lunar tables so that the rapid motion of the moon across a given fixed star could be used as a measure of longitude by sailors, provided, of course, that they knew the time at Greenwich. As he did not have a suitable mural arc until 1689, Flamsteed was reluctant to publish his results. He thus earned the hostility of Newton, who was desperately anxious to know whether Flamsteed's lunar observations bore out his own theory.

Flamsteed was succeeded at the Royal Observatory by Edmund Halley (1656–1742), professor of mathematics at Oxford. Halley was a friend of Newton, and his insistence on Newton's publication of the *Principia* would alone have sufficed to earn him immortal fame. Even so, he is mainly remembered for his observations of the comet which bears his name. He determined its orbit and, realizing that the same comet had been observed in the past, he was able to predict its return in 1758 (see p. 444). Finally, Halley studied terrestrial magnetism and, for that purpose, paid a special visit to the southern hemisphere, where he gathered valuable astronomical data on what was then a relatively unknown part of the sky.

NEWTON'S CONTRIBUTION TO ASTRONOMY

Newton's work was the crowning glory of 17th-century astronomy, as it was of so many other branches of science. The man who said: 'If I saw farther than others, 'twas because I stood on the shoulders of giants', was himself perhaps the greatest giant of them all.

Newton was born in Woolsthorpe, in Lincolnshire, on 25th

December 1642 (old style), and began to study mathematics at Cambridge in 1661. During the Great Plague (1665–1666) he was forced to return home, where he began the great work on which his renown chiefly rests. (In 1714, speaking of this period, Newton said that he was then at the height of his creative powers and more impassioned with philosophy than at any other time.)

If Newton's theory of universal attraction was, indeed, the fruit of meditation in the solitude of his home, it is easier to understand how he conceived his great idea, for as A. Koyré has shown, none of the 17th-century physicists suspected the identity of attraction and gravitation, but rather distinguished sharply between them. One was action at a distance and could occur only between similar bodies; it could not be seen. The other was directly perceived.

True, in his *Astronomia nova* (1609), Kepler had stated that gravity is proportional to mass (*moles*), but he believed that mutual attraction was exercised between only such similar bodies as the earth and the moon, and not between dissimilar bodies like the sun and the planets, which the sun moves by its own force. (Kepler was unfamiliar with the principles of inertia and conservation of momentum, and hence considered the force involved to be of magnetic or pseudo-magnetic origin.)

Since attraction implies action at a distance, Borelli (1608–1679) rejected it in his *Theoricae Medicearum planetarum ex causis physicis deducta* (Florence, 1666), where he explained that the circular motion of the planets is the result of a balance of centrifugal and centripetal forces in infinite and isotropic space. Had he not rejected attraction (the full consequences of which would, in any case, have been hidden from him by his inadequate mathematical knowledge), he might therefore have reached the same conclusions as Newton.

Only against this background can Newton's contribution be fully appreciated. Quite independently of Borelli, he considered that the planets are kept in their orbits by the interaction of centrifugal and centripetal forces, and found that the sun attracts the planets with a force inversely proportional to the square of its distance from them. Moreover, having compared the earth's pull on the moon to the force of gravity causing bodies to fall to the surface of the earth, he concluded that the two forces are identical.

Newton was too brilliant a man not to realize the provisional nature of his results, and he refused to print them. In fact, he had based his law of distances on the assumption that the planets revolve in circular orbits. Moreover, he was unable to prove the identity of terrestrial gravitation and celestial attraction while he still lacked a general law of attraction, and—though this is perhaps less important —before the mass and radius of the earth had been determined.

Though Newton then switched his main interest to optics, his reading of Huygens' *Horologium oscillatorium* (1673), and his controversy with Hooke persuaded him, in 1680, to re-examine the question of attraction in its entirety. (In his *An Attempt to Prove the Motion of the Earth from Observations*, 1674, Hooke had used the law of inertia to explain the mutual attraction of the planets and the sun, but had been unable to arrive at a *law* of attraction.) Newton now made the further assumption that, under the central attraction of the sun, the planets are deflected from the rectilinear paths which they would describe under the action of their inertia alone, and are therefore forced into elliptical rather than circular orbits. Hence it followed immediately that:

(1) All motion caused by a force acting from a central point follows the law of areas (Kepler's second law).

(2) If the central action is inversely proportional to the square of the distance, the trajectory is an ellipse with the centre of attraction in one of its foci (Kepler's first law).

Newton also showed that Kepler's laws imply that the force of attraction must be directed towards the focus, and that its intensity must be inversely proportional to the square of the distance. Finally, he showed how Kepler's third law can be derived from his own law of universal gravitation.

Newton published all these results in a small treatise, the *De motu* (1684), which Halley communicated to the Royal Society. But an essential link was still missing, for it was not until 1685 that Newton was able to prove that the attractive force of a solid sphere is equal to the attraction of its total mass assumed to be concentrated in its centre. To do this Newton had to create an entirely new mathematical tool—the calculus of fluxions.

In 1685 Newton finished his masterpiece, the *Philosophiae naturalis principia mathematica*. Meanwhile, Huygens' measurements of gravitational acceleration and Picard's measurements of the terrestrial radius had enabled him to complete his identification of the forces of gravity and attraction. The *Principia*, one of the highlights of human achievement, was published in London in 1687 and its effects were so tremendous that 18th-century astronomers devoted most of their work to the study of its consequences.

In the practical field, too, Newton made tremendous contributions to astronomy. His reflecting telescope[1] provided a more powerful

[1] This instrument, whose advantages had first been described by James Gregory in 1663, was produced almost simultaneously—and in similar form—by Cassegrain and Newton. Newton presented his instrument to the Royal Society in February 1672. The subsequent development of the telescope will be discussed in a later volume in this series, in connection with the work of William Herschel.

observational instrument and his study of light prepared the way for spectrum analysis, the full significance of which was not appreciated until the 19th century.

With Newton, modern science came of age. However, his greatness must not make us forget the contributions of lesser men, from the famous Cassini down to the obscure Gaultier de la Valette, all of whom helped to speed astronomy on its way and to infuse new life into the oldest of all sciences. By doing so, they all played a part in releasing the human spirit from shackles which had held it imprisoned for millennia.

CHAPTER 4

The Birth of Mathematical Optics

NEW EXPERIMENTAL TECHNIQUES

Optical Instruments in the Early 17th Century

Renewal of interest in optics at the beginning of the 17th century was largely the result of advances in the manufacture of lenses, microscopes and astronomical telescopes.

We know little about the early history of lenses of the kind required for optical instruments, though their invention has been attributed to Salvino degli Armati (1299); it seems more likely that they were first produced by some unknown craftsman. The earliest lenses were convex and were used as magnifying-glasses and for correcting poor sight. Up to the 15th century no one bothered to make a scientific study of their properties.

Then Leonardo da Vinci constructed a *camera obscura* and compared it with the human eye. In 1523, Giovanni Roncellai used a concave mirror as a 'microscope' and, about 1550, F. Maurolico began a systematic study of prisms, spherical mirrors and the human eye. His results, which were not published until 1611, anticipated many of the findings of Kepler, who seems to have been quite unaware of his predecessor's work.

The early physicists' indifference to the properties of lenses reflected their distrust of the results of what they considered to be mere conjurers' tricks.

The first systematic treatise on lenses was the *Magia naturalis* by Giambattista della Porta (2nd edition, 1589), who even described the possibility of constructing a telescope with a diverging eye-lens. The first of these was made in 1590; from 1604 onwards Holland became the main centre of their manufacture, in which Hans Lippershey (1608) was a pioneer.

In 1610, Galileo discovered Jupiter's satellites with this kind of instrument. His results were questioned by most physicists but were finally endorsed by Kepler (*Dioptrics*, 1611), who developed a geometrical theory of lenses, the Galilean telescope, and telescope object glasses. The use of diaphragms, by which all but the central ray could be excluded, enabled physicists to establish the object–image equation of a point source.

The Astronomical Telescope and the Microscope

Despite Galileo's great discoveries, astronomical telescopes were for a long time difficult to obtain. Their construction was so delicate that only experts could be entrusted with it. Men like Descartes, Hooke and Huygens did not disdain this kind of 'manual' activity, and made their own instruments.

The first astronomical telescopes were made of cardboard tubes sliding one within another. (Galileo's tubes were of lead.) Brass tubes were substituted soon afterwards. As greater magnifying power was demanded, the focal length of the lenses and hence the length of the tube had to be increased. Chromatic aberration was reduced by using small lenses of very great focal length so that tubes became impracticable. Huygens solved this problem with the aerial telescope, in which the tube was replaced by a rigid frame, and this limited the technical problems to the manufacture of good lenses. But it was only at about 1660 that advances in glass-polishing techniques led to the appearance of the first large object glasses.

It seemed a natural step to apply the principles of the astronomical telescope to the construction of microscopes and, in fact, no clear distinction between them was made at first. However, the manufacture of microscopes proved even more difficult than that of telescopes. The poor quality of the lenses led to blurred images, and chromatic aberration was so great that microscopes were of little scientific interest. Microscopes first became notable about 1615, and the most famous of all was Descartes', which incorporated a hyperbolic lens.

Z. Janssen made a compound microscope as early as 1590, and Galileo described an instrument which 'magnified 50,000 times [about 224 diameters, probably a gross exaggeration], making a fly as big as a hen, or a mite the size of a pea, and to walk east instead of west'. This microscope seems to have consisted of two convex lenses; the field lens, placed between the objective and the eye lens, was introduced by the brothers Huygens in the middle of the 17th century. The oldest-known drawings of objects seen through a microscope were made by Francesco Stelluti (1577–1640) and published in the *Apiarium* of Federico Cesi (1585–1630).

When Hooke's *Micrographia* (London, 1665), and the subsequent works of Swammerdam, Malpighi and Leeuwenhoek showed what remarkable results could be achieved with microscopes, microscopy was given a fresh lease of life. Leeuwenheok used a simple microscope (*i.e.* a single lens), and this kind of instrument, equipped with a movable support and a revolving stage, became very popular towards

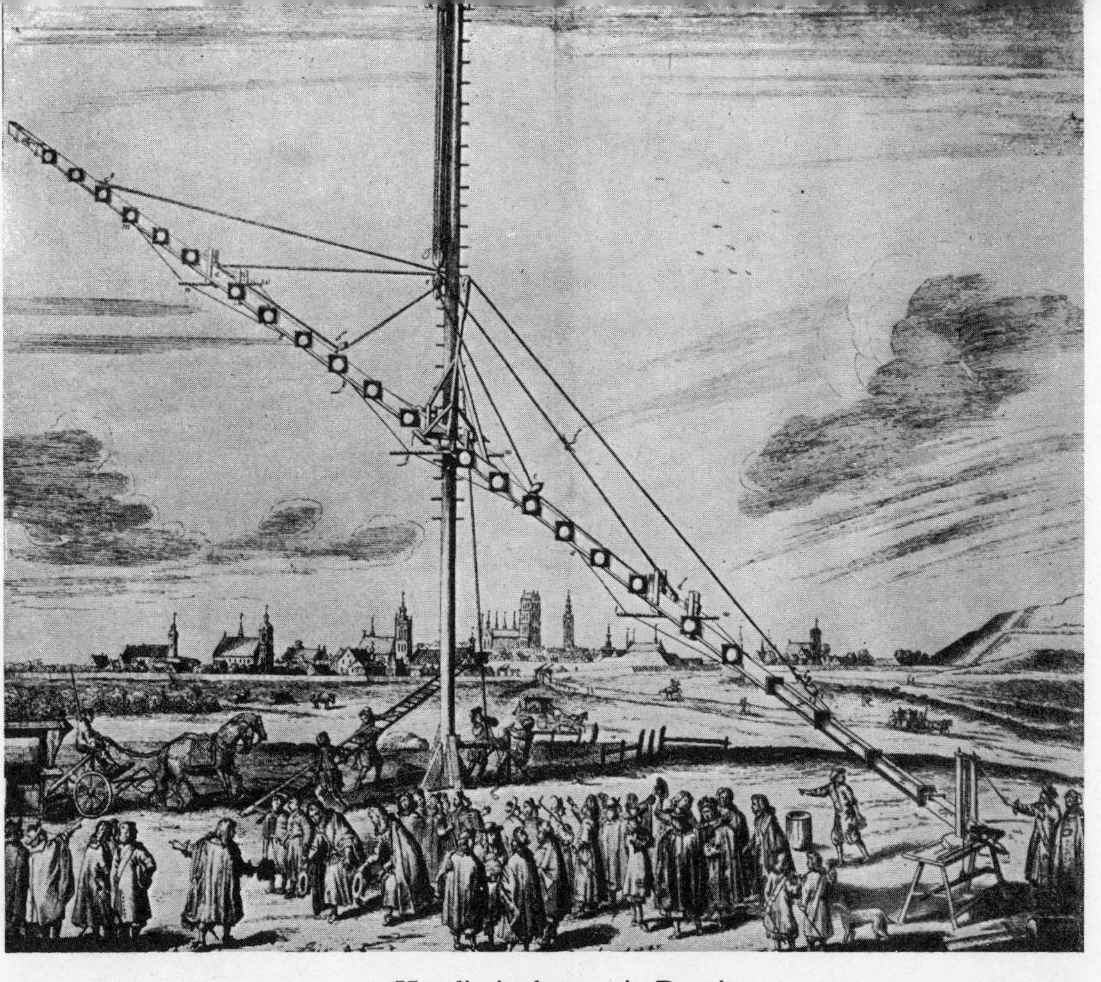

23 Hevelius' telescope in Danzig

24. Paris Observatory in 168[illegible]

the turn of the century. The very small lenses were often spherical.

Robert Hooke used a microscope made of two cardboard tubes mounted on a wooden stand by means of a ball-and-socket joint, which enabled the microscope to be tilted in any direction. It was focused by screwing the whole instrument up or down through a threaded ring in the attachment at the joint, and it magnified 30 or 40 diameters. Further improvements included the use of plano-convex lenses in the eyepiece (which included the field lens) and one —but only one—binocular microscope. Though this did not appear until 1722 it had been designed by P. Chérubin in the 17th century.

Experimental Knowledge at the End of the 16th Century

The fundamental properties of light rays—rectilinear propagation, reflexibility and refrangibility—the properties of lenses, spherical mirrors, and prisms had been described in Euclid's *Catoptrics* and in Ptolemy's and Damianus' *Optics*. Unfortunately, the clumsy notions which the Ancients had introduced precluded them from obtaining any quantitative results.

This shortcoming was the reason why, at the beginning of the 11th century, Alhazen failed in his attempts to give a mechanical explanation of the reflection and refraction of light by plane and spherical mirrors.

The early 13th century witnessed a minor rebirth of experimental activity, involving the use of the camera obscura, lenses, prisms and mirrors of all kinds. However, their properties were not understood, and though Bacon explained how a burning-glass brings the sun's rays to a focus, he failed to generalize this discovery.

In 1593, G. della Porta tried to explain the refraction of light (in the *De refractione*) but his introduction of visual processes and other extraneous notions led him to absurd conclusions. It would seem that, up to the beginning of the 17th century, experimenters in optics, even when they suspected where the correct answers lay, were unable to pose its problems correctly and hence failed to reach any kind of solution.

Advances in Experimental Techniques

It was Kepler who managed to isolate the fundamental elements from which the laws of geometrical optics were eventually derived. In his *Ad Vitellionem paralipomena* (1604) he compressed into a few propositions the principles governing the rectilinear propagation of light. He then presented what may be called a truly modern image-object theory. Every point-object has a corresponding point-image, which is 'intentional' (virtual) whenever the ray entering the observer's eye has first been 'broken' by reflection or refraction. Despite his detailed studies, Kepler failed to determine the exact law of refraction, though he did discover that, for small angles, the angle of refraction varies with the angle of incidence. The problem had at last been posed correctly.

Kepler also explained the working of the human eye, considered as an optical instrument. By separating the problem of visual optics from the associated physiological problem, he was able to show that the pupil and retina play the same role in sight as do the diaphragm and screen in physical optics. He also showed how glasses are effective in correcting poor vision.

The law of refraction was probably discovered—though not published—by Willebrord Snell. The first to state it was Isaac Voss (1618–1689), who gave it a purely empirical formulation: The distances travelled through two adjacent media (during similar time-intervals) have a constant ratio, which is that of the cosecants of the two angles (*i.e.* the angles of incidence and refraction).

In the *Dioptrics*, which he published as an appendix to his *Discours de la méthode* in 1637, Descartes failed to mention Voss and substituted sines for Voss's cosecants, attempting to prove Snell's law in terms of moving particles of light. He concluded that these must travel faster in the refracting body than in air. When Fermat argued that the opposite can be shown to follow from the 'principle of natural economy', he laid the foundations for Bartholin's and Huygens' work on double refraction and for Newton's studies of dispersion.

At the same time, practical optics assumed an increasing importance in scientific observation. Experimental advances resulting from the development of instruments led to more accurate results which, in turn, led to better hypotheses and the elimination of irrelevant observations. In 1665, Grimaldi was able to demonstrate diffraction phenomena. At the same time, Newton's experiments on thin plates, and the work of Hooke and of Huygens on interference phenomena, opened up vast new fields. Finally, the development of the infinitesimal calculus led to the construction of a truly mathematical optics, by which all the observed phenomena could be fitted into an all-embracing hypothesis.

THEORIES ON THE NATURE OF LIGHT

Theoretical Heritage of the 17th Century

According to the ancients, light is a substance whose original form was fire. Fire itself was considered by some to be the only fundamental element and the source of all things and of all colours (School of Miletos; Heraclitos of Ephesos), while others assumed it to be but one of the four elements. According to them, colours are the result of the combination of fire with the other three elements, and this theory, which probably goes back to Empedocles, was adopted by Aristotle.

Aristotle contended that fire is light in its purest state, and the brightness of the sky is fire adulterated with other elements. In nature, light can be perceived only as colour, hence optics is the study of appearances. The Stoics added further confusion by adding the notion of 'sympathy', and so did the schoolmen, who were torn between the corpuscular theory of Democritos and the doctrines of Heraclitos and Plato. Colour became a debased aspect of pure light, but no one bothered to ask how this 'debasement' was produced.

The Nature of Light and Corpuscular Theories

The corpuscular theory of light is almost as old as the theory of the basic elements. It first appeared in India, where materialist doctrines held sway before the birth of Brahmanism. According to these doctrines, colour is an essential property of all atoms. Though Buddhism denied the substantiality of matter and, *a fortiori*, of light, it, too, subscribed to a kind of evanescent atomism—all atoms are formed of immaterial sub-atoms of colour or sound.

Greek atomism was far more materialistic than that. Thus, Anaxagoras taught that all qualities correspond to particles, and that the ultimate particles of matter are homogeneous. His doctrine was taken over and modified by Democritos and Epicuros.

According to Democritos, light consists of indiscernible round particles which travel from the luminous object to the eye through an intermediate fluid—the air—which contracts under the combined effect of the material emanations of the object and the eye. Democritos' optics was therefore based on a mixed theory involving both corpuscles and a medium, and maintained that light is not a special substance but the result of a mechanical *action*: the rarefaction of air due to corpuscular collisions.

This theory was so vague that various philosophers could easily fit it into their particular doctrines. Thus Plato assumed that vision is due to the mutual encounter of rays emitted from the eye and particles emitted by the object. The existence of visual rays was generally assumed by the Greeks, especially by Pythagoras and hence by Euclid, who constructed a satisfactory geometrical optics on it. For Plato, the visual ray or 'visual fire' was made up of particles that were smaller or larger than the corpuscles emitted by the material objects. In the particular case when both have the same dimensions, no sensation is produced. Black, white or coloured vision is the result of changes in the relative dimensions of the two kinds of particles.

The theory of Epicuros, subsequently popularized by Lucretius, was altogether different—it lacked the simplicity of Democritos' theory and discarded Plato's visual fire. According to Epicuros, the surface of objects constantly emits thin and rapid corpuscles which travel through the air and preserve the form of the objects from which they have originated. When they meet the eye, they produce vision.

Dream images are caused by still smaller corpuscles which can penetrate as far as the soul, where the weakest of them may be distorted into nightmares. To Epicuros, the imagination was but a form of vision and not, as in Plato's doctrine, the dim recognition whereby the soul is enabled to transcend itself. His doctrine was a kind of psychoanalytic theory, with a censor barring entry to all unwanted impressions. Nevertheless, the Epicurean theory of light was far from scientific for it failed to give any analysis of immediate sense impressions, other than attributing them to the selective impact of atoms.

In short, Greek theories of light were based on brilliant but sporadic insights, and were quickly forgotten.

With the rise of Christianity, certainty was identified with the revealed truth: light was given directly by God; beyond that, Aristotle was held to have spoken the last word on the subject.

Despite Alhazen's contribution in the 11th century, and that of less-known scholars in the 12th and 13th centuries, most theories of light therefore continued to be based on Aristotle. That was the reason why Porta, for instance, was unable either to pose or to solve the problems to which he devoted so much of his time, and why real progress had to await the coming of Kepler.

Opinions on the Nature of Light at the Beginning of the 17th Century

By the end of the 16th century physicists had at last begun to ask whether light is a substance or the motion of a substance. However, we must not be misled into thinking that they were, in fact, choosing between the corpuscular and wave theories of light. By calling light a substance they simply stressed its substantial reality and not its relationship with other matter; by calling it a motion they simply referred to the rarefaction and compression effects produced by a central source. It was only with the introduction of the concept of vibration in a non-material medium that an independent wave theory would be born.

Thus, up to the time of Newton, theories of light were neither purely kinetic nor purely corpuscular. Antonio de Dominis (1611), for instance, considered light a substantial element that produced the colours of bodies but was not an inherent part of them. When light is pure it looks like fire, when it loses its brilliance it becomes white; when it becomes tainted with matter it produces all the other colours.

Isaac Voss (1648) held similar views, though since he knew that light rays can be brought to a focus he assumed their immaterial nature. Light was fire but, unlike Aristotle's and the Stoics', Voss's fire was not an element but a kind of heat produced by the agitation of solid bodies or 'the action which dissolves bodies'. He believed that light crossed the air instantaneously and invisibly, but becomes visible again in the solids on which it falls.

Voss's theory was neither a corpuscular theory, in the sense that it distinguished between light and the matter constituting physical bodies, nor was it a kinetic theory. To say that light is heat is not to liken it to a material body; to maintain that it is produced by the agitation of solid bodies does not make it a source of vibrations.

But at about the same period, there appeared a truly kinetic theory of light, based on the motion of 'substantial' though not necessarily material media. Marcus Marci of Kronland defined this motion as resulting from compressions and expansions of a medium whose nature he failed to specify.

Most other kinetic theories postulated, at least implicitly, the material nature of the medium, which was said to differ from common matter only by its greater subtlety. A decisive advance in this kind of theory was made when light was first likened to sound, which was known to result from the agitation of the air. Though Leonardo da Vinci seems to have suspected this kind of relationship, Galileo was the first to make it explicit.

To Galileo's mind, all physical effects, and more especially all optical effects, were produced by kinetic causes. Like sound, though travelling with a far greater velocity, light involves the motion of a medium. However, since Galileo was not certain whether this motion was due to the collision of the solid particles which make up the medium, or to waves, his optics was not very satisfactory.

The Optics of Descartes

One of the basic principles of Descartes' philosophy was the assumption that matter is extension (see pp. 246–248), and that all extension is a form of matter. As a result, his world was made up of matter with varying degrees of subtlety but basically identical in nature and held together by vortices.

In Descartes' world, the sun and the eye were separated by a layer of subtle matter in the form of small spheres packed together like lead shot. Thinner particles, which split up when they meet other bodies, tend to escape from the sun and from all luminous bodies and compress the intermediate layer, so that it begins to 'tremble'. As a result, it may be thrown against solid bodies, causing the corpuscles of the subtle medium to be refracted or reflected according to whether the 'pores' of the solid body are large enough to admit them or not.

Thus Descartes considered light, not as a true motion, but as a tendency—a *conatus ad movum*—or a kind of pressure. Once produced by the rhythmical pressure variations within an incompressible fluid, light crosses space instantaneously.

> Light is merely a certain movement or a quick and powerful action which travels towards our eyes through the medium of the air or any other transparent body, in the same way that impressions of movement or of resistance travel up to a blind man's hand through the medium of his stick.

Because Descartes' theory introduced corpuscular media, it has often been judged incompatible with any kind of wave theory. This judgment is admissible only if one assumes that the determining factor is continuity or discontinuity. In fact, the main distinction between the corpuscular and wave theories is their respective view of the nature of the medium. Though Descartes failed to introduce vibration as such, he implied it when he spoke of the instantaneous transmission of rhythmical pressure systems.

Descartes' optics was not entirely divorced from experiment, but he used experiments merely to confirm assumed truths. Like Gassendi, he considered reflection and refraction particular instances of material collisions. Thus, he proved the laws of reflection by assuming that light was thrown back like an elastic ball. A similar investigation of refraction then led him to his sine law.

We have seen that Fermat rejected Descartes' view that a dense medium offers less resistance to the passage of light than do air and other rare media. Fermat's second objection was that Descartes' physics was based on too many arbitrary analogies, such as his comparison of reflection with elastic phenomena. However, Fermat's dislike of mechanical hypotheses was by no means typical of his day.

In reality, the fragility of Descartes' physics was due not so much to his mechanistic approach as to his arbitrary introduction of *a priori* certainties, and his arrogant assumption that his deductive method was capable, by itself, of explaining the entire universe. Hence, when it became known that light does not travel with infinite speed—an essential conclusion of the Cartesian method—Cartesian optics was shaken to its very foundations.

Malebranche's Vibratory Theory: Colour and 'Promptitude'

New discoveries at the end of the 17th century led to radical changes of all the existing theories of light.

In 1665, Grimaldi demonstrated the existence of diffraction. At about the same time, Hooke was studying iridescent colours in thin flakes of mica. Double refraction was discovered four years later by Erasme Bartholin and then studied by Huygens. Finally, in 1675, came Römer's discovery (see p. 283) that light travels with a finite velocity.

This period of great experimental successes coincided with the youth of Newton. In France, Cartesianism still held full sway, so that Malebranche tried to reconcile it with the vibratory theories of Grimaldi, Hooke and Huygens.

Though a pupil of Descartes, Malebranche (1638–1715) developed a philosophy that differed greatly from his teacher's, for he substituted the idea of intelligibility for that of agnostic clarity. 'It is only faith', he wrote, 'whereby we become convinced of the existence of bodies.'

Malebranche began his optical studies by defining the Cartesian theory of subtle media. He assumed that light was a kind of pressure, propagated instantaneously and subject to periodic variations.

His next step was to change the shape of Descartes' subtle matter. Solids cohere because they are compressed, not by Descartes' tightly packed balls, but by soft and elastic matter moving in vortices, without which there would only be fluids. Malebranche therefore came close to Huygens' elastic æther.

But despite all these innovations, Malebranche continued to accept the basic principles of the Cartesian theory. When he described light as a sensation caused by very 'prompt' pressure fluctuations, he had merely converted the 'trembles' of Descartes into vibrations.

In 1712 Malebranche first read Newton's *Opticks*. He had previously associated every pure colour with a vibration of given 'promptitude' (frequency); now Newton's theory of dispersion forced him to conclude that white was a combination of vibrations of different 'promptitudes'. Malebranche felt that this constituted no real break with Cartesian principles and continued his attempts to explain the laws of reflection and refraction by the vortical structure of the æther.

In other words, Malebranche tried to preserve the best part of both theories. He finally adopted the hypothesis of the finite propagation of light. We shall return to his colour theory, which was his most important contribution.

Diffraction. The Vibrant Æther

Father Pardies and Hooke, two contemporaries of Malebranche, tried to develop Grimaldi's optics into a complete theory of the æther.

Grimaldi's own views were based on the existence of diffraction phenomena, which he himself had discovered. His experiments had convinced him that the mere notion of light rays, the basis of geometrical optics, failed to explain all optical phenomena. 'There exists', he wrote, 'a fourth method by which light can be propagated, *viz.* by diffraction, which is quite distinct from the three modes known hitherto' (rectilinear propagation; reflection; refraction). From the fact that opaque bodies can deflect light, he concluded that light must travel with a finite but undetectable velocity.

He also believed that light differs from matter not only by its subtlety but also by its generation, and that it can be compared with sound because both are produced by the rhythmical agitation of a medium. 'Light is a fluid that moves extremely quickly, vibrating through transparent bodies.'

After Grimaldi, æther theories became more materialistic and more accurate—more Cartesian, we might say. In particular, they attempted to account for motions in the æther, and while Descartes thought it sufficient to allow the æther a 'tendency' to tremble, Malebranche and Grimaldi demanded a true causal vibration, though they were vague as to the exact mode of propagation.

Like Descartes, Hooke held that Nature is constituted of only matter and motion which, he added, were interchangeable. Though this remained no more than a brilliant intuition, it forced Hooke to replace Grimaldi's non-material luminiferous æther with a material fluid, and to base the distinction between matter and light on the characteristic vibrations of particles.

This idea was so close to our own that its importance has often been exaggerated. Hooke lacked a correct definition of kinetic energy (which was provided by Huygens) to explain the connection between vibrations and material particles. As a result, he held that light was transmitted by uniform pulsations of the medium, perpendicular to the direction of propagation. In Fresnel's hands this hypothesis later became the basis of wave theory.

Hooke also considered that reflection, refraction and chromatic phenomena were produced when vibrations cross a transparent body in different directions. In that respect his theory proved greatly inferior to that of Huygens. Moreover, Hooke held that light was transmitted instantaneously, and put up a fundamentally false colour theory in opposition to Newton's.

He explained double refraction by the assumption that every light

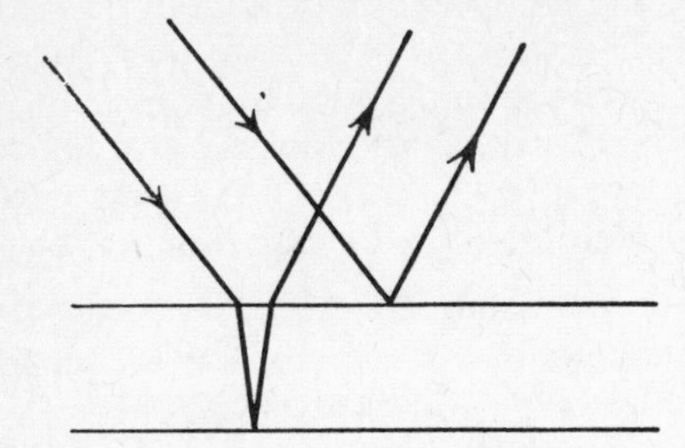

fig. 23 Reflection and refraction by a thin plate.

ray has two faces, vibrating in opposite directions, thus in some way causing near objects to look doubled when viewed through Iceland spar, and white light to be split into two fundamental colours.

Hooke's explanation of the appearance of colours in thin plates was a curious mixture of near-modern and long-forgotten notions. As a light ray travels across the plate, he maintained, it is more highly reflected and weakened by the back face than by the front face. The two reflected rays then combine to produce a series of alternating 'strong' and 'weak' impressions, the strong component travelling in front. If the interval between them is imperceptibly small, the eye perceives a single 'strong' ray which, by definition, causes a red impression; if the interval is perceptible, the 'weak' ray seems to travel in front, and the eye receives a blue impression. It was left to Newton to remedy the worst fault of this physiological colour theory.

Despite its evident faults, Hooke's theory had a number of important consequences. Thus, though he failed to appreciate its full significance, Hooke was the first to consider transverse vibrations, and his definition of the æther as the medium supporting vibrations was probably closer to the views immediately preceding relativity theory than was Huygens' more precise definition. Huygens' theory had many similarities with those of Pardies and Hooke, with both of whom he kept in close touch.

'Light', Huygens wrote at the beginning of his *Traité de la lumière* (1690), 'is the movement of the matter between us and luminous bodies.' He went on to compare light with sound. As sound needs air for its propagation, so light needs a material æther as the seat of its vibrations.

Huygens then went on to consider the fine structure of the æther, and concluded that it must consist of small elastic particles surrounded by a second, still more subtle, medium whose rapidly moving particles compress it. Though this explanation had a decidedly Cartesian flavour, Huygens' particles had neither pores nor grooves: æthereal matter fills the gaps between large particles which merely *appear* to be continuous. Each æther particle obeys the laws of impact and each may become the centre of a wave spreading infinitely far into space. Huygens then made the spherical wave hypothesis the basis of his proof of the laws of reflection, refraction and double refraction.

Huygens' theory was more quantitative than Hooke's, and hence an advance on it. He not only accepted Römer's proof that light travels with a finite velocity, but considered it the experimental confirmation of his wave hypothesis.

> If light takes time to travel, it follows that it spreads, like sound, by surfaces and spherical waves.

On the other hand, Huygens failed to adopt Hooke's idea on transverse vibrations, and though he was the first to describe polarization in noting the extinction of light by two spar crystals, he made no attempt to explain it.

It was left to Father Ango, following Father Pardies, to fill in the gaps. According to him, light originates from the intrinsic vibrations of a source, and spreads through the æther in the form of waves. These waves may be likened to ripples on the surface of the sea, and do not transport matter. Though Ango did not say this in so many words, his æther must have been a material medium, because he thought that it could communicate its vibrations to the air. Huygens, who had given a much clearer definition of the æther, had failed to be nearly as explicit about the exchange of motions between the subtle and the material medium.

Pardies, Hooke, Huygens and Malebranche wrote their main work roughly at the time that Newton was preparing his. Their opposition to his theory ushered in a stormy period in the history of optics.

Newton's Optics: the Theory of Fits

Any discussion of Newton's optics must begin with an account of his dispersion experiments. Dispersion phenomena had been observed in the past, but had been attributed to chance effects of the optical materials used. Newton was the first to realize that rays of different colour have characteristic degrees of refrangibility, and that a 'pure' ray retains its colour even after it has passed through a prism. Hence colours could not possibly be conferred on the rays by the glass, but must pre-exist in them. Prisms merely help to sort them out.

What, then, is light? In a paper which he sent to the Royal Society on 28th February 1672, Newton called it a substantial reality with a corpuscular structure. He had deduced this from his colour theory, arguing that since colours are qualities of light, light itself must be a substance, for there can be no such thing as the quality of a quality. Colour is associated with the light substance, much as mechanical properties are associated with matter.

In what respect does light differ from other matter? Newton seemed less certain on this point. While he was certain that light is a substance, he found it difficult to determine precisely what kind of substance. 'I have no wish to mix what is certain with what is uncertain', he added.

Newton's paper was strongly criticized, particularly by Hooke and Huygens. In his reply, Newton stated that his hypothesis was but one of many possible ones, and that he had decided henceforth to eschew them all.

Newton also studied the colours produced in thin plates, and particularly in the so-called Newton's rings. He experimented first with two slightly convex prisms pressed together, and later with a plano-convex lens pressed on a thin glass plate. In this way he obtained a layer of air whose thickness increased towards the edges. He found that distinct interference rings are produced by distinct thicknesses of the layers of air.

To fit this phenomenon, which we consider a direct consequence of the wave theory, into his corpuscular theory, Newton was forced to introduce a further hypothesis: the reason why the surfaces of all thick transparent bodies reflect part of the light incident on them and refract the rest is that some rays, at their incidence, are in fits of early reflection and others in fits of early transmission.

Newton explained the colour of thin plates in similar terms. Suppose that the distance between two plates is such that the rays enter and emerge in fits of early transmission. Neither the incident nor the emergent ray would then reach the eye of the observer, who would see a black spot at the point of egress of the plate. On the other hand, if the distance between the plates is such that rays enter and leave by different fits, every ray transmitted by the first surface is reflected by the second to produce a bright spot. Hence there arise alternating dark and bright zones. In other words, the theory of fits was based on periodic changes of state and not of motion.

Since interference could not be caused by secret virtues, Newton had to find a physical explanation for it. Accordingly, he suggested that the fits may result from a dissymmetry in the form or properties of the luminous corpuscles, caused by magnetic effects or by their axial position. Thus, the motion of an ellipsoid (cigar-shaped) corpuscle which rotates as it moves forward might be said to proceed in 'fits' (see *fig. 24*).

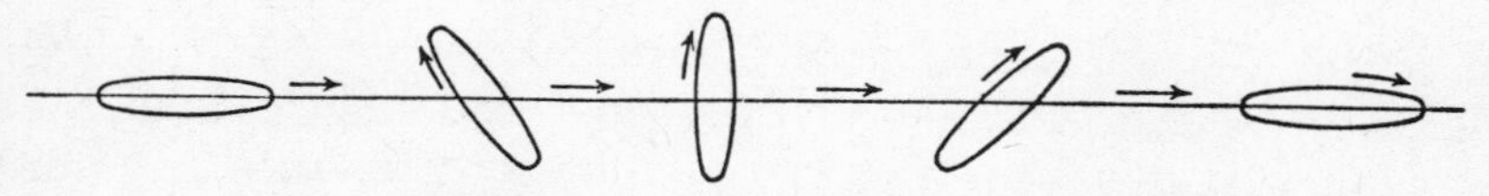

fig. 24 Possible explanation of Newton's theory of fits.

Alternatively, fits might result from the interaction of different light corpuscles, as a result of which different corpuscles move with different velocities through the æther.

Brilliantly conceived though it was, Newton's theory of fits failed to pass the experimental test. In his studies of the colours of thin plates, Newton had merely considered the behaviour of rays which had crossed the first face to be modified by the second. Now, if reflection from the first surface was eliminated by the use of polarized light, the rings disappeared when, according to the theory, they should not have been affected. Hence the rings could have resulted only from the combined reflected rays of both surfaces, *i.e.* from interference.

The Corpuscular Theory and the Existence of the Æther

Newton's earliest theories were purely corpuscular—he did not mention the æther before 1671. But his disputes with Hooke forced him to consider the existence of a subtle medium, albeit with great reserve.

Hooke, in his turn, had been compelled to change his theory of æthereal vibrations. Forced to admit the connection between colour and refrangibility, and to discard his view that light results from the combination of two basic colours, he could no longer maintain that light rays have two sides. Hence he came to explain the appearance of colours by internal changes of the rays, and to postulate that each colour corresponds to a given amplitude of the vibrant æther.

In the same year—1675—Newton published his theory of light and colours. He was pleased with the concessions Hooke had been forced to make to his own theories, and then developed a theory of æthereal waves which meant an even greater concession on his part. His theory was intended to be only provisional, but in stating it he more or less declared that light is an emanation of incandescent bodies which has the power to produce periodic vibrations in the æther.

Newton's conversion seems to have occurred for two main reasons. First, the theory of fits indicated the presence of a medium affecting the motion of light particles. Second, diffraction phenomena seemed to suggest an action at a distance from the screen. This action was reminiscent of gravity which, too, seemed to demand the presence of a medium. Newton was, of course, particularly keen on this analogy.

However, Newton argued that the æther could not possibly have the properties that Descartes had attributed to it, since any fluid, however subtle, would offer an enormous resistance to the motions of the planets. Now, Newton's studies of resistance had convinced him that no such fluid exists. Hence, the properties of the æther must depend on the matter with which it is associated, so that there is a distinction between æther in the free state and æther containing or contained by bodies. It is because of this distinction that refrangibility varies with the density and chemical nature of bodies.

But while space contains no solid matter, it could contain thin vapours and light rays. Despite this qualification, Newton's ideas had clearly undergone a great change since 1671. Nevertheless, he had not changed sufficiently to go beyond a mixed theory, in which light corpuscles act on a vibrant æther. This does not mean that his theory could have dispensed with the æther, as has often been suggested, but simply that he considered it an inadequate foundation of optics.

Newton's criticism of wave theory was rather feeble. He considered it incompatible with his theory of fits. In order to reconcile the two, it would have been necessary to introduce two vibrant æthers, the vibration of one constituting light and that of the other—travelling more quickly—producing fits of the former. He also believed that his own theory explained the rectilinear propagation of light perfectly well, while Hooke had to introduce the unnecessary complication of rays travelling at right angles to the front of a spherical wave. Knowing that wave phenomena are rarely propagated in straight lines, Newton remarked that the rectilinear propagation of light cannot be explained in that way. (Huygens almost succeeded in reconciling rectilinear propagation with wave theory, but failed to interpret interference phenomena correctly. This task fell to Young and Fresnel.)

Moreover, Newton's study of mechanics had given him a clear preference for atomic hypotheses. If light consists of material corpuscles, the laws of dynamics, and particularly the principle of inertia, can be applied directly and lead to a simple explanation of the most obvious properties of light.

Finally, Newton embraced the corpuscular doctrine for personal reasons. Hooke being the official advocate of wave theory, Newton took the opposite view almost as a matter of course.

In any case, Newton's philosophical views made it impossible to come down squarely on the side of either the corpuscular or the wave hypothesis. The choice of hypotheses, however useful, was a matter of indifference; the only important question was the observable behaviour of light. 'We cannot know', he said, 'whether light is a projection of bodies or merely an abstract motion.' This is why E. Bloch had much reason to claim that Newton's theory had to remain mixed, if it was to remain Newtonian.

COLOUR THEORIES

Colour Theories at the End of the 16th Century

Because colours are perceptible aspects of light, most theories of light have also been theories of colour.

Plato explained that colours are produced by various factors presiding over the meeting of the 'visual fire' emitted by the eye and the stream of corpuscles emitted by the object. Provided the particles are large enough, the visual fire can split them up and the eye sees black; conversely if the particles are small enough to split up the visual fire, the eye sees white. If the 'splitting' occurs close to the eye, we have a dazzling sensation, which may be quenched by the humours of the eye to produce a red impression. Gold, grey, ochre and green are obtained by different interactions of the two streams.

'As to the rest,' Plato continued, 'it is fairly clear from these examples what are the mixtures with which we ought to identify them, if we would preserve probability in our account. But should any inquirer make an experimental test of these facts, he would evince his ignorance of the difference between man's nature and God's—how that, whereas God is sufficiently wise and powerful to blend the many into one and to dissolve again the one into many, there exists not now, nor ever will exist hereafter, a child of man sufficient for either of these tasks. (*Timaios*, 68 D.)

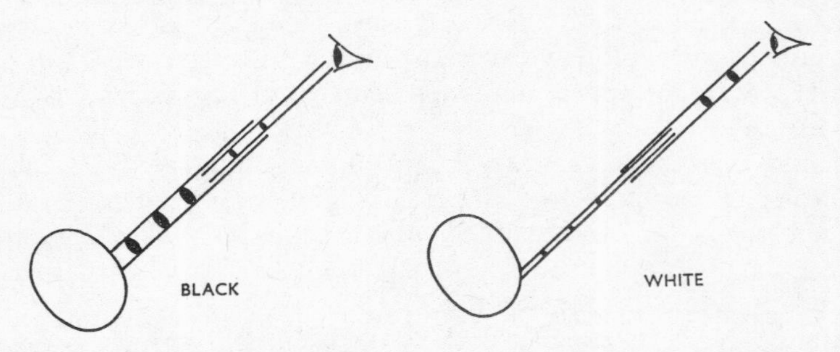

fig. 25 The formation of black and white according to Plato.

Aristotle's colour theory was quite different: colours result from different combinations of light and shade. A bright light and a shadow produce red; a dark shadow and a weak light produce violet. The other colours are produced by combinations of these two.

This theory persisted until the Renaissance, though the dispersion effects of prisms had been observed long before, and though Seneca had likened the resulting colours to those of the rainbow. But in the Middle Ages these effects seemed merely to corroborate an Aristotelian theory: light refracted from the front edge of a glass plate travels a shorter distance than light refracted from the back edge. Hence the back edge produces more shadow and less light (violet) while the front edge produces more light and less shadow (red).

Pre-Cartesian Views on the Nature of Colours

In 1617, the Jesuit Galeotto Mariscoti tried to refute the Aristotelian colour doctrine by demonstrating that colours are produced, not by the prism itself, but by the refraction of light rays. If a ray enters the prism at right angles to its surface, no colour appears. Moreover, the 'purest' ray, yellow, is not the ray closest to the apex of the prism, as Aristotle's theory would suggest, but the central ray, which must have crossed a thicker layer of glass than the red ray and ought to have been the darker of the two.

Despite these arguments, Isaac Barrow was still convinced of the basic validity of Aristotle's ideas in 1674. According to him, black is produced by the complete absorption of light; other colours, being mixtures of shadows and light, result from various degrees of reflection and absorption.

Cartesian Theories. Colours and Vibrations

At about the same time, Cartesian molecular and kinetic theories began to oust the principles of scholastic physics. According to Descartes, light is transmitted because the rotating particles of the subtle medium exert a pressure on one another. At the surface of terrestrial bodies, the boundary between shadow and light, the particles have no neighbours and are therefore subject to unilateral pressure only. That pressure either increases or decreases the velocity of their rotation, according to its direction. Colour is merely the effect of the resulting velocity differences.

Because they lacked any kind of experimental basis, Cartesian theories were the more far-fetched the more they went into detail. Boyle expressed his utter disdain of this type of explanation, but Father Pardies tried to produce a compromise between Descartes and Aristotle. Like Aristotle and Barrow, he assumed the existence of two fundamental colours: white, produced by reflection from convex surfaces, and black, produced by absorption by concave surfaces. All other colours were mixtures of these two, and all were produced by lateral motions of the agitated æthereal substance. This was also his explanation of the irization effects which Grimaldi had obtained during his diffraction experiments.

All these confused ideas were corrected by Malebranche, who propounded the first modern colour theory in 1699, quite independently of Newton.

Using the analogy between light and sound, Malebranche argued that, just as increases in the amplitude of acoustic vibrations produce increasingly louder sounds, so changes in the amplitude of light vibrations produce changes in the intensity of a given colour, but not in the nature of the colour. Different colours are produced by vibrations of different promptitude (frequency) and not of different amplitude; white corresponds to the highest promptitude, followed by yellow and blue. What differences there are between light and sound are due to the fact that colours result from æthereal vibrations whereas sounds result from aerial vibrations.

> Light, with its different colours, behaves like sound with its various tones. The strength of sound depends more or less on the intensity of air vibrations and the diversity of tones more or less on their promptitude. Similarly, the strength or brightness of colours depends more or less on the strength of the vibrations of subtle matter and differences in colour more or less on their promptitude.

At first, Malebranche had considered white a colour like any other, but, in about 1712, when he learned of Newton's work, he came to look upon it as the resultant of all possible promptitudes.

However, his original comparison of light with sound, by which he had arrived at such astute explanations, also persuaded him that there were seven fundamental colours, just as there are seven musical intervals. In that theory, violet, corresponding to the vibration of greatest promptitude, must undergo maximum dispersion, which was, in fact, proved by experiment.

After his death, Malebranche's colour theory was gradually forgotten. Euler, who adopted the hypothesis that colours are related to frequencies, made no acknowledgment to his predecessor.

Like Malebranche, Hooke, too, was forced to change many aspects of his original colour theory. Whereas he had originally explained that colours result from the random directions which the light vibrations assume once they have crossed transparent bodies, the demonstration of double refraction now convinced him that luminous rays must have two parallel faces, *i.e.* two opposite and independent vibrations. Hence there could be no more than two basic colours —red and blue. (By similar arguments, Huygens concluded that the basic colours must be yellow and green.)

Later still, after he had read Newton, Hooke came to admit the infinite diversity of colours and their close connection with refrangibility. Sticking to his wave theory, he explained that individual colours are associated with different vibratory intensities of the rays. If the most intense vibration arrives first, we see red; if it arrives last, we see blue.

25 Newton, by Sir Godfrey Kneller

Systema Ideale
PYROPHYLACIORUM
Subterraneorum, quorum montes
Vulcanii, velut spiracula
quædam existunt.

The difference between the amplitudes of vibration may be purely apparent. For instance, it may result from an imperceptible shift of two different vibrations, one strong and one weak, as happens in the case of the colours of thin plates.

Thus all pre-Newtonian physicists, with the exception of Malebranche, treated colour phenomena as substantial or kinetic modifications of pure light; all attempts to explain dispersion were attempts to explain how prisms can alter the composition or motion of light. Hence there arose such complicated theories as Mariotte's which distinguished eight principles governing the distribution of colours in a refracted beam. Newton's revolutionary contribution was to replace the problems of pure light by the colour problem.

'Pure' Colour and White Light

After his studies of dispersion, Newton propounded the theory that white light is composed of a number of 'pure' colours, each with a specific degree of refrangibility.

> Homogeneal Light has a Colour corresponding to its Degree of Refrangibility, and that Colour cannot be changed by Reflexions or Refractions. (*Opticks*, Prop. II, Theor. II.)

Newton was soon forced to realize that colours, far from being restricted to seven, exist in infinite numbers. He then asked whether colours exist in the dark, or whether they are qualities of bright objects. He concluded that they are caused by modifications of light and that, though light rays are not themselves coloured, they 'possess a certain power or disposition to stir up a sensation of this or that colour'.

Hence, 'the homogeneal light and rays which appear red, or rather make objects appear so, I call rubrifick or red-making; those which make objects appear yellow, green, blue, and violet, I call yellow-making, green-making, blue-making, violet-making, and so of the rest'.

While colours can bring out certain specific properties of illuminated bodies, these properties are not 'colorifick' themselves.

At once there was a storm of protest. Father Pardies, for instance, tried unsuccessfully to compound colours into white and then dismissed Newton's theory as a mere hypothesis. Only when he used Newton's own method was he able to carry out the experiment successfully.

Hooke argued that the simultaneous belief in the substantiality of light and in the pre-existence within it of an infinity of colours was paradoxical. If colours pre-existed in white light there could only be two fundamental colours. Only if light was not a substance but an æthereal vibration could there be an infinity of colours, and this was, in fact, the view which he finally adopted.

In his early work, Newton, faithful to his corpuscular theory, had tried to explain the variety of colours by the diversity of light corpuscles. He assumed at first that light consists of heterogeneous particles of specific refrangibility, and later that the distinction between different light particles rests purely on differences in size, and hence in mass, the smallest particles corresponding to violet.

Now, Newton thought he had proved that refraction is a kind of attraction. Like Descartes, he therefore assumed that the velocity of light increases with the density of the medium, but (and this Descartes had not appreciated) that the sine law holds only in the case of monochromatic light. This hypothesis led him into immediate difficulties.

First of all, he had to assume that violet particles, which are the most refrangible, were also the most strongly attracted, even though they are the smallest of all. Secondly, since he believed refraction and dispersion to be proportional, Newton was forced to conclude that the chromatic aberration of lenses and prisms could not be eliminated, no matter what combination of lenses was used. Newton therefore incorporated a mirror into his telescope to avoid the inevitable consequences of chromatic aberration. This 'Newtonian error', as Euler called it, was accepted without discussion during the early 18th century.

From 1672, Newton came to admit the possible existence of a vibrant æther, showing how it could be reconciled with the existence of an infinite number of colours: the corpuscles produce vibrations of the æther and the resulting waves correspond to the different colours. However, unlike Malebranche, Newton associated colours with amplitudes and not with frequencies.

Newton and Malebranche had thus laid the foundations of modern colour theory. The elaboration of their ideas in the 18th century was to become the very model of precise physics and the final justification of mathematical optics.

CHAPTER 5

Magnetism and Electricity

THE DEVELOPMENT OF MAGNETISM and electricity into a positive, albeit rudimentary, science in the 17th century is possibly one of the most remarkable chapters in the history of science. Here, more than in any other branch of physics, it would be misleading to concentrate on the chronological order of the discoveries, for magnetism is rooted in the most complex ideas. Even today the word 'magnetism' still conjures up the occult forces of the 'animal magnetizer'.

This fact alone suggests what animist and vitalist obstacles impeded the study of magnetic phenomena right up to the Renaissance. It was only in 1600, when Gilbert's *De magnete* appeared providentially as the herald of the new age, that magnetism not only took its rightful place among *physical* forces but became the basis of a new 'magnetic philosophy.[1]

THE EXPERIMENTAL AND THEORETICAL HERITAGE

THE CONTRIBUTIONS OF ANTIQUITY

Thales of Miletos is said to have been the first to have studied the Magnesian stone and the electric properties of amber (ἤλεκτρον). At the time, no clear distinction was made between magnetic attraction and electrical attraction, no electric spark had been produced, and lightning was not considered to be an electrical phenomenon.

The magnetic poles were not discovered until the 12th century, when the compass was first put to use. Meanwhile the real facts remained shrouded in a mass of legends and fabrications, many of which were recognized as such but nevertheless hampered progress.

The greatest temptation was to explain magnetic phenomena by animistic and vitalistic theories. While even the ancients had little difficulty in fitting other physical phenomena into some sort of

[1] *Cf.* J. Daujat, *Origine et formation des théories de l'électricité et du magnétisme* (Paris, 1947), from which we shall quote at length. *Cf.* also E. Bauer, *L'électromagnétisme hier et aujourd'hui* (Paris, 1949).

coherent framework, magnetism was so shrouded in mystery that it was left outside their theories of nature.

The magnet's 'virtues' of attracting iron, and only iron, and of pointing to the north were thought to be not 'manifest' (intelligible by comparison with the behaviour of other bodies) but 'occult' (original and inexplicable). Thus authors like Pliny and Porphyry reflected the general opinion when they endowed magnets with a soul, claiming that magnets attract iron as a bridegroom would his bride. Pliny lumped lodestones together with precious stones—all more or less magical—and distinguished between male and female magnets. Magnets were also said to have marvellous medicinal properties.

Plato compared magnetism to poetic inspiration. Magnets attract not only the iron ring in contact with them, but also rings in contact with the first, and so on, just as the inspired poet radiates a chain of enthusiasms (*Ion*). Plato did not leave it at that, but propounded a physical theory, based on the *horror vacui*:

> As regards . . . the marvels concerning the attraction of amber and of the Heraclean stone [lodestone or magnet]—not one of all these ever possesses any real power of attraction; but the fact that there is no void, and that these bodies exert a circular force on one another and, according as they separate or unite, exchange places and proceed severally each to its own region . . . will be evident to him who investigates them properly. (*Timaios*.)

Atomists like Empedocles, Epicuros and Lucretius also propounded mechanical theories in opposition to the current magical explanations. Empedocles' classic text on the subject was discussed by Alexander of Aphrodisias:

> Why the Heraclean stone attracts iron. Empedocles says that the iron is borne towards the stone by the effluvia emanating from both and because the pores of the stone are fitted to receive the effluvium of the iron. The effluvium of the stone then expels the air from the pores of the iron. Once the air is expelled, the iron itself is carried along by the abundant flow of the effluvium. Again, when the effluvium of the iron moves towards the pores of the stone, which are fitted to receive it, the iron begins to move with it. (*Cf.* Huygens, *Complete Works*, Volume XIX.)

Lucretius (*De rerum natura*, VI) attributed magnetic attraction to both the expulsion of air (the magnet is thrust into the vacuum produced by its effluvium), and also to the presence of special principles (*semina*). These principles emanate from the magnet and close the pores (*foramina*) of the iron which, unlike the pores of wood and similar substances, are tightly packed together. Lucretius realized that magnets could either attract or repel iron. He also saw that iron filings fell into patterns when a magnet was brought near them, but did not speak of magnetic lines of force.

The Work of Peter Peregrine

Medieval scientists did little but continue Alexander's and Averroës' interpretations of the physics of Aristotle, who had proffered no theory of magnetism himself. They rejected atomic explanations of magnetic phenomena, and adopted the theory of natural 'sympathy' of magnets for iron. Since that sympathy was purely qualitative, they never dreamt of measuring its effects.

The birth of scientific magnetism had to await the coming of the magnetic needle and the genius of Peter Peregrine, whose *De magnete*, drafted in 1269, gave evidence of an altogether remarkable sense of observation and experiment. His work was a 'model of clarity, simplicity, and order' (E. Bauer).

Peregrinus (to use his Latin name) considered that the magnet 'has an inherent resemblance to the heavens', inasmuch as a floating magnet turns its point to the geographical poles. He also found that when a second magnet is brought close to a floating magnet, the opposite poles attracted each other while like poles repelled each other. He framed his first law (*regula*) accordingly.

Then, taking a spherical magnet, he moved a needle across it, plotting its successive inclinations, *i.e.* its magnetic lines of force (though he did not, of course, speak of them as such). He found that the needle is most strongly attracted near the poles, which he therefore recognized as the centres of attraction. Finally, he broke a magnet in two and found that it now had four instead of two poles. On joining the broken parts together, he reduced the number of poles to two once again.

He must have had a rudimentary idea of the magnetic couple, for he argued that it was not the north pole alone which attracts a magnetic needle, but the combination of forces flowing from both poles. At the end of his book, he suggested a method of using magnetism to produce perpetual motion. This famous 'method' gave rise to lengthy discussions and was responsible for a great many errors, which may be readily forgiven one who, because of his remarkable observations and experiments, has been called the 'Father of Magnetism'.

The Renaissance

Peter Peregrine remained a voice crying in the wilderness, for no one—until Gilbert—paid any heed to him. Thus while the Renaissance witnessed two crucial discoveries, the inclination and declination of the magnetic needle, these were made by sailors and not by scientists or philosophers.

On the philosophical plane the Renaissance was, in fact, to revive a score of animistic and vitalistic notions. As good Neo-Platonists, most scientists of the time believed that the world had a soul and readily identified it with the magnet.

Cardan, for instance, whom Gilbert cited as one of the least objectionable representatives of that science which he wanted to supplant, contended in his *De subtilitate*, Book VII, that lodestones could grow old, like men, when they ceased to attract iron, and that a magnetized needle turns on its pivot quite spontaneously, just as an animal returns to its favourite lair.

Cardan attributed magnetic declination to the pull on the magnetic needle of a star in the tail of Ursa Major, an idea that was to hold sway for a very long time.

He also made a clear distinction between magnetic and electric attraction; while amber attracts all light bodies, magnets attract iron alone. The cause of electric attraction is the flow and return of a fatty substance to which dry things adhere. (The idea that electricity was like a moist, fat tongue grasping its prey persisted during most of the 17th century.) Cardan also designed a number of magnetic toys, which enjoyed a great vogue.

All in all, his vitalist notions did not prevent his making discoveries of some value. The same is true of G. della Porta (*Magia naturalis*), another vitalist, who broke magnets longitudinally and carried out the first magnetic measurements. He discovered that a magnet does not gain weight after it has been left in iron filings for months, and that its soul can therefore not feed on iron.

Robert Norman (1581) was the first to measure magnetic inclination and declination at different points of the earth, though it was not until the 17th century that the variation of magnetic declination with time was first discovered.

ELECTRICITY AND MAGNETISM IN THE 17TH CENTURY

When taking stock of magnetic theory at the end of the Renaissance, we must guard against a simple illusion, that the work of Peter Peregrine, della Porta, and Cardan provided adequate stepping-stones for future advances. In fact, their positive contributions had never been organized into a coherent whole.

It was the mechanists, with their hatred of all occult virtues and 'souls', who first stripped magnetism of its magic, albeit by concentrating on the behaviour of magnetic matter in the 'pores' and 'channels' of physical bodies. The only exception was Mersenne, whose *Letter on the Magnet* (1644) called for measurements rather than further theories.

At the same time, an apparently related problem aroused keen interest: the physical explanation of gravity. Thus, Roberval was able to write to Fermat: 'We do not know the principle of gravity; many hypotheses can be proposed, including that of "mutual attraction" or of natural desire of bodies to combine, as in the case of iron and the magnet.' Hence, though magnetism and gravity were eventually distinguished, we may say that 17th-century magnetic theory contained the germ of Newtonian physics—the recognition of magnetism as a natural phenomenon provided the key for unlocking all nature's mysteries.

William Gilbert

That was the view of Gilbert, who, in the preface to his *De magnete*, claimed that he was teaching a new style of philosophizing, and promised to destroy all the erroneous opinions of the ancients. Moreover he set himself a number of highly practical aims, including the determination of longitude by measurements of variations in magnetic inclination and declination at different points of the earth.

Gilbert knew the work of Petrus Peregrinus and may be called his direct heir. He distinguished clearly between electricity and magnetism, and between electric and non-electric bodies, and also showed that amber was not the only body that could be electrified. His explanation of electrification was rather curious but characteristic of his time: rubbed amber exhales something peculiar that attracts bodies by a kind of capillary action.

Much more important was his description of an electroscope of his own invention, and the first to be devised:

> Make yourself a rotating needle (*versorium*) of any sort of metal three or four fingers long, pretty light, and poised on a sharp point after the manner of a magnetic pointer. Bring near to one end of it a piece of amber or a gem, lightly rubbed, polished and shining: at once the instrument revolves.

Continuing Peregrine's experiments with spherical magnets, he inferred the existence of the earth's magnetic field, and concluded that the spherical magnet is a model of the earth. Accordingly, he fashioned a sphere of lodestone, which he called a *terrella* (small earth), and then studied the behaviour of an iron needle when moved across its surface:

> The rays of magnetic force are dispersed in a circle in all directions (*undique sparguntur in orbem*); and the centre of this sphere is not in the pole (as Baptista Porta deems) but in the centre of the [lode]stone and of the

terrella. So, too, the earth's centre is the centre of the earth's magnetic movements, though magnetic bodies are not borne direct toward the centre in the magnetic movement save when they are attracted by the poles.

In other words, a magnet is not the combination of two centres of attraction, but one whole. It follows that its lines of force must form closed circuits.

Although he still gave no quantitative data, Gilbert contended that the magnetic sphere of influence extends farther than the sphere of movement of any magnetic body (*i.e.* that the attractive force decreases with distance but never disappears completely), and that 'the velocity of the movement of a magnetic body towards a lodestone is in proportion to the strength of the lodestone, or its mass, or its shape, or the nature of the medium, or the distance within the magnetic sphere of action. A magnetic body approaches with greater velocity a powerful lodestone than a sluggish one, in the ratio of the respective energies of the two lodestones.' The experimental study of magnetic phenomena was well on the way.

Pivoting a needle across a *terrella*, Gilbert then studied the dip (inclination) of the needle. He discovered that at the equator the needle had no dip, whereas at the poles it had a dip of 90°. Comparing these results with geographers' data, Gilbert was able to show that the dip varies with terrestrial latitude, though not directly. Gilbert's geometrical construction to explain this law was the first of many elegant (although often false) attempts of the new physics to treat natural phenomena mathematically.

In his work on magnetic variation, Gilbert was able to develop his 'magnetic philosophy' to the full. He argued that magnetic attraction is quite distinct from electrical attraction, for whereas electrical attraction is due to 'matter', magnetic attraction is due to 'form'. Both are 'primal forces' inherent in the very structure of the universe. To explain them, Gilbert rejected such magical concepts as sympathy or antipathy and introduced the concept of *physical force* instead, an innovation that was greatly to influence the work of Kepler and indirectly that of Newton. For Gilbert, that force was none other than the magnetic force, which sets up a 'field' without the intervention of any material particles or moving media:

We do not mean that the magnetic forms and spheres exist in the air, or water, or any other medium non-magnetical, as though the air or water took them or were by them informated; for the forms are only effused and really exist when magnetic bodies are present.

Gilbert contended that that force was crucial to the coherence of the earth, and that it was concentrated in iron and lodestone because these two substances were more earth-like than any others. In short, the earth is not magnetic because it contains magnetic substances, but those substances are magnetic which, by their nature, are inherently 'terrestrial'. Because it is animate, the earth must have a 'magnetic soul'; Gilbert assumed that it was in the bowels of the earth, and hence near to the earth's 'soul', that the lodestone acquired its 'directing virtue' (*verticitas*). As a deflected magnet returns spontaneously to its normal position, so the earth, were it by any unlikely chance to be thrown off the course on which God originally set it, would return to its normal place under the action of its magnetic force.

As a result, the terrestrial poles are not mere geometrical points 'as all who came before us believed', but *physical* points. In fact, Gilbert believed that the magnetic and geographical poles were identical, and opposed all those who tried to explain magnetic variation by imaginary magnetic mines at some distance from the geographical poles. Gilbert was led into this error mainly because of his unqualified identification of the earth and his *terrella*.

Still, fluctuations of magnetic declination with time were an undisputable fact which Gilbert could not ignore. Hence he explained that, were the earth a perfect and homogeneous sphere, the magnetic needle would point towards the north, but as it has an uneven surface, 'marred by matters of diverse nature', and has elevated and convex parts, its total magnetic force turns magnetic bodies towards the more massive magnetic parts. Though Gilbert realized that longitude could not be determined by magnetic variation alone, he believed—and this was the crux of his whole system—that the variation is constant in a given place because of its constant distance from the more elevated magnetic parts of the earth *(fig. 26)*.

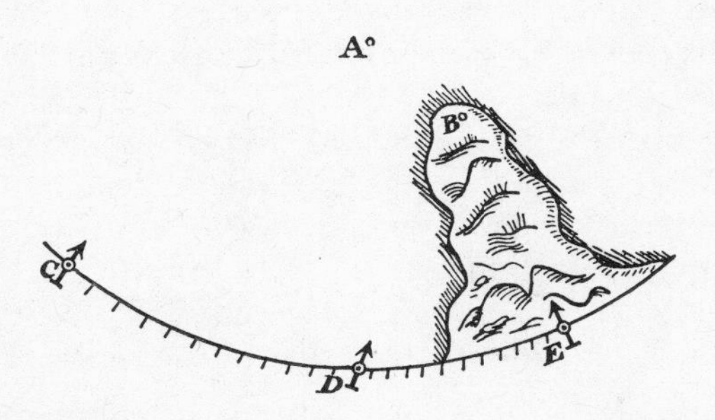

fig. 26 Action of land masses on a magnetic needle.
In a homogeneous region, C, the needle points towards the pole A (the drawing is poor); in D and E the needle is deflected by the mass B.
(W. Gilbert: 'De Magnete', p. 183.)

Paradoxically enough, this erroneous explanation showed how fruitful Gilbert's magnetic philosophy really was,[1] for it marked a half-way stage between the ancient belief that magnetism can be explained by the principle 'like attracts like' and Newton's theory of attraction. With Gilbert, attraction had become a measurable physical force, and his early attempts to compute it foreshadowed Newton's measurements, although Gilbert confused gravitational and magnetic attraction.

Gilbert also applied his ideas to astronomy, contending that the earth rotates on its axis not because of its shape, as Copernicus had believed, but under the continuous action of its magnetic force, so that the earth completes one rotation in 24 hours, precisely because the corresponding velocity agrees with the intensity of its magnetic force. Gilbert discarded the idea that the universe has a centre; to him, every celestial body was an independent whole, attracting bodies on its surface by its own force. This shows to what extent it is true that Gilbert's 'magnetic philosophy' (despite its basic confusions) contained the germs of subsequent astronomical theories.

Gilbert's Influence

Galileo and Kepler were fervent admirers of Gilbert, and Kepler turned Gilbert's system into the basic pillar of his 'new astronomy'. He believed that not only the earth, but also the sun and the planets are large magnets; that as the sun rotates on its own axis it carries the planets along by its *species motrix*; and that the planets describe elliptical orbits since, because their magnetic poles are successively attracted and repelled by the solar magnet, they travel with variable velocities (inversely proportional to their variable distance from the sun). This was, indeed, a remarkable synthesis of Gilbert's early intuitions.

Gilbert even had followers among such staunch Aristotelians as the two Jesuits, Nicolas Cabeo and Athanasius Kircher.

In his *Philosophia magnetica* (1629), Cabeo made a praiseworthy attempt to discover the mathematical laws governing the propagation of magnetic forces, and showed that at every point of a magnetic field the force must have a magnitude and a direction satisfying fixed geometrical conditions.

Kircher (*Magnes, sive de arte magnetica*, 1654) attributed tidal phenomena to the magnetic attraction of the moon, as Gilbert had done before him, but denied that the earth was a large magnet, since a magnet of that size would attract magnetic bodies with so great a force that they could not be prised off again. This objection was

[1] It is curious to note that Gilbert's theory explains changes in gravitational acceleration and not in magnetic variation.

interesting, for Gilbert had completely overlooked it. Léotaud, who shared Kircher's views on this subject (*Magnetologia*, 1668), 'was the first to have considered magnets as aggregates of small elementary magnets with equal directions, though earlier experiments on breaking magnets ought to have suggested this hypothesis long before' (Daujat).

The contribution of Gilbert and Kepler was so great that we might have kept silent about their minor lapses were it not that these lapses help to explain the Cartesian reaction. Gilbert's idea of a magnetic soul, Kepler's love of animistic notions, Cabeo's and Kircher's use of the non-material magnetic field to bolster up qualitative physics, and finally Campanella's magic views of magnetism called for a decisive attack, and Descartes was quick to launch it.

Descartes and the Cartesians

Though Descartes' magnetic theory was based on few experiments and on few calculations, and may therefore be called pure invention, it was nevertheless of great historical importance.

Descartes realized full well that, to establish his physical system, he had to give a better account of magnetic phenomena than any of his predecessors had done.

Above all, he wished to prove that magnets have 'no qualities so occult nor effects of sympathy or antipathy so marvellous as to render them inexplicable by the principles of magnitude, size, situation, and motion'. (*Principia philosophiae* IV, 187.)

He also wanted to destroy once and for all—and this was to prove a very dangerous step—belief in the existence of attractive forces, which were to him so many occult virtues. 'In truth, there is no attraction in this [magnetism]; for the moment iron enters a magnet's sphere of virtue, that virtue is communicated to it by the grooved particles [which] expel the air between them and hence draw them together.' In other words, Descartes, like Plato and Lucretius, believed that magnets and iron are thrust together as the surrounding air rushes into what would otherwise be a vacuum.

Physics has long since forgotten Descartes' grooved particles of subtle matter, threaded like screws, which constantly bombard bodies and enter their pores. Nor does it bother to ask if these particles belong to the first, the second or the third element of Descartes' cosmological system. Descartes' contemporaries, however, were greatly concerned with such problems.

Descartes took over Gilbert's distinction between magnetism and electricity. To explain electrical attraction, he discarded Gilbert's capillary theory and offered another that was no improvement:

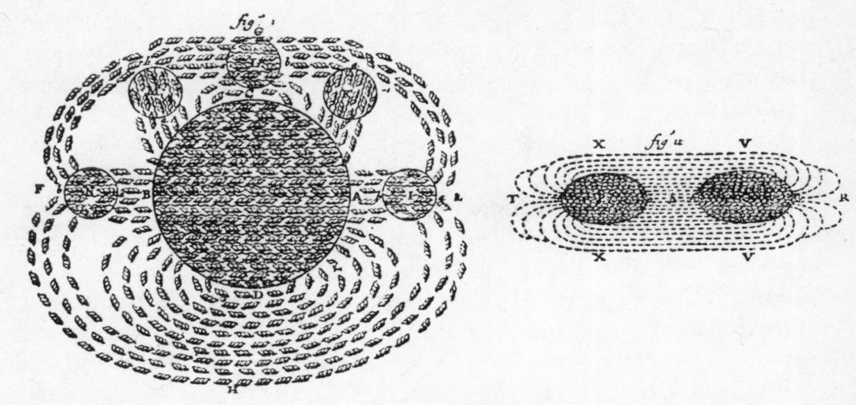

fig. 27 Magnetic lines of force (*right*) *and explanation of terrestrial magnetism* (*left*), *according to Descartes* (*Œuvres, Vol. IX, Pl. XIX.*)

subtle matter penetrates electrical bodies to form loops like elastic bands inside them.

When glass is rubbed so as to become slightly heated, the loops in its pores are forced out into the air and other surrounding bodies where, unable to find pores fitted to receive them, they return at once to the pores of the glass, carrying straws or other small bodies with them.

Descartes produced the first drawing of magnetic lines of force (see *fig. 27*, right) or of what he called 'the paths taken by the grooved particles'. According to him, there were two distinct magnetic currents, each entering one side of the magnet and emerging from the other. Terrestrial magnetism (*fig. 27*, left) was explained in the same way: one current entered the southern hemisphere and emerged from the northern, the other travelled in the opposite direction. In other words, Descartes held that, whereas there was only one kind of electricity, there were two kinds of magnetism, and that the magnetic flux ran straight through the magnet itself, whose pores contained two kinds of screw threads fitted to receive the two kinds of 'grooves' of the magnetic particles. Descartes explained the differences in the magnetic properties of iron and steel by differences in their pore structure, *i.e.* by a sort of molecular hypothesis.

He gave a strictly mechanical explanation of magnetic variation and magnetic dip. The magnetic needle is deflected by the force with which the grooved particles are made to travel in straight lines. To explain why the variation differs from place to place, Descartes adopted Gilbert's solution, adding that there are 'evidently' more magnetic mines in one region than in another, a conclusion which

Gilbert had explicitly rejected. Unlike Gilbert, he realized that the magnetic declination of a given place changes slowly with time, and explained this fact by the gradual exhaustion of the iron mines through their exploitation by man.

Like Gilbert, he described the earth as a large magnet. However, anticipating Kircher's objection, he added that 'very small lodestones often have a greater force than the earth' because 'the earth's magnetic virtue is concentrated in the bowels of the earth and is weak at the surface'.

Finally Descartes, breaking with Gilbert and Kepler, denied that magnetism played any part in the motion of either the earth or the planets, which are moved by vortices of subtle matter alone.

Descartes' ideas about magnetism were the logical outcome of his general philosophical view that the universe consists of figures and motions. Hence the earth, magnets and electrical bodies were riddled with pores or channels whose form (geometrical figure) admitted 'grooved particles' of a given type. Descartes' love of philosophy was far greater than his concern with experimental investigations—hence many of his most irritating assertions. However, the underlying idea of his system, though not the system itself, was to offer a fruitful field for experiment to even so un-Cartesian a scientist as Huygens.

Descartes' disciples added little to their master's work. Rohault (*Traité de physique*, 1671) reduced all magnetic phenomena to local effects. 'Attraction . . . is . . . a very obscure matter or rather a matter about which we know nothing.' He explained that magnetic variation and dip are caused by the direction of the flux of subtle matter.

From Régis' *Système de philosophie* (1690) we know that the change of declination with time had become a well-known fact towards the end of the 17th century. Régis faithfully repeated Descartes' explanation of this phenomenon.

Robert Boyle

Robert Boyle was the first to show that air plays no part in magnetic attraction when, placing a magnetic needle in a vessel connected to his vacuum pump, he found that the needle's response to a magnet held outside the vessel did not differ appreciably before and after the evacuation (*Works of Robert Boyle*, 1744, Vol. I). He concluded that magnetic attraction results exclusively from the 'magnetic effluvia' of the magnet or 'of that great magnet which is the earth'. Boyle suggested, with Descartes, that these effluvia might produce a change in the internal structure of bodies, thus endowing them with magnetic properties.

Other experiments enabled Boyle to establish that two bodies rubbed together have an electrical attraction for each other. As for the explanation of this phenomenon, he showed the same reserve as he did on the subject of magnetic effluvia. Reviewing the theories of Cabeo, Digby, Gassendi and Descartes (which seemed to him based on an error), he found that no choice need be made between them since all alike had rightly discarded the old physics of qualities. His conclusion shows to what extent Descartes influenced even those who did not subscribe to his general doctrine.

Gassendi and Atomism

Though strongly opposed to Descartes, Gassendi was himself a mechanist and as such rejected the idea of attraction out of hand. In the *Physics*, which he published as part of his *Syntagma philosophicum* (1649), he followed Cardan in explaining that electrical bodies 'lick up' substances with an invisible tongue. Gravity and magnetic effects are caused by corpuscles which, emanating from the earth or from the magnet, capture foreign bodies by means of 'hooks'. Like Gilbert, Gassendi believed that the earth is a large magnet, and that the spherical magnet was a 'small earth', but unlike Gilbert he held that it was gravity and not magnetism which acts on all bodies alike; only iron is driven towards the magnet by a force other than gravity. Continuing della Porta's experiment, Gassendi showed that a body is pulled towards the earth with a force greater than its mass if a magnet is placed below.

The Experiments of Otto von Guericke

Otto von Guericke's *Experimenta nova* (1672) opened a new chapter in experimental science, though it was still studded with such outworn concepts as corporeal and incorporeal virtues. Von Guericke, like Kircher, whom he quoted, denied that magnets have any magical or medicinal properties. He did not believe that the earth is a magnet, but agreed with Gilbert that it moves through space because of its magnetic force. Like Huygens, and in opposition to Kepler, he distinguished between attraction as such (*conservatio*) and magnetic virtue, which he identified with electrical attraction. Von Guericke was principally an experimenter, and believed that the miracles of nature are revealed to those who make experiment their mistress.

He was the inventor of the first electrical machine, a sulphur globe 'the size of a child's head' which could be rotated on its axis and rubbed by hand until it sparked and crackled. The fifteenth chapter of Book IV of his *Experimenta nova* is a treasure-house of experimental science—it describes experiments on electrical repulsion, on the acquisition and loss of electrical properties, on point potentials, on surface charges, on the electrification of a thread, on conductivity, on discharges, and on electrical sound and light effects.

fig. 28 Von Guericke's electrical machine. (*O. von Guericke: 'Experimenta nova', 1672, p. 148.*)

J. Daujat, who has made a special study of von Guericke's work, has stressed that he failed to fit his many experiments into a coherent theory. As a typical post-Cartesian empiricist he despised all great systems, and concentrated on collecting data without bothering about their consequences. Still, he provided the data and all that remained was to fit them together.

HUYGENS

Huygens was the author of a special *Magnetic Treatise* (1680) and of numerous papers on magnetism, all of which can be found in Volume XIX of his *Works*. Like his contemporaries, he built his world on principles: the æther, magnetic matter and gravitational matter. In this way he made a clear distinction between gravitational, magnetic and electrical attraction.

Like Descartes, Huygens considered that magnetic lines of force represent the paths of a 'substance' but not of two opposite flows. Moreover, he, too, explained magnetic forces in mechanical terms, but argued that the æther and not the air is involved in magnetic phenomena:

For firstly, I do not hold that the Universe is a *plenum*—quite the contrary is the case. . . . I say, moreover, that it is not the air but a much more subtle substance which is expelled by magnetic matter, since magnets attract each other even in evacuated vessels. (*Works*, Volume XIX, p. 585.)

In other words, magnets are thrust together by the surrounding æther into the vacuum produced by the outflow of magnetic matter.

Huygens' explanation of magnetic repulsion was much simpler. Two 'emergent' poles repel each other because their flux is in opposite directions; two 're-entrant' poles separate under the pressure of the vortices which, in trying to enter both of them, rush in between and force them apart.

Huygens also believed that when a large magnet is brought close to a small magnet, the motion of the latter is determined by two combined forces. His observations of the resulting couple, though interesting, involved no quantitative results. He explained that magnets exert a greater force on a 'keeper' joining both poles because, 'finding an easier passage through pores of iron than through air, vortical matter rushes towards the keeper'.[1] Huygens rejected the common opinion that this effect is reduced when a piece of paper is placed between the keeper and the magnet.

He showed understandable reserve in respect of the findings of the 'magnetic philosophy', and though he adopted the view that the earth is a large and weak magnet he refused to look for the cause of the earth's 'magnetic vortex'. Knowing that the earth's magnetic field can magnetize a piece of soft iron, Huygens believed that lodestones receive their magnetic power from mines running due north.

In 1687, he rejected the Cartesian doctrine of electricity (which involved the idea of 'sticky tongues') and presented a vortical theory akin to that of his magnetic doctrine.

In 1692, he began a long series of electrical experiments in the course of which he noticed that a small amber sphere produces the same effects as Guericke's very much larger sulphur ball.

Newton's Silence

Though Newton's work crowned the achievements of the 17th century, and though many of his predecessors had associated gravitational with magnetic attraction, Newton himself said very little on the subject. Oddly enough, the man who discovered the inverse square law believed that it did not apply to magnetic attractions (*Principia* III, Prop. 6, Cor. 5). But though he did not follow Kepler in identifying gravity and magnetic attraction, his polemics with the Cartesians nevertheless caused him to write:

> The Attractions of Gravity, Magnetism, and Electricity reach to very sensible Distances, and so have been observed by vulgar Eyes, and there may be others which reach to so small Distances as hitherto escape Observation; and perhaps electrical Attraction may reach to such small Distances, even without being excited by Friction. (*Opticks*, Query 31.)

In other words, Newton must have thought that all bodies have some electrical properties, however slight.

[1] Descartes explained the phenomenon in similar terms. Their simple ideas may be called rudimentary concepts of magnetic permeability.

27 William Harvey

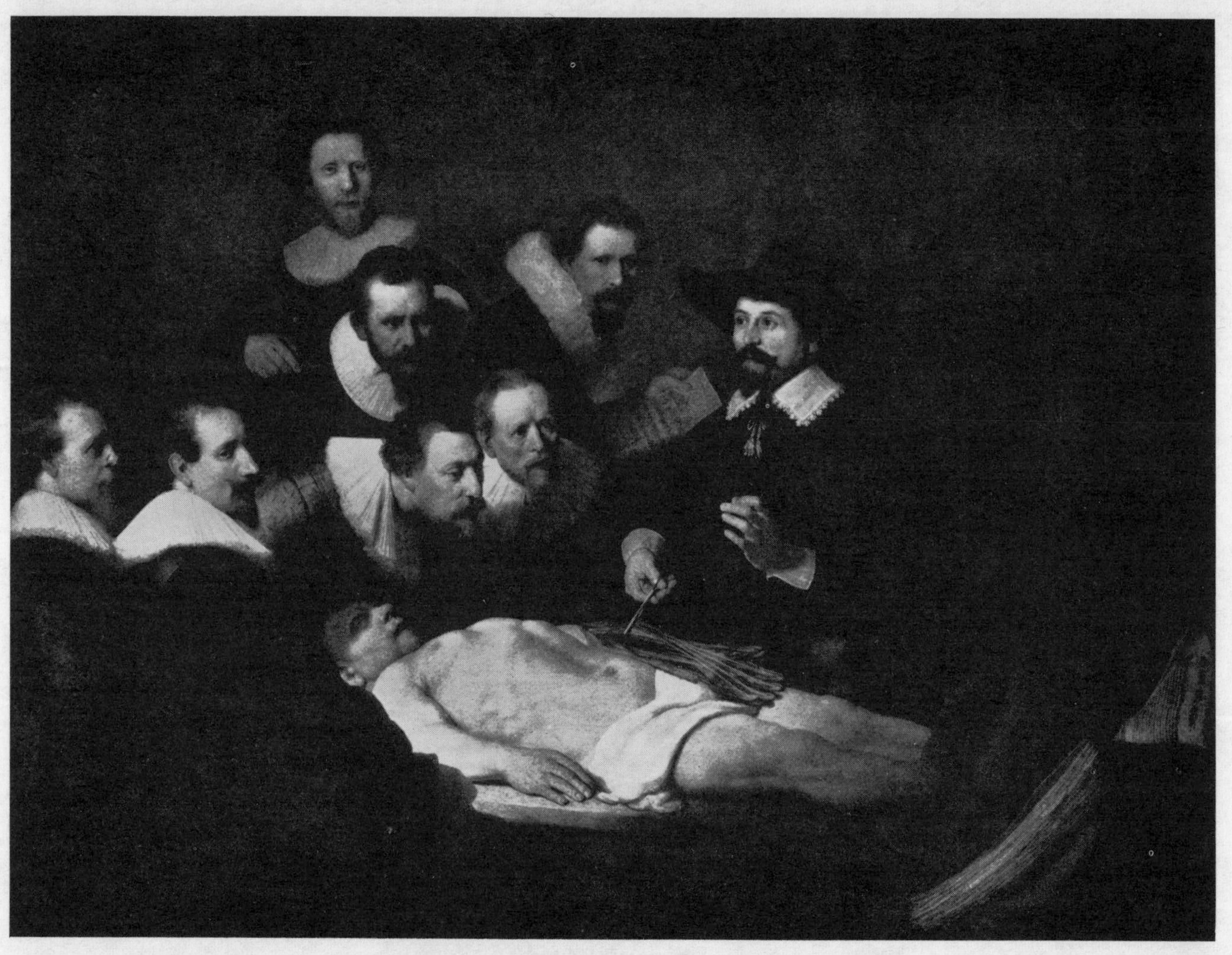

28 The Anatomy Lesson, by Rembrandt

Though the 17th century made a considerable contribution to the study of magnetism and electricity, advances in these fields were small when compared with those in other branches of physics. There were as yet no laws, no units of measurement, no distinction between the two sorts of electricity, no notion of conductibility, and so on. In short, the theory of electro-magnetism was still in its infancy.

But by his realization that a law must be found, Gilbert had taken a vast leap into the future, outpacing all his predecessors with the possible exception of Peter Peregrine. It is regrettable that leading 17th-century scientists wasted their time on studying electrical and magnetic 'substances' instead of making precise measurements. Their relative backwardness can be understood only if we remember how deeply steeped in magic magnetism had always been. But with Huygens and Newton, the tables were turned and magic finally gave place to experimental findings.

The discovery and first measurements of the magnetic field, the first attempts to give a geometrical interpretation of the forces involved, the study of the earth's magnetic field, and von Guericke's and Boyle's work on electrical phenomena were to become the cornerstones of a new scientific edifice in the 18th century.

CHAPTER 6

The Chemistry of Principles

THE SEARCH FOR THE UNIVERSAL PRINCIPLE

THE HISTORY OF 17TH-CENTURY CHEMISTRY is mainly the history of Paracelsus' quintessence, which had been turned into a kind of universal agent or solvent responsible for all chemical reactions.

If we look at chemical theories before Stahl, we cannot help being struck by the wealth of discordant conceptions that went into each one of them. Paracelsus' three immediate principles were joined to the Peripatetic elements, and the (undefined) quintessence was made to reign supreme over all. The quintessence, which could be altered at will without changing anything in the other elements, was originally a metallic principle: every metal was said to have its own quintessence. But when all metals were endowed with a tendency to turn into gold, their quintessences became, first the universal agent transforming their physical appearance, and later the universal principle of all chemical reactions.

VAN HELMONT

Johann Baptista van Helmont (1577–1644) was the first chemist to develop ideas of that kind. After studying at the University of Lausanne, he made an extended tour of Europe and then settled down at Vilvorde, near Brussels, where he spent the rest of his life studying chemistry and medicine. Among his medical writings was one on animal magnetism which earned him the condemnation of the Holy Office. His many books on chemistry were collected by his son and published posthumously under the title *Ortus medicinae* (1648). The work ran to many editions, was translated into French and English, and was read by most 17th-century chemists. Though he provided chemistry with a new experimental approach, he, like other 17th-century chemists, failed to appreciate the importance of quantitative measurements.

Van Helmont's most famous experiment was as follows. He took the shoot of a young willow tree and watered it with rain for five years. He then pulled up the shoot and found that it had increased in weight. Since he had fed it nothing but water, he concluded that the difference was due to water alone. He also studied the calcination of metals and salts (particularly of saltpetre), the combustion of carbon and sulphur, and the processes of fermentation, and then propounded a new theory of matter.

Water as the Chief Element

In this, he rejected Peripatetic elements, together with Paracelsian principles, chiefly because, being a deeply religious man, he felt bound to reject the teachings of pagan philosophers. In addition, he contended that the existence of the four fundamental elements was disproved by experiment. Fire, for instance, cannot be considered an independent element when it disappears without leaving a trace.

The Book of Genesis taught him that water had played a paramount role in the Creation, whence he concluded that water must be the material principle of all things, particularly since his willow experiment had shown him that water could transform itself into wood, and hence into fire and ashes. He also believed that, with the help of a 'seminal spirit', water could turn into metals. That spirit was not van Helmont's own invention, but had been used by the ancient chemists and especially by Paracelsus, who had attributed the natural evolution of metals to it.

The 'Alkahest'

Van Helmont, however, turned this seminal spirit into a universal solvent, the *alkahest*, suggesting vaguely that he himself had managed to obtain it in small quantities, though not soon enough to carry out a full programme of tests.

The prodigious virtues of the *alkahest* were ridiculed by many commentators who argued that, were it indeed a universal solvent, it could not be contained in any bottle, so that van Helmont could not possibly have stored it. Others, like Glauber and Becher, defended van Helmont; Glaser mentioned the *alkahest* without committing himself as to its existence; Ettmüller called it 'a white crow'. Nevertheless, few chemists felt they could ignore it altogether.

'Gas', or Spirit Sylvestre

Another term coined by van Helmont was 'gas'. Though derived from an unknown (and perhaps non-existent) root, like '*alkahest*', it passed almost immediately into the popular language because of its resemblance to the German word *Geist* (spirit). Van Helmont also used the old name, '*spiritus sylvestris*', for gas, to indicate that it is too wild to tame, and suggested that what apparent distinctions there are between different aeriform substances are merely different manifestations of one and the same 'gas'. Helmont applied the term 'inflammable gas' not only to hydrogen but also to the combustible products resulting from the distillation of vegetable matter. The fact that the production of gases was invariably associated with the appearance of water vapour confirmed van Helmont's belief that water was nature's basic element.

Van Helmont distinguished clearly between gas and air, arguing that since air cannot be converted into, or produced from, water, it plays no role in the constitution of matter. Though air can be transformed into gas by combination with volatile matter, it is restored once the gas is 'destroyed'. Contrary to age-old beliefs, van Helmont contended that the air plays no part in combustion, oxidation or respiration. Despite these errors, van Helmont's distinction between air and gas was important, for he was the first to show that air was not the only possible 'subtle spirit'. However, this distinction must have escaped his commentators, and does not seem to have had any influence on 17th-century chemists, probably because they, like van Helmont, lacked the means of collecting gases. Even when they discovered a suitable method in the end, the rise of the phlogiston theory prevented their drawing the correct conclusions.

The Chemistry of Salts

Van Helmont's ideas were given a mixed welcome. His theory of gases was so out of keeping with the general beliefs that few chemists paid it any heed. His *alkahest*, on the other hand, was in the general line of current ideas and hence exerted a great deal of influence on subsequent theoretical developments, and particularly on the continued search for the universal solvent. However, no chemist adopted van Helmont's idea that that solvent is water; most of them sought it among substances producing vigorous reactions. It was thus that they began to experiment with salts, so much so that 17th-century chemistry may be called the chemistry of salts, much as the 16th century was the century of metals and the Middle Ages the age of sulphur.

The starting-point of all these investigations was the reaction of black powder (antimony sulphide) or saltpetre (nitre, potassium nitrate) with combustible substances. Because of its explosive powers, it was tempting to consider saltpetre the universal agent responsible not only for chemical reaction but also for a host of other apparently related phenomena.

Most historians have neglected this stage in the development of chemistry, possibly because they are repelled by its infantile theories. However, if we try to read the relevant texts with the eyes of those to whom they were addressed, we see that they were not, in fact, as irrational as they have been made out to be. A number of recent studies, and particularly those of Douglas McKie, J. R. Partington, Henry Guerlac and Marie Boas, have thrown fresh light on 17th-century chemistry, showing how its ideas led directly to the formulation of the early combustion theories.

Saltpetre (Nitre) in Chemical Theories

Historians have been particularly astonished that such scholars as John Mayow (1641–1679) and Robert Hooke (1635–1703) should have attributed combustion and respiration to the actions of a 'nitro-aerial spirit'. Mayow, whose work was forgotten for a century but who is now generally recognized as Lavoisier's precursor, concentrated on the study of nitre because its properties were so well known. Nitre was used both in fireworks and in agriculture, and its combined fertilizing and detonating powers readily suggested that it was present in the air, where it bestowed its fertilizing virtue on rain and snow. Moreover, the Dutch chemist and physician Cornelius Drebbel had apparently used nitre to prepare respirable air for use in a submarine of his own invention. This, at least, is what Boyle reported in 1660 when propounding his own ideas on respiration. In any case, by the middle of the 17th century, nitre had somehow replaced water as the universal chemical agent, and Nicolas Lefebvre even claimed that it was engendered by the sun.

Though it was old knowledge that air is necessary for maintaining respiration and combustion, Robert Boyle (1627–1691) was the first to examine this idea more closely. While working with a pneumatic pump, invented by himself and constructed with the help of Hooke, he discovered that in a vacuum sulphur does not catch fire, a flame is extinguished, and no animal can survive for long.

He also knew of Otto von Guericke's observation that a burning ember is extinguished in a closed container—von Guericke's experiments had been described by the Jesuit Caspar Schott in 1657. Boyle began his own investigations of combustion in 1658, and returned to them time and again. During the next few years, many others took an interest in the subject and offered their own explanations. Hooke mentioned combustion in various papers and also in his *Micrographia* (1665), and John Mayow propounded the first theory of respiration in Part I of his *Tractatus duo* (1668) and again in his *Tractatus quinque medico-phisici* (1674).

Most of these chemists believed in the existence of a special agent in the air, which they likened to nitre. Boyle called it volatile nitre; Hooke considered it similar to, or identical with, the combustible substance contained in saltpetre; Mayow contended that the air contains nitro-aerial particles. We shall return to these theories below, and meanwhile continue to discuss the further development of the theory of universal agents.

From about 1660 to 1675, chemists looked upon 'aerial nitre' not as a gas in van Helmont's sense, but as a salt, or rather as a spirit derived from the principle which Paracelsus had called by that name. Thus the German physician, Michael Ettmüller, spoke of a salt that had been 'spread throughout the universe at the Creation and which is vulgarly called the spirit of the world because it is blended with the air'. He added, 'the universal salt engenders . . . a particular salt which is of two kinds; to wit, acid and alkali'.

Acids and Alkalis

This idea was characteristic of the times. Though the universal principle ought to have precluded chemists from making a distinction between acids and alkalis, that distinction was nevertheless drawn. However, Ettmüller maintained that alkalis are engendered by acids, and his claim was readily accepted by his colleagues, who could thereafter remain good philosophers while yet holding what we consider paradoxical views. Thus Nicolas Lémery felt free to speak of the mutual antagonism and the interpenetration of acids and alkalis.

In his *Traité de la Chimie* (1663), one of many works of the same type, Christopher Glaser described a number of operations to 'open' mixtures. In 1672, the physician Nathaniel de St. André affirmed that Paracelsus' three principles could be reduced to two simpler ones, namely acid salt and acrid or alkaline salt.

> An acid salt is a simple body of pointed shape, which ferments in the presence of alkalis and is the essence of all mixtures. An acrid salt is a simple, perforated, salt which ferments with acids and which causes Martian vitriol [iron sulphate] to become precipitated in water.
>
> The sharp points of acids fit so perfectly into the holes of the alkalis and fill them so completely that fresh acid encounters no empty pore to arrest its movement; hence the fresh acid reacts so violently that it tears the constituents of these bodies apart, ceaselessly moving and agitating them while separating them.

Since St. André wrote his treatise two years before Lémery's *Cours de Chimie*, he, and not Lémery, was the real founder of this theory.

Chemical Treatises

Lémery's historical importance has been quite generally exaggerated, mainly because Fontenelle made far too much of his alleged lucidity, contrasting it with Glaser's incomprehensible jargon. Fontenelle's assessment of Lémery's work was adopted rather uncritically by J. B. Dumas a century later.

In reality, most of the many 17th-century and, particularly, late 17th-century chemical textbooks published before Lémery's were at least as lucid and comprehensive as his. All these books sold well because they had direct applications in medicine and pharmacy, and most of them ran to a number of editions and were translated into many foreign languages. One of the oldest was published in about 1610–1612 by Jean Béguin, demonstrator at the laboratories in the *Jardin du Roy*. The original Latin was translated and amended in 1615, soon after Béguin's death, and published as *Les éléments de la chimie*. In it, Béguin defined chemistry as the art of 'preparing medicaments so as to make them more agreeable to the taste, more salubrious and less dangerous'. Glaser reverted to Paracelsus' more modern definition of chemistry when he wrote in 1663:

> Chemistry is the scientific skill of dissolving substances so as to obtain their constituents or so as to combine them into exalted bodies.

Christopher Glaser (1628–*c.* 1672) was another demonstrator at the *Jardin du Roy* where he succeeded Nicolas Lefebvre (*c.* 1610–1669), the author of a famous *Traité de Chimie*. In general, most chemical textbooks were divided into four more or less distinct parts. In the first, the author expounded his theories, described his flasks, retorts, lutes and experimental processes; in the second, he discussed minerals (*i.e.* metals and their origins); in the third, he described vegetable extracts; and in the fourth, he dealt with animal extracts.

These books filled a great need because, in the 17th century, chemistry was taught in all medical schools, and there was also a marked increase in the number of practical chemists.

Nomenclature

Once initiated into 17th-century terminology, the modern reader has little difficulty in following these authors, for their terminology had become standardized to a considerable extent.

Acids were generally described as 'spirits', oxides as 'calces' and 'earths', sulphates as 'vitriols'; the term 'regulus' was applied to antimony and arsenic. The powdery products obtained by the sublimation of such substances as sulphur and some oxides were known as 'flowers', and more 'learned' preparations as 'magistery'.

Clearly, there were still great gaps, and many authors, anxious to present 'original' medicaments, added further confusion by describing familiar products under new names. The clearest books of all were those written by such non-pharmaceutical authors as Thibaut le Lorrain or Matte La Faveur, two simple distillers.

The Definition of Acids

Even so, the modern reader cannot help being struck by the accurate descriptions of acids in most of these textbooks. While the number of known acids had not increased, their laboratory preparation had become standardized. *Aqua fortis* sometimes meant nitric acid but at others referred to a mixture of nitric and hydrochloric acids, which also had the special name *aqua regia*, while spirit of vitriol (sulphuric acid) was distinguished from oil of vitriol (fuming sulphuric acid, to judge from its method of preparation). This familiarity with strong acids explains why chemists looked upon 'acid' as the universal solvent for twenty years, until Boyle dispelled the illusion.

This great British scientist showed that the accepted definition of acids was circular and hence useless. Acids were defined as bodies effervescing in the presence of alkalis, while alkalis were defined as bodies which effervesce in the presence of acids. Boyle broke this vicious circle when, having discovered that syrup of violets assumes a different colour in acids and alkalis, he introduced the use of coloured indicators. He also developed a method of identifying copper, iron and silver salts by the colour of their reactions, and demonstrated that since acids can be decomposed, and since many bodies contain no acid, acids cannot be universal solvents or elements.

The Chemistry of Robert Boyle

Boyle's criticism of prevailing conceptions was tantamount to a rejection of Aristotelian and Paracelsian doctrines. Like van Helmont, he denied that fire had a corporeal structure, but he went further than van Helmont when he also denied that any of the other ancient 'elements' could be the sole constituent of matter. He also showed that the Paracelsian principles merely led to confusion, and that it was pointless to distinguish between them and their physical manifestations. Moreover there was no experimental or metaphysical proof that chemical compounds could be reduced to any or all of Paracelsus' principles.

Boyle then gave his own view of chemical elements: 'I mean by elements . . . certain primitive and simple, or perfectly unmingled bodies, which not being made of any other bodies, or of one another, are the ingredients of which all perfectly mixt bodies are immediately compounded, and into which they are ultimately resolved. . . .' While this definition may seem similar to the one propounded by Lavoisier a hundred years later, it merely expressed Boyle's opposition to all the outworn concepts of the schoolmen and the Paracelsians, and was actually much closer to the ideas of van Helmont than to those of Lavoisier.

However, it would be just as wrong to identify the views of the Irish physicist with those of the Flemish physician. In effect, Boyle argued that though simple bodies can form mixtures, it does not follow that the substances extracted from mixtures by fire or other means were originally in the mixtures in that form. Similarly, the decomposition of a mixture by different agents does not necessarily produce identical simple bodies. Boyle's 'elements' were as many as there were substances to which all known different bodies could be reduced.

Boyle, who was a prolific writer, is chiefly remembered for his *Sceptical Chymist*, first published at Oxford in 1661.

THE PHLOGISTON THEORY

Though Boyle's ideas were widely discussed, and though his critique of Aristotle and Paracelsus was endorsed by many of his contemporaries, most chemists nevertheless continued their search for the universal solvent or element. As in the past, they simply joined the new ideas to the old ones, leaving their main doctrines quite unchanged.

The Corpuscular Structure of Matter

Towards the end of the 17th century, chemical discussions were not mainly centred on the theory of elements and principles but on the interpretation of chemical reactions, and particularly of the reactions of acids and bases. As a result, most chemists came to adopt a rather vague corpuscular conception of matter and the related doctrine of chemical affinity. While we shall not dwell on these developments, which concern the history of metaphysics far more than the history of chemistry, we must emphasize that, by their concern with indivisible and immutable atoms, 17th-century chemists prepared the way for Lavoisier's fundamental revision of chemical principles and for Dalton's atomic theory.

The Rise of the Phlogiston Theory

At a time when discussions on the corpuscular structure of matter were still at their height, Georg Ernst Stahl developed a new theory that promised to fulfil an age-old dream of chemists.

In 1669, the German chemist Johann Joachim Becher (1635–1682) had suggested that all minerals are composed of three constituents in varying proportion: *terra pinguis* (sulphur), *terra mercurialis* (mercury) and *terra lapida* (saline constituent), and that all natural substances contained *terra pinguis* but lost it on combustion. Becher's ideas would have fallen into oblivion had not Stahl incorporated them into his phlogiston theory, and had he not republished Becher's *Physica subterranea* in 1703.

Georg E. Stahl (1660–1734) was professor of medicine and chemistry at the University of Halle, where he taught an animistic theory of medicine which enjoyed great success. He felt so passionately about his theories that he invariably rushed them into print, mixing German and Latin in long and clumsy sentences. The first account of his phlogiston theory appeared in his *Experimenta, observationes, animadversiones chymicae et physicae* (1697), and was followed by many lengthy tomes during the next twenty-five years. It was not, however, so much his own writings which helped to spread his theory as those of his commentators, Juncker in Germany and Sénac in France.

Stahl's phlogiston was a weightless element contained in all such combustible substances as sulphur, carbon, oil and (later) phosphorus. During combustion, phlogiston escapes from the combustible substances, thus changing their properties. Sulphur deprived of phlogiston becomes sulphuric acid; oil, charcoal, fats, *etc.*, burn away almost completely and are, for that very reason, extremely rich in phlogiston. (Some of Stahl's successors came to describe carbon as pure phlogiston.)

Formation and Reduction of Metallic Calces

The most interesting part of Stahl's theory bore on the conversion of metals into their calces (metal oxides) and on the reduction of calces into metals. The greater the amount of phlogiston in a given metal, the more easily it can be converted; perfect metals contain very little phlogiston or none at all. Metals lose their phlogiston when they are calcined in the presence of air, which plays an essential role in their transformation. Stahl explained this fact by the kind of mechanistic argument so typical of his day: the air agitates the phlogiston particles and hence causes them to escape.

However, the conversion of metals into calces can also proceed along a 'humid path', for calces can be obtained by dissolving metals in sulphuric or nitric acid. What happens in that case is that the body containing phlogiston (the metal) gives up its phlogiston to a body devoid of it (the acid). During reduction, calces surrender their phlogiston to the charcoal, thus regenerating the metal.

When it was found that the conversion of metals into calces by loss of phlogiston leads to an increase in their weight, and the regeneration of metals to a decrease, Stahl explained away this fact—which we should consider a flagrant contradiction of the doctrine—by arguing that phlogiston, being an immaterial principle, has neither weight nor density. What happens when metals lose their phlogiston is that they become more concentrated, and hence heavier. He could offer this puerile 'explanation' because no clear distinction between weight and density had yet been drawn.

Later, Stahl contended that the escape of phlogiston produces vacuums in metals, with a consequent inrush of denser air.

The Triumph of the Phlogiston Theory

In other words, Stahl and his successors were not willing to change their ideas to fit the facts, but preferred to fit the facts into what they considered the only possible theory. It explained so many reactions, and explained them so well, that what minor difficulties there were could be safely ignored for the time being. Moreover, phlogiston was the culmination of the chemists' age-long dream of a universal element, and therefore required no basic rethinking on the part of its proponents. It also had a clear connection with recently discovered electrical phenomena, for Guericke had obtained the first experimental electric effects by using a ball of sulphur, a substance known to be significantly rich in phlogiston.

Finally, Stahl's system demanded no break with any of the prevailing metaphysical systems. It satisfied the Cartesians because it endowed motion with a chemical and hence a material significance, and because it considered form rather than weight; it satisfied the atomists because it implied a corporeal structure of nature; and it was later to satisfy the Newtonians because it fitted their idea of chemical affinities and could, in fact, be placed at the head of affinity tables.

The Universality of Phlogiston

Unchallenged because its universality pleased the natural philosophers, phlogiston theory continued to rule supreme, so much so that Stahl felt encouraged to extend the theory to embrace other chemical processes as well. When two bodies contain an 'analogous' phlogiston principle, they combine because their molecules are attracted to one another. This attraction explains the formation of salts, their solubility in water and the formation of metallic amalgams. Salts and alkalis contain a similar principle; nitric acid is produced by the putrefaction of a 'universal acid' in the presence of phlogiston; nitric acid dissolves metals by virtue of phlogiston 'analogies'. Salts combine with phlogiston to produce alkalis, which owe their solubility to the former and their causticity to the latter.

Phlogiston was thus elevated beyond the principle of combustion to the rank of a general principle governing the chemical, and even physical, properties of bodies, including their colour and smell.

It is simple for a modern author to show that all the weaknesses and contradictions of the phlogiston theory sprang from the fundamental error on which it was based. But Stahl and his immediate successors could not have avoided this error, simply because they did not suspect the existence of gases. The historical importance of the phlogiston theory can only be assessed if we look at it with the eyes of 18th-century chemists. To them, Stahl's theory presented an escape from an age-old *impasse*. They were not, as some historians have claimed, obstinate fools determined to stick to outdated arguments at all costs, for among them were such illustrious men as Priestley, Scheele, Cavendish, Macquer, Kirwan and Richter. It seems fairer to say that Stahl's theory was rightly considered a great contribution in its day.

THE DESCRIPTIVE SCIENCES

CHAPTER 1

Human and Animal Biology

ZOOLOGICAL KNOWLEDGE

Aldrovandi's Encyclopedia

To obtain a picture of the state of zoological knowledge at the beginning of the 17th century, we can do no better than examine the enormous encyclopedia (ten folio volumes) of Ulysses Aldrovandi (1552–1605), professor at the University of Bologna. The work was written towards the end of the 16th century and published between 1599 and 1616.

Aldrovandi divided the animal kingdom into two large groups, the first of which embraced all our vertebrates:

I Viviparous Quadrupeds
II Oviparous Quadrupeds
III Birds
IV Fishes, Cetaceans
V Snakes and Dragons

The second group contained all the 'bloodless' animals (Aristotle's *anaima* and our invertebrates):

VI Molluscs
VII Testaceans
VIII Crustaceans
IX Insects
X Zoophytes

Aldrovandi set out to give the literary history of animals rather than their zoological description. Of the 294 pages devoted to the horse, for example, only three or four deal with its zoological characteristics; all the others repeat what earlier writers have had to say about horses and deal with such topics as synonymy, habitat, rearing, temperament, character (faithfulness, generosity), memory, sympathies, antipathies and uses in war, games and processions. Nothing is forgotten—neither mythology (sacrifices, metamorphoses, fabulous horses, centaurs) nor monsters. A special section is devoted to proverbs about horses, and to famous paintings and sculptures of horses. Aldrovandi's approach was typical of that of his great predecessors and of Gesner in particular.

Zoology in the 17th century remained steeped in ancient misconceptions, many dating back to Aristotle. Thus Aldrovandi continued to classify bats among birds for the simple reason that both have wings, though he appreciated that bats have fur instead of feathers and that they suckle their young. He even drew the skeleton of a bat to show how greatly it differed from those of birds.

Though cetaceans had always been considered fishes, simply because they are aquatic animals, Aldrovandi realized that they breathe through lungs and not through gills, and that their internal organs (heart, blood-vessels, kidneys, genitals, mammae) resemble those of viviparous quadrupeds. However, he lacked the courage to make a definite distinction and simply introduced a new heading: Cetaceans *and* fishes. In it he also included the seal, which is a pinniped, the seacow, which is a sirenian, and the sawfish, which is a selachoid. A mere glance at their limbs would have revealed the error of this classification.

I. Among *Viviparous Quadrupeds* Aldrovandi, like his predecessors, distinguished a number of related groups. For example, his Solipeds rightly embraced the horse, the ass, the zebra and the onager, but it also included the elephant, whose foot, though simple at first sight, has five toes. His Bisulcs, or two-toed quadrupeds, included the cow, the sheep, the goat, the stag, the camel and the giraffe, but also the rhinoceros which has three toes and belongs to quite a different group.

Though an intuitive grasp of similarities often led Aldrovandi to correct principles of classification, he frequently mistook purely superficial characteristics for basic similarities, even in large mammals which, being closest to man, are simplest to study. Hence his classification showed no promise of leading to a useful and logical natural system.

II. Aldrovandi's group of *Oviparous Quadrupeds* included reptiles and amphibians simply because both have four legs and lay eggs. Because snakes have no limbs, however, they were separated from the other reptiles and classified with dragons and the basilisk.

III. Aldrovandi's classification of *Birds* included a number of fairly homogeneous groups: birds of prey, fowls, waders and pigeons. Most of his other groups were confused, or based on such purely superficial criteria as habitat or voice.

IV. Among the *Fishes*, Aldrovandi, like Gesner, introduced the excellent distinction between bony and cartilaginous types. The cartilaginous fishes were either elongated (dogfish, shark) or flattened (ray, torpedo-fish). Following Aristotle, Rondelet, Salviani and Gesner, Aldrovandi mistakenly classified the *Angler* (a bony fish) among the rays. The bony fishes were grouped according to their habitats as pelagic, littoral, lacustrine, fluviatile, *etc*.

V. No doubt for the sake of completeness, Aldrovandi attempted to describe and to depict all such fabulous beasts as sea-serpents, griffins, harpies, stymphalian birds, and dragons, together with such natural monsters as two-headed sheep, dogs with imperfectly formed limbs, porcupine fowls and men suffering from hypertrichosis or syndactyly.

With the bloodless animals (our invertebrates), Aldrovandi came face to face with a vast and largely unexplored conglomeration of animals representing so many morphological distinctions and mysterious anatomical characteristics that, like his predecessors, he could classify them only by superficial resemblances.

VI. The *Molluscs*. This group corresponded partly to our own phylum of that name and included such cephalopods as the octopus and squid, but also the sea-hare (*Aplysia*), which is not a mollusc. On the other hand, Aldrovandi failed to include the nautilus and argonaut ('paper nautilus').

VII. Aldrovandi's *Testaceans* consisted chiefly of our shellfish or molluscs. It included the gasteropods *Murex*, whelk, top-shell, spire-shell, *etc*., and various snails. The lamellibranchs (bivalves), comprising the mussels, oysters, scallops, *etc*., were grouped together as '*Concha*' and artificially classified by the patterns on their shells. Among the testaceans, also, Aldrovandi included the two molluscs, the pearly nautilus, which is a primitive cephalopod differing from all other living representatives, and the argonaut or 'paper nautilus', which is also a cephalopod. His error arose because the only drawing he was able to consult was of a female argonaut, which expands her two uppermost arms into broad flattish shells, in which she transports her eggs. Again, the pearly nautilus lives in the last chamber of a coiled shell, and these features led Aldrovandi to conclude that these creatures are varieties of bivalve and snail, respectively.

Apart from this error, Aldrovandi's testaceans would have been a homogeneous group had he not included the acorn barnacles, which are, in fact, crustaceans. This confusion arose because these sessile animals are protected by calcified plates. For the same reason, he also included sea-urchins (*Echinus*, *Spatangus*) which are neither molluscs nor crustaceans, but echinoderms.

VIII. Aldrovandi's *Crustaceans* consisted of our own decapods, and included the crayfish, the lobster, the crab, the hermit crab and the prawn. He observed that the hermit crab outgrows and abandons its old shell and adopts a new one. He left out most of the lower crustaceans.

IX. Apart from these groups of fairly easily identifiable invertebrates, there remained a great many others which Aldrovandi, like his predecessors, lumped together as '*Insects*'. He divided them first into terrestrial and aquatic insects, and then distinguished between those with legs and those without legs. The terrestrial ones with legs were again either winged or wingless.

The winged insects were certainly what we should call insects today. They included bees, wasps, hornets, dragonflies, crickets and butterflies. Aldrovandi deserves credit for depicting various species of butterfly together with their larvae and pupae, and for treating dipterous or two-winged insects (flies and mosquitoes) as a special group. His Coleoptera included the true beetles (stag beetle, scarab, musk beetle, *Cantharis, etc.*), but also such Orthoptera as locusts, leaf insects and cockroaches.

While his classification of the winged insects was nearly correct, his *Aptera* included ants (Hymenoptera), bugs (Hemiptera), fleas, lice and, what is far more serious, scorpions and spiders, which are arachnids and not insects at all.

His group of 'apodal insects' was still more of a hotchpotch. It included earthworms, tapeworms, roundworms and, for good measure, slugs—which are in fact molluscs.

Aldrovandi's aquatic insects were an improbable mixture of annelids (*Scolopendra marina*), crustaceans (water-fleas), leeches and marine worms, together with brittle-stars, which are echinoderms. Following Rondelet, Aldrovandi classified such lophobranchiate fishes as *Syngnathus* and *Hippocampus* among the worms. (Salviani called them 'sea-refuse'.)

X. Aldrovandi, like Aristotle, described as *Zoophytes* all those animals which could not be fitted into any other group. They included corals, sea-anemones, jelly-fish, sea-cucumbers and sea-squirts. The resulting group was a conglomeration of the most varied types of creature.

Aldrovandi may be said to have reflected both the knowledge and the ignorance of his predecessors. Misled by superficial resemblances, he lumped together the sea-urchin's and the acorn barnacle's tests with the snail's shell, simply because all three are hard and calcified. Unable to detect the pentamerous symmetry of echinoderms, he classified sea-urchins among testaceans, starfish and brittle-stars among insects, and holothurians among zoophytes.

THOMAS MOUFET

Thomas Moufet's *Theatre of Insects* (1634) is sometimes said to have introduced a number of substantial advances, but that claim strikes us as baseless. The work had a long prehistory. When Gesner realized that one man could not possibly describe every kind of plant and animal, he enlisted the help of Thomas Penny. At Penny's death, his untidy notes were handed to Thomas Moufet, then a medical practitioner in London, who, braving the sarcastic remarks of his colleagues, decided to complete the work. Moufet died in 1604, thirty years before his book was finally published.

Its most interesting feature was the section dealing with bees. Moufet mistook the queen for a king, and drew a fantastic picture of life in the hive: the king inspires respect by his size and the sweetness of his manners. He is elected and can be dethroned by popular vote. While honey bees are generated by the decomposition of beef, the king and his counsellors are generated exclusively by the brains of cattle.

Moufet's Diptera included such authentic two-winged insects as the fly, the horsefly and the cranefly, but also the four-winged dragonfly. It seems hardly credible that he failed to take into account so obvious a characteristic as the number of wings. However, he also repeated Thomas Penny's interesting observations on the reproduction of flies, *viz.* that they copulate and lay eggs, which later turn into larvae or 'vermicules'.

The book was illustrated with fairly accurate drawings of some 60 species of butterfly, including a number of their caterpillars and chrysalides, though Moufet treated most caterpillars separately. He rightly combined some homogeneous groups such as the locusts and cockroaches.

When it came to the classification of wingless insects, Moufet, like all his predecessors, lumped together spiders, bugs, ticks and worms. He also described the proglottids of tapeworms, which resemble the seeds of gourds (whence their name of *cucurbit*), as worms in their own right. Among the worms, Moufet also mentioned *Dracontia*, an 'earthworm' found in Egypt and India 'which causes sub-cutaneous tumours', and which was, in fact, our own guinea-worm (*Filaria medinensis*).

The work, which remained unfinished, contained two plates (without legends) depicting a tapeworm, some spiders, scorpions, sea-slugs and caterpillars, a sea-pen, a dytiscus larva, and the traditional hippocampus (sea-horse). This unlikely mixture shows better than anything else how unable early 17th-century naturalists were to understand the nature of the insect world.

J. Johnston's *Historia naturalis*

The last great zoological encyclopedia was published a hundred years after Gesner's. It was the *Historia naturalis* by J. Johnston (1603–1675), which did little more than repeat the ideas of Gesner and Aldrovandi. Like them, Johnston distinguished between viviparous quadrupeds, oviparous quadrupeds (amphibians and reptiles), birds (including bats), fishes (including cetaceans), snakes and dragons, and insects (real insects together with spiders, myriapods, worms, slugs, lower crustaceans, leeches, sea-stars and—naturally—hippocampus).

All Johnston's molluscs were cephalopods. His testaceans included gasteropods, lamellibranchs, sea-urchins and acorn barnacles. His higher crustaceans formed a homogeneous group, but his zoophytes were made up of sea-anemones, corals, sea-squirts (tunicates) and sea-cucumbers (holothurians).

As Aldrovandi followed Belon and Gesner, so Johnston copied Aldrovandi, repeating the same errors and the same fables. From Gesner (1551–1558) to Johnston (1657–1665) zoology had therefore made little, if any, progress.

The Work of Ray and Willughby

We should have had to conclude on this pessimistic note were it not that the end of the 17th century witnessed the appearance of the work of John Ray (1628–1705) and of his friend Francis Willughby (1635–1672), whose *Ornithology* and *Ichthyology* Ray undertook to revise and complete on Willughby's sudden death. Ray himself wrote a *Synopsis methodica animalium quadrupedum et serpentini generis* (1693) and a *Historia insectorum* which was published posthumously (1710).

Ray's system of classification was still inspired by Aristotle. He divided the *Anaima* (invertebrates) into Molluscs, Crustaceans, Testaceans and Insects. On the other hand, he greatly improved Aristotle's classification of vertebrates by the use of anatomical criteria. Thus he distinguished the fishes from other vertebrates by their respiratory organs, and reptiles from amphibians by the structure of their ventricles.

Willughby had also recognized that, unlike fishes, cetaceans breathe by means of lungs, mate like quadrupeds, give birth to living young, and have organs whose structure agrees with that of viviparous quadrupeds. However, he had not dared to draw the obvious conclusion and had left the cetaceans among the fishes.

Ray's and Willughby's classification of the vertebrates was not only remarkable in itself, but it also showed the method that should be adopted to disentangle the much more complex world of the invertebrates.

ANATOMICAL KNOWLEDGE

Seventeenth-century biologists knew a great deal about human anatomy, and they applied that knowledge to their studies of vertebrates. Many of them dissected domestic or captive animals and described their internal structure. However, this work followed no general plan, and what comparisons were made were made incidentally. True, as early as 1555 Belon had indicated the homology of the principal bones of birds and man, and Leonardo da Vinci had established a clear correspondence between the human leg and foot and the hind leg of the horse, but no one else (except Aldrovandi, who simply reproduced Belon's diagram) had followed their example.

Then, in 1645, M. A. Severino (1580–1656) published a remarkable work in which he stressed the structural similarity of many animals differing in external appearance. However, his conclusions were far too general, and involved far too many comparisons between animals and plants, to be of any real value.

In his *Anatome animalium* (1681), the Belgian anatomist G. Blaes (or Blasius) listed all that was known about the anatomy of the chief domestic animals, and that of lions, tigers, hyenas, hares, rats, elephants, stags, dromedaries, *etc.* The work was illustrated with some 60 plates based on earlier illustrations. Blasius, too, followed no methodical plan, and failed to make any useful anatomical comparisons.

Of the other anatomists, we must mention Fabricius da Aquapendente (1537–1619) who described the four-chambered stomach of ruminants, and who was one of the first zoologists to study the development of the chick embryo and to distinguish between different mammalian placentas.

In 1671, the physician and architect C. Perrault (1613–1688) published a series of papers on the lion, the hedgehog, the chamois, the eagle, the guineafowl, the ostrich, the tortoise, *etc.*, which contained valuable descriptions. He also discovered the existence of spiral valves in the intestine of the shark.

Between 1676 and 1693 Duverney dissected an adder, an ostrich, a hedgehog, a panther and an elephant, and published his findings. In the *System of Anatomy* (1685), Collins concentrated on the anatomy of birds and fishes. Tyson (1680) published papers on the porpoise and the chimpanzee.

The Dutch physician Nicholas Tulp, who was probably one of the figures in Rembrandt's *Anatomy Lesson*, was the author of the *Observationes medicae* (1652), which included a short illustrated study of *Satyrus indicus*, or the orang-utang. Although his particular specimen had been captured in Angola, he mentioned that orang-utangs can also be found in Borneo where they are so strong that they attack armed soldiers. Tulp insisted on the extraordinary resemblance between this large ape and man.

Bit by bit, zoologists were thus gathering material for the future science of comparative vertebrate anatomy. (The term 'comparative anatomy' was coined by Nehemiah Grew in 1675.) Meanwhile the study of invertebrates made little progress, for zoologists were unable to discover any method of producing order among thousands of animals, built according to scores of patterns. Thus they continued to confuse the calcified test of the urchin (echinoderm) with the calcified plates of the acorn barnacle (crustacean) and the shell of the snail (mollusc), lumping all three together as testaceans.

Microscopic Anatomy

The next great advances followed the invention of the microscope, generally a simple bead of glass set in metal. Hooke used glasses of 'our English make' to excellent effect. He illuminated his objects either by filtering sunlight through oiled paper, or else by concentrating the light of an oil lamp, using a glass globe filled with water as a condenser. The results of his observations were published in his *Micrographia* (1665) which contained excellent engravings of the sting of the bee, the foot of a fly and the wings of insects. Other plates depicted gnats, spiders, fleas, lice, mites, vinegar eels, *etc.*

The *Generation of Insects* (*Esperienze intorno alla generazione degl' Insetti*), by Francesco Redi (1626–1697), discussed and depicted the external parasites of various animals (goat, camel, ass, stag, chicken, swan, peacock, tortoise, tiger). It also described ants and mosquitoes, insect galls, scorpions, and elderberry flies. Works like his greatly encouraged other naturalists to make detailed observations of their own.

Marcello Malpighi (1628–1694), when professor of medicine at Messina, published his remarkable *De Bombyce* in 1669. In it he discussed the rearing of silkworms, their cocoons, chrysalides, and the inner structure of the adult moth. He also showed that, like *Bombyx*, locusts, stag-beetles and bees use their tracheae as organs of respiration.

Malpighi was the first to describe the spiracles of insects and to identify the 'heart' of the silkworm. He discovered the glandular system now known as the Malpighian tubes, and observed that it discharges into an enlargement of the hindgut—the excretory ampulla. He also described the silk-producing glands and the reproductive organs of adult moths. His *De Bombyce*, which was profusely illustrated, may therefore be called the first complete study of invertebrate anatomy.

Another skilful microscopist, one of the great amateurs of science, was Antony van Leeuwenhoek, who discovered the red corpuscles in his own blood, the transverse striations of muscle, and the capillary circulation. He was one of the first to observe spermatozoa. He also wrote illustrated anatomical studies of the edible mussel, the flea, the bee, the ant and the spider.

Leeuwenhoek was the first to use the microscope to examine transparent objects, including rotifers and other infusoria—'flattened oval creatures with extremely fine legs in rapid motion'. He even observed the presence of bacteria (*micrococcus*, *bacillus*, *spirillum*) in dental tartar.

When opening female aphids (1695), Leeuwenhoek found to his surprise that they were viviparous—their bodies contained young aphids instead of the eggs he had expected to find. He then isolated two females by placing them on a sterilized twig in a tightly closed bottle of water. Though no males were present, one female gave birth to nine young and the other to six, within twenty-four hours.

> 'What struck me as the most extraordinary thing,' he observed, 'was that I never came upon a single one of these small creatures from which I was unable to extract a number of young in the process of formation . . . or which I could possibly consider as being a male.'

When further observations confirmed these findings, Leeuwenhoek was forced to conclude that his aphids represented the first-known case of parthenogenesis in animals.

The work of Jan Swammerdam (1637–1680) deserves quite special mention. Though a physician by profession, Swammerdam did not practise medicine, but devoted himself exclusively to the study of invertebrate anatomy. His health was poor and his life came to a sad close when he was only 43 years old. Even so, he managed to publish a considerable volume of work.

Apart from his *General History of Insects*, in which he challenged Harvey's account of the metamorphosis of insects, maintaining that the adult insect is contained in the larva, he published a number of beautifully illustrated academical treatises on the anatomy of the animals he had dissected. In his *Biblia Naturae*, he described the natural history of the mayfly, the dragonfly, the bee, the gnat, the ant, the rhinoceros-beetle, the tortoiseshell butterfly, the cheese mite, various moths, flies, gall insects, crabs, water-fleas, scorpions, snails, cuttlefish, frogs and many others.

While dissecting a pulmonate freshwater gasteropod (*Viviparus*), he discovered the young, and so showed the viviparous nature of the species. He also found a number of 'vermicules' (the sporocysts of a parasitic roundworm), which turned into larvae and began to swim about rapidly by flapping their tails. In short, Swammerdam's observations were unusually rich and varied and opened up a vast new field of study for the naturalists.

In 1662, the painter Jan Goedaert published a book in which he had illustrated a host of unrelated observations. He mentioned that he had come across a caterpillar teeming with 'vermicules' which turned into flies, but failed to appreciate the nature and origin of these parasites.

We may sum up by saying that it was mainly due to Malpighi, Leeuwenhoek and Swammerdam that invertebrate anatomy was given the solid foundations on which the great systematizers of the future were able to base their work.

THE DISCOVERY OF THE CIRCULATION OF THE BLOOD

It seems odd that early 17th-century physicians and naturalists should have had no suspicion of the circulation of the blood, when familiarity with wounded soldiers must have shown them that blood often escapes in spurts. Once again direct observation proved impotent in the face of deep-rooted preconceptions, for Galen had taught that only the veins contain blood and few dared to challenge his authority.

According to Galen, blood is produced in the digestive organs from chyle and passes by the portal vein to the liver, whence it is carried by the vena cava to the right ventricle of the heart. From here it is distributed to the body through the veins, the 'arterial vein' (now called the pulmonary artery) taking a special supply to the lungs to 'nourish' them. A small quantity of blood was believed to pass through imagined perforations in the inter-ventricular wall to the right ventricle, to be mixed with air drawn from the lungs through the 'venous artery' (pulmonary vein). This mixture was a process akin to fermentation and produced 'arterialized' blood charged with 'vital spirits'. It consisted chiefly of air, and was distributed to the body through the arteries. Evidence of this was adduced from the fact that the arteries of a dead body are found on dissection to be very nearly empty, while the veins are always filled with blood.

Galen thus maintained that there are two separate and independent systems, the veins containing 'natural' blood and the arteries 'vital' blood (mostly air). Within these systems the two sorts of blood surged to and fro like the tides. So great was Galen's authority that Vesalius' protest in 1643 that no one had ever seen the mysterious perforations in the inter-ventricular septum fell on deaf ears.

Another critic of Galen's theory was Miguel Servet (Servetus, 1509–1553). This talented Spanish physician, whom Calvin burnt at the stake for his heretical views, argued that the pulmonary artery would not be as large as it is if its function was merely to 'nourish' the lungs. He concluded that the blood from this artery actually passes through the lungs and enters the left heart by the pulmonary vein, and is there combined with air. His was therefore the first attempt to introduce the idea of a connection between the venous and arterial systems outside the heart.[1]

Similar ideas were expressed in 1559 by Realdo Colombo (1516–1559) who had observed the movements of the heart during a vivisection. Finding the pulmonary vein filled with blood and not with air, he concluded that the blood must pass through anastomoses connecting the arteries with the veins.

It was William Harvey (1578–1657) who finally discovered the systematic circulation of the blood. After studying at Cambridge and later at Padua, Harvey returned to England in 1602 and in 1604 was admitted to the Royal College of Physicians in London. Here, as Lumleian lecturer, he began to teach anatomy in 1616. In 1618 he became physician to James I, and in 1625 to Charles I. He developed his theory between 1615 and 1618 and published it in 1628, in his famous *Exercitatio anatomica de motu cordis et sanguinis in animalibus*.

Relying on direct observation and 'not on the writings of others', Harvey distinguished between a phase of muscular contraction (systole) during which the blood from the ventricles is forced into the arteries, and a phase of dilatation (diastole) during which the blood is readmitted to the heart. With characteristic shrewdness Harvey began his observations with the dissection of cold-blooded animals (eel, frog, newt, snail, shrimp) in which the movements of the heart are slower and hence easier to follow.

Fishes, in particular, have only a single auricle and a single ventricle, so that Harvey had little difficulty in discovering that the auricle contracts to force the blood into the ventricle, and that the latter contracts in turn, to force the blood through the gills into the aorta. The function of the gills was not then known so that Harvey disregarded them and perceived a simple circulation. In animals with a four-chambered heart, the two auricles contract first, driving their blood into the corresponding ventricles, which then contract,

[1] See R. Taton (ed.), *Ancient and Medieval Science*, in this series, p. 420, where Ibn al-Nafīs of Damascus is mentioned as a possible precursor of Servetus.

the right chamber pumping its blood into the pulmonary artery and the left into the aorta.

Harvey could therefore assert as a general principle that the blood is received by the heart through the veins and leaves it through the arteries, and he began to wonder by what means the blood from the arteries is returned to the veins.

Since the capillary circulation was not observed until later (in the lung of a frog by Malpighi in 1661, in the tail of a tadpole and in young fishes by Leeuwenhoek in 1668), Harvey had to leave the solution of this problem to his successors, but was convinced that a peripheral connection between the arteries and the veins existed.

As we might expect, Harvey's great discovery was greeted with almost universal scepticism. Because of the bitter attacks of James Primerose (1630), the glib gibes of Guy Patin, the sarcastic comments of Riolan, Hoffmann, Johannes a Turro, Piso, Parisanus and others, Harvey died long before his fundamental discoveries were accorded the universal recognition which they so richly deserved.

THE MYTH OF SPONTANEOUS GENERATION

'Every dry body which turns moist,' Aristotle had affirmed, 'or every moist body which turns dry, produces animals provided only that it can serve them as nourishment.' Lucretius had argued similarly when he claimed 'that living worms can be seen to emerge from the earth as, soaked by excessive rains, it begins to putrefy'. This legend survived into the 17th century, when naturalists believed that even highly organized animals may be produced spontaneously from organic and inorganic matter.

For instance, maggots in corpses and in putrefying flesh were said to have originated in this way. It was only in 1668 that Redi gave a convincing demonstration that such maggots had, in fact, hatched out from eggs which flies had deposited on the flesh. He did this by placing meat, dead fish and dead snakes in jars covered with paper or with a piece of linen fine enough in mesh to keep the flies out. The meat was found to have no maggots, whereas meat left in the open invariably crawled with them. Twenty years later, Leeuwenhoek, who knew nothing of Redi's experiments, had to carry out similar experiments to persuade a surgeon that the 'worms' in an anatomical specimen had hatched out from the eggs of flies.

A similar belief, namely that gall insects are produced spontaneously, was destroyed by Vallisnieri (1671–1730), who described how certain Hymenoptera deposit their eggs in buds and leaves, thus producing the galls in which their larvae develop.

It was far more difficult to destroy the belief in the spontaneous generation of intestinal parasites, since the only alternative was that God must have created them together with Adam—even before Adam had sinned. There was some mention of 'seeds' entering the human body from the air, but there was no means of testing this hypothesis at the time.

THEORIES OF GENERATION

Though it was generally known that most animals are hatched from eggs laid by the female, and that the male plays some role in fertilizing them, that role had never been defined precisely. Even less was known of the reproduction of viviparous animals and of man in particular. Though ovaries (called 'didymes' or female testes) had been discovered by Herophilos, no eggs had ever been discovered in the ovaries of mammals. The reason, as we know today, was that mammalian ova are too small to be observed with the naked eye or with simple lenses. (The ovum of a dog is $\frac{9}{100}$ mm. in diameter, the ovum of a woman $\frac{17}{100}$ mm.) Hence the question how mammalian young are produced remained completely unsolved.

The Doctrine of the Two Seeds

The first attempt to provide an answer was that of Empedocles of Agrigentum (*c.* 440 B.C.). According to Empedocles, the female ejaculates a seed like the male and the combined male and female semina engender the various parts of the foetus. Pythagoras, too, held that the contribution of each parent was dissimilar and complementary.

This theory was also adopted by Democritos, though with some slight modifications. Hippocrates believed that the two sexes produce seeds in the head, whence they travel to the kidneys through the spinal cord. Once mixed, they are heated in the female body, whereupon 'hot spirit' escapes while 'cold spirit' is drawn in with the mother's breath. Under the action of this mixture of hot and cold spirits, the menstrual blood becomes flesh.

Aristotle, too, took the menstrual blood for the formative substance, but believed that it was animated by the 'spirit' of the male seed. That theory was so well-established that it survived into the 16th century, when Paracelsus and the Portuguese physician Amatus Lusitanus tried to verify it by pouring a mixture of menstrual blood and male sperm into a vial and then heating it. They claimed to have observed the gradual formation of a small being.

Galen, who also adopted the doctrine of the two seeds, rejected the role of the menstrual blood. During dissections of female monkeys, he had observed 'didymes' (female testicles) which, according to him, produced not eggs but a special 'seed', a kind of spirituous liquor which travels in the blood. In the womb, this liquor mixes with the male seed, which is more copious, hotter and drier than the female seed, and hence plays a greater role in the formation of the foetus.

This doctrine, which took into account the apparent contributions of both parents and 'explained' the hereditary characters of the child, was adopted by the leading 16th-century philosophers, including Bacon, Paré and van Helmont. In the 17th century, Descartes expounded it at length in his *Traité de l'homme* (published posthumously in 1664):

> The seed of animals, being very fluid, and being ordinarily produced by the conjugation of the two sexes, appears to be but a confused mixture of the two liquors which serve each other as leaven and which become so heated that some of their particles acquire the same agitation as fire, dilating and compressing the others in such a way that they are gradually shaped into the limbs.

The heart is formed in much the same way. Once that is done, the dilated particles 'tend to continue their movement in a straight line, and because the heart now formed resists them, they move away from it and take their course towards the place where afterwards the base of the brain will be formed. They enter into the place of those that were there before, which for their part move in a circular manner to the heart, and there, after waiting for a moment to assemble themselves, they dilate and follow the same road as the aforementioned ones.'

This passage is so characteristic of the whole book, that Descartes' views on embryology may be dismissed as so much pretentious theorizing, all the more dangerous because they are presented as if they were ascertained facts.

'The alleged female seed', Nicolas Andry (1658–1752) later remarked, 'is merely the viscous humour secreted by the vaginal glands, whose only function is to soften the parts which it moistens'.

Ovism

Since their doctrine of the two seeds could obviously not be applied to oviparous animals 17th-century biologists developed the ovist theory, according to which the male seed emits a vapour or *aura seminalis* which merely stimulates the development of the egg, but has no other influence on the development of the embryo.

This theory was shown to apply also to viviparous animals by Nicholas Steno (Stenson), who demonstrated in 1667 that sharks (which are viviparous) have ovaries containing large ova. In fact, even Aristotle had known that female sharks and adders develop ova to maturity within their oviduct, but Steno was the first to suggest that 'the "testes" of women must be regarded as exactly the same organ as the "roe" of sharks, for, like the sharks, they discharge eggs or related matter into the uterus'. A year later, in a paper devoted more especially to the male organs, J. van Horne adopted the same hypothesis.

William Harvey, too, was interested in solving the mystery of mammalian reproduction. Though he has often been called the founder of ovism because he coined the phrase *ex ovo omnia*, he was, in fact, referring to eggs in the widest possible sense of the word, and merely coined that phrase to stress that the foetus is invariably born from a material substance.

As physician to King Charles I, Harvey had occasion to dissect the reproductive organs of a great many does and hinds killed during royal hunts. Unable to observe any changes in the female 'testes' or ovaries immediately before or after copulation, he concluded that they played no role in generation and that they must be looked upon as mesenteric ganglia.

He had no greater success with his investigations of the uterus of pregnant hinds, in which he noticed a kind of sac filled with 'an aqueous sticky substance resembling the white of an egg'. Though he called this sac the 'egg' it was, in fact, the chorion and the amniotic sac surrounding the foetus. Thus Harvey's contribution to the theory of ovism was almost negligible.

Steno's hypothesis that the 'testes' of female mammals produce eggs was apparently verified in 1671 by Theodor Kerckring, a Dutch physician, who claimed that he had been able to remove eggs from the 'egg stores' of women, that he cooked them and ate them, and found that they had an extraordinarily disagreeable taste. From his illustrations it is clear that he mistook the Graafian follicles for ova.

It was the remarkable studies of Regnier de Graaf (1672) which finally gave the ovist theories of mammalian reproduction a solid basis. Though the vesicular bodies which Graaf observed in the ovaries of rabbits, hares, dogs, sows, sheep, cows, cattle and women were not, as he believed, the ova of mammals (which are too small to have been seen with the simple instruments of the times) they were nevertheless follicles containing ova. Apart from this unavoidable error, Graaf came to a sound conclusion. Seeing that eggs are found in all animals, including mammals, he stated that 'the role of the female testes is to produce eggs and to bring them to maturity' and that they must therefore be called 'ovaries' and not testes.

In pregnant cows, de Graaf observed the presence of globular yellow bodies which Malpighi later called *corpora lutea*. De Graaf realized that these were follicles which had released their ova into the uterus, and was thus able to connect the number of *corpora lutea* (*i.e.* of ova that have left the ovary) with the foetuses in the uterus. Three days after coition, the right ovary of doe rabbits contains three *corpora lutea* and there are three 'eggs' in the right horn of the uterus; the left ovary contains one *corpus luteum* and there is one foetus in the left horn of the uterus. De Graaf confirmed this conclusion by repeating his observations 3, 5 and 6 days after coition.

For the first time, a connection had been established between changes in the ovary and foetal development in the uterus: 'There are as many *corpora lutea* in the ovaries as there are foetuses in the uterus.'

De Graaf's work was violently criticized and he died two years after his discovery, his health being undermined by the constant attacks of his adversaries.

In the end, however, de Graaf's opinion prevailed, so much so that it was argued that, since all animals, viviparous and oviparous alike, spring from maternal eggs, the egg alone must be the generative element. This was the view expressed particularly by C. F. Garmann, according to whom the male seed plays no other role than to emit a vapour which rises through the horns of the uterus to the ovary of viviparous animals and 'stimulates the eggs into fermentation'.

Preformation in the Egg

Though the new theory helped to explain the mechanics of generation, it said nothing about the development of the foetus in the egg. This gap was filled by the theory of preformation, according to which the foetus pre-exists complete, though in miniature, within the egg. In the course of gestation, it swells up and eventually 'sheds its envelopes'—the etymological origin of the word 'development'.

One of the founders of the theory of preformation was Jan Swammerdam, who believed that the egg of a louse is itself a louse in miniature. He concluded that the adult louse was hidden in the egg, and so also with the ant, the butterfly, and the frog. 'In nature, there is no generation but only propagation, the growth of parts. When their stock of eggs is finished, the human race will cease to exist.'

These erroneous views received unexpected support from Malpighi's study of the development of the chick. Malpighi was astonished to see in a fresh egg, which had been laid the previous night and which had not been incubated, 'an entirely formed chicken'. What had happened, in fact, was that he had carried out his experiments during the hot summer months, so that the chick had reached a stage that would normally have required six hours of incubation. No wonder that he concluded that 'the chicken pre-exists in the egg' long before incubation.

This theory was soon associated with another, that of *emboîtement*, according to which a female foetus must have ovaries containing the eggs of the foetuses of the next generation, and so on. In other words, each egg contains an infinite number of ever-smaller foetuses of future generations, and Eve's ovaries must have contained all mankind. This hypothesis delighted Swammerdam, for it explained original sin—'all men lay hidden in the kidneys of the first woman'.

The theory led to demonstrably absurd conclusions, and Hartsoeker was able to show that the foetuses of the final generation would have had to be impossibly small. The discussion was continued with much passion during the 18th century.

The Discovery of Spermatozoa: Animalculism

In 1677, Leeuwenhoek wrote a letter to the Royal Society, in which he described a momentous discovery. A young student by the name of Ham had brought him a specimen of human semen, claiming that his microscope had revealed the existence of 'living animalcules' in it. Leeuwenhoek immediately examined the material for himself and found that Ham was right. After repeated observations, he was able to inform the Royal Society that semen contains an immense number of moving animalcules, each with a tail 'five to six times the length of its body'.

Within a year, Leeuwenhoek had observed similar animalcules in the semen of a dog, a horse, a rabbit and, later, in the melt of a cod and a pike, and in the semen of snails and oysters. The hunt for animalcules was on. When Homberg, Geoffroy, Lister, Camerarius, Lancisi and Vallisnieri had confirmed Leeuwenhoek's discovery, the ovist hypothesis was challenged by the animalculist. Its first exponent was Leeuwenhoek himself, who argued that generation cannot possibly be attributed to 'imaginary eggs' but must 'surely be wrought by the living animalcules or vermicules contained in the male semen'. The egg itself 'serves purely as nourishment for the spermatic worm, which feeds on it as other worms feed on fruit'.

Preformation in the Spermatozoon

The problem of foetal development had now to be re-examined, for if the spermatozoon is the only reproductive agent, the foetus must be preformed in *it* rather than in the egg. This view was presented by Hartsoeker in 1694:

> I think that every worm in the seed of birds contains either a male or a female bird belonging to the same species as the bird in whose seed it was

formed. . . . The same may be assumed of the animalcules found in the seed of men and quadrupeds, to wit that each animalcule contains . . . a male or female animal of the same species in miniature. . . . If we could see the animalcule through its covering skin, we should perhaps find that it looks like the accompanying figure, though its head might well be a little larger in proportion to the rest of the body.

Hartsoeker's famous sketch of a 'homunculus' crouching inside the head of a spermatozoon was mistaken by many, including even N. Andry (1699), for a drawing from real life. Thus when the secretary of the *Société Royale*, François de Plantade (1670–1741), published an illustrated thesis on Hartsoeker's homunculus as a practical joke (using the pseudonym of Dalempatius), most of his contemporaries were completely taken in by it.

Animalculism was also adopted by the Swedish physician van Hoorhn (1709), who considered it 'more in keeping with the dignity of man', and by E. F. Geoffroy, professor of medicine at the *Collège Royal*.

From the preceding remarks it will have become clear that, despite two important discoveries—that of ova in viviparous animals by Steno and de Graaf, and that of spermatozoa by Leeuwenhoek—the 17th century was completely unable to solve the problem of reproduction and that it was compelled to disguise its ignorance with the absurd doctrines of preformationism and *emboîtement*.

CHAPTER 2

Medicine

IF THE 16TH CENTURY MAY BE CALLED the age of anatomy, the 17th century was the age of physiology, a science that could develop only on solid anatomical foundations. True, the 17th century produced anatomists as well, but the great anatomical treatises had already been written. Its greatest contribution to medicine was the discovery of the circulation of the blood.

In the 17th century, medicine was still considered a branch of philosophy, so that the ideas of Galileo, Descartes, Bacon, Newton and Leibniz had a marked influence on its development. Thus Bacon inspired medical philosophy, Galileo medical observations, and Descartes medical methods. Newton and Leibniz introduced mathematical rigour into medicine, but their influence was not to be fully manifest until the 18th century.

MORPHOLOGY

THE LYMPHATIC SYSTEM

While Harvey was studying the circulation of the blood, other physiologists discovered the lymphatic system. Gasparo Aselli demonstrated the presence of the lymphatic glands bearing his name; Jean Pecquet discovered Pecquet's cistern and the thoracic duct, which he traced from its junction with the left subclavian vein, showing that Aselli's lymphatics do not feed the liver, as was commonly believed, but the cistern. Of the many other physiologists who studied the lymphatic system we can mention only Olof Rudbeck and Thomas Bartholin.

HUMAN ANATOMY

Other 17th-century contributions to anatomy and physiology were far less important. Of all branches of anatomy, osteology, which had ceased to be a branch of osteopathy, was perhaps the easiest to study. Hence many anatomists made a detailed examination of the cranial bones, and of the sphenoid and the ethmoid, in particular. Others concentrated on myology, examining, for instance, the tensor tympani. Steno was the first to show that the heart is a muscle—an idea which created a great stir.

Harvey caused renewed interest in angiology. The coronary circulation was now described in greater detail and many physicians concentrated on the study and treatment of aneurisms. At the same time, they continued to believe in the non-existent neuro-lymphatic capillaries.

Neurology proved to be particularly attractive. The brain and its neuraxis were the subjects of many studies, and there were numerous discussions on whether or not it was the seat of the soul. Thomas Willis studied the cranial nerves (not all of which had been discovered), and so did Raymond Vieussens, who also examined the peripheral nerves. Others concentrated on the sense organs, and A. M. Valsalva founded the science of otology. Medical ophthalmologists vied with such physicists as Peiresc, Scheiner and Mariotte.

The internal organs were also studied in greater detail. A. van der Spiegel described the liver, Lorenzo Bellini the kidneys, J. C. Peyer and J. C. Brunner the intestines, J. G. Wirsung, Steno and Thomas Wharton the larger glands. The sexual organs were studied particularly by N. Highmore and Regnier de Graaf.

Physiology

At the same time, physiology scored many new successes. Malpighi discovered the presence of arteriovenous capillaries in the lung, which led to the abandonment of the traditional theory that air is exchanged between the lungs and the rib cage. Borelli demonstrated the respiratory role of the intercostal muscles, though he and all others neglected the diaphragm.

Many turned to neurophysiology, investigating the mysterious flow of 'animal spirits', the Cartesian 'nervous circulation' and the supposed 'neuro-lymphatic capillaries'. It was quite generally believed that the dura mater contracts to drive the nervous fluid to the rest of the body.

The study of digestive processes was greatly complicated by the theories of Franciscus Sylvius (De la Boë), and though the main digestive juices were known—de Graaf succeeded in collecting pancreatic juice—their functions were not clearly understood. While the spleen continued to puzzle physicians who, like Sylvius, wondered why it lacks a duct, the kidneys became better known through the microscopic studies of Bellini and Malpighi, whose names are associated with the kidneys to this day. The sexual organs continued to pose a host of complicated problems, and there was a great deal of discussion on whether the embryo obtains its food and respiratory air from the mother's blood-stream or from her digestive juices.

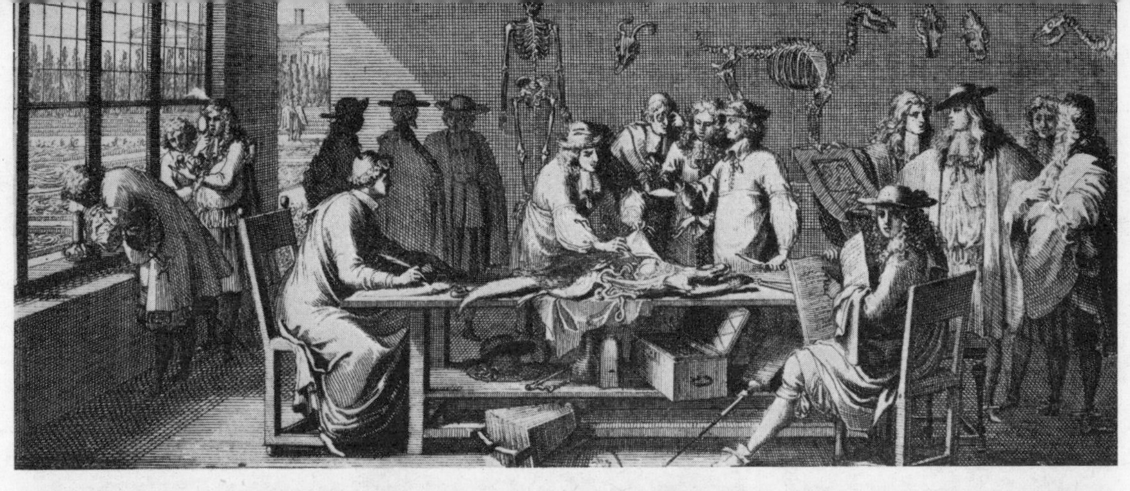

29 Lessons in anatomy and pharmacology at the Jardin du Roi, by Sébastien Leclerc

30 Ward in the Charité Hospital, Paris, by Abraham Bosse

All things considered, physiology may be said to have got well into its stride in the 17th century. However, its progress was to be impeded more than once by the appearance of theories that were not, strictly speaking, physiological theories at all.

Microscopic Anatomy

Another great 17th-century achievement was the creation of histology (or 'microscopic anatomy' as it was then called). Chief among its founders were Robert Hooke, Antony van Leeuwenhoek and Marcello Malpighi. Frederik Ruysch also made a signal contribution when he developed the technique of vascular injections, and a method of preserving corpses which he never divulged.

Pathological Anatomy

Though pathological anatomy became an independent discipline in the 17th century, it did not become important until the 18th. Théophile Bonet, J. J. Manget, Richard Morton and (perhaps) Sylvius made the first studies of miliary tuberculosis and of caverns in the lung; Richard Wiseman investigated white swelling.

It seems odd that, at a time when Redi's experiments disproving the theory of spontaneous generation went largely unheard, Father Kircher and A. Hauptmann should have suspected the existence of microbes, which the former called 'invisible creatures' and the latter regarded as worms or maggots.

THE GREAT SYSTEMS

Chemiatric Medicine

Though chemistry had been introduced into medicine in the 16th century by Paracelsus and his disciples, 17th-century 'Paracelsians' were still busily trying to perfect purely chemical cures. Chemiatric medicine was taught mainly in France and Germany. Among its most vociferous enemies were the two Galenists, Guy Patin and Jean Riolan; among its staunchest advocates were Joseph Duchesne (Quercetanus) and T. Turquet de Mayerne. There was also a neutral camp led by A. Sala and D. Sennert.

Iatrochemistry

Chemiatric medicine continued to flourish until the middle of the 17th century, when it made way for a new 'science'—iatrochemistry—which, as P. Delaunay has described it, turned man into a retort. This approach was, of course, most tempting, for once it is assumed that the human organism is governed exclusively by chemical processes, therapy becomes the simple addition or removal of appropriate chemicals.

Among the leading iatrochemists were two men of great renown: Johann Baptista van Helmont (1577–1644) and Franciscus de la Boë or Sylvius (1614–1672).

Van Helmont believed that the human body as a whole was ruled by an immaterial principle which he called the chief *archaeus*, and that lesser *archaei* preside over the fermentations of the different organs. He placed the chief *archaeus* in the stomach, arguing that even the brain, which he recognized as the centre of movement, memory, imagination and volition, depends for its nourishment on the stomach and cannot function without it.

Van Helmont attributed all pathological conditions to disequilibrium between the chief and the secondary *archaei*. Though disequilibrium might be triggered off by external factors, it was never caused by them, for, unless the body was suitably predisposed, external factors were powerless to affect it in any way. To cure pathological conditions, the physician must help the chief *archaeus* to regain its mastery over its subject *archaei*, and must ignore all external symptoms. Since bleeding and purging merely weaken the body, van Helmont prescribed opiates and wine instead.

Though this theory was quickly forgotten, it had a great many adherents, especially in Holland, Germany, England and France. In particular, it became the basis of the system of Sylvius (de la Boë), in which digestion played much the same role as van Helmont's chief *archaeus*. According to Sylvius, digestive processes are caused by ferments which are released when food comes into contact with saliva, pancreatic juice and bile. Most diseases are caused by excessive acidity, and must therefore be treated with alkaline medicaments, and also with bleedings and purgatives. Sylvius' theory was therefore the more truly 'iatrochemical' of the two. It had as many advocates and enemies as van Helmont's, and caused an even greater stir.

While controversies of this kind were going on, less ardent philosophers like Lémery and Charas concentrated on the more humdrum tasks of publishing new pharmacopoeias and chemical textbooks.

Man as a Machine

The arrogant claims of the iatrochemists produced an equally exaggerated reaction. As physics had benefited so greatly from the development of experimental and mathematical techniques, it seemed only natural to introduce similar concepts into medicine and, in particular, into physiology. The wish to create yet another all-embracing system was so overriding that what truth this new view may have contained was quickly swamped in another bog of idle speculation.

This mathematical approach to medicine had been prepared by Descartes, whose *Traité de l'homme* (1664) described man as a self-contained machine. Descartes used such ancient notions as the fire of the heart and the cooling effects of respiration, and taught that the heart beats because the blood arrives in it 'drop by drop'. From the heart, the blood is driven to the centre of the brain where it is filtered by 'a certaïn small gland'. As a result, the most subtle elements are squeezed through invisible holes and become animal spirits, which act on the nerves and produce movements. Clearly, Descartes had felt no need to encumber his theory with experimental studies.

Iatromathematics or Iatromechanics

Much more serious were the studies of Santorio Santorio (Sanctorius, 1561–1636) who spent part of his life sitting on a balance and weighing his food and excreta. From the difference in their weights he inferred the existence of an imperceptible kind of perspiration whose fluctuations were responsible for diseases. His theory proved extremely popular, even though he expounded it by way of aphorisms. He was the first to introduce such instruments as the balance, the thermometer and the pulsimeter (*pulsilogium*) into medical practice, and hence to give quantitative results of biological phenomena.

However, the real founder of iatromathematics was Giovanni Alfonso Borelli. Although many of his predecessors had compared the organs of the human body to the wind, scissors, pumps, presses, *etc.*, Borelli was the first to associate all vital movements with the actions of the three orders of lever, and later with the structure of muscle fibre. Italy adopted the new theories with enthusiasm; in Newton's country they were welcomed as further evidence in favour of the theory of universal attraction. The chief iatromathematicians were Giorgio Baglivi and Lorenzo Bellini in Italy, and J. Keill, W. Cole, A. Pitcairn and G. Cheyne in Britain.

The circulation of the blood was another favourite subject of iatromathematical studies. Adepts measured its velocity, the resistance of the vascular walls, the diameter and curvature of the vessels, and the collision and friction effects of red corpuscles. Others investigated the elementary corpuscles of which they thought the plasma was made up, computing fluctuations in their flow—the alleged cause of all secretions—or estimating their mutual attractions and repulsions in the blood-stream and in the tissues—the alleged causes of assimilation. Unfortunately, not all iatromathematicians agreed on the interpretation of these 'basic' facts, so that they often arrived at diametrically opposed conclusions.

Other iatromathematicians, or iatromechanists as they came to be called more and more often, studied the movement of the dura mater, which was assumed to be synchronous with the heart-beat and to drive the nervous fluid towards the periphery of the body. At about the same time, Francis Glisson began his studies on irritability, which were to cause so much of a stir in the next century, while others tried to explain digestion by grinding, friction, coction, molecular structure, *etc.*

The iatromechanists, many of whose ideas make us smile, nevertheless deserve credit for having had a single praiseworthy aim: to eliminate the cause of disease. That cause was quickly found: when the nerve fluid which normally produces muscular contractions turns acrid, it engenders spasms or atony, vascular disorders, stagnation, various kinds of inflammation, digestive troubles, and so on.

In other words, many iatromechanists were forced to adulterate their purely mechanical theories with chemical notions. Others again, for instance Baglivi, forgot their theories altogether when they had to deal with their patients. It gradually became clear that neither a purely chemical nor a purely mechanical system could explain the sum total of all biological phenomena. Unfortunately, the alternative systems substituted during the 17th and 18th centuries proved equally abortive, and it was not until all these systems had been scrapped that a synthesis of all that was best in each could finally be constructed.

MEDICAL PATHOLOGY

Neo-Hippocratism

The search for systems was rejected by even many 17th-century physicians, a number of whom turned back to the Hippocratic doctrine that medicine must be based on clinical principles. These neo-Hippocratic practitioners must not be confused with the many surviving Galenists, who still implicitly followed Galen and the Arabs, and were so steeped in the past that they proved a serious obstacle to medical progress. Foremost among those to break with tradition was Thomas Sydenham, who is said to have read so little of Hippocrates that he had to rediscover many of his precepts for himself. He belonged to no particular school and devoted his entire life to the care of his London patients.

Using the Hippocratic principle of studying the patient rather than his symptoms, he distinguished between variolar, morbiliform, dysenteric, grippal and other constitutions. He also considered such factors as the season of the year, and treated intermittent, remittent and continuous fevers and, finally, the plague. Like Hippocrates, Sydenham treated the organism as a whole, helping rather than supplanting the healing action of *natura medicatrix*. His therapy was wise and logical; he popularized the use of quinine and wine of opium, which is still known as 'Sydenham's laudanum'.

Although he headed no school, Sydenham had a number of disciples who were responsible for the general adoption of his method of constitutional diagnosis towards the end of the 18th century. He has been called the 'English Hippocrates'.

The Compilation of Medical Data

At about the same time, other practitioners began to publish their clinical observations. These publications were the forerunners of our medical journals, although unlike them, they concentrated on therapy and ignored etiology. Hence many of the diseases they described are difficult to identify by the modern reader. Some physicians, like Lazare Rivière, supplemented their own notes with the observations of surgeons; others, like Théophile Bonet and Jean-Jacques Manget, attempted to summarize the most important medical, surgical and pharmacological findings of their predecessors and contemporaries. It is mainly thanks to these two great compilers that we have any idea of the state of medical knowledge at the end of the 17th century.

Epidemiology

Though epidemic diseases, and especially plague, continued to lay waste city after city, no new counter-measures were discovered in the 17th century. Though the palustral fevers were recognized as such, as they had been for a long time, erythematous conditions were still mistaken for measles, and most of the other fevers were also confused with one another. Sydenham was the first to recognize and describe scarlet fever.

In general, 17th-century physicians simply distinguished between what they called intermittent, remittent, continuous, comatose, nervous, bilious, haematic, verminous, mucous and catarrhal fevers, each of which could be either malignant or benign. With the introduction of quinine, a further distinction was made between quinine-positive and quinine-negative fevers, a division which foreshadowed 18th-century classifications.

At the same time, what anti-plague measures were in vogue were enforced most rigorously. Suspected victims were quarantined regardless of protests, and it became customary to sprinkle oneself with aromatic 'disinfectants'. (From F. Ranchin's account of the plague in Montpellier, it appears that these were not entirely ineffective.) Every French and German town had a special sanitary corps whose task it was to keep the plague out at all costs. The corps usually included a surgeon, who had to deal with the victims on the spot, at a time when most ordinary physicians had usually taken to their heels. There were also outbreaks of cholera and smallpox, but leprosy was so much on the decline that the lazar-houses were being rapidly closed down. On the other hand, tuberculosis (then called consumption or phthisis) was markedly on the increase.

Among non-epidemic diseases, the most commonly described were gout, dropsy, hypochondria, catarrh, ulcerations of all kinds, the itch (scabies) and venereal diseases. The latter were, however, mentioned less frequently in 17th- than they had been in 16th-century texts, probably because syphilis had ceased to be a novelty and also because mercury therapy must have proved of some benefit.

Hygiene and Hospitalization

Anti-epidemic measures helped to crystallize hygienic concepts, though the term 'hygiene' sorts badly with a century that has rightly been called the 'age of dirty hands'. Even so, as many new hospitals sprang up—particularly in the France of Louis XIV—the decrepit hovels in which poor patients had previously been lodged made way for more salubrious institutions. Special pesthouses were opened in the stricken areas, and military hospitals rose up in regions ravaged by wars. Some German princes engaged a full-time medical corps, but most military leaders engaged their surgeons for only the duration of a given campaign. Field surgery, crude though it may have been, offered excellent training for surgeon-apprentices, many of whom flocked to the colours to learn their trade. The 17th-century manuals on military surgery and hygiene were full of hints that can be used to advantage even today.

Tropical Diseases

The great trading companies also employed a special staff to tend the men in the West and East Indian settlements. Like the sailors, these physicians generally returned with reports of new diseases and new medicaments, thus opening a fresh field of study—tropical medicine. The men who helped to spread this new knowledge did not necessarily belong to the great maritime nations, for French and German physicians played at least as important a part in it as their Dutch and British colleagues.

Though many remedies, for instance those for sleeping-sickness, were of no more than curiosity value in Europe, many exotic drugs and therapeutic techniques proved extremely valuable. These included such methods as moxa and acupuncture from China, and such drugs as quinine and ipecacuanha from South America. At the same time, opium was put to far greater use than before. Some physicians made a special study of the flora and fauna of foreign countries, thus adding greatly not only to pharmacology but also to botany.

Botany thus became virtually a branch of medical science—the medical faculties were the only centres in which it was taught. In particular, botany had special links with histology, for both disciplines were the favourite fields of microscopists. Hence many of the anatomists we have mentioned were also famed for their contributions to plant physiology.

Forensic Medicine

The 17th century also saw the beginnings of serious forensic medicine, though even in the late 16th century Jan Wier, for instance, had protested against torturing witches, on the grounds that witches are mentally sick and not possessed by the devil.

The new discipline covered a vast field: it embraced murder, abortion, rape, traumatology and lunacy. As a result, a great many people participated in its development, including some who believed in such medieval fantasies as magic and the evil eye. However, G. B. Condronchi, Séverin Pineau and their successors Fortunato Fedeli, Johann Bohn, J. G. Zeller and, above all, Paolo Zacchias (1584–1659) made a lasting contribution to forensic medicine and gave it a scientific basis. Italy, Germany, France and Holland, in that order, were leaders in this field.

SURGERY

General Surgery

In most countries, surgery continued to be divorced from medicine, as it had been in the past. Only Italy and Holland continued to follow a medieval tradition of their own, placing surgery on a par with medicine and having it taught and practised exclusively by qualified doctors. All other countries regarded surgery as a purely manual skill, and left it in the hands of barbers and other uneducated persons. Apart from the College of Saint-Côme in Paris, there were no schools of surgery, and what lectures some medical faculties devoted to the subject were mainly theoretical. The College of Saint-Côme itself was greatly weakened by its struggles with the medical faculty, which looked down upon it with disdain. In general, surgeon-apprentices learned their trade by working for individual masters or by joining the army.

Despite their low status, some surgeons made a considerable contribution to medicine. The greatest of all was Ambroise Paré, who may be called the heir of Guy de Chauliac. Most of the texts which appeared in the 17th century were no more than pale reflections of his work.

Obstetrics was taken out of the hands of the midwives and lithotomy was turned into a real art, especially by Jacques de Beaulieu, who helped to develop a number of special instruments.

Other great names in the early development of general surgery were Pierre Dionis, who gave lectures on 'anatomy explained by the circulation' (1673), and J. G. Duverney in France; Wilhelm Fabry (Fabricius Hildanus) and M. G. Purmann in Germany; M. A. Severino and Cesare Magati in Italy; and Richard Wiseman in England.

While many surgeons concentrated on osteology and pathology, others introduced such advances as the treatment of torticollis by subcutaneous section of the sternomastoid. Vascular surgery was mainly restricted to treating aneurisms and tying blood-vessels. Surgeons also treated intestinal wounds, hernias, tumours of all sorts, and fistulas. In addition, some surgeons performed tracheotomies and even more delicate operations, especially in gynaecology, while most were experts on head and chest injuries. Trepanations and amputations were commonly performed, and so were operations on the eye, ear and nose.

In short, though 17th-century surgery was far less brilliant than that of the Renaissance, it did much to develop past knowledge and techniques and to prepare the field for surgical specialization.

Obstetrics

Obstetrics, though still considered a branch of gynaecology, had already become a speciality and women no longer thought it scandalous to be delivered by a man. Obstetrics was, from its very beginning, a French science led by the famous François Mauriceau and the equally famous Louise Bourgeois. Holland soon followed suit with Henrik van Deventer.

As a result of their efforts, important advances were made. The various obstetric techniques were standardized, and new techniques, *e.g.* Mauriceau's method, were adopted. Labour was no longer artificially induced and Caesarean sections, which had been introduced during the previous century, were abandoned as being too dangerous—at least in France, where Mauriceau advised against them. Symphyseotomy was not yet known. The 17th century saw the general introduction of the use of forceps, said to have been invented by the Chamberlen family, who kept it a close family secret. Though a fatal operation caused French surgeons to lose interest in this instrument, other surgeons took a different view; the Dutch in particular bought the Chamberlens' instrument in large numbers. It was some time before the manufacture of forceps ceased to be a family monopoly.

PHARMACOLOGY AND THERAPEUTICS

The 17th century witnessed a pharmaceutical revolution, brought about largely by the introduction of new drugs against the bitter opposition of diehard Galenists.

The most important of all these was undoubtedly quinine, or *cinchona*, imported from Peru where it had been known as fever-bark. From Spain, it was brought to France by the Jesuits, whence it became known as Jesuits' or Cardinals' bark. Because of the Jesuits' bad reputation, the new drug was quickly abandoned in France, and it had to be re-introduced from England, where Robert Talbor (Tabor), aided by Sydenham, had popularized its use. The drug was officially recognized after it had cured the King of France.

The second American drug to appear at the time was ipecacuanha, with which Jean Adrien Helvetius managed to cure the Dauphin. Opium, too, though known of old, became very popular, partly from Sydenham's praises of it. Other new vegetable products, then regarded as of medicinal value, included tea, coffee and chocolate.

At the same time, such chemical compounds as the sulphates of sodium, magnesium and potassium, and various acids and alkalis, were prescribed in ever-growing numbers. Mercury was considered a particularly effective sialagogue, and antimony was at last admitted into the French pharmacopoeia. The 17th century also witnessed the introduction of many compound 'balms', of eau-de-Cologne, of such effervescent medicaments as Rivierus' Draft, and of magnets as painkillers.

Two New Techniques

In addition, there were two further innovations: injection and blood transfusion, both of which became the subjects of bitter controversies. Blood transfusion, in particular, was proscribed in France and Italy, when the first spectacular results were followed by a number of fatal accidents. The most famous advocates of intravenous injections were

Sir Christopher Wren in England, and J. D. Major and M. Ettmüller in Germany. The leading advocates of blood transfusion were G. Colle and F. Folli in Italy, R. Lower in England and J. B. Denis in France.

* * *

In short, the 17th century threw new light on many medical topics neglected or misunderstood during the Renaissance. Medicine had ceased to be the secret skill of a few masters and a few schools; the new discoveries were available to any student of the subject. Colleges of medicine and surgery sprang up in Italy, England, France and Germany, and published their findings in journals and papers. It is worth noting that the father of modern journalism, Théophraste Renaudot, was a physician, and that other physicians, too, devoted part of their time to journalistic activities.

At the same time, new medical schools sprang up alongside the ancient universities of Paris, Montpellier, Bologna, Padua, Pisa, Pavia, Cambridge, Oxford, Louvain, Tübingen, Heidelberg and Basle—particularly in Germany and Italy, where every prince insisted on having a university of his own, for political, national or religious reasons. The most famous of all these new institutions was the University of Leyden in Holland. However, the older universities did not thereby lose their attraction for foreign students, who continued to flock to them as before. It was the done thing to begin one's studies with a grand tour of France, Holland, Switzerland, Italy and England, and to conclude them at home.

The universities, which had been the meeting-ground of nations in the Middle Ages, had now become a melting-pot of ideas. As a result, and with the added help of printing, the medical teaching of the schoolmen was transformed into a universal corpus of medical knowledge which benefited all mankind.

CHAPTER 3

Botany

THOUGH 16TH-CENTURY BOTANISTS had described a vast number of plants, they had done little to classify them. This task was largely accomplished by their 17th-century successors, and particularly by three brilliant men.

CLASSIFICATION

John Ray (1628–1705), who has been called the 'English Pliny', began his work in 1660 by publishing a catalogue of the plants he had collected near Cambridge. Soon afterwards, he made a number of trips to various parts of Britain and published the results in a more comprehensive work which included an accurate description of many cryptogams. Continuing his travels, he visited the Continent in the company of Francis Willughby, and published a further account in 1673. He had previously written the *Tables of Plants* for Dr. Wilkins's *An Essay towards a Real Character and a Philosophical Language* (1668), but it was in his own *Plantarum methodus nova* (1682), and, above all, in his *Historia plantarum generalis* (1686–1704), which described 18,699 plants, that Ray presented his famous system of classification. Though it, too, used the old categories of herbs, trees and shrubs, and though Ray grouped the algae, fungi, mosses and ferns together as 'imperfect herbs', he must be given credit for classifying plants by the characters of leaf, flower and fruit and for introducing the distinction between monocotyledons and dicotyledons. Among his 19 genera of *Floriferae*, classified by their leaves, flowers and seed vessels, some (*e.g.* the *Umbelliferae* and *Asperifoliae*) corresponded to natural groups. This was a great advance, indeed, even though Rivinus and Tournefort claimed that their own corolline classification (based on the form and disposition of the corolla) led to far better results. Ray was also the first to use the term 'species' and to define it by constancy of descent. Though, like all naturalists of his time, he believed in the fixity of species, Ray observed that seeds can degenerate to produce what he called *transmutatio specierum*. Ray's varied and extensive contributions to botany make him one of the greatest naturalists of his time.

Another great systematizer was the Scottish botanist Robert Morison (1620–1683), who was the first to classify plants by the form and structure of their fruits alone, and who criticized Ray for paying too much attention to the character of the leaf. He began by studying the umbellifers, and then applied his principle of classification to plants in general (*Plantarum historia universalis oxoniensis*, 1680).

In 1690, A. Bachmann (Rivinus, 1652–1723), professor of botany at Leipzig, published an *Introductio ad rem herbarium* in which he propounded his corolline system of classification, emphasizing the importance of the general structure of the flower. He distinguished 18 classes and 91 sections of plants, using such criteria as perfect and imperfect, simple and compound, regular and irregular, monopetalous and polypetalous flowers. The greatest achievement of his classification was that it combined trees and herbs into one group. Rivinus' system was widely acclaimed when it first appeared, but was challenged by Ray, Dillenius and others.

All these classifications were overshadowed by the system of the great French naturalist J. Pitton de Tournefort (1656–1708). An ardent botanist from early youth, Tournefort collected plants near Montpellier and in the Alps for his famous *Herbal*, which is still one of the great treasures of the Paris Museum. In 1683, Tournefort was appointed professor at the *Jardin du Roy*, where his lectures and collections began to attract considerable crowds. He continued his botanical travels, visiting Spain, Portugal, England and Holland, and in 1694 he published his *Éléments de botanique* in three volumes, with 451 plates by Aubriet. This work, a Latin translation of which, the *Institutiones rei herbariae*, appeared soon afterwards, represents a milestone in the history of botany, for in it Tournefort used his corolline system to distinguish first between apetalous, monopetalous (gamopetalous) and polypetalous (dialypetalous) plants, and then to subdivide them into 22 sections according to the form and structure of the flowers. Though he retained the clumsy distinction between trees and herbs, and though he exaggerated the role of the corolla as a criterion of classification, his system introduced far greater order than any preceding system had done. Ray and Vaillant failed to appreciate this fact, and criticized him accordingly. Though Tournefort was not the first to use the term 'genus', he gave it a clearer definition, showed its importance, and generalized its use. Practically all his genera were retained by Linnaeus and so were most of his natural sections (orders): *Flore Labiato*, *Cruciformi*, *Rosaceo*, *Caryophyllaceo*, *Liliaceo*, *Papilionaceo* and *Amentaceo*. Finally, Tournefort distinguished carefully between individual species. He published an amended version of his system in the *Corollarium institutionum rei herbariae* (1703), the preface of which (*Isagoge in rem herbariam*) constitutes one of the earliest histories of botany.

When Paul Renaulme (1560–1624) argued in favour of grouping together all species with obvious affinities, Pierre Magnol (1638–1715) suggested that genera, too, could be combined into natural families. However, as Magnol used the calyx as the sole criterion of classification, he was forced to combine such unrelated plants as *Equisetum* and *Humulus*.

The Italian botanist Fabio Colonna (1567–1650), who tried to identify the medicinal plants described by the ancients, coined the term 'petal', and was one of the first to illustrate his work with intaglio prints from metal plates. Prince Federico Cesi (1585–1630) prepared an illustrated version of F. Hernandez's *Natural History of Mexico* in which he introduced a system of plant classification heralding that of Linnaeus. The work did not appear until 1651. Cesi also published a small book on fossilized trees.

L. Plukenet (1642–1706), Keeper of the Royal Gardens at Hampton Court, compiled a very beautiful *Herbal* and published a *Phytographia* and an *Amaltheum botanicum* which listed 6,000 plants, including 500 new species, in the alphabetical order of their names. In 1667, Plukenet's compatriot, C. Merret, published a *Pinax rerum naturalium britannicarum* which discussed 1,400 plant species.

The German botanist Joachim Jung published a set of criteria for distinguishing species. His *Isagoge phytoscopica* (1639), in which he rejected the time-honoured division of plants into trees and herbs, was the most scientific treatise on botany to appear since the time of Aristotle. Jung coined the terms 'petiole' and 'perianth' and distinguished between leaf arrangements.

In 1690, P. Hermann (1640–1695), professor of medicine at Leyden, published a catalogue of 5,000 plants, divided into 25 sections. His study of Dutch plants, illustrated with beautiful and accurate plates, was published by Sherard after the author's death.

In 1685, C. Knaut, professor at Halle, listed 1,476 species of plants in their alphabetical order (although he suspected that there was a natural method of classification). At about the same time, L. Bausch published a number of interesting botanical papers. The *Isagoge in rem herbarium* (1606) by A. van der Spiegel, professor at Padua, deserves mention chiefly for its attack on the theory of the 'signature of plants'. Other works of classification included the *Florilegium* by E. Sweerts, the *Theophrastian Commentary* by J. Bodaeus (1644), the *Botanotheca* (1626) by the Danish physician W. Laurenberg, in which plants were divided into 38 natural sections, and the *Histoire admirable des Plantes* by C. Duret (1605), an uncritical compilation of all that was known about unusual aspects of plants.

FLORAS

After the systematizers came the compilers of floras, particularly in France. In 1653, the Parisian physician J. Cornut published one of the first floras of the surroundings of Paris, mentioning 462 plants and their precise localities. While Garidel compiled a flora of Provence, Father Barrelier (1606–1673) explored not only Provence but also Languedoc, Spain and Italy. The manuscript version of his *General History of Plants* was destroyed by fire, but the plates illustrating 100 species were rescued, and published by A. de Jussieu in 1714.

The best flora of Paris was the *Botanicum parisiense* by Sébastien Vaillant (1669–1722), Secretary to the Director of—and later professor at—the *Jardin Royal* (*Jardin du Roy*) in Paris. Vaillant worked on it for 36 years, and the book, which was published by Boerhaave one year after the author's death, with 300 figures by Aubriet, is kept in the Paris Museum.

In 1698, Tournefort published a *Histoire des plantes qui naissent aux environs de Paris*, which is of great historical interest, since many of the sites described have long since disappeared. The work was annotated by Bernard de Jussieu and republished in 1725.

In 1676, Magnol published a flora of Montpellier and its environs, and in 1689 he published his chief work, the *Prodromus historiae generalis plantarum*, in which plants were listed in 67 tables and described briefly by two or three adjectives. This was the first attempt at a simple method of identifying plants.

J. Burser's herbal of European plants was sent to J. Bauhin, and published (in part) in 1724. Floras of Germany were published by L. Jungerman and M. and H. Hoffmann (flora of Altdorf and Giessen), J. Lösel and J. Gottsched (flora of Prussia), and J. Volkhamer (flora of Nuremberg). A flora of Holland was published by J. Commelin.

By the side of J. Ray's important work on the botanical geography of Europe and on the plants of Great Britain we must mention W. How's *Phytologia britannica*, which mentioned 2,200 plants, and R. Sibbald's *Scotia illustrata*. Olof Rudbeck the Younger (1660–1740), who was one of Linnaeus' teachers, described the flora of Lapland. The flora of Sweden was studied by O. Bromel, that of Spitsbergen and Greenland by F. Martens, and that of Denmark by S. Paulli, who actually coined the general term 'flora'.

The flora of Sicily was studied by P. Castelli, Bonsiglioli and P. Boccone (1633–1703), who also described the flora of Corsica, Malta, Piedmont, France and Germany. In 1692, F. Cupani published a *Catalogus plantarum Sicularum*, and in 1661, G. Grisley compiled one of the first floras of Portugal.

Other botanists turned their attention to the lower plants,

particularly Nicolas Marchant, physician to Gaston of Orleans, who was one of the chief authors of the *Description des plantes* published by the French Academy in 1676. His son Jean, Keeper of the *Jardin du Roi* (to adopt the modern spelling), published numerous papers on mosses and named the common liverwort, *Marchantia*, in honour of his father.

The Structure of Plants

The development of the simple microscope and the discovery of the compound instrument gave a great impetus to plant histology. Leeuwenhoek published his botanical results in his letters to the Royal Society and in his *Arcana naturae detecta* (1695–1719). He was the first to present drawings of plant sections and to describe the sieve tubes and scalariform vessels which had earlier been observed by Henshaw. Leeuwenhoek was also able to show that monocotyledons have scattered vascular bundles whereas dicotyledons have their phloem and xylem arranged in a definite vascular ring. He mentioned the presence of crystals in the root of *Iris florentina* and of starch grains in flour. Incredible though it may seem, he also observed bacteria. Unfortunately, though he was an exceptionally talented observer, he failed to fit his discoveries into an ordered system.

Robert Hooke discovered that plant tissues have a characteristic cellular structure. His *Micrographia* contained magnified illustrations of cork cells, seeds, spores, algae, mosses, *etc.*

In 1671, another great Englishman, Nehemiah Grew (1641–1712), presented to the Royal Society the results of work which had taken him seven years to complete. He called it *The Anatomy of Vegetables Begun* and incorporated it into his *Anatomy of Plants* (1682), in which he examined the cellular structure of the chief plant organs. Grew invented the terms 'radicle' for the embryonic root and 'plume' for what we now call the plumule. His plates illustrate sections of the roots and stems of trees (oak, alder, pine, elder, *etc.*). Grew, who had a most picturesque style, described the root parenchyma as 'a most curious and exquisitely fine-wrought sponge', 'a fine piece of manchet' (white bread), and again as 'the froth of beer or eggs'.

By far the greatest advances in plant anatomy were made by Marcello Malpighi (1628–1694), professor at the Universities of Messina, Pisa and Bologna, and later physician to Pope Innocent XII. In his *Anatome plantarum* (34 plates, 1675–1679), he observed that the utricles (cells) of plants are joined together by a substance soluble in hot water. He drew sections of woody stems and, in particular, illustrated the spiral vessels, which he believed to be subject to peristaltic movements and therefore to be comparable to the tracheae of insects. This error was due to his persistent delusion that animals and plants have similar structures. He also discovered the existence of the lactiferous ducts in certain plants, described stomata, the pits of coniferous wood, *etc.*

Malpighi was also the first to give a good account of the development of the seed in monocotyledons and dicotyledons. He published a plate of the embryo of the walnut in various stages of development, and described the seedlings of the kidney bean, the common bean, the pea, wheat, millet and the date palm. He also depicted the small nodules which appear on the roots of beans and which we now know to contain useful bacteria, and a great number of galls. In short, Malpighi must be considered one of the greatest botanists of his day.

Reproduction

Though the Italian Jesuit F. Buonanni depicted pollen grains on the stigma of a flower (*Althaea hirsuta* L.) in 1691, no botanist seems to have made an experimental study of plant sexuality before Rudolph J. Camerarius (1665–1721). His epoch-making *De sexu plantarum epistola* (1694) described how the removal of the anthers almost always prevented a flower from forming a fruit. Camerarius concluded that anthers are as necessary in the production of embryos as are the pistils. Though the existence of male and female reproductive organs had been suspected earlier, particularly by A. Zaluzhansky (1604), no one before Camerarius had been able to prove it experimentally. Camerarius also showed that certain plants are dioecious (having unisexual male and female flowers on separate stems), and tried to turn this fact into a systematic criterion. His sound ideas, on which Linnaeus based his system, were attacked by many botanists and particularly by Tournefort.

In June 1717, Sébastien Vaillant delivered a discourse on the occasion of the formal opening of the reorganized *Jardin Royal*, in which he defined the flower as a collection of sexual organs. His lecture did much to spread the idea of plant sexuality.

Grew, who had been the first to distinguish pollen grains, and who was therefore the real founder of palynology, also carried out experiments (in conjunction with Jacob Bobart, Keeper of the Oxford Physic Garden) on the fertilization of *Lychnis dioica* L. (red campion) and found that ovules remain sterile in the absence of pollen. The role of pollen in plant reproduction was confirmed by S. Morland. Paolo Boccone studied the fertilization of palm trees.

Plant Physiology

It was at about the same time that studies of the flow of sap, of the chemical structure of plants, and of irritability, led to the birth of

31 The Jardin du Roi in 1636

32 Thistle (*Eryngium alpinum* L.), by Nicolas Robert

plant physiology. We saw earlier that van Helmont concluded from his willow experiment that plants built up their substance from water alone. Joachim Jung propounded the idea that they are also able to select other nutriment from the soil, assimilating certain substances and rejecting others.

The most famous of all 17th-century plant physiologists was the Abbé Edme Mariotte (1620?–1684). In his *First Essay on the Vegetation of Plants* (1679) he contended that every plant has 'a certain number of visible principles', which originate from the action of lightning on atoms of air, dissolve in rainwater and pass into the soil where they are absorbed by the hairs of the roots and sucked up with the sap. His idea that plants synthesize material by chemical processes which vary from species to species was borne out by much later research, so that Mariotte was greatly in advance of his time.

These and similar problems were so much in the minds of botanists that the *Académie royale des Sciences* decided in 1676 to publish a special work on plant physiology, the *Mémoires pour servir à l'histoire des plantes*. They entrusted this task to Mariotte, Perrault, de la Hire, N. Marchant and D. Dodart, and instructed them to produce a true account of the physiology and the virtues of plants, their chemical composition, the methods of cultivating them and so on. Dodart was the first to use incineration as a means of analysing the chemical composition of plants; he also tried to explain the opposite tropisms of root and stem, but his ideas on that subject were challenged by de la Hire, who also investigated hybridization and stem growth.

Claude Perrault (1613–1688) proved the existence of two types of sap, ascending and descending, but, misled by the then fashionable analogy between plants and animals, he endowed the vessels of plants with valves. At about the same time, Linocier studied the distillation products of plants (1619).

The Italian botanist G. Aromatari (*De generatione plantarum*, 1625) showed that the seed is a plant in miniature, and compared its food reserves (oil and aleurone) to the albumen in eggs. His compatriot G. M. Ciassi studied germination, the circulation of sap, and plant irritability.

In England, Robert Boyle showed the effects of 'nitro-aerial spirit' on the germination of plants and on respiration, C. Merret presented the Royal Society with his experimental results on the absorption by plants of moisture from the air, and J. Woodward published the first paper on the mechanics of plant tissue.

Many 17th-century botanists concentrated on the study of plant movements. Borelli and Camerarius studied the irritability of centaury stamens, and Hooke made an anatomical and physiological study of the leaves of *Mimosa pudica*. In his *Historia plantarum*, Ray dealt at length with the movement of leaves, flowers and stamens. He also made a systematic study of the responses of leguminous leaves to temperature changes, and attributed them to variations of mechanical tension in the tissues. J. Cornut studied the relationship between temperature and the opening of flowers and also the periodic movements of locust-tree (*Robinia*) leaves, a phenomenon which Linnaeus later called the sleep of plants.

At about the same time, Sharrock published his famous experiments on the bending of stems in the presence of light. This work was continued in 1700 by Dodart, who also investigated the effects of gravity on the growth of roots and stems.

Agriculture and Horticulture

Two French botanists dominated 17th-century agriculture: Olivier de Serres and J. de la Quintinie. De Serres (1539–1619) spent his entire life in his manor at Pradel (Languedoc) where he set up a number of experimental fields. He was a close friend of Henri IV, for whom he published a book on the art of silk collecting in 1599. His *Théâtre d'agriculture* (1600), which ran to very many editions, remained the standard textbook of agriculture for more than a century. It dealt with the nature of soils, methods of tilling, dressing and sowing, the art of pruning and grafting, the care of kitchen gardens, the planting of trees, and 'honest comportment in the solitude of the country'.

J. de la Quintinie (1626–1688) was attracted to horticulture during a visit to Italy, and later became chief steward of Louis XIV's Versailles estates. His beautifully illustrated *Introduction pour les jardins fruitiers et potagers* ('Orchards and Vegetable Gardens'), published in 1690, was reprinted time and again. In it he set out what work the gardener should do month by month, and presented his own excellent method of pruning fruit trees. The book contained illustrations of most of the garden tools then in use, and had a special section devoted to the orange.

Among other 17th-century treatises on gardening, those of Jacques Boyceau, P. Laurenberg and the Abbé Le Gendre (who dealt particularly well with grafting) deserve special mention. Le Nôtre, Louis XIV's famous gardener at Versailles, was responsible for establishing many 'French' gardens, whose geometrical perfection was generally admired. Outside France, the most important works on agriculture were the *Dendrographias* by J. Jonston (Poland, 1662) and the treatises by A. Munting and J. Commelin (Holland).

Medicinal Botany

The 17th century produced few original works on medicinal plants. Among the writers to deal with this subject were N. Lémery, P. Pomet, G. Wedel and S. Dale. Others continued to publish works on the 'signatures' and medical virtues or 'temperaments' of plants, giving their astrological signs and allocating to them various degrees of 'hot', 'dry', 'cold' and moist'. Among these writers in Britain was Nicholas Culpeper (1616–1654), who, with Peter Cole, published *The English Physician Enlarged* in 1653. This book described 334 medicinal plants, illustrated by 126 woodcuts, and included 369 'new' herbal remedies. It became known as *Culpeper's British Herbal* and ran through many editions until 1809. An important West Indian herbal was compiled by the German physician P. Hermann from 1670 to 1677, but this was not published until 1747, by Linnaeus.

Botanical Gardens

The cultivation of medicinal and ornamental plants in gardens began to flourish greatly at the end of the 16th century and influenced the development of botany in a great many ways. In England, John Gerard (1545–1612) established a physic garden on Holborn Hill, London, overlooking the river Fleet. It contained more than a thousand different species of plants, of which he published a list in 1596. His *Herball or Generall Historie of Plants* was based on the *Pemptades* of Dodoens (1583), and illustrated largely by woodcuts derived from the *Eicones* of Tabernaemontanus (Frankfort, 1590).

In Paris, the brothers Robin opened a botanical garden which inspired the ladies of the capital with *motifs* for their embroidery. It was for their sake that Pierre Vallet, embroiderer to Henri IV, published his illustrated *Jardins du roi très chrétien Henri IV* in 1601. J. Robin, the director of the botanical garden of the Parisian medical school, published a catalogue of the plants in it during the same year.

In 1635, Guy de la Brosse, physician to Louis XIII, founded the Royal Physic Garden (now the *Jardin des Plantes*) which became famous all over the world. He subsequently described the virtues of all its plants and published a catalogue. It was in that garden that S. Vaillant erected the first heated greenhouse. Gaston d'Orléans opened a 'remarkable garden' near Blois, containing a great number of rare plants. Its catalogue was published by A. Brunger in 1653 and was republished by Morison in 1699. Sherard published the *Schola botanica*, a catalogue of the plants in the *Jardin du Roi*, Wienus a catalogue of the Lille Physic Garden, and Mappus a catalogue of the Strasbourg Garden.

In Italy, where botanical gardens flourished more than in any other country, G. Schenck compiled a catalogue of the Padua

Gardens, the brothers Ambrosini, F. Zanoni and G. B. Trionfetti one of the Bologna Gardens, T. Belucci one of the Pisa Gardens, and P. Castelli and F. Cupani one of the Messina Gardens. T. Aldini published a catalogue of the Farnese Gardens, in which he was the first to describe *Acacia farnesiana*. Many great artists (including Guido Reni) helped to illustrate G. B. Ferrari's *De florum cultura* (1633). T. Schenck published a catalogue of the Jena Gardens (1659), P. Ammann one of the Leipzig Gardens, R. van der Spiegel one of the Leyden Gardens, G. Commelin one of the Amsterdam Gardens and James Sutherland one of the Edinburgh Gardens, which had been founded by A. Balfour in 1680. In 1664, the Dutch physician H. Munting published his *Hortus et universae materiae medicae gazophylacium* and, in 1653, S. Paulli wrote the first collective catalogue of plants in the leading botanical gardens of his day: Copenhagen, Oxford, Paris and Padua.

Transatlantic Plants

The study of exotic plants made great advances in the course of the 17th century, thanks largely to the work of French botanists, missionaries and sailors, and to the support of Guy Fagon, chief physician to Louis XIV, who used his considerable influence to further his work. It was Fagon who was responsible for sending Plumier and Feuillée to America, and Tournefort to the Levant.

As early as 1635, J. Cornut described 79 Canadian plants, including *Robinia*, from specimens found in the botanical garden of the brothers Robin. In 1620, Vespasien Robin (1579–1662) published a natural history of the plants of Virginia. A Virginian flora was also compiled by J. Banister and published by Petiver. In 1634, the English physician T. Johnson published a list of American plants, as also did John Tradescant, who brought back numerous plants himself. From 1571 to 1577 Francisco Hernandez (1517–1578) organized a vast investigation of traditional Mexican drugs, the results of which were published in a number of incomplete texts (F. Ximenes, Mexico, 1615; N. A. Recchi, Rome, 1628; F. Cesi, Rome, 1651).

But Europe acquired most of its knowledge of American plants from the work of the Minimite Father C. Plumier (1646–1706). After working with Tournefort and Garidel in France, Plumier left for the Antilles in 1689 accompanied by the physician J. D. Surian, whose special task it was to examine plants for their possible medicinal virtues. The two men returned after an absence of eighteen months, and Surian published a catalogue of the plants and the drugs they had jointly collected. Father Plumier was appointed Royal Botanist and soon afterwards went on a second voyage to

America, publishing the new results in his *Description des plantes de l'Amérique* (1693). To illustrate it, Plumier had traced the outlines of actual plants. In the course of a further voyage, Plumier visited Guadeloupe, Martinique and St. Domingo, and was able to describe 106 new genera, which he named after the most famous botanists of his day (1703). Finally, in 1705, he published an important treatise on American ferns.

The Dominican Jean Baptiste du Tertre (1610–1687) was sent to the Antilles by Richelieu, and his *Histoire générale des Antilles* may be called the first book on applied botany. Claude d'Abbeville and Yves d'Évreux, who lived in Brazil from 1612 to 1614, published a description of some 40 Brazilian trees. It was also from Brazil that G. Marcgrav and W. Piso introduced ipecacuanha, the benefits of which they described in their *Historia naturalis Braziliae* (1648).

The Dutch pharmacist O. Cluyt, who visited North Africa, published the 'Art of packing and despatching trees, plants, fruits and seeds'. P. Hermann and J. Cunningham gathered numerous plants in the Cape of Good Hope and on Ascension Island, respectively. During a visit to Madagascar, Étienne de Flacourt, Director General of the *Compagnie de l'Orient*, gathered material for his natural history of the island (1688), which was profusely illustrated and contained descriptions of a number of new species, including the carnivorous *Nepenthes*. In 1620, John Tradescant explored the flora of the Mediterranean islands; in 1638, J. Vesling published a study of Egyptian plants; the Frenchman J. Spong and the Englishman J. Wheler visited Greece and a part of Asia Minor, and described more than a hundred plants they had found there (1677). William Sherard, who had been made consul in Smyrna, compiled one of the most important herbals of his day.

In 1700, Tournefort left for the Levant accompanied by the painter Aubriet and by the German botanist A. von Gundelsheimer. Together they visited Crete, the Greek islands, Constantinople, the shores of the Black Sea, Armenia (where Tournefort climbed Mount Ararat), Georgia and Asia Minor. On his return to Marseilles on 3rd June 1702, 'full of the riches of the East', Tournefort wrote an account of their journey, which he published in 1717. This work contained drawings of 1,356 plants.

H. van Rheede tot Draakenstein, who travelled extensively before becoming Governor of Malabar, described the vegetation of the Indies in his monumental *Hortus indicus malabaricus* (12 volumes, 794 plates, 1673–1703). J. Commelin (1629–1692) wrote a commentary on Part II of this work, and also a special study of edible plants in the Indies. In 1642 J. de Bondt published a study of the medicinal plants of India, and in 1712 the German botanist E.

Kaempfer, who visited Iran, Ceylon, the Gulf of Bengal, Sumatra, Batavia, Siam and Japan, published a description of the many plants he had collected. His special study of Japanese plants was not published until 1791, by Joseph Banks, a notable 18th-century collector.

The flora of Hindustan was studied by N. Grim; that of China and Japan by the Polish Jesuit M. Boyn and others, including the German physician A. Cleyer, C. Mentzel, J. Nieuhof (who described tea, China root, *etc.*, in 1655) and J. Cunningham, who sent his specimens to Ray, Plukenet and Petiver. P. Camelli, the Moravian physician after whom the Camellia is named, studied climbing plants in Manila and sent specimens to Petiver and Ray, who catalogued them. A magnificent flora of the Sunda Islands was prepared by the German botanist G. Rumph (1626–1707) and published in seven volumes by J. Burman (1741–1750). This work was far more descriptive than Rheede tot Draakenstein's, but the plates were of poorer quality. General surveys of exotic plants were published by C. Mentzel and J. Breyn, whose work was a typographical masterpiece.

The English mariner W. Dampier (1652–1715) may be considered a perfect example of all those 17th-century sailor-botanists who did such valuable work. His guardians sent him to sea as a child, and he took part in buccaneering expeditions to Central and Southern America. He also visited the East Indies, which had just been discovered by Tasman, and later described their flora. He lived in the forests of Jamaica for three years and went back to them in 1679. From there he went to Virginia in 1682. He arrived in China in 1687 and visited Tonking, returned to England in 1691, and left again for New Holland. On his way back he was shipwrecked on Ascension Island, but was rescued two months later. He described his many adventures in his *New Voyage Round the World*, which epitomizes the achievements of all those adventurous men to whom Europe owed most of its knowledge of exotic plants.

CHAPTER 4

The Birth of Geology

THE BASIS FOR GEOLOGY as a serious science was laid in the 17th century. The true nature of fossils had been appreciated for a long time—by Herodotos, Leonardo da Vinci and Bernard Palissy—but no one, save Leonardo, had suggested any connection between them and the study of geological processes. But Leonardo, who described the sedimentary formation of fossiliferous rocks in many parts of Italy, and accepted fossils as evidence of changes in sea-level which could not be accounted for by the Flood, was far ahead of his time.

In the Middle Ages, the term *geologia* was applied to all secular, as opposed to religious, studies and hence embraced such unlikely bedfellows as mineralogy and jurisprudence. It appears that it was first used in its modern sense in 1657, when the Danish naturalist M. P. Escholt called his book on earthquakes and minerals the *Geologia norvegica*. The work was translated into English by Daniel Collins in 1663 and was followed, in 1690, by Erasmus Warren's *Geologia, or a Discussion Concerning the Earth before the Deluge*.

At that time, geology had not yet become an independent discipline. Its students were mainly philosophers, physicians, physicists and travellers, who tried to rid science in general of Aristotelian prejudice—a dangerous task in a period when the Church forced Galileo to recant his heretical views on the earth.

In France, Descartes, though no geologist, introduced mathematics into cosmography by arguing that all celestial phenomena were governed by mechanical laws.

In England, Robert Hooke used the microscope to study foraminifera and the comparative anatomy of fossilized and living trees, and thus prepared the way for the theory of evolution. Harvey's discovery of the circulation of the blood suggested the idea that the earth was a living body in which water circulated freely. Steno introduced the first notions of stratigraphy, at about the same time that the German Jesuit Athanasius Kircher presented the first 'plutonist' theory. Leibniz explained the geological history of the earth in terms of the action of fire and water. Mineralogy was begun by Steno, Huygens, and Boethius de Boodt. Large collections of fossils and rocks were being accumulated and led to the creation of natural history museums.

The Cartesian Synthesis

The discovery of sunspots in 1610 had been one of the most spectacular contributions of the new astronomy. In 1630, Father Scheiner prepared the first map of these spots and their movements, thus demonstrating that the sun was neither immutable nor immobile. As a result, the whole Aristotelian picture of the sun and the earth became changed.

Though the case against Galileo persuaded Descartes to defer the publication of his *Traité du Monde,* he nevertheless stuck to his revolutionary ideas on the evolution of the universe.

> 'I showed', he wrote in his *Discourse on Method,* 'how the greatest part of the matter of this [original] chaos must, in accordance with these laws, so arrange and dispose itself as to resemble our skies, and how some of the remaining parts constitute an earth, others the planets and comets, and others the sun and fixed stars.'

And in his *Principles of Philosophy* he added: 'It is not difficult to conclude from all this that earth and the heaven are made of but one and the same matter.'

Descartes was therefore the first to express the idea that the entire universe is built up of the same sort of matter, and hence obeys the laws of mechanics. According to him, the earth and the other planets had 'once been stars . . . and differed in no way from the sun except possibly in size' (*Principles of Philosophy*). Pursuing these ideas, Descartes concluded that changes in the earth's contours are the result of the gradual and continuous cooling of its central mass.

Fig. 29 is a reproduction of Plate XV of Descartes' *Principles,* illustrating the structure of the earth. In the centre is the element I (heat and light from the time when the earth was still a star). Next comes the sphere M which is made up of the same matter as sunspots; then comes the 'very solid and very heavy crust' C and the lighter crust E, floating on the internal sea D. As fragments of the crust E tilt, they become immersed in the sea and protrude as mountains.

This internal sea is vast enough to explain the Flood. The reason why the oceans on the surface of the earth do not overflow is that they communicate with the internal sea. 'The course of the water in the earth imitates that of the blood in the bodies of animals.'

Descartes also proposed a highly ingenious theory of the formation of metals from metallic vapours rising from the depths. A similar idea had been propounded earlier in von Kalbe's *Bergbüchlein* (1505); afterwards it was adopted by Steno and Hutton. All in all, Descartes'

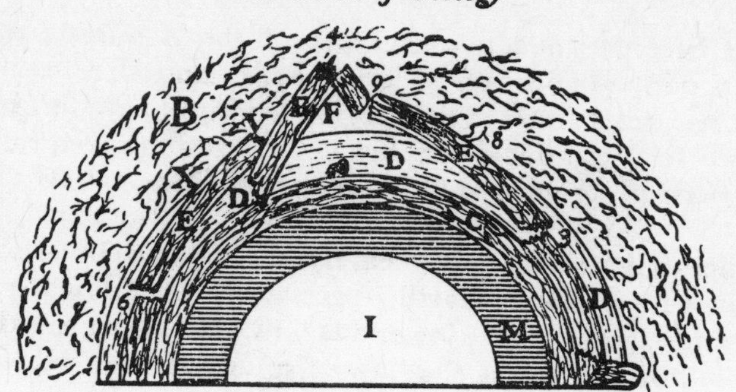

fig. 29 The structure of the earth according to Descartes. ('Principia philosophiae', 1644.)

work helped to introduce into cosmography intelligible ideas of motion, impetus and centrifugal forces. His principle that matter is the same throughout the universe was borne out by 19th-century spectrum analysis, and his idea that the earth has a molten centre was to have a tremendous influence on the development of geological theories.

The Circulation of Water

In 1643, the French Jesuit Georges Fournier, who was a great traveller, published his *Hydrography*, in which he gave an explanation of sea currents and propounded the theory that all oceans have the same level. He also established that the water which rivers carry down to the sea accounts for only a small proportion of the volume of the oceans.

In 1674, Pierre Perrault (1608–1680) published his *Origin of Fountains* in which he contended that the rain contributes the major proportion of sea water. In order to substantiate this claim he measured the rainfall in Paris for three years, the figure he obtained being 600 mm. (24 inches) per annum, which is fairly in accord with modern measurements. He also estimated the catchment area of the headwaters of the Seine and concluded that the rainfall alone is sufficient to feed the river and to maintain the life of trees and fields. Then, like everyone from Aristotle to Descartes, he contended that water rises up from the bowels of the earth in the form of subterranean vapour.

The Work of Steno

Niels Steensen (1638–1686), who is better known as Nicolaus Steno, studied in his native Copenhagen, and later in Amsterdam and Leyden. After a short stay in Paris (1664–1666), he left for Florence, where he became an active member of the *Accademia del Cimento* and was appointed court physician to Ferdinand II, Grand Duke of Tuscany. A careful study of that region led him to a number of quite unexpected stratigraphical conclusions. He summarized his findings in the *Prodromus de solido intra solidum naturaliter contento* (Florence, 1669).

Steno not only explained the real nature of fossils, but also realized that distinct layers of the earth's crust were laid down by marine sedimentation, and that the lower a layer the earlier it was deposited, a principle now known as the 'law of superposition'. He attributed faults and other disturbances in horizontal strata to the action of fire and water. He was also the first to give a diagram of an unconformity.

Moreover, Steno distinguished between 'primary rocks', older than the first plants and animals, and 'secondary rocks', which contain fossils. He made a comparative study of fossilized and living shells, and distinguished between freshwater and marine fossils. Finally, he established six great geological periods, based on advances and retreats of the oceans.

As a result of all these contributions, Steno must be called the first modern geologist. We have seen that he was also a great anatomist, so that his conversion to religion and his consequent loss of interest in his former activities dealt a severe blow to science as a whole.

The English School

Robert Hooke, one of the greatest of all 17th-century scientists, came to geology through his microscopic studies of small fossilized animals and particularly of foraminifera of the genus *Rotalia*. He also made a comparative study of the anatomy of living and fossilized plants. His *Micrographia* (1665) contains a very beautiful drawing of the structure of a silicified tree, the more remarkable since the technique of preparing thin sections was still in its infancy.

Hooke was also among the first to advocate a theory of evolution, for he wrote:

> There may have been divers Species of things wholly destroyed and annihilated, and divers others changed and varied, for we find that there are some Kinds of Animals and Vegetables peculiar to certain Places and not to be found elsewhere. . . . There may also have been divers new Varieties generated of the same Species, and that by the Change of the Soil on which it was produced; for since we find that the Alteration of the Climate, Soil, and Nourishment does often produce a very great Alteration in those Bodies that suffer it, 'tis not to be doubted but that Alterations also of this Nature may cause a very great Change in the shape and other Accidents of an animated Body. . . .

Edward Lhuyd was the author of the remarkable *Lithophylacii britannici iconographia* (1699), which contained a description of 1,600 British fossil animals and plants, and 23 excellent octavo plates illustrating 250 species. Lhuyd observed the similarity between English and Irish fossils, both of which he thought were produced by the germination of small organisms spread by the air and by water. Nevertheless he was the first to describe the brachiopod genus *Terebratula* and the trilobite *Trinucleus*. He realized, too, that certain fossils are characteristic of certain strata, and that the echinoderms found in the English and Irish Chalk are identical.

John Woodward also held traditional ideas on the origin of fossils but he was also a shrewd observer and noticed that 'stone and other terrestrial matter' containing fossils is divided into layers.

Martin Lister continued the work of George Owen, who, in his *Description of Pembrokshire* (1603), had followed the course of 'lymestone vaynes' to the sea. Lister described and illustrated the fossils of England and observed that the English Chalk is continued across the Channel. He also decided to construct one of the first geological maps, but failed to carry this project into practice.

The German School

The Jesuit naturalist Athanasius Kircher (1601–1680) began his geological studies during a visit to the Rhineland. In 1635 he arrived in Rome where, together with Father Scheiner, he observed the sun and prepared the extraordinary solar map which he published later in his *Mundus subterraneus* (1664). On it, the sun was shown as a 'central fire' with a number of 'glory holes of nature' and 'volcanic mountains'. Even so, Kircher was the first to consider the sun as a star in the process of development. Hence it was but a short step to think that the earth, too, was constantly changing, and this is, in fact, how Father Kircher depicted it in a drawing (*Mundus subterraneus*, Vol. I, p. 194), to which he attached the legend: 'Ideal System of Subterranean Fire Cells from which Volcanic Mountains arise, as it were, like Vents.' The whole idea was a fantasy, and so was Kircher's view that the ocean level is maintained by subterranean channels, through which the tides could drive the sea water to the top of the mountains. Even so, Kircher may be called a modern geologist, for he maintained that 'neither within nor without has the earth remained in its original state', and that it is constantly changed by erosion, incursions by the sea, river deposits and earthquakes, which latter he blamed for the disappearance of Atlantis.

Gottfried Wilhelm von Leibniz was born in Leipzig in 1646. In 1676, he was appointed librarian to the Duke of Brunswick-Luneburg at Hanover, and in 1680 he was given the task of writing a history of the House of Hanover and of the Duchy of Brunswick. While crossing Italy in search of documents, he met Steno, whose geological ideas captured his imagination. Leibniz had read Descartes and was attracted to the mechanical philosophy, but felt that the mainspring of mechanical actions must be sought in metaphysics. He had also read Kircher, whom he quoted at some length.

He started his Hanoverian history with a geographical and geological introduction based on a study of the earth as a whole. The results of that study, the *Protogea*, were not published until 33 years after his death, in 1749, the very year in which Buffon's *Theory of the Earth* first appeared.

Like Descartes, Leibniz assumed that the earth was of igneous origin, that it had a central fire, and that it abounded in 'vitreous matter', volcanic substances and thermal waters.

Leibniz believed that the earth had been, and was being, transformed by the continuous action of fire and water—a view which bore witness to his great intellectual courage. Like all his contemporaries, Leibniz believed that the Flood had been caused by the sudden release of subterranean waters resulting from the collapse of the earth's rocky 'vault'. He distinguished between igneous and sedimentary rocks, and thought that the contours of the earth had been shaped by water and wind, though the mountain chains had appeared during antediluvian eruptions.

Leibniz's *New Essays* (written in 1703 and published in 1765) contained what was probably the earliest definition of a 'species': 'We define species through generation, considering that like types produced by like seeds must necessarily be of the same species.' However, 'one cannot invariably assign fixed limits to a species'. 'Species are related and do not differ from one another except by imperceptible degrees.' 'Everything in nature proceeds by degrees; nothing proceeds by jumps.' By adding that, 'perhaps at some time . . . species of animals have been, or will be, more subject to change than they are at present', Leibniz clearly foreshadowed the views of 18th-century evolutionists.

The Mineralogists

The science of mineralogy can be studied by mathematical, chemical and geological methods, and can therefore be divided into: *crystallography* or the study of symmetrical properties, *chemical mineralogy* or the study of the chemical composition of minerals, and *petrography* or the study of their origin and mode of occurrence as the ingredients of rocks. Mineralogy, originally a branch of geology, became an independent discipline as early as the middle of the 17th century, when the term 'mineral kingdom' was first coined.

While Hooke, Leeuwenhoek and Boyle observed crystals and merely remarked on their strange properties, Steno made a profound study of the shapes of different types and especially of the prismatic crystals of quartz. His compatriot and teacher, Erasmus Bartholin (1625–1698), investigated the structure of crystals of Iceland spar (calcite) and was the first to describe double refraction (*Experimenta crystalli Islandici disdiaclastici*, Copenhagen, 1669). In 1690, Huygens described the structure of calcite in his *Traité de la lumière*, in which he assumed that calcite consists of minute ellipsoidal particles pressed closely together, having definite orientations in regard to the optical axis of the crystal, and forming a system of rhombohedra. This view was close to that which Haüy propounded a century later.

Anselmus Boethius de Boodt (1550?–1632) was born in Bruges. In 1604 he was summoned to Bohemia and appointed physician and lapidary to the Emperor Rudolf II. During his stay in Prague, he wrote a *Historia gemmarum et lapidum* which was published in 1609, the very year in which Kepler, another servant of the Emperor, published his first laws of planetary motion.

In this book, de Boodt discussed the properties, uses and locations of precious, semi-precious and other stones. He strongly emphasized the value of experiment and also presented an experimental method of distinguishing between five degrees of hardness in stones: earths, soft stones, hard stones which can be filed down, harder stones which can be worked with emery, and very hard stones which can be cut only with diamonds. He made careful studies of the properties of diamonds, rubies, garnets, sapphires, opals, emeralds, topazes, quartzes, corals and pearls. He coined the term *nephrite* (jade) and discussed the therapeutic properties of precious stones. He described 647 fossils and rocks—a considerable achievement for that time. His work, which was widely read, and republished in 1636, 1647 and 1649, was translated into French in 1644.

Geological Collections

Though the true nature of fossils was not generally understood, fossils had become collectors' items and the subject of many learned discourses. It had become clear that in order to make a proper study of them it was essential to assemble and compare specimens and to publish illustrated catalogues. The first such catalogue was probably compiled by Johann Kentmann (1518–1574), whose classification was based on Agricola's system. Kentmann also published a sketch of his 'cabinet' which he called *arca rerum fossilium*.[1]

[1] The term *Museum*, which had been applied to the university building erected by Ptolemy Soter in Alexandria, was resurrected in the 16th century when it came to be used for collections of coins, in spite of protests by purist philologists.

The first large geological collections were set up in Italy. The most important of all was the Vatican Collection, which was catalogued by Michele Mercati in 1574. This catalogue (which was not published until 1719) included an unintended lesson in comparative anatomy, for Mercati pictured, side by side, 'tongue-stones' and shark's teeth, showing the resemblance between them though never suspecting that they are, in fact, identical.

Another great collection was that of Ulysses Aldrovandi. According to Misson, who inspected it in 1668, it was labelled and catalogued in 187 volumes. Aldrovandi's *Musaeum metallicum* was published by Ambrosini in 1648, and the collection was transferred to the Bologna Museum. Another important collection was the *Calceolarius* in Verona. It was founded by Francesco Calceolari (1522–1609), and many catalogues of its contents were published.

In England, the first important catalogue to be printed was that of John Tradescant's collection (1656). It described pyritized trees, and specimens of petrified holly from Loch Ness, both of which created great interest. The collection was exhibited at Lambeth and transferred to the Ashmolean Museum at Oxford in 1683 (where it no longer exists). The University of Cambridge was more fortunate in that it was able to preserve John Woodward's collection. The Royal Society acquired the collection of Robert Hubert (*alias* Forges) and published a catalogue in 1664.

The creation of a national British Museum was advocated by Robert Hooke, who said in a lecture:

> It is not only in the description of species of Shells and Fishes, that a very great Defect or Imperfection may be found among Natural Historians, but in the description of most other things. . . . It were therefore much to be wish't for and indeavoured that there might be made and kept in some Repository as full and compleat a Collection of all varieties of Natural Bodies as could be obtain'd, where an Inquirer might be able to have recourse, where he might peruse, and turn over, and spell, and read the Book of Nature. . . . And I could heartily wish that a Collection were made in the Repository of as many varieties as could be procured of these kinds of Fossile-Shells and Petrifactions. . . .

Hooke's dream was realized in 1753, when Parliament voted £20,000 for the purchase of Sir Hans Sloane's collection. This collection, thenceforth called the British Museum, was housed and arranged in Montagu House, Bloomsbury.

Conclusion

It would be idle to attempt a brief summing-up of the achievements of a century that saw so many advances in scientific methods and so many new discoveries. All we can say is that it gave an impetus to scientific research which it has not lost to this day. Future mathematicians, physicists, geologists, biologists and particularly chemists had merely to follow the course charted by their predecessors, and to extend and co-ordinate their findings.

As a direct result of 17th-century achievements, scientific ideas came to play a growing part in the intellectual preoccupations of Europeans. Their liberating role, which had appeared so forcefully during the revolt against the official Aristotelian and medieval traditions, was to culminate in the 'age of enlightenment', which was the direct consequence of the hard battles fought and won by the innovators of the 17th century.

BIBLIOGRAPHY

Historical Background

'Peuples et civilisation': *La prépondérance espagnole (1559–1600)* (by H. HAUSER, 3rd ed., Paris, 1948), *Louis XIV (1660–1715)* (by P. SAGNAC and A. DE SAINT-LEGER, 3rd ed., Paris, 1949).

R. K. MERTON, 'Science, Technology and Society in Seventeenth Century' in *Osiris*, Vol. IV, 1938.

Histoire générale des civilisations, Vol. IV, *Les XVIe et XVIIe siècles* (by R. MOUSNIER, Paris, 1954).

L. OLSCHKI, *Galilei und seine Zeit*, Halle, 1927.

Collection 'Clio': *Le XVIIe siècle* (by E. PRÉCLIN and V.-L. TAPIÉ, Paris, 1943).

P. M. SCHUHL, *Machinisme et philosophie*, 2nd ed., Paris, 1947.

H. A. P. SMITH, *History of Modern Culture*, 2 vols., New York, 1930–34.

B. WILLEY, *The Seventeenth Century Background*, Cambridge, 1934.

General Science

M. BOLL *et al.*, *La science, ses progrès et ses applications*, Vol. I, 2nd ed., Paris, 1950.

H. BUTTERFIELD, *The Origins of Modern Science*, London, 1949.

F. ENRIQUES and G. DE SANTILLANA, *Compendio di storia del pensiero scientifico*, Bologna, 1948.

G. HANOTAUX, *Histoire de la nation française*, Vols. XIV and XV, Paris, 1929 (articles by E. PICARD, H. ANDOYER, P. HUMBERT, C. FABRY, A. COLSON, M. CAULLERY).

R. LENOBLE *et al.*, 'Les sciences au XVIIe siècle' in the review *XVIIe Siècle*, January 1956.

S. F. MASON, *History of the Sciences*, London, 1953.

H. PLEDGE, *Science Since 1500*, London, 1939.

Works already cited of DAUMAS, HALL, MIELI, PAPP and BABINI (Vols. V–VII), POGGENDORFF, RUSSO, SARTON, WOLF (see Bibliography of Part I, p. 172).

Scientific Institutions

Archives du Museum d'histoire naturelle, Tricentenary volume, Paris, 1935.

H. BROWN, *Scientific Organizations in Seventeenth Century France*, Baltimore, 1934.

M. DAUMAS in *Histoire de la science*, Paris, 1957.

A. FAVARO, 'Documenti per la storia dell' Accademia dei Lincei' in *Bull. di bibl. e di storia delle scienze . . .*, Vol. XX, 1887.

R. T. GUNTHER, *Early Science in Oxford*, 14 vols., Oxford, 1920–45.

SIR H. LYONS, *The Royal Society, 1660–1940*, Cambridge, 1944.

E. MAINDRON, *L'Académie des Sciences*, Paris, 1888.

M. ORNSTEIN, *The Rôle of Scientific Societies in the Seventeenth Century*, 2nd ed., Chicago, 1928.

D. STIMSON, *Scientists and Amateurs. A History of the Royal Society*, New York, 1948.

Monographs

A. CARLI and A. FAVARO, *Bibliografia galileiana*, Rome, 1896.

G. BOFFITO, *Bibliografia galileiana, 1896–1940*, Rome, 1943.

F. SHERWOOD TAYLOR, *Galileo and the Freedom of Thought*, London, 1928.

A. KOYRÉ, *Études galiléennes*, Paris, 1939.
Galilée et la révolution scientifique du XVIIe siècle, Paris, 1955.

G. ABETTI, *Amici e nemici di Galileo*, Milan, 1945.

G. DE SANTILLANA, *Le procès de Galilée*, Paris, 1955.

P. M. SCHUHL, *La Pensée de Bacon*, Paris, 1949.

R. W. GIBSON, *Francis Bacon: a Bibliography of his Works and of Baconiana . . .*, Oxford, 1950.

I. BEECKMAN, *Journal*, ed. by C. DE WAARD, 4 vols., The Hague, 1939–53.

C. DE WAARD (ed.), *Correspondance du P. Marin Mersenne*, 4 vols., Paris, 1933–55.

Pierre Gassendi, Paris, 1955.

Tricentenaire de Pierre Gassendi, Paris, 1957.

C. ADAM, *Descartes, sa vie et son œuvre*, Paris, 1910.

G. MILHAUD, *Descartes savant*, Paris, 1921.

E. GILSON, *Etude sur le rôle de la pensée médiévale dans la formation du système cartésien*, Paris, 1930.

J. F. SCOTT, *The Scientific Works of René Descartes*, London, 1952.

A. VON BRAUNMÜHL, *Christopher Scheiner . . .*, Bamberg, 1891.

P. HUMBERT, *Un amateur: Peiresc*, Paris, 1933.

L'œuvre scientifique de Blaise Pascal, Paris, 1947.

A. MARRE, *L'œuvre scientifique de Pascal*, Paris, 1912.

H. GOUHIER, *La philosophie de Malebranche*, Paris, 1928.

L. BLOCH, *La philosophie de Newton*, Paris, 1908.

F. CAJORI, *Sir Isaac Newton*, London, 1928.

E. A. BURTT, *The Metaphysics of Sir Isaac Newton*, London, 1925.

L. T. MORE, *Newton*, London, 1934.

R. W. and G. M. BABSON, *A Descriptive Catalogue . . . of the Works of Sir Isaac Newton . . .*, New York, 1950.

E. N. DA C. ANDRADE, *Isaac Newton*, London, 1954.

Mathematics

Works already cited of BECKER and HOFMANN, BOUTROUX, BRAUNMÜHL, CAJORI, CANTOR (Vols. II and III), CHASLES, COOLIDGE, KÄSTNER, LORIA, MONTUCLA, SMITH, TROPFKE, ZEUTHEN.

F. CAJORI, *A History of Mathematics*, 2nd ed., New York, 1919.

W. W. R. BALL, *A Short Account of the History of Mathematics*, London, 1901.

E. T. BELL, *The Development of Mathematics*, 2nd ed., New York, 1945.

R. C. ARCHIBALD, *Outline of the History of Mathematics*, 6th ed., Math. Ass. of America, 1949.

J. E. HOFMANN, *Geschichte der Mathematik*, 3 vols., Berlin, 1953–57.

J. F. SCOTT, *A History of Mathematics*, London, 1958.

L. BRUNSCHVICG, *Les étapes de la philosophie mathématique*, 4th ed., Paris, 1947.

P. BOUTROUX, *L'idéal scientifique des mathématiciens*, 2nd ed., Paris, 1955.

P. SERGESCU, *Les recherches sur l'infini mathématique . . .*, Paris, 1949.

C. B. BOYER, *The Concept of the Calculus*, 2nd ed., New York, 1949.
L. GEYMONAT, *Storia e filosofia dell'analisi infinitesimale*, Turin, 1947.
L. E. DICKSON, *History of the Theory of Numbers*, 3 vols., Washington, 1919–23.
I. TODHUNTER, *History of the Mathematical Theories of Probabilities . . .*, Cambridge, 1865.
J. L. COOLIDGE, *History of Geometrical Methods*, Oxford, 1940.
A History of Conic Sections and Quadric Surfaces, Oxford, 1945.
A. AMODEO, *Origine e sviluppo della geometria projettiva*, Naples, 1939.
C. B. BOYER, *The History of Analytical Geometry*, New York, 1957.
P. TANNERY, *Mémoires scientifiques*, Vol. VI, Paris, 1926.
H. BOSMANS, various articles, listed in *Arch. int. hist. des sci.*, III, 1950.
F. RITTER, *François Viète*, Paris, 1895.
J. ITARD, *Pierre Fermat*, Basle, 1950.
G. KNOTT (ed.), *Napier Tercentary Memorial Volume*, London, 1915.
R. TATON, *L'œuvre mathématique de G. Desargues*, Paris, 1951.
A. FAVARO, *B. Cavalieri*, Venice, 1914.
E. WALKER, *A Study in the 'Traité des indivisibles' of Roberval*, New York, 1932.
F. CAJORI, *William Oughtred*, Chicago, 1916.
P. H. OSMOND, *Isaac Barrow*, London, 1944.
J. F. SCOTT, *The Mathematical Work of J. Wallis*, London, 1938.
H. W. TURNBULL, *James Gregory*, London, 1939.
The Mathematical Discoveries of Newton, London, 1945.
G. W. LEIBNIZ, *Die mathematische Schriften* (ed. Gerhardt, 7 vols., Berlin, 1849–63).
J. E. HOFMANN, *Die Entwicklungsgeschichte der leibnizschen Mathematik . . .*, Munich, 1949.
Works of VIETA (Leyden, 1646); FERMAT (5 vols., Paris, 1891–1922); DESCARTES (12 vols., Paris, 1896–1911); TORRICELLI (5 vols., Faenza, 1919–44); PASCAL (14 vols., Paris, 1908–14); HUYGENS (22 vols., The Hague, 1888–1950).

Mechanics

Works already cited of DIJKSTERHUIS, DUGAS, DUHEM, JOUGUET, MACH, OLSCHKI.
R. DUGAS, *La mécanique au XVIIe siècle*, Paris, 1954.
E. A. BURTT, *The Metaphysical Foundations of Modern Physical Science*, 2nd ed., London, 1932.
E. W. STRONG, *A Study in the Philosophy of Mathematical-physical Science in the 16th and 17th Centuries*, Berkeley, 1931.
R. LENOBLE, *Mersenne et la naissance du mécanisme*, Paris, 1942.

M. BOAS, 'Establishment of the Mechanical Philosophy' in *Osiris*, X, 1952.
A. E. BELL, *Christian Huygens and the Development of Science in the 17th Century*, London, 1947.
I. TODHUNTER, *A History of the Theory of Elasticity*, 2 vols., Cambridge, 1886–93.
A. KOYRÉ, *Études galiléennes*, Paris, 1939.
A Documentary History of the Problem of Fall from Kepler to Newton, Philadelphia, 1955.
C. DE WAARD, *L'expérience barométrique*, Thouars, 1936.
M. GUÉROULT, 'Métaphysique de la force chez Descartes et chez Malebranche' in *Rev. de métaph. et de morale*, 1954.
Dynamique et métaphysique leibniziennes, Paris, 1934.
F. ROSENBERGER, *Newton und seine physikalischen Principien*, Leipzig, 1895.

Astronomy

Works already cited of BERTRAND, DELAMBRE, DREYER, KOYRÉ, ZINNER.
A. G. PINGRE, *Annales célestes du XVIIe siècle*, Paris, 1901.
J. S. BAILLY, *Histoire de l'astronomie moderne*, 3 vols., Paris, 1785.
J. LALANDE, *Bibliographie de l'astronomie*, Paris, 1803.
J. C. HOUZEAU and A. LANCASTER, *Bibliographie générale de l'astronomie*, 2 vols., Brussels, 1882–89.
E. DOUBLET, *Histoire de l'astronomie*, Paris, 1922.
F. BOQUET, *Histoire de l'astronomie*, Paris, 1924.
G. BIGOURDAN, *L'astronomie. Évolution des idées et des méthodes*, Paris, 1911.
H. MACPHERSON, *Makers of Astronomy*, Oxford, 1933.
G. ABETTI, *The History of Astronomy*, New York, 1952; London, 1954.
F. JOHNSON, *Astronomical Thought in Renaissance England*, Baltimore, 1937.
A. KOYRÉ, *La gravitation universelle de Kepler à Newton*, Paris, 1951.
'La mécanique céleste de J. A. Borelli' in *Rev. Hist. Sci.*, VI, 1952.
A. DANJON and A. COUDER, *Lunettes et télescopes*, Paris, 1935.
H. C. KING, *The History of the Telescope*, London, 1956.
C. ANDRÉ and G. RAYET, *L'astronomie pratique et les observatoires . . . depuis le milieu du XVIIe siècle*, 5 vols., Paris, 1874–81.
C. WOLF, *Histoire de l'Observatoire de Paris*, Paris, 1902.
G. BIGOURDAN, *Histoire de l'astronomie d'observation et des Observatoires en France*, 2 vols., Paris, 1918–30.
H. SPENCER JONES, *The Royal Observatory, Greenwich*, London, 1943.
P. HUMBERT, *Les astronomes français de 1610 a 1667*, Draguignan, 1942.

J. A. REPSOLD, *Zur Geschichte der astronomischen Messwerkzeuge*, 2 vols., Leipzig, 1908–14.

M. CASPAR, *J. Kepler*, Stuttgart, 1948.

Works of GALILEO (20 vols., Florence, 1890–1909); of KEPLER (8 vols., Frankfort, 1858–70; new ed., Munich, 1938); Engl. ed. of GALILEO's *Dialogo* (Chicago, 1953; Berkeley, 1953), of NEWTON's *Principia* (Berkeley, 1946).

Physics

Works already cited of POGGENDORFF, GERLAND and TRAUMÜLLER, LASSWITZ, ROSENBERGER.

E. HOPPE, *Histoire de la physique*, Paris, 1928.

F. CAJORI, *History of Physics*, 2nd ed., New York, 1929.

W. F. MAGIE, *A Source Book in Physics*, New York, 1935.

H. VOLKRINGER, *Les étapes de la physique*, Paris, 1929.

R. CAVERNI, *Storia del metodo sperimentale in Italia*, 6 vols., 1891–1900.

P. MOUY, *Le développement de la physique cartésienne*, Paris, 1934.

M. DAUMAS, *Les instruments scientifiques aux XVIIe et XVIIIe siècles*, Paris, 1953.

C. SINGER, E. J. HOLMYARD and A. R. HALL, *A History of Technology*, Vol. III (1400–1650), Cambridge, 1957.

A. P. USHER, *A History of Mechanical Inventions*, 2nd ed., Harvard Univ. Press, 1954.

L. T. MORE, *Life and Works of . . . Robert Boyle*, New York, 1944.

J. F. FULTON, *Bibliography of Robert Boyle*, 2nd ed., London, 1954.

M. ESPINASSE, *Robert Hooke*, London, 1956.

H. W. ROBINSON and W. ADAMS, *The Diary of Robert Hooke, 1672–1680*, London, 1935.

J. PRIESTLEY, *History and Present State of Discoveries Relating to Vision, Light and Colours*, 2 vols., London, 1772.

E. VERDET, *Leçons d'optique physique*, 2 vols., Paris, 1869–70.

D. N. MALLIK, *Optical Theories*, 2nd ed., Cambridge, 1917.

E. HOPPE, *Geschichte der Optik*, Leipzig, 1926.

C. E. PAPANASTASSIOU, *Les théories sur la nature de la lumière de Descartes à nos jours*, Paris, 1935.

C. PLA, *El enigma de la luz*, Buenos Aires, 1949.

V. RONCHI, *Histoire de la lumière*, Paris, 1956.
Galileo e il cannochiale, Udine, 1942.

I. B. COHEN, 'Roemer and the First Determination of the Velocity of Light' in *Isis*, XXXI, 1943.

M. ROBERTS and E. R. THOMAS, *Newton and the Origin of Colours*, London, 1934.

K. J. A. HALBERTSMA, *A History of the Theory of Colours*, Amsterdam, 1949.

R. S. CLAY and T. H. COURT, *The History of the Microscope*, London, 1932.
E. FRISON, *L'évolution de la partie optique du microscope*, Leyden, 1954.
M. ROOSEBOOM, *Microscopium*, Leyden, 1956.
J. PRIESTLEY, *History and Present State of Electricity* . . ., London, 1767.
T. MARTIN, *La foudre et le magnétisme chez les Anciens*, Paris, 1866.
E. SARTIAUX and M. ALIAMAT, *Principales découvertes et publications concernant l'électricité*, Paris, 1903.
P. F. MOTTELEY, *Bibliographical History of Electricity and Magnetism*, London, 1922.
E. HOPPE, *Geschichte der Elektrizität*, Leipzig, 1884.
D. M. TURNER, *Makers of Science: Electricity and Magnetism*, Oxford, 1927.
J. DAUJAT, *Origine et formation des théories de l'électricité et du magnétisme*, Paris, 1947.
M. GLIOZZI, *L'electrologia fine al Volta*, 2 vols., Naples, 1937.
E. BAUER, *L'électromagnétisme hier et aujourd'hui*, Paris, 1949.
E. T. WITTAKER, *History of the Theories of Aether and Electricity*, 2nd ed., 2 vols., Edinburgh, 1951–53.

Chemistry

Works already cited of DELACRE, DUVEEN, FERGUSON, FIERZ-DAVID, HOLMYARD, JAGNAUX, LEICESTER and KLICKSTEIN, VON LIPPMANN, OSTWALD.
M. P. CROSLAND, *Historical Studies in the Language of Chemistry*, London, 1962.
H. METZGER, *La chimie*, Paris, 1930.
Les doctrines chimiques en France du début du XVIIe siècle a la fin du XVIIIe siècle, Paris, 1923.
La genèse de la science des cristaux, Paris, 1918.
J. R. PARTINGTON, *A Short History of Chemistry*, London, 1948.
T. S. PATTERSON, 'J. Mayow's Contribution to the History of Respiration and Combustion' in *Isis*, Vol. XV, 1931.
G.-E. STAHL, *Œuvres médico-philosophiques*, Vols. 2–6, Paris, 1859–65.
H. DE WAELE, *J. B. van Helmont*, Brussels, 1948.

Geology

Works already cited of ADAMS, GEIKIE, VON GROTH, KOBELL, DE MARGERIE, MATHER and MASON, MEUSNIER, ZITTEL.
M. DAUBRÉE, 'Descartes, l'un des créateurs de la cosmologie et de la géologie' in *Journal des savants*, 1880.
W. N. EDWARDS, *Guide to an Exhibition Illustrating the Early History of Palaeontology*, London, 1931.
R. FURON, *La paléontologie*, 2nd ed., Paris, 1951.

J. G. GARRET, 'The Prodromos of Nicolaus Steno's Dissertation . . .' in *Univ. Michigan Studies*, Hum. ser., XI, 1916.

J. E. HILLER, 'Boèce de Boodt, précurseur de la mineralogie moderne' in *Ann. Guétard-Séverine*, 1935.

R. LENOBLE, *La géologie au milieu du XVIIe siècle*, Paris, 1954.

C. PÉCAUT, 'L'œuvre géologique de Leibniz' in *Rev. gén. des sci.*, 1951.

Biology

See Bibliography of Part I, p. 175. Also:

G. CUVIER, *Histoire des sciences naturelles*, 5 vols., Paris, 1831–45.

J. ROSTAND, *Esquisse d'une histoire de la biologie*, Paris, 1945.

E. GUYÉNOT, *Les sciences de la vie aux XVIIe et XVIIIe siècles*, 2nd ed., Paris, 1956.

G. CANGUILHEM, *La connaissance de la vie*, Paris, 1952.

La formation du concept de réflexe aux XVIIe et XVIIIe siècles, Paris, 1955.

F. J. COLE, *Early Theories of Sexual Generation*, Oxford, 1930.

F. W. OLIVER, *Makers of British Botany*, Cambridge, 1913.

C. E. RAVEN, *English Naturalists from Neckam to Ray*, Cambridge, 1947.

John Ray, Naturalist, 2nd ed., London, 1950.

J. F. FULTON, *A Bibliography of the Writings of W. Harvey*, 2nd ed., Cambridge, 1953.

L. CHAUVOIS, *William Harvey. His Life and Times; his Discoveries; his Methods*, London, 1957.

J. METZLER, *Niels Steensen*, Copenhagen, 1928.

C. DOBBEL, *Antony van Leeuwenhoek and his 'Little Animals'*, London, 1932.

A. SCHIERBEECK, *The Collected Letters of A. van Leeuwenhoek*, Amsterdam, 1939–52.

Medicine

See Bibliography of Part I, p. 176. Also:

J. GUIART, *Histoire de la médecine française*, Paris, 1947.

E. H. GUITARD, *Manuel d'histoire de la littérature pharmaceutique*, Paris, 1942.

D. GUTHRIE, *History of Medicine*, London, 1945.

E. KREMERS and G. URDANG, *History of Pharmacy*, Philadelphia, 1940.

P. LECÈNE, *L'évolution de la chirurgie*, Paris, 1923.

J. LÉVY-VALENSI, *La médecine et les médecins en France au XVIIe siècle*, Paris, 1933.

F. R. PACKARD, *Guy Patin and the Medical Profession in Paris in the Seventeenth Century*, London, 1924.

J. F. PAYNE, *Thomas Sydenham*, London, 1900.

P. PIC, *Guy Patin*, Paris, 1911.

A. PORTAL, *Histoire de l'anatomie et de la chirurgie*, 6 vols., Paris, 1770.

M. RAYNAUD, *Les médecins au temps de Molière*, Paris, 1863.

L. REUTTER DE ROSEMOND, *Histoire de la pharmacie*, 2 vols., Paris, 1931.

J. ROUSSET, *Les thèses médicales soutenues a Lyon aux XVIIe et XVIIIe siècles*, Lyons, 1950.

R. H. SHRYOCK, *The Development of Modern Medicine*, Philadelphia, 1936.

C. SINGER, *A Short History of Medicine*, Oxford, 1928.

K. SPRENGEL, *Histoire de la médecine*, 9 vols., Paris, 1815.

A. C. WOOTTON, *Chronicles of Pharmacy*, 2 vols., London, 1910.

PART III

The 18th Century

IN LESS THAN A CENTURY—from Gilbert's *De magnete* (1600) to Newton's *Principia* (1687)—the face of science had changed almost beyond recognition. The immense progress made had engendered confidence in the practical value of science and the 18th century opened in an atmosphere of optimism. Most European rulers founded and supported scientific academies, where students could work in relative peace and with few financial worries. Though they thus owed much to aristocratic patronage, the scientists were nevertheless instrumental in preparing the ground for liberalism. Their belief that social conditions could be ameliorated by the realization of scientific objectives became one of the mainsprings of the French encyclopedists and hence of the French revolution.

In mathematics, 18th-century students concentrated, in the main, on extending, co-ordinating and applying the discoveries of their predecessors. The development of the differential calculus and the introduction of new methods—differential equations, partial differential equations, calculus of variations—helped to complete the work Newton had so brilliantly begun in mechanics, and to introduce mathematics into acoustics and hydrodynamics.

At the same time, physics was rid of the last remnants of Cartesianism. As Newton's 'experimental physics' spread from England and Holland to the rest of Europe, spectacular advances were made in the study of electricity, magnetism and chemistry. Geological problems were being tackled far more open-mindedly than ever before, and biology took a great leap forward, thanks mainly to the rise of natural methods of classification, to detailed studies of plant and animal physiology, and to renewed interest in the problem of generation. All in all, the 18th century may therefore be said to have continued along the path blazed by its brilliant forerunner and to have made many original contributions as well.

The Century of Enquiry

THE 'AGE OF ENLIGHTENMENT', as the 18th century came to be called, began and ended at different times in different countries. In England it was ushered in by the 'Glorious Revolution' of 1688; in Russia it did not begin until 1763, with the accession of Catherine the Great; in Germany, or rather Prussia, it began in 1740 with the reign of Frederick the Great; in France it is said to have begun in 1715. Nevertheless, it is true to say that scientists all over Europe reached much the same stage within a few years of one another.

The spirit of the 18th century was one of scientific enquiry—enlightenment was no longer sought in revealed truth, but in reason. While the new outlook crystallized, the centre of European culture began to shift from the Mediterranean to the shores of the Atlantic. The old trade routes across Asia lost importance as the maritime powers drew increasingly on the wealth of America and Asia by sea.

THE EMERGENCE OF NEW TASTES

Small quantities of exotic products for the extremely rich had been coming into Europe for centuries, but now that they were pouring in they revolutionized the taste of Western Europeans. New species of plants were being cultivated in botanical gardens; new foodstuffs and beverages began to fill the larders, and new materials and dyes appeared in the markets to capture and delight the eye.

As his tastes changed, so 18th-century man began to despise many earlier customs. What had seemed luxurious to the courtiers of Louis XIV, struck the subjects of Louis XV as merely tawdry. The atmosphere became lighter; men questioned and joked; manners were easier; intellectual adventure was the order of the day.

THE SCIENTIFIC SCENE

The 18th-century scientific scene was dominated by Newton's brilliant explanation of the doctrines of Copernicus and Kepler, one of the greatest achievements in the history of science. Newton's importance went far beyond astronomy and mathematics: his idea that the universe could be summed up by a set of equations (for that was what 18th-century scientists read into the *Principia*) inspired natural philosophy with a new vision.

That vision was given a further impetus by the expanding needs of daily life, which forced craftsmen to turn inventors. Architecture, town-planning, interior decoration, textile design, were all directed towards a new goal—comfort. Houses were no longer built and furnished for mere show; street lighting was introduced, and pavements were provided for pedestrians. By the end of the century, many houses had running water. Furniture became less heavy and ornate; chairs were designed to fit the human body; rooms became spacious, light and comfortably arranged. There was less gold and marble; their place as decorative materials was more and more taken by embroidered silks and printed cottons. At the same time, cookery became an art. The fashion for beef and mutton, hitherto regarded as inferior foods, resulted in a better knowledge of animal anatomy and animal husbandry.

Most 18th-century French town houses were decorated with plant and animal motifs inspired by the great Buffon. Heating became a subject of special study: the reflection of heat by various materials and the construction of efficient chimneys were closely investigated. It emerged that the more air was admitted to a fire the better it burned, and also that the draught increases with the temperature. In short, the fireplace assisted in the development of a number of branches of science: calorimetry, aerostatics, the kinetic theory of gases and, above all, modern chemistry, which Lavoisier founded on his studies of combustion.

The quest for comfort and gracious living resulted in many other scientific discoveries as well, or at least it created a favourable climate for them. For instance, interest in music led to the formulation of the quantitative laws governing the vibrations of strings and organ pipes.

Conversely, abstract scientific studies led to improvements in practical life. Better knowledge of astronomy enabled navigators to perfect a method of determining longitude at sea; better knowledge of mathematical acoustics led to the improvement of musical instruments. Theoretical studies also had repercussions on the techniques of dyeing, bleaching, spinning, weaving and engineering, thus preparing the ground for the industrial revolution.

It would be wrong, however, to think that scientific findings were applied to industrial techniques in the consistent way in which they are applied today. In the 18th century they were still the inspired improvisations of particularly gifted craftsmen. True, astronomy and mathematics had reached a stage where laymen could no longer make any considerable contribution, but physics, chemistry, and even medicine remained fields in which skill counted for more than theoretical perfection.

Scientific Education

While Stendhal could still argue that the Red and the Black, the Army and the Church, were the only means of social advancement, at any rate for those not born into the nobility, less than a century later anyone could rise by his own initiative in trade and in education. Thus Voltaire achieved fame by his pen alone, and Jean le Rond became d'Alembert by his mathematical talents (and some discreet influence). Much more surprising still was the rise of such scientific 'dynasties' as that of the Bernoullis.

However, education was not easily obtained, even in the 'Age of Reason'. There were few scholarships and few schools; knowledge had to be gathered from books or, better still, from personal tuition by an acknowledged master. As a result, opportunity was unequal: a peasant's son would have no chance at all but a tradesman's son might just make the grade, in which case he could gain the same advantages as a young aristocrat.

Whereas science had never before been a means of earning one's livelihood, it now became a recognized profession. Thus 18th-century mathematicians played a considerable role in industry and commerce, weighing, computing, designing and working on actuarial problems. In other respects, too, scientists had an ever-growing effect on the development of civilization, which became more and more bound up with the progress of science.

* * *

In discussing the 18th century we have dealt only with Europe because, in fact, no contribution came from outside. Asia had played a considerable part in scientific discovery in pre-Christian and medieval times, and America and Russia were to come to the fore in the 19th and 20th centuries, but the 18th century was truly the century of Western Europe. As human needs then began to grow, as they were successively fulfilled and as education came to reach wider and wider afield, Europe, which had taken so much from the rest of the world, began to repay her debt—and to repay it several times over.

THE THEORETICAL SCIENCES

CHAPTER 1

The Rise of Analysis

IN MATHEMATICS, the 18th century opened with the sharp conflict between the Newtonians in Britain and the Leibnizians on the Continent, continued with the work of Euler, d'Alembert and Lagrange, and ended with Laplace, Monge, Legendre and Lacroix.

THE BRITISH AND CONTINENTAL SCHOOLS

In Great Britain, Newtonian mathematics was taught in all the main seats of learning: Cambridge, Oxford, London, Glasgow and Edinburgh. Its chief proponents included Roger Cotes, James Stirling, Abraham de Moivre, Brook Taylor, Nicholas Saunderson, Robert Simson and Matthew Stewart. However, because of its dogmatic adherence to the letter of Newton's word, the British school lost its vitality in the second half of the century.

On the Continent, on the other hand, 18th-century mathematicians not only consolidated the great achievements of their 17th-century predecessors but also enlarged the scope and effectiveness of mathematics with original contributions. The impetus came from Leibniz's pupils, Jean and Jacques Bernoulli and Guillaume de l'Hôpital, ably assisted by the school of mathematics associated with the Paris Academy of Science. That school did not rise to its full height until a generation later, when its fame was spread by such illustrious men as Maupertuis, Clairaut and particularly d'Alembert, who developed the calculus into a powerful mathematical tool. D'Alembert took a keen interest in the French *Encyclopédie* and carried all his associates with him. The considerable prestige the school had acquired by the end of the century was due not only to the exceptional combination in it of such brilliant men as Lagrange, Laplace, Legendre and Monge, but also to the fact that French had become the *lingua franca* of Continental mathematics and liberal reformism.

The notorious shortcomings in French scientific education were partially remedied by the appearance of advanced military academies and technical colleges during the second half of the 18th century. French scientific life was also quickened by the *Académie Royale des Sciences* whose annual lectures were attended by most leading

European scientists. Following the French example, Frederick the Great of Prussia tried his utmost to infuse greater life into the Berlin Academy—founded by Leibniz in 1700—by attracting Maupertuis, Euler (from 1741 to 1766), Lagrange (from 1766 to 1787), Lambert (from 1763 to 1767) and many other leading mathematicians. As a result, the Prussian Academy prospered as never before. The opening of a modern university in Göttingen (1737) was a further landmark in the history of German science, for it culminated with the early writings of Gauss at the end of the 18th century.

In Russia, Peter the Great founded the Academy of St. Petersburg (1724) and attracted a number of Swiss mathematicians, including Daniel and Nicolas Bernoulli and J. Hermann. Euler joined the Academy from 1727 to 1741, and again from 1766 to 1783.

Dutch universities, which enjoyed world renown, concentrated on experimental studies and neglected theoretical research. Switzerland had two brilliant scientific centres: Geneva and Basle. Basle supplied the leading lights of the Russian Academy. Though Italy continued to be a great centre of learning, producing such talented men as the Ricattis, Michele Manfredi, Guido Grandi, Malfatti, and even Fagnano and Ruffini, she failed to rise to her former heights. It was, incidentally, Italy which appointed the first woman to a chair of mathematics: Maria Gaetana Agnesi (1718–1799), the author of a treatise on differential calculus which was translated into French and English. Spain, Portugal, the Scandinavian countries and Central Europe produced few mathematicians of great standing.

The Status of Mathematicians

While the 17th century was the age of great amateur mathematicians, the 18th century was almost exclusively the age of professionals—university professors and members of scientific academies.

To a greater extent than their predecessors, the 18th-century mathematicians widened their activities beyond purely theoretical studies. Thus Euler took an interest in music, optics and shipbuilding; d'Alembert contributed to philosophy, music, applied mechanics and astronomy, and played an important part in the publication of the French Encyclopedia. Laplace, who did such important work in pure mathematics, celestial mechanics and probability theory, also collaborated with Lavoisier in writing a fundamental paper on heat. While the great natural historians, Buffon and Réaumur, began their scientific careers as mathematicians, great mathematicians like Monge, Legendre, Meusnier and Laplace took a keen interest in, and sometimes repeated, Lavoisier's experiments on the composition of water.

Our study of 18th-century mathematics will be restricted to only the most important contributions. As mathematics grew more complex, detailed discoveries increased considerably in number, and it would be quite impossible to go fully into every one of them. Though we are forced to present these contributions under various special headings, we must stress that most of the 18th-century mathematicians contributed to the development of mathematics as a whole.

THE DEVELOPMENT OF INFINITESIMAL ANALYSIS

The First Followers of Leibniz and Newton

Calculus on the Continent

When Leibniz's first paper on the 'new calculus' was published in the *Acta eruditorum* (Leipzig, 1684), the only mathematicians to pay any serious attention to it were E. W. von Tschirnhaus, who used it to correct a number of errors in his own work, J. Wallis and J. Craig. The next mathematician to consider it was Jacques Bernoulli, who was appointed professor at the University of Basle in 1687, and he became a staunch supporter of Leibniz's new method. In 1690, he taught it to his brother Jean, who, during a stay in Paris (1690–1691) explained it to Malebranche's circle, and particularly to the Marquis de l'Hôpital, for whose benefit he published a special pamphlet on differential and integral calculus. The first part of this pamphlet became the basis of de l'Hôpital's *Analyse des infiniment petits*.

The *Acta eruditorum*, in which Leibniz published most of his papers, also opened its pages to his first followers, who, convinced of the great potentialities of the new calculus, tried to develop it in a number of different ways. Most of their findings and discussions were published in the *Journal des sçavans*. Newton's disciples replied with attacks in the *Philosophical Transactions*.

In 1690, Jacques Bernoulli, who had begun his important work on series in 1689, succeeded in solving the isochronous line problem which Leibniz had posed in 1686. At the same time, he made a fairly exhaustive study of the catenary problem (the curve in which a chain or rope hangs), which was later solved by Huygens, Leibniz and Jean Bernoulli. In 1691, the year in which Leibniz published his study on the quadrature of conics, Jacques Bernoulli determined the tangents to parabolic and logarithmic spirals and to the loxodrome, and also rectified these curves. In the same year, Jean Bernoulli determined the tangents, inflections and radii of curvature of numerous plane curves, and was the first to use polar co-ordinates.

Subsequently, his brother investigated all sorts of curves, including caustics, cycloids, hypocycloids, *etc.* Leibniz determined the envelope of a one-parameter family of curves and presented a new theory of evolutes and involutes. Many other problems in differential geometry, in mechanics and in integral calculus were solved in the course of challenges which appeared more and more frequently in the periodicals of the time. Two of these merit quite special mention: the famous problem in differential geometry posed in 1692 by Viviani, and the brachistochrone problem or the problem of the path of quickest descent, which Leibniz applied to Fermat's proof of Snell's law. Another controversy, on the isoperimetric problem, brought into the open the quarrel between the brothers Bernoulli, and enabled Jacques to lay the foundations of the calculus of variations. His solution (1701) was subsequently perfected by Taylor, Jean Bernoulli and Euler. Other important solutions bore on the problem of orthogonal trajectories and on the determination of the geodesics of certain surfaces.

The First Difficulties

While the Marquis de l'Hôpital's *Analyse des infiniment petits* (1696) helped to spread knowledge of the practical applications of the new calculus, it also led to the neglect of unresolved theoretical problems. True, isolated attempts were made to remedy this failure, but they did little to weaken the force of the logical objections to the basic contradictions in the theory. The 'robust confidence' with which 18th-century mathematicians ignored these objections earned them the scorn of Cauchy, Abel and Bolzano in the 19th century.

In 1694 and again in 1695, B. Nieuwentijt asserted that the methods of Barrow, Newton and Leibniz were dangerously obscure. In his reply Leibniz did little to elucidate the nature of differential expressions. The discussion was reopened in about 1700 when de l'Hôpital's book was defended by Varignon and Saurin against violent attacks by Cartesian members of the Paris Academy. However, the conversion to calculus of one of the most eminent critics, the algebraist Michel Rolle, and the appearance of Carré's *Méthode pour la mesure des surfaces* (Paris, 1700) and of Reyneau's *Analyse démontrée* (Paris, 1708) marked the final victory of the new method in France.

The Famous Priority Dispute

It was at this point that infinitesimal analysis gave rise to an even more acrimonious debate with particularly deplorable consequences.

In 1685, shortly after the publication of Leibniz's first paper, J. Wallis and J. Craig accused Leibniz of plagiarizing Barrow and

Newton. The Swiss mathematician Fatio de Duillier repeated this accusation, first privately and later publicly. When Leibniz replied, he was careful not to attach any blame to Newton himself. The quarrel was reopened in 1708 when one of Newton's pupils, John Keill, once again accused Leibniz of plagiarism, and refused to retract this accusation despite many protests. Leibniz then requested Newton and the Royal Society to act as arbitrators. A commission was set up to study all the relevant documents and to publish a detailed report.

This report, the *Commercium epistolicum* (1712), suggested that Leibniz must have developed his calculus after a study of Newton's method of fluxions. Leibniz, who had not been invited to submit any evidence, was bitterly offended, and the resulting enmity between him and Newton greatly enlarged the century-old rift between English and Continental mathematicians. Exacerbated by the appearance of Raphson's biased *History of Fluxions* (London, 1750), the quarrel persisted into the 19th century, when fresh evidence revealed that Leibniz could not possibly have had access to the sources mentioned in the *Commercium epistolicum*.

The Work of English Analysts

Newton's method of fluxions spread far more slowly than Leibniz's calculus, probably because of Newton's reluctance to publish his papers, but also because his early followers—C. Hayes (1704), H. Ditton (1706), J. Hodgson (1736), T. Simpson (1737), C. Maclaurin (1742), J. Rowe (1751) and N. Saunderson (1751)—were unquestioning admirers of Newton's theory and unwilling to discuss criticisms of it.

Fortunately, Newton also had followers of far greater merit. One of the most eminent of these was Roger Cotes (1682–1716), the editor of the second edition of the *Principia* (1713), whose *Harmonia mensurarum* (1722) dealt with the roots of unity, the integration of rational fractions, the theory of differentials, and many problems of differential geometry.

The name of Brook Taylor (1685–1731), another of Newton's great disciples, is attached to the well-known series for the expansion of variables in powers thereof, *viz.*:

$$f(x+h)=f(x)+hf'(x)+\frac{h^2}{2!}f''(x)+\dots$$

Taylor first published this theorem in his *Methodus incrementorum directa et inversa* (London, 1715). (The particular case where $x=0$, known as Maclaurin's theorem after Colin Maclaurin, who rediscovered it in 1742, was also considered by Taylor; it was first stated by Stirling in 1717.) However, since Taylor did not recognize the need for convergence when dealing with infinite series, his proof of the theorem lacked rigour. The importance of his series was not fully appreciated until 1772, by Lagrange, and a rigorous proof was not supplied until 1823, by Cauchy. Taylor also gave some treatment of finite differences, of interpolation, and of the change of the independent variable. Finally, he was one of the first to use mathematical physics to determine the frequency of vibrating strings from their length, weight and tension. Two other mathematicians to do spadework in the treatment of infinite and recurring series were A. de Moivre and J. Stirling.

Content with developing Newton's method of fluxions, few of these mathematicians bothered to examine its basic principles. A salutary reaction was triggered off in 1734, when George Berkeley, Bishop of Cloyne, published a pamphlet in which he derided fluxions as 'ghosts of departed quantities'. The first Newtonian to reply, James Jurin, was easily refuted by Berkeley and was attacked by B. Robins and H. Pemberton. As a result of these and similar discussions, attention was focused on some of the greatest weaknesses of the method, and on the need of a more logical approach. Maclaurin's *Treatise of Fluxions* (1742) marked an important stage in this development, though, by discarding analytical in favour of geometrical techniques, it helped to steer British mathematics into rather unfruitful paths. Another important contribution came from John Landen (*The Residual Analysis*, 1764), who tried to found the calculus on generally valid algebraic and geometrical principles 'without recourse to some external principle such as the imaginary motion or incomprehensible infinitesimals'. It was not, however, until 1820 that English analysis recovered its lost vitality, thanks mainly to greater familiarity with Continental methods and particularly with Leibniz's notation.

Extensions and Applications of Infinitesimal Analysis

With the death of Maclaurin in 1764 and of Jean Bernoulli in 1748, the era of Newton's and Leibniz's immediate followers was closed. Even before that, the progress of analysis had already passed into the hands of the next generation, led by Daniel Bernoulli (1700–1782), Euler (1707–1783), Clairaut (1713–1765) and d'Alembert (1717–1783), who, in turn, handed it on to the generation of Lagrange (1736–1813), Monge (1746–1818), Laplace (1749–1827) and Legendre (1752–1833). Euler and Lagrange proved to be the most brilliant of this remarkable team.

After studying under Jean Bernoulli, Leonhard Euler left his native Basle at the age of 20, joining first the St. Petersburg Academy of Science (1721–1741), later the Berlin Academy of Frederick the Great, and finally returning to St. Petersburg in 1766 at the invitation of Catherine II. His scientific contribution was exceptionally rich—his *Opera omnia* consists of 69 quarto volumes containing 866 papers devoted to mathematics, optics, astronomy, naval science, actuarial practice, *etc.* His *Letters to a German Princess* (first Russian edition, 1768) was translated into more than ten languages, and his less popular writings played a considerable part in the co-ordination of the various branches of analysis and in the training of many future generations of mathematicians. The most famous of these works was his *Introductio in analysin infinitorum* (Lausanne, 1748), which was translated into French and English and quickly became a mathematical classic. The first of its two volumes was devoted to functions in general, and to exponential, logarithmic and trigonometrical functions in particular. It also dealt with series, with the appoximate solutions of equations, and with various problems in number theory. The second volume gave an analytic treatment of plane curves and surfaces. The whole was exceptionally lucid, and contained many new results of great value. Euler also published an *Institutiones calculi differentialis* (1755) and an *Institutiones calculi integralis* (3 volumes, 1768–1770), in which he surveyed the work of his predecessors, adding numerous contributions of his own. These works remained the standard textbooks on differential and integral calculus until the end of the century, when they were supplanted by Lagrange's *Mécanique analytique* and by Lacroix's *Traité du calcul differentiel et du calcul intégral* (Paris, 1797–1800; 2nd edition 1810–1819).

Lagrange, who was born at Turin in 1736, proved an exceptionally gifted mathematician at an early age. He resigned his professorship at the Turin Artillery College in 1766, to succeed Euler at the Prussian Academy. In 1787, after the death of Frederick the Great, he accepted the invitation of Louis XVI and came to Paris, where he spent the rest of his life. In 1788, he published his first great work: the *Mécanique analytique*. He became professor at the *École normale* in 1795 and later at the *École polytechnique*, and published his lectures under the titles of *Théories des fonctions analytiques* (1797); the *Traité de la résolution des équations numériques* (1798); and *Leçons sur le calcul des fonctions* (1799). Napoleon, who greatly admired his talents, made him a senator and a nobleman. Though a less prolific writer than Euler, Lagrange was Euler's equal in the variety and importance of his work, and in his concern for clarity and elegance.

Although other analysts made contributions of undoubted value, they were all overshadowed by these two mathematical giants. Some of them, like Daniel Bernoulli, Clairaut, Lambert, Landen and Legendre, concentrated on particular aspects of analysis; others looked upon analysis as a means towards different ends: astronomy and probability in the case of Laplace, differential geometry in the case of Monge. Only d'Alembert brought his great talents to bear on problems touching analysis as a whole, but his mathematical work suffered from his activities in other fields. Had he not spent so much time on the French Encyclopedia and on philosophical questions, he might easily have rivalled the achievement of Euler and Lagrange.

Differential Equations

While developing infinitesimal calculus, early analysts came up against an ever-growing number of differential equations which they generally tried to solve by special techniques. However, as results accumulated, and as the notation became more precise, they were able to state the first general rules. Euler made Jean Bernoulli's integrating factor (1691) the basis of a new theory, which also involved the criteria of integrability studied by Clairaut, Fontaine and Euler himself. He also developed the constant of variation which Jean Bernoulli had first used in 1693. In 1750, he was the first to integrate linear differential equations with constant coefficients. In 1724, J. F. Riccati solved the equation named after him, $y' = f(x) + yg(x) + y^2h(x)$, for several particular cases. D'Alembert demonstrated how certain differential equations can be solved by means of an equivalent system. The existence of singular solutions, which Taylor had predicted, was confirmed by Clairaut who used the method of differentiating the initial equation. The study of singular solution was then taken up by Euler, Laplace, Lagrange and Monge, who solved most of the difficulties. Euler also introduced the hypergeometric series, on which he based the solution of second-order linear differential equations and various other functions, including beta and gamma functions.

Total differential equations were studied particularly by Euler and Lagrange. Monge defined the geometrical significance of total differential equations that do not satisfy the condition of integrability, thus foreshadowing the work of J. F. Pfaff.

The calculus of finite differences was studied particularly by Taylor, Cotes, Euler, Lagrange and Laplace, who, following Montmort and de Moivre, applied it to probability theory.

Partial Differential Equations

Though derivatives of functions with more than one variable, or partial derivatives, had first appeared in the writings of Newton,

Leibniz and the Bernoullis, partial differential equations were not introduced explicitly until 1734, by Euler. Even then, they were not studied systematically for another 13 years. In 1747, d'Alembert was able to show that the vibrating string equation $\frac{\partial^2 u}{\partial t^2} = a^2 \frac{\partial^2 u}{\partial x^2}$ has a solution of the form

$$u = f(x + at) + \varphi(x - at)$$

where f and φ are two arbitrary functions, partially determined by the limiting conditions. The restrictions which d'Alembert imposed on the choice of these functions were criticized by Euler, who insisted on the necessity of admitting every function defined by any line placed at random, and by Daniel Bernoulli, who proposed to define these functions by trigonometrical series. All the mathematicians of the time had something to say on the matter, which was only solved in the 19th century when the concepts of functions and trigonometrical series were given more rigorous definitions.

Apart from studying the applications of the new equations in mechanics and physics, mathematicians also investigated their purely theoretical consequences. Lagrange developed a general method of solving first-order equations and Monge a method of interpreting them geometrically. Both mathematicians also made a study of different types of second-order equations which led them to the expansion of functions in trigonometrical series, and of simple or general spherical functions, *etc.* While Lagrange clarified many aspects of the new theory from a purely analytic point of view, Monge concentrated especially on its relevance to differential geometry, and created a new method of integrating an important class of partial differential equations of the form $Ar + 2Ks + Lt + M = 0$. His theory of characteristics was a model of analytical geometry and inspired many 19th-century mathematicians, including Sophus Lie, who admitted that his own theory of tangential transformations was based on the work of Monge.

The Calculus of Variations

In 1728, an examination of Leibniz's studies of various problems involving the maxima and minima of integrals convinced Euler of the need of introducing greater generality into the problem. After first stating and examining the famous isoperimetric problem, he went on to publish his *Methodus inveniendi lineas curvas maximi minimive proprietate gaudentes* (Lausanne, 1734) in which he presented the first general method of solving extremum problems, thus creating a new discipline: the calculus of variations. His arguments, though complicated by his simultaneous consideration of geometrical elements, successive differences and series, led him to simple and elegant formulae which he was able to apply to excellent effect.

In a famous paper which appeared in Volume II of the *Miscellanea Taurinensia* (1762), Lagrange introduced a more suitable notation and established Euler's formulae on a purely analytic basis, which enabled him to dispense with Euler's condition that the extrema of the integral function must remain fixed. Euler admitted the superiority of this proof and adopted Lagrange's method. Lagrange devoted numerous papers to the new calculus, which he applied quite particularly to the problem of minimum surfaces and to developing his system of analytical mechanics. In 1788, Legendre offered a criterion for distinguishing between maxima and minima; his proof, which lacked rigour, was corrected by Jacobi in 1836.

The General Concept of a Function

The concept of functions goes back to the creation of analytical geometry by Fermat and Descartes, who expressed the ordinates of a curve in terms of the abscissa. The analytical definition, however, had to await the creation of the infinitesimal calculus. Leibniz was the first to speak of functions as such, and, in 1718, Jean Bernoulli defined the functions of a variable as 'the quantities composed in any way whatsoever of that variable and of constants'. The modern notation, $f(x)$, was introduced by Euler and Clairaut.

In his *Introductio in analysin infinitorum* (1748), Euler presented a systematic study of elementary functions, and distinguished between algebraic and transcendental, explicit and implicit, and uniform and multiform functions. This classification was a tremendous advance, even though Euler's original definition of a transcendental function was much too narrow. Euler realized this himself in 1749, after a study of d'Alembert's partial differential equations. As a result, he came to hold that a general function might well be defined by any curve traced at random on a plane. The ambiguity resulting from the coexistence of these two views was not resolved until the 19th century, when Fourier and Lejeune-Dirichlet were able to show independently the connection between the general concept of a function and Daniel Bernoulli's trigonometrical series.

D'Alembert and the Theory of Limits

Though they failed to pay enough attention to the basic principles of the new calculus, 18th-century mathematicians did not take them altogether for granted. Thus Fontenelle's dogmatic view of the subject (*Éléments de la géométrie de l'infini*, Paris, 1727) was keenly discussed and challenged.

In the French Encyclopedia and in his *Éclaircissements sur les éléments de philosophie* (1767) d'Alembert discussed the properties of different order infinitesimals in a strikingly modern way, and based infinitesimal analysis on the theory of limits. D'Alembert's theory was criticized by Euler, whose own views were less clear and closer to those of Fontenelle.

Lagrange and Functions

Lagrange, too, believed that the method of limits was shrouded in metaphysics, and tried to base it instead on algebraic methods and especially on Taylor's series. He expounded his own views on the subject in his *Théorie des fonctions analytiques* (1797) and in his *Leçons sur le calcul des fonctions* (1799), where he studied the expansion by Taylor's series of a function in the neighbourhood of a value a of the independent variable. He appreciated the importance of the remainder, and defined the derived functions—which he expressed by $f'(x)$, $f''(x)$, *etc.*—by means of successive coefficients of the series. Lagrange's notation was considered clumsy by his contemporaries, and suffered from his (and Taylor's) failure to recognize the need for convergence and for a rigorous definition of the concept of functions. Nevertheless, Lagrange deserves credit for having drawn attention to what, in the hands of Cauchy, Riemann and Weierstrass, became the theory of functions of a real variable.

Other New Problems

Among the many unsolved problems which Newton bequeathed to his successors was that of the shape of a rotating fluid mass. Maclaurin and Clairaut were able to show that it must be an ellipsoid, as Newton had assumed it would be, and Maclaurin determined the attractive action of a homogeneous ellipsoid on a point in its interior or on its surface.

These two problems were taken up by d'Alembert, Lagrange, Laplace and Legendre, who developed special methods of calculation for this purpose. Legendre, for instance, extended the solution to the attraction exerted by a spheroid on a particle outside it, by introducing the homofocal ellipsoid (1783) and the famous Legendre's polynomials, *i.e.* the coefficients of increasing powers of α in the expansion of $(1-2\alpha x+x^2)^{-\frac{1}{2}}$; Clairaut introduced the potential function which Lagrange was to apply to dynamics and analysis. In 1785, Laplace showed that this function, V, satisfies the Laplace's differential equation $\frac{\partial^2 V}{\partial x^2}+\frac{\partial^2 V}{\partial y^2}+\frac{\partial^2 V}{\partial z^2}=0$, which plays so important a role in various branches of theoretical physics.

Another problem—the rectification of the ellipse and of the hyperbola, which had eluded 17th-century analysts—led to even more significant discoveries. Unable to grasp the root of this problem, 18th-century mathematicians began with a search for elliptic integrals. In 1750, G. C. Fagnano (1682–1766) was able to show that the integral which expresses the arc of a lemniscate has properties analogous to those of the integral which represents an arc of a circle. Euler extended the theory to elliptic functions in 1756, and showed that elliptic integrals are characterized by the presence in the element of the square root of a quartic polynomial. In 1780, J. Landen showed that the rectification of an arc of a hyperbola is tantamount to the rectification of two arcs of an ellipse—a conclusion which Lagrange obtained by more direct methods. In 1786, A. M. Legendre made his first contribution to the theory of elliptic integrals, to which he devoted the best part of his life. His first two papers (1786 and 1793) dealt with the classification of these integrals, with their reduction to canonical forms, and with their approximate evaluation. But since Legendre's most important works, the *Exercices du calcul intégral* and the *Traité des fonctions elliptiques*, did not appear until the 19th century, we shall begin the detailed discussion of his contribution in a later volume.

ADVANCES IN ALGEBRA

Though it introduced no spectacular innovations into algebra, the 18th century nevertheless laid the foundations of the revolutionary developments which took place a century later.

The Theory of Equations

The Fundamental Theorem of Algebra

In 1608, Peter Roth, a Nuremberg *Rechenmeister*, asserted that all algebraic equations of the nth degree must have n roots. This law was next propounded by Girard (1629), and more clearly expressed by Descartes (1637), Newton (1685) and Euler (1742). Attempts to prove what came to be known as the 'fundamental theorem of algebra' were made by d'Alembert (1746), Euler (1751) and Lagrange, and the first rigorous proof was given by Gauss (1799), who assumed, like Lagrange, that every algebraic equation must have at least one root, real or imaginary.

Determinants

At the end of the 17th century, Leibniz had occasionally solved systems of linear equations with more than one unknown by an algorithm resembling our determinant. A similar notation was used by Gabriel Cramer in 1750, by Bezout in 1764, by Vandermonde and Laplace in 1772, and by Lagrange in 1773. Though various new results were obtained in this way, no systematic study of the properties of the new algorithm was made before the early 19th century (Binet, Cauchy, Jacobi). Gauss (1801) was the first to speak of determinants as such, and the modern notation was introduced in 1841 by A. Cayley.

Higher Equations

As mathematicians acquired greater skill in manipulating complex numbers, and as the theory of cubic and quartic equations made considerable advances, attention was quite naturally brought to bear on higher degree, and particularly on quintic, equations. In 1683, von Tschirnhaus thought wrongly that he had discovered a general method of solving algebraic equations. In fact, his method was useless in dealing with equations beyond the quartic, but his substitutions enabled his successors to reduce the general quintic to the canonical, trinomial form: $x^5+ax+b=0$.

The many failures to solve general equations beyond the quartic forced mathematicians to make a more careful analysis of even the two general methods for solving lower-order equations: substitution and combination. Two important studies on this subject were made by Vandermonde (1770, results published in 1774) and by Lagrange (*Réflexions sur la résolution algébrique des équations*, 1770–1771).

Vandermonde was able to show that the general solution of an equation of whatever degree depends on the possibility of constructing an irrational function of the roots, certain values of which must be identical with the roots, and which must be so transformable as to depend on only the symmetrical functions of the roots under investigation. Hence Vandermonde was able to obtain formulae for solving the general quadratic, cubic and quartic equations, but not the general quintic and higher equations, though he did solve the equation $x^{11}-1=0$, and even foresaw that the equation $x^n-1=0$ must have a solution whenever n is a prime. Gauss was the first to give that solution in his *Disquisitiones arithmeticae* (1801).

Lagrange, too, studied the rational functions of the roots of algebraic equations, and particularly the effects on these functions of root permutations, thus making an important contribution to root theory. Observing that all the methods of his predecessors for solving equations up to fourth degree reduced to the procedure of obtaining solutions by means of an 'auxiliary' equation of one degree lower, and that the quintic leads to an auxiliary equation of degree six, he concluded that it was impossible to solve equations of a higher degree than the fourth. In 1798, he discussed the whole problem in his *Résolution algébrique des équations* but was unable to supply a formal proof. A partial proof was given in Pietro Ruffini's *Teoria generale delle equazioni* (1799), and a rigorous proof was supplied by Abel in 1826. The role of Ruffini in extending Lagrange's theory of roots is generally overlooked; in fact, with Vandermonde, Lagrange and Gauss, he prepared the way for the great revolution of 1826–1830, which overcame the difficulties in the path of the theory of equations and helped to give algebra an entirely new look.

Other Advances

Among less spectacular 18th-century advances in algebra, we must mention the development by Lagrange (1768) and E. Waring (1770 and 1782) of the theory of the symmetrical functions of the roots of algebraic equations, which had been begun by Girard and Newton. The elimination of one unknown from two equations with two unknowns—a problem equivalent to finding the points of intersection of two curves—had been studied by Stevin, Fermat and Hudde in the 17th century. In 1750, Cramer explained the difficulties introduced by the possible existence of numerous points of intersection, and, in 1771, Bezout gave the definite proof that two algebraic curves of degrees m and n have mn common points.

Leibniz, de Gua, Segner, Waring and Gauss attempted to develop and prove Descartes' rule of signs. The separation of roots was discussed in Michel Rolle's *Traité d'algèbre* (1690), which contained an account of Rolle's 'cascade method'. In this a series of auxiliary equations of descending degree is considered to 'straddle' the real roots of certain types of equation. In 1691, Rolle published his famous theorem: $f'(x) = 0$ has at least one real root lying between two successive roots of $f(x) = 0$.

The Numerical Solution of Equations

In his *Arithmetica universalis*, Newton had presented various methods of determining the maximum number of real roots, the minimum number of imaginary roots, and also the maximum number of positive and negative roots. (The last problem was not solved satisfactorily until the 19th century.)

Newton also studied the important problem of the approximate determination of the roots of an equation. His method, which Wallis used in his *Algebra* (1685), was simple and elegant.

Let $(f)x = 0$, and let a be the approximation to one of its roots. Put $x = a + y$, and write the auxiliary equation $(g)y = (f)a + y = 0$; this equation in y has a root whose approximate value b is obtained by reducing the equation to its two terms of least degree; hence $a + b$ is a further approximation to the root we are seeking. This procedure can be repeated *ad lib.*

Newton's method was slightly modified by Raphson (1690), who introduced the approximate value $b_1 = a - f(a)/f'(a)$, and it was subsequently developed by Lagrange and Fourier.

Of the many other 18th-century methods of obtaining approximate solutions of higher-degree equations we can only mention that of Lagny, which was based on differencing the function $f(x)$; that of Taylor, which was based on his famous series; and that of Lagrange, which was based on continued fractions.

Imaginary Numbers

The Nature of Imaginary Numbers

Imaginary numbers, which had been introduced during the 16th century in attempts to solve cubic equations, assumed an increasing importance in 18th-century algebra. Though they were considered artificial aids to calculation, and no more, and hence a logical blot in the copybook of mathematics, they led to many advances in various branches of analysis.

Most 17th-century authors had thought that roots of different degree corresponded to different types of imaginary numbers, even though Leibniz had shown that the number $\sqrt[3]{a+bi} + \sqrt[3]{a-bi}$ is real. During the early 18th century, better methods of solving cubic and quartic equations, and the increasing use of imaginaries in the study of functions and series, led to far greater ease in their manipulation. In 1746, d'Alembert took the decisive step of asserting that all imaginary numbers are of the type $a+bi$ (the symbol $i = \sqrt{-1}$ was introduced by Euler). Although d'Alembert's proof lacked rigour, it convinced many of his contemporaries, and, in any case, prepared the ground for Cauchy's analytical theory.

Another method, the graphic representation of imaginary numbers, first suggested by Wallis (1673), was taken up by the Danish mathematician C. Wessel (1797) but failed to make progress until the 19th century.

Extension of the Concept of Logarithms

The question of the admissibility of imaginary numbers was closely bound up with the study of logarithmic, trigonometrical and exponential functions.

While integrating rational fractions, Leibniz, Jean Bernoulli (1702) and G. C. Fagnana (1716) were quite naturally led to consider the logarithms of imaginary numbers. This question gave rise to heated discussions between Leibniz and Jean Bernoulli (1712), between the latter and Euler (1727), and finally, between Euler and d'Alembert

(1747). In two papers which he published in 1751, Euler was able to show conclusively that every real or imaginary number n has an infinite number of logarithms, all of which are imaginary except one, which is real when $n>0$.

At the same time, the study of the logarithmic function was radically transformed. Previously, three methods had been brought to bear upon it: the old procedure of relating arithmetical to geometrical progressions, the use of series, and the definition of the logarithmic as a primitive function. However, because Wallis, Newton and Jean Bernoulli had demonstrated that the logarithmic function is the inverse of the exponential function, whose properties are particularly simple, W. Jones suggested (1742) that the logarithmic function should be studied in this new light, a view adopted by Euler and by all later mathematicians. Euler also introduced the use of the symbol e for the base of Naperian logarithms, and proved that e and e^2 are irrational.

Imaginary Numbers in Trigonometry

At about the same time, imaginary numbers made a brilliant entry into trigonometry. From the formula $ix=\log(\cos x+i\sin x)$ which Roger Cotes had established in 1714, de Moivre (1730) and Euler (1748) derived the fundamental formulae $(\cos x+i\sin x)^n=\cos nx+i\sin nx$, and $e^{ix}=\cos x+i\sin x$.

Euler also introduced the exponential equations:
$\cos x=\frac{1}{2}(e^{ix}+e^{-ix})$ and $\sin x=\frac{1}{2}i(e^{ix}-e^{-ix})$, and the formula $e^{i\pi}=-1$, which connects two of the most 'mysterious' analytical numbers in simple fashion.

Abandoning its reliance on geometry, trigonometry thus became a branch of the theory of functions, and particularly of the theory of exponential and logarithmic functions. That development had been foreshadowed by 17th-century studies of series and by Cotes's trigonometrical reduction of x^{n-1} into its real linear and quadratic factors. In his *Introductio in analysin infinitorum*, Euler gave trigonometry its modern form when he defined functions as ratios, made the *sinus totus* equal to 1, and introduced the modern formulae together with series and the continued products of various trigonometrical functions.

Mention must also be made of Fantet de Lagny's discovery of the periodicity of trigonometrical functions and of the introduction of new formulae by F. W. Oppel and T. Simpson. Spherical trigonometry was given a near-modern form by Euler, and was also studied by Cotes, Lambert, Lexell, Legendre and Laplace, either for purely analytical reasons or else for its geodesic and astronomical applications.

Following in Vieta's path, J. Machin, J. Hermann and Euler expressed π by means of series or infinite products, which enabled them to obtain far better approximations. The term π was first introduced by W. Jones in 1706; the use of that symbol was popularized by Euler, and the irrationality of π was proved by Lambert (1769). Although the impossibility of squaring the circle was not proved until 1882 (Lindemann), the Paris Academy of Science refused, as early as 1775, to accept any papers on this subject, on the duplication of the cube, or on the trisection of an angle. This refusal shows clearly how much real progress had been made in this controversial field.

In the same connection, we must also mention V. Riccati's introduction in 1757 of hyperbolic functions, whose close connection with trigonometric function was established by Wallis and Lambert in 1768.

New Algorithms

The Study of Series

Work on series, which had yielded such astonishing results in the 17th century, was continued in the 18th, particularly by Jean Bernoulli and Euler. Taylor's theorem came to play an essential role in the work of Lagrange; Newton's binomial theorem (1676) was proved ingeniously by Euler for fractional powers (1773); Euler also showed that the exponential series converges to e^x for every value of x.

Despite their great skill, even these famous mathematicians succumbed to the pitfalls of infinite series. Though they were familiar with the idea of convergence, Euler and Lagrange saw no objection to using semiconvergent or divergent series; by calling a series 'converging', 18th-century mathematicians meant no more than that the general term tended towards zero. Thus Lagrange asserted that the sum of the series $\cos x + \cos 2x + \cos 3x + \ldots = -\frac{1}{2}$, and that $1 - 1 + 1 - 1 + 1 - \ldots = \frac{1}{2}$. In general, Euler considered that if, for certain values of x, $f(x)$ can be expressed as the sum of a converging series, that series applies for all values of x for which $f(x)$ is determinate, even if convergence can no longer be verified. This approach was bound to lead to manifest contradictions which one would have expected a mathematician of Euler's rank to have appreciated.

Hence we can sympathize with Abel's sweeping judgment, 'With the exception of the simplest cases, there is hardly a single mathematical series of which the sum has been determined rigorously; in other words, the most important topic in mathematics has been left without any foundations' (letter to Holmböe, 16 Jan. 1826).

INFINITE PRODUCTS AND CONTINUED FRACTIONS

Although they had been discussed by Vieta, infinite products were not used systematically until Euler, recognizing their importance, obtained results which were later to play a fundamental role in the theory of functions and in number theory.

Interest in infinite series was bound to lead mathematicians to the theory of continued fractions. Euler, who treated the problem systematically in 1737, developed a special notation, generalized the method of reduction, and studied the problems of the convergence and transformation of series into continued fractions, and their application to the solution of algebraic or indeterminate equations. Lagrange concentrated on recurring continued fractions, and applied them to the integration of differential equations.

Number Theory

Though renewed interest in Diophantine analysis had led to brilliant results in the 17th century, 18th-century mathematicians lost interest in it, and reverted instead to number theory. In 1736, Euler proved Fermat's theorem (if p is a prime, $a^p - a$ is divisible by p), which he later (1760) generalized by introducing the φ function of an integer, *i.e.* the number of integers not greater than the given integer and relatively prime to it. In particular, he proved Fermat's Last Theorem for $n=3$ (Lagrange later proved it for $n=4$). In 1741, Euler studied the partition of integers, *i.e.* the number of ways in which a positive integer n can be written as a sum of positive integers. He presented his conclusions in the *Introductio in analysin infinitorum*. Lagrange proved Fermat's theorem that every integer n is the sum of at most four squares; Euler proved that every prime number of the form $4n+1$ can be expressed as the sum of two squares.

Euler's studies of continued fractions enabled him to improve the method of solving the indeterminate equation $ax+by=c$, and also Pell's equation (developed earlier by Wallis and Brouncker) $x^2 - Dy^2 = 1$, where D is a positive integer not a square; Lagrange proved the existence of the roots of that equation in 1766.

In 1771, E. Waring presented (without proof) a whole series of propositions in number theory: the decomposition of a number into a sum of cubes, biquadratics, *etc.;* the decomposition of every even number into the sum of two prime numbers (foreshadowed by Goldbach in 1742); and the theorem (attributed to J. Wilson but known to Leibniz) that $(p-1)!+1$ is a multiple of any prime p. (This theorem was proved by Lagrange in 1771.)

Euler and Lagrange also made important contributions to the theory of quadratic residues. In 1772, Euler propounded a series of propositions which were tantamount to the quadratic reciprocity law, a law which Legendre formulated in 1785 and which Gauss was the first to prove rigorously in 1796. Legendre and Gauss were, in fact, to open the new phase in number theory discussed in a later volume in this series.

Probability and Statistics

PROBABILITY THEORY

When it was created in about 1650 by Pascal, Fermat and Huygens, probability theory appeared to apply almost exclusively to games of chance. While the late 17th-century contribution to the new theory was insignificant, the early 18th century produced many works which helped to chart its future course.

The first of these was P. R. de Montmort's *Essay d'analyse sur les jeux du hazard* (Paris, 1708) which contained a thorough analysis of the 'stake problem'. Jacques Bernoulli's *Ars conjectandi*, published posthumously in 1730, included a copy of and a commentary on Huygens' *De ratiociniis in ludo aleae* and a special treatise on combinatorial analysis. In particular, it stated Bernoulli's theorem or the 'law of large numbers':

Let (1)p be the probability of an event A on a trial, and (2)m/n be the observed proportion of the event A in n trials. Then the probability is that $\left|\frac{m}{n}-p\right|<\varepsilon$ has a limit of one, as $n\to\infty$, for any arbitrary ε.

This theorem, which was given its definite form by Laplace, and which Burron and Poisson tried to verify experimentally, was proved to be of increasing practical importance. Further studies by de Moivre, Stirling, Maclaurin and Euler led to very many important analytical results, including the formula:

$$s!=s^{s}e^{-s}\sqrt{2\pi s}(1+\varepsilon),$$

which was discovered by de Moivre and Stirling in 1730. In this connection, we must also mention Jacques Bernoulli's introduction of the so-called Bernoulli's numbers, *i.e.* the numerical values of the coefficients of $x^2/2!$, $x^4/4!\ldots$, $x^{2n}/2n!\ldots$ in the expansion of $x/(1-e^{-x})$.

Abraham de Moivre, a French Protestant who was forced to seek asylum in London, wrote a number of important papers and also the *Doctrine of Chances* (London, 1718; 2nd edition, 1738), the *Annuities upon Lives* (1725) and the *Miscellanea analytica* (1730), in which he defined the principles and applications of probability theory. He discovered the rule for determining the probability of a compound event, and introduced finite difference equations.

In 1738, Daniel Bernoulli tackled the problem which had been posed by Nicolas Bernoulli in 1730, and which became known as the 'St. Petersburg paradox':

A and B play a game of heads or tails, in which A throws the coin. If the coin comes up heads, A must pay B a crown; if it comes up tails, A pays nothing but throws the coin once more. If it comes up heads again, A pays B two crowns; if the first head be on the third throw he will pay four crowns, if it be on the *n*th throw he will pay 2^{n-1} crowns. What should B pay to be allowed to take part in this game?

This is a question of mathematical expectation, defined as the sum of all possible gains multiplied by the chance of getting it. Accordingly B's expectation is

$$\frac{1}{2}\times 1+\frac{1}{2^2}\times 2+\frac{1}{2^3}\times 2^2+\ldots=\infty.$$

Now this is contrary to common sense, as no one in his right mind would pay A any great sum for his expectation. To solve this paradox, Daniel Bernoulli developed the idea of the moral value of money. He maintained that if a man have a fortune of x the moral value of an increase dx in it is dx/x.

In a posthumous paper (1763), Thomas Bayes posed the problem of determining the probability of causes from their observed effects. This idea was taken up by Laplace, who formulated the so-called Bayes's theorem in 1774. By combining this theorem with theorems on total and compound probability, Laplace and Condorcet were able to determine the probability of numerous events from prior observations.

The continuous variable was first introduced into probability theory with the famous needle problem, which Buffon studied in 1733 and again in 1777 (*Arithmétique morale*, suppl. to Vol. IV, *Histoire naturelle*). In this problem a floor is ruled with parallel lines whose distance apart is d. A needle of length $l<d$ is thrown at random on the floor. What is the probability that it will fall across one of the lines? Geometrical probability was subsequently generalized by Lagrange, Laplace and Gauss.

Probability theory had one of its most important applications in metrology. R. Cotes (1722) suggested that to interpret a series of measurements correctly, different weight should be given to different observations; Simpson, Lagrange and Laplace recommended the use of the arithmetical mean. The law of least squares, propounded by Legendre in 1806, was proved in 1809 by Gauss, who developed the theory of observational errors and stated the famous law which bears his name.

The Work of Laplace

In a series of papers published between 1771 and 1818, the main conclusions of which he incorporated in his *Théorie analytique des probabilités* (Paris, 1812), Laplace made a most important contribution to probability theory. By stating and proving every one of its theorems and by discussing the solution and applications of every classical problem, he produced a gigantic synthesis crowning the work of all his predecessors. He gave a lucid account of the psychological foundations of probability theory and also introduced a new theory, that of generating functions. In addition, he suggested ways in which probability theory could be applied to demographic studies, to certain legal problems, and to a large number of scientific questions, including the planetary inequalities, the mean inclination of the orbits of comets, the distribution of stars, the theory of errors, *etc.*

Laplace also published an *Essai philosophique sur les probabilités* (Paris, 1814, many subsequent editions), which was a simplified version of his main work. With Laplace probability theory may be said to have become an independent branch of mathematics.

Early Applications

Though Cardan had discussed life expectancy as early as 1750, the serious application of probability theory to mortality tables began with John Graunt's *Natural and Political Observations* (1662), which included a set of results based upon records of deaths in London from 1592. Further studies of the subject were made by Huygens in 1669 and by Jan de Witt in 1671. The first tables of great importance were those of Edmund Halley (1693), which included a study of annuities.

As life-insurance companies expanded in the 18th century, especially in England, so a need was felt for greater actuarial knowledge. To fulfil that need, de Moivre published his *Annuities upon Lives* and A. Deparcieux his *Essai sur les probabilités de la vie humaine* (1746–1760). In the second half of the century, demographic studies were greatly developed by Euler, Laplace and Condorcet. Condorcet also studied such problems in political arithmetic as the fairest method of holding elections, the influence of the composition of juries on the course of justice, *etc.* (*Essai sur l'application de l'analyse aux probabilités des décisions rendues à la pluralité des voix*, Paris, 1785). These very delicate questions were also treated in Laplace's *Essai philosophique.* Although premature, and hence incorrect in many respects, these early attempts merit special mention if only because they impinged on what came to be known as the theory of games.

THE REVIVAL OF GEOMETRY

Though the successes of the new calculus had led to the almost total neglect of pure geometry, the work of Gaspard Monge ushered in an unexpected revival of that branch of mathematics. As a result, the whole approach of mathematical research was transformed in the late 18th century.

Classical Geometry

Textbooks

Intensified teaching of mathematics in the 18th century gave a great impetus to the publication of geometrical textbooks, many of which introduced novel ideas. Though different editions of Barrow's *Euclid* (1655) continued to be published in England until 1751, other translations also appeared, including those of J. Keill (1708) and R. Simson (1756, nearly thirty editions), and an adaptation by J. Playfair (1795). In other Western countries, most geometries abandoned the rigour and formalism of Euclid and adopted an easier style more fitted to the didactic needs of mathematical novices. Though the new approach reflected the humanist ideals of the Encyclopedists, a clear reaction against it and a return to more rigorous methods set in towards the end of the century, with the appearance of two new textbooks that were to have a lasting effect on the teaching of geometry: Legendre's *Éléments de géometrie* (Paris, 1794) and S. F. Lacroix's *Éléments de géometrie* (1799).

Critical Examination of Euclid's Postulate of Parallels

Mathematicians had for a long time tried to remove the uncertainty surrounding the validity of Euclid's parallel axiom. In 1693, J. Wallis translated Nāṣir al-Dīn al-Ṭūsī's 13th-century study on that axiom, which showed that it implied that every figure must have a similar figure of arbitrary size. In 1733, the *Euclides ab omni naevo vindicatus* ('Euclid vindicated from every blemish') by the Italian Jesuit Girolamo Saccheri threw much fresh light on the indispensable role which this axiom played in the structure of the Euclidean edifice. Although Saccheri thought he had proved Euclid correct, he was the first to discuss the consequences of denying the parallel axiom and to suggest the construction of a geometry independent of it. Unfortunately, his book was not read widely enough to have much influence.

In a posthumous work (*Zur Theorie der Parallellinien*, 1786) J. H. Lambert also questioned the validity of the axiom, and showed how spherical geometry could dispense with it. J. Playfair, developing an idea suggested by Proclos, gave the axiom its modern formulation (1795). Legendre made a determined effort to prove its validity by showing that it was a consequence of Euclid's other axioms, and particularly of the postulate that the angles of a triangle are together equal to two right angles. But interest in these studies was soon afterwards eclipsed by the work of the founders of non-Euclidean geometry, Gauss, Lobachevsky and Bolyai, which we shall be discussing in a later volume.

Perspective

Another 18th-century revolution in geometry was based on the introduction of geometrical transformations, a concept which was to play a crucial role in 19th-century geometry.

Though perspective techniques go back to prehistory, the geometrical aspects of perspective were not studied seriously before the 15th century, when Guiberti, Brunelleschi, Alberti, Piero della Francesca, Leonardo da Vinci and Benvenuto Cellini established the theory of perspective as an aid to painters. In 1505, J. Pélerin was the first to discuss the vanishing point. Other 16th-century works on perspective were written by Dürer (1525), Commandino (1558), Barbaro (1559), Barozzi and Danti (1582), Guidobaldo del Monte (1600) and many others. In the 17th century, the major contributions came first from the Netherlands—Stevin (1605), Salomon de Caus (1612), d'Aiguillon (1613) and Marolais (1614), and later from France—J. L. Vaulezard (1631), Aleaume and Migon (1638), J. Dubreuil (3 vols., 1642–1649) and A. Bosse (2 vols., 1648–1653). The first to appreciate the importance of perspective, considered as a central projection, to geometry was Girard Desargues, whose *Brouillon project* (1639) introduced the projective geometry of conics. Desargues also tried to interest practical men in perspective methods, but despite the support of Bosse, Pascal and de la Hire his attempts proved largely abortive. Though excellent books on perspective were written by van 's Gravesande (1711), Brook Taylor (1716 and 1719) and J. H. Lambert (1759 and 1774), it was not until the 19th century that perspective theory was officially incorporated into geometry—as the direct result of attempts by Gaspard Monge (1746–1818) to spread the use of descriptive geometry.

The Rise of Descriptive Geometry

Though descriptive geometry was not invented by Monge—it had been used in Dürer's *Underweysung* (1525) and in Frézier's *Stereotomy* (3 vols., 1737–1739, 2 vols., 1760)—no one before Monge had been able to define its principles and methods, or to show its applications in pure and even in differential geometry. Monge, who had taught descriptive geometry as professor at the military school at Mézières well before 1770, and who had mentioned it in many of his memoirs, did not publish a complete treatise on the subject, the *Géométrie descriptive*, until 1799. The practical advantages of this method were propagated by his pupils, who gave it a much narrower definition than Monge himself would have wished. For Monge, descriptive geometry was only one aspect of the theory of projections, which, despite its applications in draughtsmanship, was nevertheless a branch of pure geometry. Monge himself did not develop a general theory of projection.

Other Advances

Among lesser 18th-century contributions to geometry we must mention L. Mascheroni's *La geometria del compasso* (Pavia, 1797), which discussed fixed compass constructions. These had been treated previously by G. Mohr (1672), and by Lambert (1774), whose work was developed in the early 19th century. The theory of transversals, to which Ceva had made a signal contribution in 1678, became the object of a number of 18th-century studies before it was generalized by Carnot in 1806. Euler and Wallis studied the geometrical properties of triangles; Castillon and Malfatti published their famous construction problems; Euler (1752) rediscovered Descartes' formula connecting the number of faces, vertices and edges of a convex polyhedron.

Under the lasting influence of Newton, British mathematicians continued to take an active interest in classical geometry. Though Newton wrote no special work on geometry as such, his *Principia* included important theorems on the generation of conics. In addition, he had shown how different types of cubics were generated by five types of 'divergent parabolas'. Many of Newton's theorems were generalized by Cotes and Maclaurin; the latter, in his *Geometria organica*, presented a new method of describing conics and also studied such curves as the cissoid, the strophoid and the lemniscate. Maclaurin also generalized the theory of Pascal's mystic hexagram. His pupil, Matthew Stewart, set forth a number of new theorems, some of which were related to the theory of transversals.

Obtained as they had been without any general plan, these diverse results were not built into a coherent doctrine until the 19th century. Nevertheless, they show to what extent 18th-century mathematicians had returned to geometrical studies.

Analytical Geometry

At the beginning of the 18th century, analytical geometry was still clearly influenced by Descartes, according to whom it was an 'application of algebra to geometry', that is to say an algebraic technique for solving geometrical problems beyond the normal scope of Euclid's methods. Curves were not studied as such; straight lines and planes, which were considered as belonging to pure geometry, were neglected. Moreover, the study of solid analytical geometry had not yet been begun, and the use of a single axis introduced an artificial dissymmetry between the co-ordinates of two-dimensional geometry. It was against this background that 18th-century mathematicians, by their systematic study of plane curves and three-dimensional problems, and by the reorganization of basic principles, took analytical geometry beyond 'the application of algebra to geometry'.

The Theory of Plane Curves

Newton made systematic use of negative co-ordinates, introduced the method of undetermined coefficients in the *Arithmetica universalis* (1707), and developed analytical methods of studying cubics in his *Enumeratio liniarum tertii ordinis* (1704). He showed that there are seventy-two possible forms of a cubic—the remaining six were discovered by his successors—which he arranged in genera and classes, claiming that all could be derived by central projection from five fundamental types. Newton also perfected methods of determining the tangents and infinite branches of a cubic, and introduced the analysis of curves in the neighbourhood of a point by means of power series. Many of his pupils, including Stirling and Maclaurin, took these studies further still, while Dionis du Séjour, Goudin, Waring, Riccati and Saladini made an analytical study of higher-degree curves. The most decisive work in this field was Gabriel Cramer's *Introduction à l'analyse des lignes courbes algébriques* (Geneva, 1750), in which plane curves were classified by their order and special attention was paid to their infinite branches and singular points. Cramer, who eschewed integral calculus, was able to show that an nth-order curve is generally defined by $\frac{1}{2}n(n+3)$ points, but mentioned a number of exceptions.

Euler's *Introductio in analysin infinitorum* also made an important contribution to the theory of plane curves. Though Euler asserted that the two co-ordinate axes are equivalent, he did not apply this principle consistently. A prior study of co-ordinate changes enabled him to relate the equation of the conic to two conjugate diameters, and then to the principal diameters, a procedure which led him to the modern classification and to a detailed study of these curves. He went on to apply his studies of the infinite branches and of the asymptotes to the classification of curves of the third and fourth order. Though Euler failed to give analytical geometry a new basis, he nevertheless went much further than the Cartesians.

The Beginnings of Solid Analytical Geometry

The application of analytical geometry to the study of three-dimensional problems, first suggested by Descartes and Fermat, and more precisely by Philippe de la Hire in 1679, was begun seriously in 1700 by A. Parent, who formulated the equations of some surfaces, including the sphere and the hyperboloid of one sheet, and studied their tangential planes. The first complete work on solid analytical geometry, A. Clairaut's *Recherches sur les courbes à double courbure* (Paris, 1731), contained a systematic study of numerous types of space curves and surfaces, both from the algebraic and also from the differential point of view. In 1732, J. Hermann discussed various problems relating to planes and studied numerous surfaces, particularly quadric surfaces, of which he gave the first, though incomplete, classification.

In the last chapter of his *Introductio*, Euler co-ordinated all the known results, studied the transformations of space co-ordinates, made an analytical study of second-order surfaces based on that of conics, and gave their first complete classification.

The Creation of Modern Analytical Geometry

Lagrange's *Sur les pyramides triangulaires* (1773) was a much more 'modern' work. Anxious to demonstrate the efficiency of analytic methods, Lagrange made a definite break with the Cartesian tradition, affirmed the absolute equivalence of the three co-ordinate axes, and emphasized the fundamental character of straight lines and planes. Consequently, he was able to simplify calculations, to improve the notation, and to present the results in a more symmetrical and more general form.

At about the same time, Monge published a number of papers in which he incidentally solved the classical problem of planes and straight lines. His notation was particularly well suited to the nature of the problems under investigation; in 1785, he introduced the famous axial co-ordinates of the straight line (which Plücker rediscovered in 1865). Monge's *Feuilles d'analyse* (1795), based on his lectures at the *École Polytechnique*, was the first complete account of modern analytical geometry. In addition to this concise and elegant study, which laid great stress on symmetry, Monge also published a more comprehensive *Application de l'algèbre à la géométrie* (1802) which contained a thorough analysis of co-ordinate transformations and a detailed study of second-order surfaces. With it, elementary analytical geometry had come of age. The appearance in the early 19th century of a vast number of textbooks, including that of Lacroix (1798), shows how quickly the new discipline was able to make headway subsequently.

The Application of Analysis to Geometry

THE BEGINNINGS

Although partial results had been obtained earlier, differential geometry was undoubtedly the direct result of 18th-century studies, particularly by the followers of Leibniz. Their contributions included the determination of the radii of curvature, of points of inflection, of evolutes and involutes, of envelopes of one-parameter families of straight lines, of the orthogonal trajectories of certain families of curves, of the geodesic lines of certain surfaces, *etc.*

However, interest in these problems declined, and was not revived until the appearance of Clairaut's *Recherches sur les courbes à double courbure*. Unfortunately, Clairaut turned his attention to other subjects soon afterwards, so that many aspects of differential geometry remained neglected.

In 1728, Euler and Jean Bernoulli made a study of geodesic lines, whose mechanical significance Euler defined in 1763. His study of the calculus of variations led him to define minimal surfaces (of constant curvature) in 1744—Lagrange expressed these in partial derivatives in 1762. In 1760, Euler tackled an entirely new subject: the study, in a point M on a surface S, of the radius of curvature of different plane sections of S passing through M. He arrived at the famous formula expressing this radius as a function of the principal radii of normal curvature of the surface at the point. We must also mention Euler's study of the isometric mapping of surfaces (1770), and his paper on developable surfaces in which he introduced curvilinear co-ordinates.

MONGE AND THE RENEWAL OF DIFFERENTIAL GEOMETRY

Euler's geometrical studies were too dry and analytical to appeal to most mathematicians, but then, in 1771, Gaspard Monge began his remarkable studies, which were to revolutionize differential geometry, and which quickly received general recognition.

Monge not only had an exceptional sense of spatial relations, but was also a first-class analyst who invariably emphasized the close connection between the analytical, geometrical and practical aspects of every problem. In that way he always managed to hit upon the most direct and fruitful method and to derive the maximum benefit from every result.

Monge's first contribution (1771) was an overall survey of the general properties of space curves, in which he presented many important and original results with great elegance. He discussed their evolutes, rectifying planes, osculating spheres, the torsion of space curves, *etc.* In 1775, he continued Euler's study of developable surfaces, interpreting their properties by means of the partial differential equation $rt - s^2 = 0$, and then applying the results to the theory of umbrae and penumbrae. In 1776, his pupil J. B. Meusnier published a geometrical study of the curvature of surfaces which contained Meusnier's theorem, and also discussed the geometrical integration of the partial differential equation of minimal surfaces. Soon afterwards, Monge made the practical cut-and-fill problem the basis of a study of two-parameter families of straight lines (congruencies), defined the lines of curvature of a surface, and brought out their essential properties. At the same time he studied different families of surfaces, particularly the first-order surfaces (cylinders, cones, *etc.*), second-order surfaces (developable surfaces, directrices of ruled surfaces, *etc.*), and third-order surfaces (ruled surfaces in general), from their partial differential equations. Geometrical integration led him to the study of the envelopes of surfaces, of characteristics, *etc.*, and to the introduction of contact transformations. In 1795, he made his main results the subject of a course of lectures, which he published in 1795 and again in 1799 as the *Feuilles d'analyse appliquée à la géométrie*, and which he republished in more complete form in his great classic, the *Application de l'analyse à la géométrie* (1807).

It was largely due to the success of Monge's approach and to his lasting influence that geometry recovered the prestige it had lacked for so long.

CHAPTER 2

The Organization of the Principles of Classical Mechanics

BECAUSE OF THE EXTRAORDINARY DEVELOPMENT of science in the 17th century, the successes of experimental methods, and the development of mathematics from the rule of three to integral calculus, 18th-century scientists were freed from many of the metaphysical speculations that had hampered the work of the founders of classical science. This new freedom found its clearest expression in their treatment of mechanical problems.

THE SPREAD OF NEWTONIAN IDEAS

In England, Newton's system took a long time to spread. Newton's brief lectures at Cambridge were poorly attended because, as Whiston explained, they proved too hard to follow. At the time Rohault's *Physics*, in Latin and English translations, was still the main textbook, and it was to the 1723 English edition of that work that Samuel Clarke added a running commentary of notes based on quotations from Newton, which was, in fact, a complete refutation of the author. Paradoxically, Newton's ideas were thus spread in Cambridge in the margin of a purely Cartesian work.

The growing Newtonian faction then launched an attack on their Continental detractors in Roger Cotes's preface to the second edition of the *Principia* (1713). Cotes told the Cartesians that their imperceptible vortices had the very occult qualities which they so bitterly condemned. The Newtonians also accused their opponents of despicable impiety in denying God's constant intervention in natural phenomena. This argument was criticized by Leibniz, who poked fun at the Newtonian view that absolute space was the *sensorium* of God.

THE RISE OF NEWTONIAN IDEAS ON THE CONTINENT

By 1730, Newton's ideas had spread to Holland (van 's Gravesande, Musschenbroek) but not as yet to France. The *Académie des Sciences* first heard of them from Maupertuis, who had this to say about their reception:

It took more than fifty years to acquaint our Academies with the concept of attraction, which remained shut in its island, or, if it did cross the sea, appeared as a mere replica of a monster that had just been slain; scientists were so pleased about having banished occult qualities from philosophy, that they felt everything smacking of these as a dire threat. So delighted were they with the mechanical explanation of nature that they condemned unheard the true mechanism they were now being offered.

Maupertuis went on to show that Cartesian principles failed to provide an exhaustive description of physical reality. Since there is no necessary connection between extension and impenetrability, he contended that attraction is not *a priori* less admissible than impulsion; even if attraction were conceived as an inherent property of matter (a view which Newton never propounded) that conception would not be metaphysically absurd and did not lead to any contradictions. In any event, attraction must be considered a physical fact.

Maupertuis had a distinguished supporter in Voltaire, who proclaimed himself a convinced Newtonian in his *Lettres philosophiques* (1734), and who wrote a popular *Éléments de la philosophie de Newton* (1738), and a preface to the French translation of Newton's *Principia* by Madame de Châtelet. In it, he rounded on all those of his contemporaries who had 'grown old with the errors of Descartes and now refused to see the light of reason'.

Thus it was not until 1738 that the great battle, begun in the 17th century, was won on the Continent. Meanwhile, English science, as if oppressed by the lonely majesty of Newton's work, had begun to languish and the torch England had lit passed out of her hands.

THEORETICAL MECHANICS

Euler and the Mechanics of a Particle

In 1736, Euler was the first to turn the mechanics of a particle into a theoretical science (*analytice exposita*), and to show that the composition or the equivalence of forces (or powers) in statics could be extended to their mechanical effects. Euler assigned the same force to a body at rest as he did to a body in motion, holding that, in both cases, the body is subject to the same action. He introduced the mass indirectly by asserting the proportionality between the forces necessary to produce an effect and the quantities of matter involved—a truly Newtonian synthesis.

D'ALEMBERT'S PRINCIPLE

D'Alembert explained his philosophy of mechanics in a special preface to his famous *Traité de dynamique* (1743). He asserted that, once the nature of motion and the laws of impact are understood, mechanics can be shown to be a purely rational science based on principles that are necessarily true and clear in themselves. Although he protested to the contrary, d'Alembert was, in fact, a Cartesian, inasmuch as he proposed to banish the forces inherent to bodies in motion as obscure and metaphysical, and to make mass and motion his basic principles. He reduced the general problem of dynamics to the solution of the following general problem:

Let there be a system of bodies arranged in any way with respect to one another; and suppose that a particular motion is impressed on each of these bodies, which it cannot follow because of the action of the other bodies: to find the motion that each body must take.

'Clearly,' d'Alembert explained, 'the motions a, b, c, . . . impressed respectively on the bodies A, B, C, . . . of a given system can each be compounded of two motions *a* and α, *b* and β, *c* and γ, . . . where *a*, *b*, *c*, . . . are the acquired motions, *i.e.* the motions we require to find, and α, β, γ, . . . the motions which must cancel out among themselves'.

From this solution, d'Alembert derived his principle for finding the motion of several bodies which act upon one another:

Decompose each of the motions a, b, c *etc.* which are impressed on the bodies into two others *a* and α, *b* and β, *c* and γ, *etc.* which are such that if the motions *a*, *b*, *c*, *etc.* had been impressed on the bodies, they would have been retained unchanged; and if the motions α, β, γ, *etc.* alone had been impressed on the bodies, the system would have remained at rest. It is clear that *a*, *b*, *c*, *etc.* will be the motions that the bodies will take because of their mutual action. This is what we had to find.

Though d'Alembert's principle was very clear, its application often proved laborious. Hence, Lagrange suggested that it was more practical 'to establish immediately the equilibrium between the forces and the motions they generate, but taken in the opposite directions'. This method had already been recommended by Hermann (1716) and by Euler (1740), but despite this priority, and also that of Jacques Bernoulli, who had linked together the problems of the centre of oscillation and of the equilibrium of the lever (1703), d'Alembert deserves credit for having raised the method to a unifying and generalizing principle.

It has often been said that d'Alembert's principle reduces all dynamics to statics. In fact, d'Alembert himself stressed that 'the three principles of the force of inertia, of compound motion, and of equilibrium are essentially different from one another'. D'Alembert applied his principle to the systematic solution of all the problems discussed in his *Traité*, including the behaviour of bodies supported by threads or rods, and of bodies oscillating in planes. He also solved the problem of different modes of impact.

Moreover, he set out to show that the principle of the conservation of 'living' (active) force was a consequence of the laws of dynamics for systems with restraints composed of threads and inflexible rods, just as the laws of impact were a consequence of the same principle. He demonstrated this fact for 'every particular case'.

The Principle of Least Action

In 1744, Maupertuis intervened in the debate between Fermat and the Cartesians on the former's use of his principle of 'natural economy' to explain the laws of refraction (1664).[1] The strange thing is not that he succeeded in finding the answer; rather is it that in extending the minimum principle almost arbitrarily to the field of dynamics, he was led to a valid law, turning Newton's optical error into a mechanical truth.

According to Maupertuis, nature does not follow the *shortest* path, as Fermat's principle suggested, but the path by which the *quantity of action* is the least. By means of a simple differential argument, he then succeeded in combining Newton's law of the propagation of light and Snell's law of refraction in one simple extremum law. It seems reasonable, however, to assume that Maupertuis had reversed the order of the arguments; that he first produced (or borrowed from Leibniz) the differential argument and then presented it as the consequence of an economic principle—which, moreover, he believed was the expression of a final cause, the very proof of the existence of God. 'It cannot be doubted that all things are governed by a supreme Being who has impressed on matter forces that reflect His power, and has destined them to produce effects that reveal His wisdom.'

Maupertuis' contribution to the laws of impact (1747) was more constructive. He argued that the total action produced by the impact of bodies can be expressed as the *sum of living forces resulting from the lost velocities*. Since the quantities of action produced by nature are minimal, that sum must be minimal as well, no matter whether the colliding bodies are 'hard' or 'elastic'. In other words, he showed that the law of least action reduces to the conservation of total momentum. Once again, Maupertuis had arrived at a successful synthesis.

Maupertuis, who declared that 'my only fault was that I discovered a principle that created something of a sensation', was the object of

[1] See p. 461.

many bitter attacks. Thus J. G. Koenig (1751) alleged that he had taken his principle from Leibniz, who had, in fact, propounded no such thing; Voltaire hurled the grossest insults at him, and d'Alembert rounded on him for his revival of final causes (*Traité de dynamique*, 1758 edition).

Meanwhile Euler had expressed the law of least action in the integral form $\int mvds$ in Appendix II of his *Methodus inveniendi lineas curvas maximi minimive proprietate gaudentes*, adding that the law also governed the fall of heavy bodies, the parabolic motion of a particle subject to a central force, and even that of a particle attracted by any number of fixed centres. Called in to settle the dispute between Maupertuis and Koenig in 1753, Euler found for the former.

Euler and the Mechanics of Solid Bodies

In 1760, Euler published a *Theoria motus corporum solidorum seu rigidorum*, which was amended and amplified by his son in 1790. For every solid, Euler defined a centre of mass or centre of inertia, remarking that the term 'centre of gravity' implies the more restricted concept that the body is acted on by external forces, while the centre of inertia is defined by means of inertia alone. He also defined *moments of inertia*—a concept which would have helped Huygens to avoid many circumlocutions. In the same treatise Euler introduced the classical differential equations which express the general motion of a solid body about a fixed point in terms of the forces applied to the solid, the components of instantaneous rotation of the solid and their derivatives, and the moments of inertia of the solid about a fixed point.

HYDROSTATICS

Clairaut and the Shape of the Earth

Continuing Huygens' and Newton's studies of the earth's shape, Clairaut arrived at the following formulation of the general law of equilibrium of a fluid mass:

> In order that a mass of fluid be in equilibrium, it is necessary that the efforts of all the parts of the fluid contained in a duct re-entrant upon itself should cancel each other out. (*Théorie de la figure de la terre*, 1743.)

Clairaut went on to apply this principle to the study of the equilibrium of a fluid mass rotating about its axis, and concluded that, for equilibrium to be established, the differential of gravity must be a complete differential.

Comparative measurements of the meridians, at different latitudes, and particularly those obtained by the French Lapland expedition of which Clairaut was a distinguished member (see p. 450), indicated that the earth has a polar flattening of the order of 1/300, and that Newton's figure had been much too large. Clairaut concluded that the earth was formed of layers which were flatter as they were farther from the centre, the flattening following a law that depended on the decrease of the density between the centre and the surface.

Daniel Bernoulli's Hydrodynamics and Jean Bernoulli's Hydraulics

In 1738, Daniel Bernoulli published his remarkable *Hydrodynamica sive de viribus et motibus fluidorum commentarii*, which embraced both hydrostatics—the science of equilibrium—and hydraulics, the science of fluid motion. Bernoulli's guiding principle was the conservation of living forces, *i.e.* the equality between the actual descent and the potential ascent of a fluid in the course of its normal flow. In this way, he introduced the kinetic concepts of Huygens into hydrostatics. In addition, he assumed that the particles of a slice of fluid which is perpendicular to the direction of the motion move with the same velocity, and that this velocity is inversely proportional to the cross-section of the slice. With these hypotheses he was able to solve numerous problems in a novel way.

Daniel Bernoulli was roundly attacked by his father Jean Bernoulli, who reproached him with starting 'from an indirect principle which, though true, has not yet been adopted by all philosophers', and who suggested that the study of fluid motions should dispense with the assumption of the conservation of living forces. Moreover, he accused Daniel of having taken the idea of slices from his own *Hydraulics*, which was published in 1742 but which, he alleged, he had conceived as early as 1729.

D'Alembert and the Motion of Fluids

D'Alembert wrote that, while the mechanics of solid bodies 'depends only on metaphysical principles which are independent of experiment, the foundation of the theory of fluids, on the other hand, must be based on experiment, from which we receive only a very little enlightenment'.

In 1744, d'Alembert published a *Traité de l'équilibre et du mouvement des fluides*, in which, following Jean Bernoulli, he tried to base hydrostatics on purely dynamic principles. Adopting the hypothesis of flow by parallel slices of fluid, d'Alembert then extended to fluids the equilibrium principles he had used as a basis for his dynamics. As a result, he was able to treat many of Daniel Bernoulli's problems in a quite novel manner.

D'Alembert and the Resistance of Fluids

In his *Traité de l'équilibre* d'Alembert also treated the resistance of fluids with the aid of a mechanical model in which the motion of fluids was likened to collisions between 'small balls' and a solid body immersed in the fluid. By 1752 (*Essai d'une nouvelle théorie de la résistance des fluides*) he had discarded this flimsy model and returned instead to Clairaut's principles: The velocity v of a fluid particle at the instant t, can be considered as the sum of v', its velocity at the instant $t+vt$, and a velocity v''. By the principles of hydrostatics, 'the particles of the fluid would be in equilibrium if they tended to move with only the velocity v'', in which case the fluid pressure would be the same as if the fluid were at rest and as if its particles were forced into motion by the accelerating force $\frac{v''}{dt}$. In this way, he managed to obtain (at least for plane motions) the general equations of the motion of fluids, which make his *Essai* a great pioneering work.

Considering the case of a symmetrical, fixed and immovable solid placed into a steady uniform stream of a homogeneous weightless fluid, d'Alembert observed that 'the body would suffer no resistance from the fluid, which is contrary to experience'. He had thus discovered the hydrodynamical paradox with which his name is still associated, and which he 'bequeathed to the geometers, that they may explain it'. This paradox, emphasizing the gulf between everyday experience and a theory that was unencumbered with arbitrary hypotheses, provided 18th-century mathematicians with much food for thought.

Euler's Hydrodynamics

In 1755, Euler presented a number of papers to the Berlin Academy on the theory and practice of hydrostatics, which were so perfect that little of their contents has aged with time. Here we can give only a brief analysis of the most important points.

In his paper dealing with hydrostatics, Euler considered a fluid, either compressible or not, which was subjected to any given forces.

> 'The generality that I include,' he wrote, 'instead of dazzling us, will rather discover the true laws of Nature in all their splendour, and there will be found yet stronger reasons for admiring their beauty and simplicity.'

Euler's 'generality' was based on Clairaut's principle, and had the advantage of introducing pressure explicitly and of relating it to the accelerative force at each point.

In a series of other papers dealing with hydrodynamics, Euler developed his famous equations of the motion of a perfectly compressible fluid, and also his equation of the kinematics of continuous media which involved the concept of the conservation of mass.

Lagrange was able to declare that 'by the discoveries of Euler the whole mechanics of fluids was reduced to a simple matter of analysis alone'. Euler himself was too good a mathematician to overlook the remaining difficulties of this 'simple matter'. He summed up his own, and the work of his contemporaries, with the following rather ironic comment:

> However sublime the investigations on fluids for which we are indebted to MM. Bernoulli, Clairaut and d'Alembert may be, they stem so naturally from our two general formulae that one cannot but admire this agreement of their profound meditation with the simplicity of the principles from which we have deduced our two equations, and to which we were led directly by the first axioms of mechanics.

FRICTION

Coulomb's Work on Friction

In 1699, Amontons had stated that friction was proportional to the mutual pressure of the parts in contact, and De Camus and Desaguillers had contended that friction at rest is greater than friction in motion.

In 1781, the *Académie des Sciences* chose the subject of the laws of friction and the stiffness of ropes for a competition, and called for new experiments, made on a large scale and applicable to 'machines valuable to the navy, such as the pulley, the capstan and the inclined plane'.

The prize was won by Coulomb, who was then a captain of the Royal Corps of Engineers and whose paper was a model of experimental analysis. Coulomb assumed that in order to draw a weight along a horizontal plane it is necessary to deploy a force proportional to the weight plus a small constant depending on the 'coherence' of the surfaces. Coulomb also established the quantitative law governing the tension of ropes.

Borda and the Resistance of Fluids

The Chevalier de Borda deserves credit for having drawn attention to 'hydrodynamical questions in which a loss of living force must be assumed'. Such a loss appears in a tube whose diameter is suddenly enlarged or reduced. Borda compared this phenomenon to an impact in which a loss of kinetic energy is involved, *i.e.*, in the language of the time, to an impact of hard bodies.

Borda also carried out systematic experiments on the resistance of fluids and on the resistance of air. He showed that the total resistance cannot be calculated as the sum of the partial resistances of each of the elements, and went on to demonstrate that Newton's theory of fluid resistance is incorrect. Finally, he showed that the law of the square of the sine does not hold for oblique resistance, since 'when the angles of incidence are small the resistance does not decrease as much as the simple sine'.

Borda's experiments were closely related to those of the Abbé Bossu, who studied fluid resistance in the basin of the Military College, and also to the work of du Buat.

Lazare Carnot's Mechanics

In 1783, Lazare Carnot published his *Essai sur les machines en général* which he later extended under the title of *Principes généraux de l'équilibre et du mouvement* (1803).

Carnot was the first to assert the experimental character of the principles of mechanics, in contrast to the ideas professed by Euler and d'Alembert. He applied the laws of mechanics to the reasoned observation of problems of impact, reducing the action of a continuous force, *e.g.* gravity, to that of a series of infinitely small impacts.

In his studies of the mechanics of systems, Carnot introduced the concept of *geometrical motions*, that is to say motions that have no effect on the actions which are exerted between the bodies of the system but depend only upon the conditions of constraint between the parts of the system. In modern language, Carnot's 'geometrical motions' are *virtual displacements* compatible with the restraints between the bodies of the system.

Carnot then established his theorem of the impact of 'hard bodies': 'In the impact of hard bodies, the sum of the living forces before the impact is always equal to the sum of the living forces after the impact together with the sum of the living forces that each of these bodies would have if it moved freely with only the velocity which it lost in the impact.'

He also developed some interesting ideas on animated systems: 'It seems that, as far as its physique is concerned, an animal may be considered as an assembly of particles separated by more or less compressed springs which, by this fact, store a certain quantity of living forces; and that these springs, by extending, may be considered to convert the latent living force into real living force.'

Carnot's highly original ideas were to inspire Laplace, Barré de Saint-Venant and probably Coriolis as well.

THE 'MÉCANIQUE ANALYTIQUE' OF LAGRANGE

We now come to a work which crowned all 18th-century efforts to develop a rational mechanics—Lagrange's *Mécanique analytique* (1788). Its main object was the following:

> To reduce the theory of mechanics, and the art of solving the associated problems to general formulae, whose simple development provides all the equations necessary for the solution of each problem.
>
> To unite, and present from one point of view, the different principles which have, so far, been found to assist in the solution of problems in mechanics; by showing their mutual dependence and making possible a judgment of their validity and scope.

Lagrange also made the following declaration on the mathematical structure of his work:

> No diagrams will be found in this work. The methods which I expound require neither constructions nor geometrical and mechanical arguments, but only algebraic operations subject to a regular and uniform development. Those who love analysis will, with pleasure, see mechanics become a new branch of it, and will be grateful to me for thus extending its field.

Lagrange related all problems of statics to the principle of virtual work (or the principle of 'virtual velocities' as he still called it) 'which is not sufficiently clear in itself to be formed into a first principle . . . but can be deduced from two principles' (of the lever and of the composition of forces). Lagrange himself preferred to base it directly on the *principle of pulleys*.

In order to express problems of statics quite generally by means of mathematical equations, Lagrange introduced the elegant method of multipliers.

In dynamics, Lagrange did not openly take sides between Euler and d'Alembert. Because he felt that his predecessors had solved it, he considered that there was no need to study the mechanics of the particle, and felt free to concentrate on the dynamics of systems.

He successively analysed the four principles of dynamics: the conservation of living forces; the conservation of the motion of the centre of gravity; the conservation of moments or the principle of areas; and the principle of the least quantity of action.

He observed rightly that the first of these principles went back to Huygens, though in a different form from that which Leibniz and Jean Bernoulli had given it subsequently; that the second was due to Newton; and that the third, discovered by Euler, Daniel Bernoulli and d'Arcy, was merely the generalization of a theorem of Newton concerning several particles attracted by the same centre.

Lagrange described Maupertuis' principle as vague and arbitrary, and extended Euler's method, 'which alone merits the attention of the geometers', to the motion of any system of bodies interacting in any way. We cannot go into the details of the analysis which enabled Lagrange to put the general equations of dynamics into the concise and classical form he gave them, except to say that he regarded the sums of forces acting upon a system equal to the sum of the given accelerating forces acting in each element, and that he established, better than d'Alembert had been able to do, that the conservation of living forces is a consequence of the equations of dynamics, as long as the restraints are without friction and independent of time.

In this way, he was able to relate the living force (T) of the system to the generalized co-ordinates q_i, the generalized forces Q_i, and the time t by the famous Lagrange equations:

$$\frac{d}{dt}\left(\frac{\partial T}{\partial \dot{q}_i}\right) - \frac{\partial T}{\partial \dot{q}_i} = Qi \ (i=1, 2 \ldots n)$$

Here $\dot{q}_i$ denotes dq_i/dt. (There is one equation for each of the n degrees of freedom possessed by the system.)

He was able to show that Huygens' principle of the conservation of the living force was a simple corollary of these equations, and that the principle of least action reduces to the following principle: 'The sum of the instantaneous living forces of all bodies, from the moment that they start from given points to that when they arrive at other given points, is maximum or minimum.' Lagrange suggested that it should therefore be called the *principle of the greatest or least living force*.

The *Mécanique analytique* also dealt with a great many other problems which we cannot discuss here. Let us merely note that, as part of his treatment of dynamics, Lagrange made a detailed study of the motion of a heavy solid of revolution suspended from a point on its axis, and expressed the solution in terms of elliptic integrals. He also developed a general method of approximation for solving problems in dynamics and in celestial mechanics. This method was based on the variation of arbitrary constants. Moreover, he developed the theory of small motions, and stated that equilibrium is necessarily stable when the potential of the given forces is a minimum.

Lagrange also introduced the variable with which his name is associated into the kinematics of continuous media, as a supplement to Euler's variables. It is only fair to state, however, that Euler had in some cases made use of variables of the Lagrangian type.

Finally, Lagrange established a fundamental theorem on the permanence of the irrotational property in fluid motion, and studied the motion of a fluid in an almost horizontal shallow canal. He showed that this motion is governed by an equation similar to the equation of the propagation of sound.

* * *

Readers may object that we have dwelt far too long on debates which have no bearing on the structure of modern mechanics. Our justification is that only in this way could we illustrate the tortuous path which has led mechanics to its present state. The works of Euler and Lagrange, which have remained standard texts, cannot possibly be understood if they are read outside their historical background. Moreover, though d'Alembert could assert that mathematics had expelled the love of systems even in his day, he had to admit that the 'spirit of mathematics' had limitations and might easily lead to flimsy physical theories—as it did in hydrodynamics.

In short, the philosophic premisses of mechanics remained, and were to remain for a long time, the subject of keen controversy, in the course of which many new facts were brought to light.

CHAPTER 3

The Solar System

NEWTON'S MAGNIFICENT SYNTHESIS of most of the astronomical facts known in his day enabled astronomers to turn celestial mechanics into an exact science in the course of the next two centuries, during which astronomy became more and more institutionalized in England and France.[1]

Though their instruments became increasingly accurate and powerful, 18th-century astronomers neglected the stellar universe. The main object of their studies was the solar system, and particularly the application of planetary motions to the determination of longitude at sea—a task in which they were greatly aided by governments anxious to improve methods of navigation.

THE GRADUAL ADOPTION OF THE LAW OF UNIVERSAL GRAVITATION

The first edition of Newton's *Philosophiae naturalis principia mathematica* (1687) ran to no more than 250 copies, the second (1713) to 750. These were followed by the 1726 edition, Motte's English edition (1729), Madame du Châtelet's French edition (1756)[2] and by many others.

We have seen that Newton's law of attraction was given a poor reception on the Continent, where most scientists were staunch Cartesians and, as such, rejected all actions at a distance as unscientific abstractions. When Newton objected that attraction was not a hypothesis—*hypotheses non fingo*—but only a useful method of interpreting the facts, he was told that this viewpoint had no tangible advantages. In fact, since Newton's geometrical arguments and approximations were not born out by analytical studies of the

[1] The Paris Observatory was founded in 1677, the Greenwich Observatory eight years later. Observatories in Holland, Russia and Italy were still poorly equipped at that time; Leyden and St. Petersburg did not become famous until very much later.

[2] Madame du Châtelet's translation was studded with errors. There is no critical French edition of the *Principia*.

principal inequalities in the moon's motion until much later, the Cartesians had every right to consider them specious at the time.

Newton's two great contemporaries—Huygens and Leibniz—also offered criticisms, though of a different kind. Huygens, whose studies of circular motion had first led Newton to his inverse square law, adopted that law in 1690 but questioned the idea of the *mutual* attraction of celestial objects; gravity, according to him, was a purely terrestrial phenomenon. Even so, he tested the hypothesis of mutual attraction in his theoretical calculations of the flattening of the earth but found that the evidence then available was insufficient to prove or to disprove Newton. Leibniz's uncompromisingly negative attitude, on the other hand, cheated him of discoveries which he might have made himself but which, as it was, were made by Clairaut, d'Alembert and Euler fifty years later.

Since the struggle between the Newtonians and their adversaries gave rise to a great deal of experimental research, Newton's theory played a considerable part in the history of science long before it was generally accepted.

The popularization of Newton's ideas on the Continent was largely the work of Voltaire, who attended Newton's funeral in 1727 and returned with the *Principia* in his bags. Seven years later the Paris Academy of Science presented a prize to Daniel Bernoulli for his analytical description of Newton's theory (1732). Descartes' mysterious vortices vanished from the mathematical horizon soon afterwards; other opponents were silenced when measurements of the flattening of the earth in 1737, and the predicted return of Halley's comet in 1759, confirmed Newton's theory beyond the shadow of doubt.

OBSERVATIONAL INSTRUMENTS

The 18th-century astronomers, who, as we saw, were mainly interested in the motion of the planets, expected their instruments to be accurate and stable rather than powerful. The most common type was the sector (sextant or quadrant) and later the meridian circle. The basic form of these instruments was a telescope pivoted near its object glass so that the eyepiece could be raised or lowered in a vertical plane. The degree of movement was measured on a graduated arc. This was generally fixed to the telescope and moved with it, readings being taken by means of a plumb-line suspended from the pivot. The whole instrument was sometimes supported on another, vertical pivot, so that it could be turned horizontally and orientated. There were also very large sectors in which the telescope alone moved, the graduated arc being inscribed on a wall.

Before the invention of the achromatic lens, chromatism was reduced to a minimum by making the simple object glass as thin as possible. It was therefore small in diameter and of very great focal length. A Keplerian eyepiece, consisting of a single plano-convex lens, was generally used. Before telescopes came into use sights were taken with the naked eye through pinholes, the last instrument of this type being Hevelius' alidad. But eighteen years before Hevelius' death, in 1687, the Abbé Picard was already using a telescope fitted with cross-wires in the focal plane of the object glass.

Early instruments were made either by the astronomers themselves or, more often, by craftsmen of repute. Among the prized possessions of museums are instruments inscribed with the names of Langlois, Graham, Bird and Ramsden, and it is to men like these that observational astronomy owes many of its early successes.

Observations of Altitude

Observations of altitude and declination were made more accurate by fixing a horizontal wire in the focal plane of the telescope. Further refinement was provided by the micrometer, invented in the previous century and developed by Römer, who adjusted a fine movable wire (parallel with the fixed wire) by means of a screw. The star was sighted against the movable wire, the reading giving its displacement from the fixed wire. The value of such measurements depended upon the accuracy of the screw thread and the absence of play in the mechanism moving the wire, and these qualities were achieved only by gradual improvement. Bradley's observations, to which we shall return, owed their precision to a different arrangement. Instead of using a micrometer to measure the displacement of a wire in the telescope, he applied it to the movement of the telescope itself.

Transit Observations

Exact observation of the transit of a star across the meridian could not be made until chronometers providing an accurate measurement of time were invented. Ever since Huygens applied the pendulum to the regulation of clocks in 1657, inventors had been busy devising more reliable timepieces, but these were generally distrusted by the astronomers, who demanded a degree of precision not yet attained. Practical chronometers did not appear until after the invention of Graham's escapement (1715) and mercury pendulum (1726), and Harrison's bimetal grid pendulum (about 1730). The new escapement reduced to a minimum interference with the pendulum's swing by the impulse imparted to it, and the pendulums automatically compensated for changes in their length with the changes in temperature.

Transit observations could now be made by means of a vertical wire in the focal plane of the telescope. In practice, several vertical wires crossed by a single horizontal wire were used, and observations were taken by Bradley's *eye and ear* method, which continued to be used until the development of electric recording instruments 150 years later. In this method, the observer counted the audible beats of a seconds pendulum while noting the passage of the star across five vertical wires. The resulting readings were accurate to within a tenth of a second.

Transit Instruments

Although Bradley's method was subject to systematic errors depending on the observer, it was not so much these as the flexure of the instrument which vitiated his results. Römer therefore invented his *machina domestica* (1690), which had all the chief characteristics of a modern instrument. Its axis passed through the centre of the telescope, whose tube was composed of two cones joined at their bases, thus eliminating the effects of flexure. The pressure of the telescope upon the axis of the instrument was counterpoised by a weight tending to pull it upwards at the centre, and the micrometer wires were illuminated. Unfortunately this instrument fell into disuse, and Römer's ingenious ideas had to be rediscovered after much quite unnecessary trial and error.

The same fate befell the *rota meridiana*, the first 'meridian circle', which Römer used from 1704 onwards to observe meridian altitudes. Like modern instruments, it had a full graduated circle fixed to the telescope, and the whole instrument rested upon two solid supports. It was received with understandable misgivings; the necessarily reduced dimensions of the circle and the telescope prevented the use of simple object glasses with focal lengths sufficient to offset the effects of chromatic aberration.

Compound Object Glasses

Achromatic object glasses were first introduced in the middle of the 18th century (see p. 457). Until then, all objectives consisted of a simple lens, so that chromatic aberration had to be offset by reduction of the aperture, *i.e.* by using objectives whose aperture ratio (the ratio of the diameter of the lens to the focal length) ranged from 1/50 to 1/300.

All that was changed in 1758 when John Dollond produced his classical achromatic lens, a combination of a convex lens of crown glass with a concave lens of flint glass.

The theory of spherical and chromatic aberration and of the design of optical objectives was propounded between 1760 and 1768 by

Clairaut and d'Alembert; Clairaut also designed and produced the first aplanatic objective.

THE APPARENT POSITION OF CELESTIAL POINTS

The apparent position of a point in the sky is determined by its *declination* and its *right ascension*, which are defined with reference to the celestial equator and the ecliptic. Observations made at two different times would tally only if the earth were stationary with respect to these celestial planes; as it is, the earth's motion produces an aberration effect, while the relative motion of the celestial planes produces a cumulative (secular) precession and a periodic nutation. As a result of the latter, the celestial co-ordinates appear to wobble about a mean position. Observations must take all this into account.

Of these three effects, the first and third were established by Bradley, and the second, known of old, by Newton. Hence an important chapter in the history of astronomy was written at the beginning of the 18th century, though the problem on which it largely hinged—the determination of stellar parallax—was not solved until the 19th century.

The parallax of a star is defined as the angle subtended at the star by the radius of the earth's orbit; the (horizontal) parallax of the sun and the planets is defined as the angle subtended at the sun or the planets by the radius of the earth itself. Astronomers use parallax to measure the relative distances of celestial bodies.

Since the earth revolves about the sun, a near star close to the pole of the ecliptic appears to move against the background of the more distant stars (whose apparent motion is too slight to be observed), and it is precisely the amplitude of this annual motion which constitutes its parallax. The measurement of stellar parallaxes was therefore a decisive means of establishing the physical reality of the earth's motion about the sun, which until then had been no more than a mathematical hypothesis.

Discovery of Aberration

Early demonstrations of parallactic effects were based on what was considered the most reliable method, the determination of the zenith distance at the culmination of a star which passes near the observer's zenith. By choosing a star in that vicinity, refraction effects were minimized; hence it is not surprising that the same star, γ Draconis, was used for parallax measurements for 60 years.

This star was observed by Hooke in 1669, who estimated an annual variation of about 30″. In fact, he was misled by observational errors.

When Picard, the founder of precision astronomy, observed the latitude of γ Lyrae a few years later, he was unable to detect the slightest trace of parallax, and subsequent observations showed that the same was true of γ Draconis. It was at this stage (1727) that Bradley constructed his famous 12½-ft. zenith sector. With it, he was able to make a choice of more than 200 stars of different magnitudes, with an experimental error of less than 2″. Soon afterwards, Bradley noticed a uniform annual shift in the apparent positions of *all* the stars, and observed that that shift could not be due to parallax since it lagged behind by six months; moreover, it did not take place along the line joining the sun to the earth, but perpendicularly to it, *i.e.* in the direction of the earth's motion.

Newton's theory of the emission of light then enabled Bradley to explain the shift as resulting from the gradual propagation of light, discovered by Römer in 1675 (see p. 283), combined with the motion of the earth in its orbit. He called the phenomenon the *stellar aberration*, and showed that it is greatest when the two components are perpendicular. In this case its value is equal to the *solar aberration*, which is the angle of the earth's displacement during the time the light of the sun takes to reach it. Bradley estimated the maximum of aberration at about 20″.

When Bradley submitted his results to the Royal Society in September 1728, his paper (which was published in the *Philosophical Transactions*) caused a considerable stir: the revolution of the earth about the sun had at last been established experimentally, and in a quite unexpected way.

Nutation

Bradley made his second important discovery, the nutation ('wobbling') of the earth's axis, after long study of the annual changes in the stars' *mean declination*. From these changes he deduced the existence of a complex inequality with a period of 18 years.

Now that period is also that of the motion of the moon's nodes. Newton had explained that the earth's axis must be affected by an oscillatory motion arising from the variable position of the plane of the terrestrial equator with respect to the direction of the sun's and the moon's disturbing force; Bradley now explained the additional irregularity he had discovered by the periodic variation in the position of the plane of the lunar orbit with respect to the plane of the terrestrial equator. Both effects may be accounted for by imagining the pole of the equator to describe a small ellipse round its mean position, and Bradley was able to show that the axes of that ellipse are 18″ and 16″ respectively (the corresponding modern values are 18″ 4‴ and 13″ 8‴).

ASTRONOMICAL REFRACTION

A further factor influencing the apparent position of a celestial body is the change of direction which a light ray undergoes as it passes through the terrestrial atmosphere. This phenomenon, which is in excess of 30′ at the horizon, had not escaped the attention of ancient observers, who had, however, supposed that it was restricted to stars of low altitude. The first astronomers to assert that the effect is continuous, and decreases from a maximum at the horizon to a minimum at the zenith, were Kepler, who calculated a table of refraction by an empirical rule, and Cassini, who used Snell's law in 1666. However, their measurements were so inaccurate that they masked the real importance of their hypothesis.

Other refraction tables were computed by Bradley and by Bouguer (see p. 450), who discovered a difference of 3′ in horizontal refraction measured at sea level and in Quito (altitude *c.* 10,000 ft.), and of 7′ between refraction measured at latitude 50° and at the equator. The latter difference was, in fact, the result of temperature changes, as Bouguer himself suspected. Imperfect though his tables were, they proved to be in tolerably satisfactory agreement with observation, at least for zenith distances less than 45°.

The theory of atmospheric refraction remained rather vague until 1804, when Laplace offered an explanation which has not since been improved upon to any considerable extent.

THE MOTIONS OF COMETS AND OF THE MOON

Though the motions of the planets seemed to be satisfactorily accounted for by Kepler's laws, those of the moon and of comets were not; hence they attracted the special attention of 18th-century astronomers. Long before then, Pliny the Elder had complained that the capricious behaviour of the moon tortures the spirit of the observer (*torsit ingenia contemplantium*), and Newton said that it caused him headaches and insomnia.

COMETS

Tycho Brahe had taught that since comets have no observable parallax, they must travel 'beyond the moon's orbit'. Their trajectories were variously supposed to be rectilinear, circular or parabolic. Newton, applying his law of attraction to comets, determined their orbits on the supposition that they describe flattened ellipses which may be considered parabolic in the zone near the sun where they can be observed. This assumption greatly simplified the problem and led to no appreciable error when the eccentricity of the orbit was very great.

We have seen (p. 283) that Halley attempted to determine the orbit of the comet of 1682; he also tried to compute the orbits of comets whose appearance in the past was recorded with sufficient care: twenty-four in all. He found that two of these had practically the same orbital elements as the comet of 1682, and that there were three whose perihelia had been at the same distance from the sun, and whose periodic return (1531, 1607, 1682) suggested that they were one and the same object moving in an elliptical orbit with a period of 76 years. He also remarked that in the summer of 1681, when the comet was approaching its perihelion, it passed so close to Jupiter that the force exerted by that planet amounted to 1/50 of the sun's force.

On the basis of his calculations and observations, Halley then predicted that the comet would return in 1758. When, in fact, it did return—in 1759, having been delayed by the pull of Jupiter and Saturn—the Newtonian theory scored one of its greatest triumphs.

The Orbits of Comets

The next periodic comet was not detected until 1818. It was Encke's comet, which had previously appeared in 1795 and 1808 but whose periodic nature had merely been suspected. In the meantime, the identification of comets had been perfected by improvements of Newton's method of calculating orbits from three observations. Newton had provided no means of ascertaining the value of the mean distance in the case of the orbit's being elliptical, and this element could be determined only by means of its relation to the periodic time, deduced from three successive observations of the comet. The problem has no algebraic solution.

The problem of the parabolic orbit was solved by Olbers in 1790, who used Euler's formula (1744) linking, for two positions, the time interval, the radius and the chord. This formula is often associated with the name of Lambert, who rediscovered it independently a few years after Euler. Lambert was also one of the first to appreciate that the Milky Way was only one of many stellar systems.

The case of elliptic motions in general was treated theoretically by Laplace in 1780 and by Lagrange in 1778–1783; his methods have not been made full use of to this day.

Lunar Tables

The disturbing effects of planets on one another were discussed by Newton, who thought them so considerable that only the periodic intervention of a Supreme Being could offset them—a view which presented Leibniz with an excellent target for his critical shafts. In reality, these actions are far less dramatic than Newton thought and, in practice, they affect mainly the computation of lunar tables.

These tables, so essential an aid to navigation, continued to be rough and ready until the middle of the 19th century. The most famous were those of Halley and Mayer. Mayer's, which were printed posthumously in 1770, were found to come within the limit of accuracy fixed by the British Board of Longitude, and earned his widow an award of £3,000.

The Secular Acceleration of the Moon

Among the complex elements of the moon's motion, the *secular inequality* deserves special mention. In 1693, after an extensive comparison of ancient with modern eclipse records, Halley discovered that the mean motion of the moon had been becoming continually more rapid. T. Mayer subsequently fixed this *secular acceleration* first at 13″ and later at 18″ per century.

Now, by the law of areas, this acceleration can be shown to entail a continuous decrease of the distance separating the moon from the earth, and hence an ultimate collision between the two. This impending catastrophe caused general anxiety, which only abated in 1787 when Laplace announced that he had discovered the cause of the inequality in the gradual diminution of the mean action of the sun, arising from the secular diminution of the eccentricity of the terrestrial orbit. He added that once the earth has reached a circular orbit, and the orbit begins to open out again, the sun's mean action will increase and the acceleration of the moon's mean motion will be converted into a secular retardation.

Laplace computed the inequality first at 10″ and later at 14″ (the modern value is 25″). We know today that the observed values must, in fact, be corrected, since the unit of time—the mean solar day—is not uniform but subject to a secular increase resulting from the retardation of the earth's rotation. This effect is largely produced by the tides, a fact which Immanuel Kant had the genius to appreciate in 1754.

The Problem of n Bodies

The study of the moon's motion is intimately linked with the problem of perturbation, *i.e.* the problem of the mutual attraction of n material particles.

In the case of comets, whose mass is negligible, the problem is simplified: all that need be done is to calculate the perturbing effect of the largest or nearest planets. Clairaut, for instance, predicted the date on which Halley's comet would reach its perihelion after computing the actions of Saturn and Jupiter. His date, 13th April 1759, was one month behind the actual event. Clairaut's error would have been smaller still had he been in possession of more accurate values of the masses of the two planets.

A much more complicated problem was that of the disturbing effects of planets on one another. The first effect of this kind was discovered in 1675, when Halley observed an anomalous irregularity in the motions of Jupiter and Saturn. The theory of these two planets was proposed by the Paris Academy of Science as the subject of two prize essays in 1748 and 1752. Both prizes were won by Euler, who solved the problem by his now classical *variation of parameters* method. In this method, a general solution is found from n linearly independent particular solutions, which are multiplied by an arbitrary parameter. The arbitrary parameters are assumed to be undetermined functions of x. Their sum is substituted in the original equation, and the undetermined functions are determined so that the result is an identity.

Though Clairaut, d'Alembert, Euler, Lagrange and Laplace failed to solve the 'three-body' problem completely, they nevertheless produced correct formulae for treating the various cases independently. Among the most important results springing from their immense labours were the following:

In 1749, d'Alembert gave a more rigorous explanation of the phenomenon of precession than Newton, and a mathematical interpretation of nutation which was not to be bettered for a hundred years (by Poinsot).

Lagrange made the solution of the three-body problem dependent on the solution of a system of twelve differential equations—the classical Lagrange equations of celestial mechanics—which became the basis of all subsequent studies, and of the work of Le Verrier in particular. They also led to the computation of planetary tables.

Stability and Origin of the Solar System

In 1773, Laplace arrived at the important conclusion that from the time of the earliest recorded observations, the mean motions of Saturn and Jupiter had not been appreciably altered by their mutual attraction, though he left it uncertain whether an inequality might not exist among the terms involving the higher powers of the eccentricities and inclinations. Three years later, Lagrange established the general law that the mean distances of the planets are not subject to any secular variations whatsoever, at least within the first approximation.

As Newton had synthesized the knowledge of his time, so Laplace (*Mécanique céleste*, 1799–1825) analysed the knowledge of Newton's successors, to which he himself had contributed a large share.[1] In

[1] Other aspects of the work of Laplace will be treated in a later volume.

addition, Laplace also wrote a short work of synthesis, the *Exposition du système du monde* (1796), in which he put forward the hypothesis that the solar system had developed from a nebula. Although Laplace produced no quantitative evidence in its favour, his view was generally acclaimed as the first attempt to elaborate a truly scientific cosmogony.[1] His theory was later rejected, but has been recently resuscitated in a modified form.

THE DIMENSIONS OF THE SOLAR SYSTEM

Observations had supplied the orbits of the planets, and Kepler's third law their relative distances from the sun. The real distances could be found only after parallax measurements, *i.e.* after determining the angle subtended at a planet by the radius of the earth. From the parallax of one planet, that of the sun and the other planets can be deduced directly. (The moon represents a special problem.) Parallax measurements may be compared to the triangulations of surveyors, a planet being sighted from two stations an accurately measured distance apart.

The Cayenne Expedition

Cassini proposed to solve this problem by determining the parallax of Mars, at opposition, from simultaneous observations at two widely separated points on the earth. For this purpose, Jean Richer was sent by the *Académie des Sciences* to Cayenne (1672–1673), while Cassini, Römer and Picard observed the planet from various points in France. A comparison of their results showed that the parallax of Mars at opposition was 25″.

Since, at opposition, the distance of Mars is 0.38 of the radius of the terrestrial orbit, the solar parallax was established at 9″.5 (the correct value is 8″.8). Before this determination was made, all hypotheses on the dimensions of the solar system had been pure fantasy.

Though more than three hours separate the transit of a planet over the meridians of Paris and Cayenne, the resulting variations in the declination of Mars were small and known. The declination of the moon, on the other hand, varies so considerably from place to place that the precise determination of its parallax can be carried out only from stations on one and the same meridian. Accordingly, an attempt had been made in 1704 to measure it simultaneously in Berlin and in the Cape of Good Hope, but because of inadequate preparations the Cape observations had to be ignored.

[1] In his *Allgemeine Naturgeschichte und Theorie des Himmels*, Kant had put forward a similar hypothesis which is therefore often called the Laplace-Kant hypothesis.

The Operation of 1751

In 1751, during another opposition of Mars, simultaneous observations of the meridian altitudes of the planet and of the moon were made by Lacaille in the Cape, Lalande in Berlin, Cassini de Thury in Paris, Zanotti in Bologna, Bradley in Greenwich and Wargentin in Stockholm. A comparison of their results enabled Lacaille and Lalande to determine the lunar parallax at 57′ 11″ (the correct value is 57′ 02″). However, a similar value had been used much earlier by Newton, who had assumed that the moon was 60 terrestrial radii from the earth.

The observations also established a parallax of Mars of 27″.7 and hence a solar parallax of 10″.25. Though the 1751 operation failed to fulfil the high hopes that had been placed in it, what it did do was to provide the first example of scientific collaboration on an international scale.

Transits of Venus

The inferior planets, and especially Venus, come very close to the earth during conjunction, but since their transit then occurs in broad daylight, their positions cannot be related to that of the stars. Now, this difficulty is obviated whenever the planet is in conjunction at a node of its orbit, since, in that case, it is projected on the solar disk. In 1716, Halley suggested how the duration of this phenomenon, which is different at different terrestrial longitudes, could be used for the accurate determination of the solar parallax.

Transits of Venus are rare; they occur in eight-yearly groups of two, at intervals of 113 and 130 years. The transits of 1761 and 1769 were watched by so many astronomers, from Siberia to the Cape of Good Hope and from California to Tahiti, that we cannot possibly mention them all by name. We shall, however, report the fate of the most unfortunate among them—Guillaume Le Gentil.

Le Gentil was sent by the *Académie des Sciences* to Pondicherry, which he reached after a twelve months' voyage, only to be prevented from landing by the British. The transit of 1761 therefore took place while he was at sea. He decided to return in time for the next transit, and meanwhile cruised in the Indian and Pacific Oceans. When he returned to Pondicherry in 1769, the Seven Years War was over but a cloud obstructed his view. He reached France in 1771, to find that he had been presumed dead and that his heirs had divided his estate between them.

The results of the numerous observations of these two transits were so incompatible that they led to values of the solar parallax ranging from 8″ to 10″. After a detailed study of all the data, Encke adopted the value of 8″.58 in 1824. In 1870, better evaluations of the longi-

33 Leonhard Euler in 1737, after J. G. Brucker

34 An eclipse of the Sun in 1724

tudes of the observation stations brought the figure up to 8″.83, though this close approximation to the correct value (8″.80) was purely fortuitous.

It has since become clear that 18th-century astronomers took too sanguine a view of the possibility of measuring the solar parallax by timing transits of Venus, whose durations are, in fact, difficult to determine. The modern method is to rely on the oppositions of certain asteroids which come particularly close to the earth.

THE FIGURE OF THE EARTH

Early Theories

Newton was led to assume that the earth was not a perfect sphere, after considering the relative equilibrium of a homogeneous mass in uniform rotation. He *postulated* that the earth was originally in a fluid state and that its density was homogeneous;[1] he *proved* that the mutual gravitation of its particles, combined with the effects of the diurnal rotation, would occasion a flattening of the earth at the poles so as to make the ratio of the polar to the equatorial axis 229/230.

In 1690, Huygens published his *Discours sur la cause de la pesanteur*, in which he rejected Newton's idea of mutual attraction, assuming instead that each particle is attracted independently and with a constant force to the centre of the earth, the figure of the earth being determined by the relation between this force and the centrifugal force generated by the diurnal rotation. As a result, he concluded that the earth's ellipticity is 1/578.

Now, though Huygens based his view partly upon the fact that Richer, working in Cayenne in 1672, had been forced to shorten the pendulum of his clock, this effect had merely revealed that gravity diminishes towards the equator; it was not evidence of the oblateness of the earth's figure.

Geodesic Measurements

The correct form of the earth could be determined only by measurements of two meridian arcs in different latitudes.

This work had been begun by Picard who, in 1670, measured the arc from Sourdon to Malvoisine (1° 22′). In 1683, attempts were made to measure the larger arc from Collioure to Dunkirk, and the results were published and analysed in 1720 by J. D. Cassini. It appeared that the length corresponding to one degree of arc was greater at 6° south of Paris than it was at 2° north of Paris. Though

[1] Laplace alleged that Newton also assumed that gravity varies with latitude, an allegation which, though often repeated, has no substance in fact.

the difference had arisen from experimental errors, it seemed to prove that the Cartesians were right to regard the earth as an ellipsoid.

Peru and Lapland

Since Cartesianism was on the wane, these results were immediately questioned. In 1735, the *Académie des Sciences* sent a mission to measure the meridian arc on the Equator itself. The Peru expedition, which included Bouguer and La Condamine, worked for eight years in mountainous regions that made triangulation extremely arduous and hazardous, and in a climate that proved unfavourable to astronomical observation. To add to their troubles, they suffered from financial difficulties and from personal quarrels. Only because of Bouguer's determination was the mission successfully completed. The results which he brought back in 1744 were practically identical with those of the mission of Commander Bourgeois (1901–1906) who, moreover, suffered from the same difficulties and complained particularly that the Indians kept destroying their geometric points.

Meanwhile, Maupertuis, afraid that the investigations of the Peru expedition might lead to differences as great as those established between the degree at Paris and that at the equator, decided to lead a second expedition, this time towards the Pole. With Clairaut as an able assistant, this expedition left for Lapland in 1736 and there, within a year, measured an arc of one degree. As a result, Maupertuis was able to prove the earth's flattening towards the Pole beyond any doubt. However, comparisons with the degree at Paris led him to the erroneous conclusion that the difference in length between the two degrees was about 1,000 metres (the correct figure being about 300 metres).

In 1740, J. Cassini's measurement of a degree in France was checked by his son, Cassini de Thury, and increased by 300 metres. When the Lapland degree was remeasured in 1801–1803, it was found necessary to reduce the figure given by Maupertuis by 400 metres. It is evident that comparisons based on the work of Maupertuis were of no real value.

The Peru expedition, which returned seven years after Maupertuis' visit to Lapland, brought results which were consonant with his general findings. A remark in an account of the Peru expedition written in 1748 by one of the two Spanish officers who had accompanied Bouguer is of historical interest. The author felt compelled to qualify his reference to the motion of the earth by adding '*Pero aunque esta Hypóthesis sea falsa*' ('However, this hypothesis may be false'). Clearly, the Spanish Inquisition continued to be feared even in the 18th century.

MAP OF FRANCE

In 1744, Cassini de Thury, also called Cassini III, the first official Director of the Paris Observatory, commissioned the preparation of a topographical map of France based on geodesic triangulation. That map, the first of its kind, had a scale of 1/86,400 and was completed by Cassini IV, the last distinguished member of the Cassini dynasty, who presented it to the National Assembly in 1789.

STAR CATALOGUES

Of all the work of astronomers, the compilation of star catalogues was both the most laborious and one of the most essential, for the fixed stars serve as reference points for studying the motions of the sun and planets. In the 18th century most of this work was done by British astronomers.

After its foundation, the Greenwich Observatory was directed by Flamsteed, the first Astronomer Royal. Without assistants, and lacking adequate financial backing, Flamsteed constructed a mural arc of radius seven feet at his own expense. With that instrument he made systematic observations of the planets and the bright stars until his death in 1719; his partial results were published in 1712, against his will and on the insistence of Newton, who was impatient to verify his own theories. Flamsteed's main work, the *Historia Coelestis Britannica*, was published posthumously in 1725. It was the first modern star catalogue and showed the right ascensions and polar distances, as well as the longitudes and latitudes, of nearly 3,000 stars to within an error of 10″. Moreover, it contained various subsidiary tables, and its data were directly related to regular observations of the sun.

In 1719, Flamsteed was succeeded at the Royal Observatory by Edmund Halley, who, in 1721, procured a transit instrument 5 ft. 6 inches long with which he proceeded to make regular observations. Previously, Halley had taken advantage of a visit to St. Helena in 1677 to compile a star catalogue of the southern sky, but the atmospheric conditions there limited this to 350 stars.

The third Astronomer Royal, James Bradley, devoted his twenty years of office to transit observations. Bessel, who undertook to put them in order, published the results in his *Fundamenta astronomiae . . .* (1755) which showed the positions of 3,222 stars. Because of the accuracy of the observations from which they were obtained, these results became the basis not only of all 19th-century determinations of the proper motions of the stars, but also of successive computations of the precession.

With the exception of the star catalogues of Lacaille (400 bright stars, 1757) and of T. Mayer (1,000 zodiacal stars, 1756–1761), the Greenwich catalogues were the only ones to be generally adopted. Their superiority was assured by the fact that their right ascensions had been obtained with transit instruments.

In 1761, Tobias Mayer, Director of the Göttingen Observatory, published his famous correction formulae, which made allowances for instrumental deviations. Though he applied these specifically to his mural quadrant, it was the meridian circle which chiefly benefited from them. They provided rules for correction which led to increased accuracy and stability in astronomical instruments in general.

Star Counts

While some astronomers concentrated on recording the precise positions of the stars, others were content with making inventories of the sky. During an expedition to the Cape (1751–1752), Lacaille, working with an object glass of less than 1.5 cm., managed to make a count of 10,000 stars in the southern hemisphere. It was on Lacaille's station that the great Cape Observatory, the largest in the southern hemisphere, was erected in 1820.

In his *Histoire céleste française*, Jérôme de Lalande presented a list of observations, most of which had been made by his nephew Michel de Lalande from 1789 to 1798, with a view to establishing a systematic count of stars between the pole and declination −20°. The list consisted of 50,000 stars, including many hundreds visible with the naked eye but not mentioned by earlier writers.

NAVIGATIONAL ASTRONOMY

In the 17th century, the only means of determining longitude at sea was the unreliable method of consulting the ship's log. This method of 'dead-reckoning' sometimes led to errors of hundreds of miles and was felt to be so serious a deficiency that, as we saw, the Greenwich Observatory was founded for the express purpose of remedying it.

The problem can be solved by referring local time, as determined by the stars, to a chosen standard time, such as Greenwich mean time, or from observations of the moon when it is visible. The first method requires a reliable ship's chronometer (today we use radio signals) and the second accurate lunar tables.

The Sextant

The fundamental method of observation involves the measurement of angular distances. On the land the two observations necessary to determine an angle may be made successively, but at sea the motion of the ship requires that they be made simultaneously; this could not be done before the invention of a special nautical instrument. This instrument, which had been proposed by Newton in 1699, was first constructed in 1731 by the English optician John Hadley. His 'sea octant' consisted of a telescope and a movable mirror (index glass) which could be turned so as to reflect images on to a fixed mirror (horizon glass), silvered over half its surface and left clear over the remainder. The horizon glass was placed in line with the telescope so that the eye could see the horizon through the clear half; then the index glass was turned until the star under observation appeared simultaneously in the silvered half of the horizon glass. The angle through which the index must be turned is half the altitude of the star. In 1747, Captain John Campbell suggested that Hadley's octant be enlarged to a sextant, so as to measure angles up to 120°. The instrument evolved was very similar to that used in our day.

Chronometers

Marine chronometers cannot be regulated by pendulums, which the motion of the ship would throw out of order. In 1714 the British Government offered a prize of £20,000 for a method of determining longitude at sea to within an accuracy of 30′ at the end of a voyage to the West Indies. This was virtually a prize for an accurate chronometer and a similar, but smaller, prize was offered by the *Académie des Sciences*. These prizes were won by Harrison in England and Leroy and Berthoud in France.

In Harrison's early chronometer (1735), which is preserved at the Greenwich Museum, the place of the pendulum was taken by two massive balances, controlled by four balance springs. Compensation was provided for the variations of the resistance of the balance springs with varying temperature, by connecting the fixed ends of the springs to a manifold of brass and steel rods. By 1770, marine chronometers had been so greatly improved that tests at sea showed them to lose no more than a few seconds over a number of seasons.

Observations of the Moon

Since the moon travels across the sky at a rate of approximately ½′ per minute, its motion is more difficult to detect than that of the hands of a chronometer, but more reliable. While the motion can be referred to a neighbouring fixed star (method of lunar distances) by the marine sextant, the modern method is to observe occultations of stars by the moon. However, since occultations of the bright stars are rare, and since the other stars were still poorly catalogued, this method could not be used in the 18th century.

Both methods had been known of old. In 1499, in the course of his first voyage, Amerigo Vespucci took his bearings by measuring the separation between Mars and the moon soon after one of their conjunctions. However, the usefulness of all such measurements depends on the possibility of consulting reliable lunar ephemerides, whose compilation was accordingly encouraged by many governments and academies, and which engaged the attention of Clairaut, d'Alembert, Euler and Mayer. Their work contributed to the general progress of celestial mechanics but did little to further the determination of longitudes at sea, for which chronometers continued to be an essential instrument.

Today, the observation of occultations plays an important, though quite different, role in astronomy. The local time being known, the position of the moon enables observers to detect errors in the tables, and hence to evaluate the irregularities in the velocity of the earth's rotation.

* * *

In the course of the 18th century three new sciences were born: geodesy, astrometry and analytical celestial mechanics. Their methods were established, their tools perfected and their first-fruits reaped. The earth and the planets were measured and even weighed. But, just when the sky appeared to have lost its mystery, Herschel discovered Uranus, and other new bodies appeared in rapid succession. Clearly, the universe was far from being completely explored.

THE PHYSICAL SCIENCES

THE DISTINCTION WE HAVE MADE between 18th-century physical and theoretical sciences is based on the fact that whereas mechanics and astronomy had become highly mathematical, physics and chemistry had not.

This does not mean, however, that theoretical considerations played no part in 18th-century studies of the physical sciences. Considerable advances were, in fact, made in acoustics with the use of partial differential equations, the theoretical foundations of thermodynamics were laid, electrostatics and magnetism became Newtonian sciences and chemical theory was revolutionized.

Though the late 17th century had witnessed the remarkable experiments of Hooke, Boyle, von Guericke and Mariotte, and the organization of systematic observations on a large scale by the *Accademia del Cimento*, the Royal Society and the *Académie Royale des Sciences*, interest in science had remained restricted to a very small stratum of society. In the 18th century, on the other hand, science was spread by the universities and by public lectures to all educated men, and more gradually to the masses. The popularization of science was begun by Desaguliers in England, and by Boerhaave, van 's Gravesande and Musschenbroek in Holland, and the movement soon spread to the rest of Europe. Public lectures on experimental science became the order of the day, and the results were published in an ever-growing number of popular journals, particularly towards the middle of the century, which witnessed the most spectacular experiments in electricity, and towards the end of the century, when the brothers Montgolfier sent up their man-carrying balloons.

However, while the masses watched, the real work was still done by professional scientists and those enlightened amateurs who did not allow themselves to be seduced by the purely spectacular aspects of fashionable experiments. Hence the chapters that follow will describe not so much the sensational effects of science as the hard work of those who made them possible.

CHAPTER 1

The Spread of Newtonian Optics

The Construction of Optical Instruments

During the entire 18th century, no fundamental changes were introduced into prevailing methods of constructing optical instruments. What advances there were in the manufacture of microscopes were purely mechanical: interchangeable objectives, better stages, finer focusing, *etc*.

The manufacture of telescopes, which had always been impeded by technical difficulties in the way of the construction of large mirrors, was greatly improved when W. Herschel introduced better polishing techniques.

Achromatism

The manufacture of achromatic objectives came relatively late in the day, and only after a number of theoretical and practical problems had been solved.

Newton believed that refraction is invariably associated with dispersion, and hence that it is impossible to combine lenses into an achromatic system. His influence was so great that when an English magistrate, Chester More Hall, discovered the principle on which the optician George Bass was able to produce achromatic objectives in 1733, the new discovery was dismissed as a fraudulent trick.

However, in 1747 Euler established a set of formulae from which he concluded that Newton had been wrong. He also asserted that the human eye is, in fact, an achromatic optical system realized by Nature herself.

Newton's law of dispersion was analysed by Samuel Klingenstierna (1755), who corroborated Euler's view, and showed that by passing rays through prisms of water and glass in succession, it was possible to neutralize the dispersion without neutralizing the refraction or, by choosing a glass prism of different angle, to suppress the refraction and not the dispersion.

In 1757, John Dollond (1706–1761), a London optician who had previously criticized Euler, was persuaded by Klingenstierna to reconsider his opinion. After experimenting first with glass and water

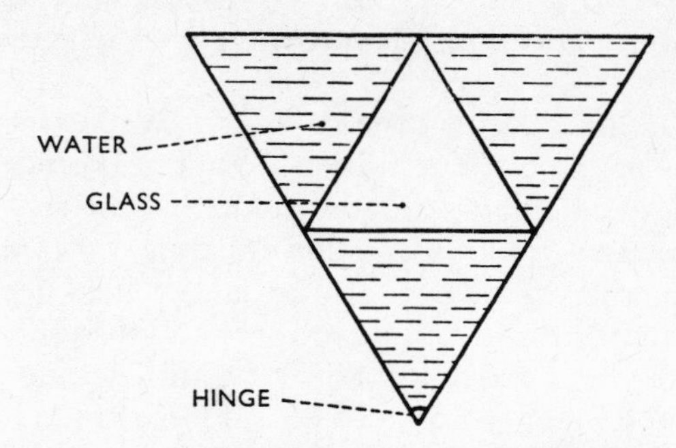

fig. 30 Experimental demonstration of achromatism. (Klingenstierna, 1755.)

lenses, Dollond eventually managed to reduce chromatic aberration to a minimum by using combined flint glass and crown glass lenses.

Despite the work of Euler, Fuss and, later, of Clairaut (1761), the manufacture of achromatic lenses continued to be a hit-and-miss affair. Even in England, the grinding of flint glass remained a matter of chance for a long time; on the Continent the problem was not solved until the beginning of the 19th century.

Experimental Discoveries

Bradley's discovery of the aberration of light (see p. 442) provided a means of checking, and hence of corroborating, Römer's measurements of the velocity of light.

In the late 17th and the early 18th centuries, a number of scientists made systematic studies of phosphorescence, a phenomenon which, according to Priestley, had first been observed by V. Cascariolo in 1630, and which continued to elude theoretical interpretation.

Late 18th-century physicists also took a keen interest in human vision—Buffon, Bouguer, Lambert, Rumford and Himly may be called the founders of physiological optics. However, measurements proved difficult to make and interpret, for there was no known way of eliminating the subjective factor. The first photometric studies were published in Buffon's *Essai d'optique sur la gradation de la lumière* (1728) and in Bouguer's *Traité d'optique* (1760). J. H. Lambert's *Photometria* (1760) presented a general survey of the new methods.

The Influence of Newtonian Theory on Philosophical Discussion

The success of his celestial mechanics, and the general recognition of Newton's genius, ensured his *Opticks* of a wide circle of readers, even outside the universities. One of Newton's most fervent admirers was

Voltaire, whose *Éléments de la philosophie de Newton* (London, 1738) emphasized the close connection between universal gravitation and optical phenomena.

According to Voltaire, light consists of small particles whose fundamental nature requires no definition. When solids act on these particles in some unspecified way they cause them to be reflected and refracted. Like Newton, Voltaire believed that the denser the medium, the greater the velocity of light in it. For instance, when a light ray passes from air into water, its proper motion is increased by the attraction of the water particles. Similarly, diffraction is caused by the attractive action of solid bodies. Voltaire added that the mutual attraction between particles of light and other particles, especially of glass, is not governed by the inverse square law but by an inverse cube law.

Voltaire also argued that though cohesion, hardness, capillarity and chemical reaction were due to attractive forces, the rotation of the earth about its axis and electricity and magnetism probably had different and unknown causes.

OPPONENTS OF NEWTONIAN OPTICS: MARAT AND GOETHE

Newton's optics also had a number of distinguished opponents, including particularly Marat and Goethe, whose opposition was based on misconceptions springing from their general philosophical views.

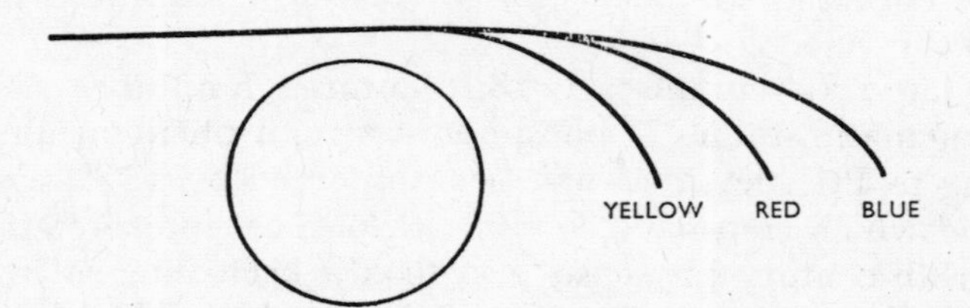

fig. 31 Decomposition of light in the vicinity of an opaque body according to Marat.

Marat was the founder of the strange science of 'peridioptrics', which was quickly forgotten, and which he expounded in his *Découvertes . . . sur la lumière constatées par une suite d'expériences nouvelles* . . . (1780). Its principles were the same as those of dioptrics, but its laws were quite different. According to Marat, all opaque bodies attract light rays passing in their vicinity with a force directly proportional to their surface density and to an affinity factor, and inversely proportional to the square of their distance from the rays.

Each of the three 'constituent' colours of light—yellow, red and blue—is attracted in a characteristic way by opaque bodies, but all three are refracted in the same way by transparent bodies. For this reason, Marat asserted that the rays in Newton's diffraction experiment must have been decomposed *before* they reached the prism. 'One must regret', Marat concludes, 'that this great genius [Newton] wasted so much of his time on so much idle research.'

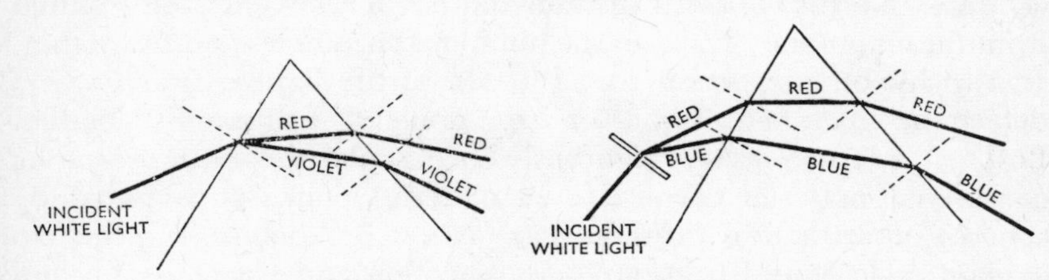

fig. 32 Dispersion according to Newton (left); deflection and refraction according to Marat (right).

The views of Goethe (*Beiträge zur Optik*, 1791; *Zur Farbenlehre*, 1810) were even more radically anti-Newtonian. His travels in Italy (1786) and his enthusiasm for Italian painting had gradually convinced Goethe that man and nature are one, and that neither could be explained by mathematical abstractions.

Goethe's views on optics were suffused with Platonic or Neo-Platonic notions. Thus he said: 'The eye is formed . . . so that the outer light may meet the inner. . . . It responds to darkness with light, to light with shadow, to one colour with another, complementary colour.'

Goethe's first experimental verification of his theory consisted of looking at a white wall across a prism. He found that the irizations appeared exclusively at the edges. (In fact, what he saw was a superposition of the various monochromatic images.) Hence he concluded that the 'border of shadow and light is the generator of all colours'. All colours are the result of a 'natural antagonism': colour is 'the action and the perception of light'. Like Plato, Goethe took the exaggerated view that the microcosm reflects the macrocosm completely. Thus he wrote to Eckermann: 'Had I not borne the world within me, I should have been blind for ever.'

Scientific Assessments of Newton's Theory: R. G. Bošković

Scientists criticized Newton's *Opticks* on quite different grounds. Most of its weaknesses had been shown up by Huygens and Leibniz, and Newton's disciples merely drew attention to the shortcomings of Newton's theory when they tried to refute its critics.

It is a remarkable fact that R. G. Bošković (1711–1787), who was a disciple of Newton, nevertheless struck a blow against Newton's theory when he showed that the rectilinear propagation of light is neither proven nor even demonstrable (*Dissertatio de lumine*, Rome, 1749).

Bošković also tried to clarify Newton's theory of fits. Newton had assumed that fits of easy transition and fits of easy reflection resulted from the combined actions of the luminous corpuscles and the aether. In this hypothesis, waves travel ahead of the light corpuscles and determine their admission or rejection by transparent bodies. Bošković adopted a more rigorously corpuscular theory, in which he considered material corpuscles as material points surrounded by spheres of attraction or repulsion. When he used this theory to explain opacity and transparency, reflection and transmission, and even double refraction and diffraction, he merely emphasized the pitfalls in the path of a purely corpuscular conception of light.

Euler

In 1735, Euler had drawn attention to a serious flaw in one of Newton's main arguments, namely that dispersion and refraction are proportional to each other, and that achromatic lenses are a theoretical impossibility.

From a full analysis of the optics of both Descartes and Newton, Euler concluded that Newton's universe, filled as it was with light corpuscles moving in all directions, was no emptier than Descartes' *plenum*. Moreover, he argued that Newton's theory was based on as improbable a hypothesis as were Descartes' postulates: the emission of light particles must lead to the exhaustion of the sources of light; the various motions of the light corpuscles must conflict; the propagation of light through transparent bodies presupposes the existence of pores running straight in all directions. Because of these objections, Euler adopted the view that light phenomena are produced by vibrations of an elastic aether, much as sound is produced by vibrations of the air. In that case, luminous bodies do not lose any of their luminous substance.

'Light is merely the agitation or perturbation of particles of the aether', Euler explained (*Letters to a German Princess*). Light travels much faster than sound simply because the aether is far less dense and far more elastic than the air. While we do not know what force causes its agitation, 'we must be content with ideas which, at least, do not outrage reason'.

According to Euler, 'opaque' (*i.e.* non-luminous) bodies do not reflect light rays, for if they did we should see the source of light reflected in them as by a mirror. What happens is that, when light falls on them, opaque bodies become agitated. Hence the rays they emit are their own rays which travel in all directions, whereas a mirror reflects external rays in straight lines.

Euler compared this phenomenon with acoustic resonance: just as the resonance of taut strings depends on the frequency of the external source of sound, so the pulsation of the molecules of opaque bodies (which produce the colour impression) depends on the frequency of the incident rays.

Whereas Newton had held that the colours of opaque bodies result from the selective absorption of the incident light, Euler believed that they were due to total absorption followed by selective re-emission. This explanation is similar to the one introduced by the modern theory of fluorescence and phosphorescence. In fact, Euler observed that certain opaque bodies continue to be luminous after the external source has ceased to act upon them. Such bodies have 'a particularly highly developed tendency to produce vibrations'.

Euler's theory did not eliminate the main difficulties raised by the wave theory which was then gaining ground, particularly since he was forced to introduce the aether and to endow it with a great many improbable characteristics. However, Euler pointed out certain gaps in Newton's theory of light which could no longer be neglected. As a result, physicists were forced to make a closer examination of the views of Malebranche, Grimaldi, Huygens and Leibniz. In this way, Euler prepared the field for the important work of Malus, Young and Fresnel.

The Principle of 'Natural Economy'

In the middle of the 18th century, another of Fermat's theories, his principle of natural economy (*cf.* p. 428), became the subject of renewed discussion. Fermat had shown that Snell's law of refraction results directly from the assumption that a light ray takes the path of least time in going from a point in the first medium to one in the second. But Fermat's deduction carried the corollary that light travels less rapidly in a dense than in a rare medium; this was a direct contradiction of the prevailing theories, both of Descartes and also of Newton, and was therefore rejected.

Fermat had still failed to distinguish between the principle of the shortest time and the principle of the shortest path. This was done by Leibniz in 1682, who contended that the path taken by a light ray is shortest when the product of its length and the resistance it meets is least. Like Fermat, he assumed the correctness of Snell's law and would therefore have reached the same impasse had he not postulated that the resistance of the medium is inversely proportional to the velocity of light in that medium. Thus, while defining the refractive index in the same way as Fermat (water resistance/air resistance > 1) Leibniz nevertheless arrived at the opposite conclusion (velocity in water/velocity in air > 1).

In 1744, Maupertuis, who was unaware of Leibniz's work in this field, propounded the theory (*cf.* p. 428) that refracted light travels, not along the shortest path, but along the path of least action, measured by multiplying the distance travelled in each medium by the velocity of light therein. According to Maupertuis, the action is least if the sine law is satisfied and when the velocity of light increases with the refractive power of the medium. Despite his application of a satisfactory law to a clearly defined 'action', Maupertuis was therefore led to erroneous conclusions.

This was not surprising, for before the principle of least action could be applied to light phenomena a more precise definition was needed of the quantity of action within the framework of wave theory. The connection between the principle and the general laws of mechanics was first established by Hamilton and Jacobi, and later generalized by Louis de Broglie in his work on quantum mechanics, based on the wave-corpuscle duality.

CHAPTER 2

Sound in the 17th and 18th Centuries

Vibrating Strings

Since the Greeks had studied the behaviour of vibrating strings, it is not surprising that modern acoustics began by taking up the same problem. Thus Galileo's *Discorsi* (1638) introduced the concept of the frequency of vibrations, explained that the relative pitch of two sounds depends on the ratio of their frequencies, and showed how the frequency of a vibrating string is affected by its length, tension and mass. At about the same time, Mersenne proved experimentally that the frequency of a stretched string varies inversely as the square root of its mass per unit length, and directly as the square of the tension. He also observed that a stretched string produces not only a fundamental note but also its harmonics, the study of which he did not, however, pursue.

That task was performed by W. Noble and T. Pigot; the first results were presented by Wallis in 1677. Similar but independent studies were made by Joseph Sauveur (1700), who determined the position of the nodes and antinodes of vibrating strings by means of paper riders. He suspected the existence of stationary waves, and used beats to determine the frequency of vibrating bodies.[1] Despite the embryonic state of his theory, Sauveur was able to establish that what he called the 'higher harmonics' of a vibrating string are in simple numerical ratio to the basic tone.

According to Louis Carré (1709) and Philippe de la Hire (1716), the sound produced by a vibrating string results from the 'trembling' of its molecules; according to Newton it results from the vibration of the string itself. In order to solve this and related problems, 18th-century physicists carried out a series of fundamental studies on vibration, with which they opened a brilliant chapter of theoretical mechanics. In 1715, Brook Taylor enunciated his famous formula, which in its modern form connects the frequency (n) of vibration of

[1] Towards the middle of the 18th century, Sorge, Romieu and Tartini attracted attention to what are now called combination-tones, which are produced whenever two pure tones are sounded together.

a string with its length (L), tension (T), and mass per unit length (m):

$$n = \frac{1}{2L}\sqrt{\frac{T}{m}}$$

Daniel Bernoulli was the first to express the form and motion of vibrating strings by means of differential equations. In 1747, d'Alembert stated and integrated the fundamental differential equation of wave motion:

$$\frac{\partial^2 y}{\partial^2 x} = a^2 \frac{\partial^2 y}{\partial t^2}$$

where y is the transverse displacement of the wave travelling in the direction of the x axis.

The interpretation of two arbitrary functions in the solution of that equation led to long discussions which contributed to the rapid development of the theory of partial differential equations by Euler, d'Alembert, Daniel Bernoulli, Monge, Lagrange and Fourier. Daniel Bernoulli and Lagrange began the theoretical study of vibrating rods; Bernoulli and Euler also analysed the vibrations of rings, bells and various membranes.

These theoretical studies gave rise to a number of experimental investigations. Ernst Friedrich Chladni (1756–1827), in particular, demonstrated the existence of longitudinal and torsional vibrations, besides transverse vibrations. Chladni made a detailed study of the vibrations of disks, square plates, *etc.*, and hit upon the idea of scattering sand upon horizontally clamped plates and then setting them into vibration by drawing a violin bow across their edges. The sand shifted from the vibrating to the non-vibrating parts of the plates to form what are known as 'Chladni's figures'. He also experimented with bells filled with water, and analysed the resulting surface waves.

Sound Waves

The concept of waves and the propagation of vibrations by a movement called 'undulatory' began to take form in the late 17th century. Huygens' *Traité de la lumière* (1690) summarized the prevailing views, while Grimaldi's *Physico-mathesis* (1665) compared the propagation of light to that of water waves. Father Ango (*Optique*, 1682) had this to say of wave motion:

> It is the motion used by contemporary philosophers to liken the rarefactions and compressions of parts of the air which, according to Aristotle, are needed for the production of sound, to the waves which appear on the surface of still water when a small stone is thrown into it.

35 Microscope belonging to the Duc de Chaulnes

36 Launching a balloon in Paris (1783)

According to Father Ango, the only distinction between sound and light waves is that the latter produce unusually rapid vibrations in a much rarer medium than air—the aether. Huygens adopted the same view; he also considered both sound and light as resulting from longitudinal vibrations. Newton, on the other hand, explained that sound results from molecular collision effects, which spread out uniformly in all directions with a velocity proportional to the square root of the elasticity of the medium divided by its density. This view was not proved empirically until 1826, when Laplace substituted adiabatic for isothermal compressibility. In short, though the problem of sound waves was not solved in the 17th century, it had at least been posed.

Otto von Guericke, the inventor of the pneumatic pump (1650), showed that sound, unlike light, is not propagated in a vacuum. Boyle, Denis Papin and Hauksbee continued his experiments, and demonstrated that it is indeed the air which transmits sound vibrations. However, it was not until 1779 that Priestley was able to show that the intensity of sound varies with the density of the gases in which it is propagated. Derham, experimenting on the velocity of sound along Newton's lines, found that the velocity of sound is independent of the intensity, but that it is greater when there are easterly or northerly winds than when there are westerly winds. Mersenne applied his special studies of the reflection of sound to the measurement of its velocity. In 1671 Morland invented the speaking trumpet. From all these investigations and discoveries, Father Ango concluded that sound is more than a pure 'quality'. Though he lacked the correct terminology, he made a clear distinction between intensity (amplitude) and pitch (frequency), thus showing how much progress the analysis of sound had made in the 17th century.

The 18th century brought many further developments. In 1738, the Commission appointed by the Paris Academy of Science, which included Jacques Cassini, Maraldi and Lacaille, established that the velocity of sound in air is 1,106 ft. per second, thus improving upon the earlier results of Mersenne, Gassendi, Borelli and Viviani. The Commission also showed that the velocity of sound is independent of the pressure of the medium, but increases with its temperature.

Because liquids were thought to be incompressible, most 17th-century physicists held that sound could not be propagated in them. It was only in 1743 that Nollet, after diving into the Seine, was able to prove that sound signals can be heard under water and that their pitch is not altered by the change of medium. By using water from which all the air had been expelled, he was also able to show that sound is not conducted in water by dissolved air. In 1791, Pérolle demonstrated by various experiments that sound travels farther in a liquid than it does in air. Chladni measured the velocity of sound in various solids and gases.

In short, 18th-century physicists provided better knowledge of the propagation of sound in air, and demonstrated that the frequency of sound vibrations is not affected by the medium, thus preparing the ground for the study of interference and resonance, and for the analysis of complex sounds.[1]

The Human Voice

Plato had argued that the human voice obeys the laws of harmony, and that vocal sounds are different combinations of high and low notes. Samuel Reyher (*Mathesis mosaïka*, 1690) observed that every sound consists not only of a fundamental note but also of its overtones. Taking up this idea, Rameau (*Nouveau système de musique théorique*, 1726) studied the sounds produced when different vowels are sung, and made the first attempt at vocal analysis. C. F. Hellwag (1780) and H. G. Flörke (1803–1804) confirmed Reyher's assumption that different vowels are associated with different tones.

No further progress was made until the discovery of the vocal cords, and the invention of special resonators whereby the ear could be taught to distinguish between various complex sounds.

The Ear

Sauveur (1700) was probably the first to study the limits of hearing of the human ear. Euler (*Tentamen novae theoriae musicae*, St. Petersburg, 1739), who studied the same problem, stressed the difficulty of eliminating the subjective factor. Their actual results were less important than the fact that they expressed them in terms of vibrations. Even before the auditory process was understood, there were a number of studies in consonance and dissonance, particularly by Euler, Tartini (*Trattato di musica*, 1754) and d'Alembert (*Éléments de musique*, 1762). However, all these studies were limited to the investigation of the simple ratios of sound frequencies received simultaneously by the ear.

* * *

To sum up, the mathematical analysis of the vibration of strings and other sounding bodies remained incomplete until the 19th century, when the use of Fourier's series at last turned acoustics into an exact science.

[1] The effects of overtones on the quality or timbre of sound were suspected by Rameau (1726) and clearly understood by Monge (towards 1780), but were ignored for almost a century.

CHAPTER 3

Heat in the 17th and 18th Centuries

The First Thermometers

Ever since ancient times it had been known that when a 'hot' body is brought into the proximity of a 'cold' body, the first surrenders its heat to the second until both are in thermal equilibrium. It was also known that most bodies expand when they are heated. However, it was not until the 17th century that Galileo (*c.* 1592), Santorio (1612), Bacon (1620), Torricelli and von Guericke (1672) began to use thermal expansion in the construction of thermometers—that is to say, for quantitative measurements. The first of these instruments was a vessel containing air whose expansion or contraction moved a column of liquid up or down in a narrow open tube. However, since increases in atmospheric pressure cause decreases in the volume of the air, this kind of instrument responded to atmospheric pressure fluctuations as well as to temperature fluctuations. The readings were therefore inconclusive.

Advances in Thermometry

In 1688, and again in 1703, Amontons suggested a more reliable method when he proposed to measure temperature by the variations in pressure of a fixed mass of gas maintained at constant volume. In this way, he was led to the concept of absolute zero, defined as the temperature at which the gas pressure vanishes completely. He used a tube of mercury to indicate the changes in pressure.

In 1693, Renaldini had been the first to propose that the boiling point of water be used as a fixed thermometric point. His suggestion was not taken up, doubtless because the boiling point was found by G. H. Fahrenheit to be inconstant in the absence of corrections for variations in atmospheric pressure. It was not, in fact, until later that Boyle, Papin and Mariotte, and above all Amontons, showed how to overcome this difficulty. Fahrenheit, in 1714, based his scale on two other fixed points, but his great contribution was to use the expansion of mercury instead of a gas, and he showed how to purify it sufficiently by straining it through leather. This was a great practical

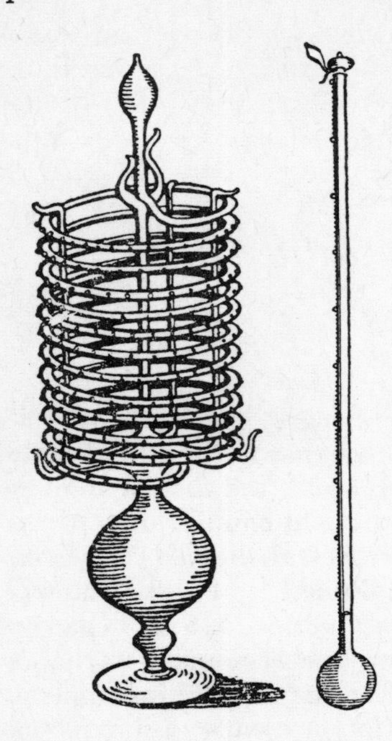

fig. 33 Two thermometers of the 'Accademia del Cimento', c. 1660. (Museo di storia della scienza, Florence.)

convenience, though Dalton and Gay-Lussac, and later Magnus and Regnault, were able to show that 'perfect gases' are still the ideal thermometric substances, and that measurements of their uniform expansion could obviate the use of any arbitrary fixed point.

The choice of the actual thermometric scale was immaterial provided it was related to two stable and easily reproduced temperatures. Galileo had divided the difference between the temperature of ice and the blood-heat of a cow into 40°, while Fahrenheit, assuming human blood-heat to be 100°, and the coldest available freezing-mixture to be 0°, found the freezing-point of water to be 32° and its boiling-point 212°. (When Fahrenheit's boiling-point became accepted as a standard, his temperature for blood-heat had to be modified to 98·4°.) René de Réaumur, in 1731, preferred 0° for the freezing-point of water and 80° for its boiling-point, while A. Celsius, in 1742, suggested 100° to represent the freezing-point and 0° the boiling-point. In 1750, M. Strömer adopted Celsius' calibration but inverted the scale, thus giving us the present 'centigrade' measure denoted by 'C' (which, nevertheless, was intended to commemorate Celsius).

Two Famous Discoveries

Until the end of the 18th century, the problem of thermometry was therefore closely bound up with that of thermal expansion. In this connection we must now mention two famous discoveries: van 's Gravesande's demonstration that when a ring or tube expands, the internal diameter increases as the external diameter, and Hope's demonstration (1805) of the anomalous expansion of water. Hope showed that between 0°C (the melting point of ice) and 4°C the volume of a given mass of water diminishes as the temperature increases, but above 4°C water behaves like all other liquids and its volume increases with the temperature. This implies that water has a maximum density at 4°C.

The Theory of Caloric: Specific Heat

A great advance in the theory of heat was made when Joseph Black (1760) introduced the distinction between temperature and 'quantity of heat'. According to Black, heat must be considered as a fluid—the 'caloric'—which is as indestructible as matter. When a body is heated, it accumulates caloric, when it cools it loses caloric. The unit of the quantity of heat is the amount of caloric fluid needed to raise the temperature of a given body of mass m by 1 °C, or the quantity of heat surrendered by the body of mass m when it cools by 1 °C. If that cooling produces an increase of temperature of 1 °C in another body of mass m', it follows that in order to raise a mass m of the second body by 1 °C, m/m' the amount of heat must be supplied to it. That quantity is its 'capacity for heat' or its *specific heat*, as we now call it. Once the specific heat of various bodies is established, it does not matter which is chosen as a standard. J. C. Wilcke (1732–1796) arrived at similar conclusions independently.

The Conduction of Heat

It was commonly known that certain bodies, and particularly metals, conduct heat well, while others, like wood, are bad conductors. At the end of the 18th century, Jan Ingenhousz (1789) and Rumford (1792) inserted various rods, all of the same dimensions and all covered uniformly with wax, into a metallic trough containing hot water. By measuring the length of each rod from which the wax had melted, they established the relative conductivity of the rods, thus introducing the first quantitative measurements of conductivity. In 1760, Black also introduced the concept of latent heat, when he showed that the melting of a fixed mass of ice requires a constant quantity of heat. Lavoisier and Laplace designed the first practical ice calorimeter, which was perfected by Bunsen but was later discarded in favour of Berthelot's calorimeter, based on Black's original 'method of mixtures', *i.e.* the measurement of the quantity of heat by the rise in temperature of a given mass of water.

The Problem of the Conservation of Energy

Now, the 'method of mixtures' was generally thought to corroborate the theory that the caloric fluid is indestructible, a theory which continued to prevail even though it was known that friction releases heat; that heat could be transformed into motion, as Denis Papin had shown; that mechanical energy is always conserved, as was established by Galileo, Huygens, Leibniz and Jean Bernoulli; and that perpetual motion is impossible, as had been proved by Stevin on the principle of the conservation of energy. As a result, the most far-fetched hypotheses were put forward, including the idea that the calorific capacity of bodies can be changed by rubbing. It was not until 1798 and 1799 that Rumford's and Davy's experiments proved beyond the shadow of a doubt that no such changes occur, and that heat, too, is subject to the general law of the conservation of energy.

The Beginnings of the Kinetic Theory of Gases

In 1728, Daniel Bernoulli had suggested that the pressure exerted by a gas on the wall of its containing vessel was the result of innumerable collisions between the atoms and the wall. In that hypothesis, the temperature of a gas was related to the velocity of its atoms, *i.e.* to their kinetic energy. It was not, however, until the 19th century that Maxwell and—in particular—Boltzmann were able to develop this theory more fully.

The Steam Engine

By his great discovery of the 'steam engine' (1681) Papin demonstrated that when water is heated in a closed vessel enough pressure is generated to raise a heavy lid. Starting from this principle, Papin described, first in 1687 and much better in 1707, a steam engine of which a model was made in 1698. In that year, also, Savery invented the first practicable steam pump for use in mines, and about 1710 Newcomen built the first beam engine which was later improved by James Watt. These were 'suction' engines and worked by atmospheric pressure when the steam in a cylinder was condensed. It fell to Watt to invent the 'expansion' engine in 1763, in which the pressure of the steam itself was used. When Watt further improved this by introducing the slide-valve and centrifugal governor (1776), the economic success of the steam engine was assured. The first Watt engine was installed in a mine in 1784 and by 1800 his engines were in daily use in 52 mines and 84 cotton mills in the north of England.

CHAPTER 4

Electricity and Magnetism in the 18th Century

THE SCIENTIFIC REVOLUTION that was begun in the 17th century had been almost completed by the beginning of the 18th. Newton's letter describing his 'new theory about light and colours', which was a model of experimental analysis and theoretical induction, was written in 1672 (the *Opticks* appeared in 1704); the first edition of Newton's *Principia*, a model of physico-mathematical synthesis, was published in 1687. In 1660, Otto von Guericke developed his electrostatic machine, the first of many inventions that were to open vast new possibilities to physicists. He described it in 1672, together with the experiments which the machine had enabled him to make.

Even so, advances in magnetism and electricity remained sporadic, and it was not until the end of the 18th century that precise quantitative measurements were able to fit these disciplines into the general framework of Newtonian science. There were many reasons for this delay. First of all, electrostatic experiments proved capricious, and the behaviour of magnets, each with two poles, seemed to elude mathematical analysis.

Proud of their rejection of animist theories and anxious to find alternative explanations, the 18th-century physicists began to encumber science with mechanical models which hid the real facts behind the notions of subtle fluids, atmospheres and vortices. As Hooke remarked in 1703, they preferred to rely on pleasant fables rather than make the sustained effort of advancing science by experiment and precise deduction.

Finally, they misunderstood or forgot von Guericke's experiments and even his electrical machine, so that these experiments had to be rediscovered some forty years later. The only 18th-century electricians who can be read with enjoyment and profit today are Charles François de Cisternay Du Fay and Benjamin Franklin, both of whom were brilliant observers and lucid theorists.

Francis Hauksbee

In 1675, the Abbé Picard, a Parisian astronomer, made a curious observation: carrying a barometer at night, he noticed that each violent motion of the mercury caused the appearance of a bluish light inside the tube. During the next thirty years this phenomenon was generally explained as due to the presence of phosphorus and sulphur in the mercury.

In 1705, Francis Hauksbee, a pupil of Boyle from whom he had learned vacuum techniques (two important improvements of von Guericke's pump were made by Boyle and Hauksbee respectively), began his systematic studies of what he called the 'fine purple light'. His experiments, though inconclusive, may be called the first empirical investigations of electrical discharges in rarefied gases.

Hauksbee showed that the phenomenon was due to the friction of the mercury on the sides of the glass tube. To extend his proof to other materials, he constructed a machine for rotating amber on wool in an exhausted vessel. With it, he repeated the earlier but forgotten observations of Cabeo and von Guericke on electrical repulsion. He also observed the 'induced' glow in an exhausted glass sphere when another, rubbed, sphere is brought near it, and would therefore have been the discoverer of electrostatic induction had he been able to grasp the connection between electricity and the luminous phenomenon he had observed. As it was, he believed that the luminosity was caused by the friction of the 'effluvia' of the first sphere on the second.

GRAY AND DU FAY

Twenty years later, the rhythm of electrical discoveries was greatly speeded up when Stephen Gray (1666?–1736) and Charles François Du Fay (1698–1739) carried out more careful experiments, from which they were able to deduce a number of general principles. As a result, they were able to provide a more systematic description of electrical phenomena than any of their predecessors.

The Discovery of Electrical Conduction

The starting-point of Gray's electrical studies was a chance observation made in February 1729. (Von Guericke had made a similar observation fifty-five years earlier, but his record had been completely forgotten, partly because he had failed to follow the matter up.)

Gray found to his surprise that when a corked glass tube was excited, not only the tube but also the cork attracted and then repelled a feather. He concluded that the tube must have communicated its attractive virtue to the cork.

He next took a wooden rod and thrust one end of it into one of the corks and the other end through a hole in an ivory ball, and obtained the same results. He then tried longer and longer rods, and finally wires or pack-thread, the longest of which was 34 ft., to connect the excited tube with the ball. He found that the attractive power continued to be communicated.

In June 1729, Gray and his friend Granvil Wheeler found that the experiment broke down when the conducting lines were suspended in a horizontal position by means of pack-thread. Wheeler suggested that silk, being smaller than pack-thread, would give better results because it would carry away fewer effluvia, and in fact, using silk, they managed to transmit the influence through 293 ft. When they next used brass wire and again failed, they concluded that success depended not on the suspension lines being small, but on their being of silk.

When the effluvium comes to the wire or pack-thread that supports the line, it passes by them to the timber, to which each end of them is fixed, and thus goes no farther forward in the line that is to carry it to the ivory ball.

Although he did not use the terms conductors and insulators, Gray had, in fact, discovered the fact that certain materials are good conductors of electricity, while others are not. More interested in making observations than in theorizing about them, he failed to investigate whether silk was, in fact, the only insulator. Gray and Wheeler finally succeeded in conducting an electric charge from a glass rod through 886 ft. of damp thread.

Electrical Induction

Gray's other important discovery was that of induced charges, or electrification by influence. Having suspended a lump of lead from the ceiling by a thread, he brought a rubbed glass tube near it, and found that the lead attracted and repelled brass filings. He concluded that the electrical virtue can be transmitted *without contact.*

Some years later, Du Fay repeated these experiments, publishing his results in 1733. His first and second papers were remarkable both for their lucidity and for their fairness: he acknowledged his indebtedness to his predecessors, and particularly to Otto von Guericke, whose work in this field thus came to be known.

Having verified that 'not all bodies can become electrified by themselves' (by friction), Du Fay went on to show that 'they can all acquire a considerable [electrical] virtue when the tube [of rubbed glass], wood, metals or liquids are brought near them', provided only that they are insulated by being stood on 'a support of glass or of sealing-wax'.

Du Fay, like Gray, was primarily an experimenter, but though he was prone to eschew theoretical speculations, defining electricity simply as 'the property of attracting light bodies', he nevertheless tried to deduce some basic principles from his observations.

Thus he ended his third paper (1733) with the following conclusion:

> We are content, for the present, to have recognized and established as a principle that the bodies least likely to become electrical by themselves are those which are the most easily attracted and which transmit electrical matter farthest and most abundantly, whereas those which have the greatest propensity to become electrified by themselves are those which are the least suitable of all to acquire extraneous electricity and to transmit it over a considerable distance.

This was the first time that Gilbert's distinction between electrics and non-electrics in themselves had been related to the scale of increasing conductivities. (By his idea that electrical matter is transmitted, Du Fay, like Gray, was using an image suggested by the experiments themselves.)

The Discovery of Two Kinds of Electricity

Du Fay was also the first to assert that there are two types of electricity.

> I had imagined that an electrical body may perhaps attract all those that are not electrical and repel all those which have become electrical by its approach or by the communication of its virtue.
>
> But what disconcerted me prodigiously was the following experiment. Having raised a gold leaf by means of the tube (of electrified glass, which repelled it after attraction and caused it to float in the air), I brought close to it a piece of rubbed copal [resin]; the leaf came and attached itself to its edge. . . . I must confess that I had expected the opposite effect, since, according to my reasoning, the copal and the gold leaf, which are both electrified, should have repelled each other.

Du Fay then recorded similar results with amber and sealing-wax.

> But when I brought an electrified ball of rock crystal up to the leaf, it repelled the leaf just as the tube had done. . . . Finally I could no longer doubt that glass and rock crystal had precisely the opposite effect of resin, amber and sealing-wax, so that the leaf which was repelled by the former because of its electricity was attracted by the others; this made me think that there might well be two different kinds of electricity. . . .

After a number of control experiments, Du Fay concluded:

> Thus there exist two electricities of distinct natures, to wit that of transparent and solid bodies like glass, crystal *etc.*, and that of bituminous or resinous bodies like amber, copal, sealing-wax *etc.* Both kinds repel all such as are of the same electricity as their own, but, on the contrary, attract all such as are of different electricity. . . . Bodies which are not electrical can (if they are insulated) acquire either of these two electricities, when their effects become similar to those of the bodies which have communicated the electricity to them. . . . I shall call the one resinous electricity and the other vitreous electricity.

The preceding quotations show how rigorously Du Fay deduced his scientific principles from observations. Hence it seems odd that, under the influence of Descartes, he should have developed—though incidentally—a vortical theory first of electrical, and later of magnetic, attractions and repulsions.

Later Studies

In a work published in 1731, Du Fay described the results he had obtained with two magnetometers. In 1737, he published two further papers on this subject, in which he mentioned how the electric forces can be compared accurately by the separation of the ends of a freely suspended thin wire. He was, in fact, describing the first of many pith ball, gold leaf and wire electroscopes.[1]

From 1734 until Gray's death in 1736, Du Fay exchanged many letters with his English colleague on the subject of electrical sparks. In the course of this correspondence, Gray remarked that whereas an electrified object surrenders its electricity gradually and silently when a pointed conductor is brought into its vicinity, it produces a sudden discharge accompanied with a spark when a thick rod is brought near it. He added: 'One day, we shall perhaps discover a means of collecting larger quantities of this electric fire which, many experiments suggest, may be of the same nature as lightning.'

The First Successes of Gray and Du Fay

Gray's work was continued by J. T. Desaguliers (1683–1744), who coined the term 'conductor', and whose remarkable *Course of Experimental Philosophy* exerted a profound influence on Benjamin Franklin. Du Fay's pupil, the Abbé Nollet, was above all a great popularizer of science. His theory of simultaneous affluences and effluences (1746) was 'one of those Cartesian theories which teach nothing and predict even less' (Barbeu Dubourg, 1773).

[1] Du Fay also made an important discovery in optics, namely the relation between crystalline structure and double refraction.

ELECTRICAL MACHINES AND THE LEYDEN JAR

Technical improvements and an accidental observation gave rise to a quick succession of important discoveries from 1745 onwards.

The Development of Electrical Machines

Gray had carried out his experiments with a glass tube, and Du Fay with rods of different materials. However, between 1743 and 1745 von Guericke's and Hauksbee's crude electrical machines were so much improved, particularly in Germany (Bose, Gordon, Winkler *etc.*) that they began to replace all other methods of electrification. In most of these machines, a large sphere or cylinder of glass was rapidly rotated by a belt drive, while the experimenter, standing on the ground, held his hand against it. Later, a leather cushion replaced the experimenter's hand and the electricity was collected by a broad strip of metal ribbon, woven of fine wire, which brushed against the top of the sphere. This 'collector' was attached to a gun-barrel suspended by silk threads, which served as a single pole. In this way, noisy sparks could be produced, to the delight of all those who flocked to watch the experiments.

The Discovery of the Leyden Jar

Public enthusiasm became greater still with the invention of the Leyden jar. This discovery had its roots in the common belief that the gradual leakage of electricity, due to the 'evaporation of electrical matter', could be reduced by electrifying water in an insulated bottle. Experiments were carried out independently by Ewald von Kleist, a Pomeranian parson, in October 1745, and by Pieter van Musschenbroek, professor of physics at Leyden, in January 1746.

Von Kleist filled a bottle with water and then plunged a nail through the cork. Holding the bottle in one hand, he applied the nail first to the gun-barrel, the pole of his electrical machine, and then to a non-insulated object, when an extremely strong spark was produced. When he used his other hand as the object he felt a violent shock. He therefore concluded that 'the human body must play some part in the effects'.

Musschenbroek repeated the experiment independently, but with the bottle resting on a table. Thus he realized that the effects had nothing to do with the observer. He wrote at once to Réaumur, who communicated the contents of the letter to the *Académie des Sciences*. The Abbé Nollet commented thus on Musschenbroek's discovery:

> This surprising experiment gave a great boost to electricity, which henceforth became a general subject of conversation. . . . All the electricians of Europe tried to repeat it, and to study its significance.

New Experimental Discoveries

In 1746, Benjamin Wilson wrote that 'the amount of electrical matter in the bottle is proportional to the thickness of the glass and to the surface of the non-electric bodies [conductors] in contact with its internal or external surfaces'. In the same year, L. G. Le Monnier thought of connecting the plates of a condenser by means of a long metal wire. He observed the resulting discharge phenomena and had, in fact, carried out the first experiment in current electricity. He tried to measure the speed of the flow but could show only 'that electrical matter travels through an iron wire with a speed at least thirty times greater than that of sound'. This conclusion was confirmed by the more comprehensive experiments of Watson and other members of the Royal Society.

Le Monnier also established that 'electricity is communicated to like bodies according to their surface area rather than according to their mass'.

Electrical Theories

It was Le Monnier whom Diderot and d'Alembert commissioned to write the articles on magnetism and electricity in the French Encyclopedia. The following passage from it is a good illustration of the ideas that were held at the time:

> Though physicists hold divided views on the cause of electricity, they all agree on the existence of electrical matter, concentrated more or less on electrified bodies. They hold that the movement of this electrical matter produces the electrical effects we perceive, though they explain the causes and direction of these movements in different ways. . . . As nothing is yet known about the essence of electrical matter, it is impossible to define it except by its principal properties.

At that time, therefore, the existence of an electrical substance or fluid was taken for granted, and the propagation of the 'electrical virtue' and its accumulation in the Leyden jar had become well-known phenomena. However, the existence of two electrical fluids, which Du Fay's discoveries ought to have suggested, was not yet suspected. Du Fay had been far too anxious to keep to the facts, and was far too accustomed to Cartesian views, to state a two-fluid theory in formal terms.

Moreover, electrical (and magnetic) experiments had all been described in terms of effluvia, virtues, matter, vortices, fluids and atmospheres, so that, as Le Monnier's articles in the French Encyclopedia show, the modern concepts of charge and field failed to emerge from the confusion.

The word 'charge' was invented by Franklin, though he used it merely as a special term for electrical 'atmosphere', and these concepts did not become clarified until Coulomb introduced quantitative considerations. Even after the work of Ampère and Faraday the 'reality' of electric charges and magnetic poles continued to be discussed. The question was not really settled until the discovery of the electron and the proton in the 20th century.

THE WORK OF BENJAMIN FRANKLIN

Watson's Experiments

William Watson (1715–1787), Franklin's great precursor, is chiefly remembered for his observation that electric sparks are less intense when the operator turning the electric machine stands on an insulated platform, for his conclusion that the 'electrical fire' can only travel from the ground to the gun-barrel if the two are connected by a chain of non-electric bodies, and for his ingenious demonstration that 'the electrical force always describes a circuit'. The demonstration required two lines of persons, four to a line, each standing on wax. Persons A, B, C, D formed a chain by grasping hands, and so did persons E, F, G, H. A grasped an electrified bottle and H the gun-barrel; if D then touched E, all felt the shock, but if D touched F, E was not in the circuit and did not feel the shock. From this and similar experiments, Watson concluded that 'the glass globes circulate the electrical fire which they receive from friction against the hand of man, and which is constantly supplied to these last from the floor'. He must therefore have had a vague idea of electrical quantity and its conservation.

On the other hand, he propounded a complicated mechanistic theory based on the belief that an 'electrical aether' extends to a considerable distance around charged bodies. 'The electrical aether is much more subtile than common air . . . since it passes to a certain depth . . . through all known bodies. . . . It has the property of extending itself round excited electrics and non-electrics to a considerable distance . . . and of carrying with it all the light bodies it encounters.' To explain electric repulsion as well as electric attraction, Watson adopted Nollet's theory of effluences and affluences.

Clearly, an entirely new approach to the subject was needed, and only a man of genius could sweep away all the mechanistic and metaphysical lumber handed down by Lucretius, Descartes and their successors. Such a man was Benjamin Franklin.[1]

[1] Franklin's work is also discussed on pp. 625–627.

BENJAMIN FRANKLIN: THE CONSERVATION OF ELECTRIC CHARGE; POSITIVE AND NEGATIVE ELECTRICITY

Benjamin Franklin (1706–1790) made his first discovery, 'the wonderful effect of pointed bodies both in drawing off and throwing off the electrical fire', in 1747. (The same observation had been made previously by von Guericke and Gray, but Franklin was unaware of this.) Though it later led him to the invention of the lightning conductor, at this time his observations merely suggested the opinion 'that the electrical fire was not created by friction, but collected, being really an element diffused among, and attracted by, other matter, particularly by water and metals'. (*Experiments and Observations on Electricity*, 1750.) Franklin soon afterwards verified this opinion by an admirable experiment which, though simple and conclusive, was merely qualitative, like all the other electrical experiments of the time:

> 1. A person standing on wax, and rubbing the tube, and another person on wax drawing the fire, they will both of them (provided they do not stand so as to touch one another) appear to be electrised to a person standing on the floor; that is, he will perceive a spark on approaching each of them with his knuckle.
>
> 2. But if the persons on wax touch one another during the exciting of the tube, neither of them will appear to be electrised.
>
> 3. If they touch one another after exciting the tube, and drawing the fire as aforesaid, there will be a stronger spark between them than was between either of them and the person on the floor.
>
> 4. After such strong spark, neither of them discover any electricity. (*Experiments and Observations on Electricity*, London, 1750.)

Franklin added that these facts can be explained immediately by assuming that 'B is electrised positively; A negatively; or rather B is electrised plus and A minus', *i.e.* that B has more and A less than his normal share of electricity. 'Thus you may circulate it (the electrical fire) as Mr Watson has shown; you may also accumulate it or subtract it' (*ibid.*).

Franklin, who knew next to nothing about the work of his predecessors, invented terms which were to become classical. The reason why he, nevertheless, spoke of an 'electrical fire' was simply that, in the 18th century, fire was considered the prototype of subtle matter.

Franklin next applied his new ideas to the Leyden jar:

> At the same time that the wire and the top of [Musschenbroek's] bottle &c is electrised positively or plus, the bottom of the bottle is electrised negatively or minus, in exact proportion, *i.e.* whatever quantity of electrical fire is thrown in at the top, an equal quantity goes out at the

bottom. . . . So wonderfully are these two states of Electricity, the plus and minus, combined and balanced in this miraculous bottle! (*Ibid.*)

Here is one of his famous experiments which confirmed these ideas directly:

Fix a wire in the lead, with which the bottom of the bottle is armed, so as that bending upwards, its ring-end may be level with the top or ring-end of the wire in the cork, and at three or four inches distance. Then electrise the bottle, and place it on wax. If a cork suspended by a silk thread hang between these two wires, it will play incessantly from one to the other, 'till the bottle is no longer electrised; that is, it fetches and carries fire from the top to the bottom of the bottle, 'till the equilibrium is restored.

In this way, Franklin gradually evolved the theory of electricity as a single 'fluid', which he published in his *Opinions and Conjectures concerning the Properties and Effects of the Electrical Matter* (1750):

1. The electrical matter consists of particles extremely subtile, since it can permeate common matter, even the densest metals, with such ease and freedom as not to receive any perceptible resistance. . . .

3. Electrical matter differs from common matter in this, that the parts of the latter mutually attract, those of the former mutually repel each other. . . .

4. But though the particles of electrical matter do repel each other, they are strongly attracted by all other matter. . . .

6. Thus common matter is a kind of spunge to the electric fluid. And as a spunge would receive no water if the parts of water were not smaller than the pores of the spunge; and even then but slowly, if there were not a mutual attraction between those parts and the parts of the spunge; and would still imbibe it faster . . . if, instead of attraction, there were a mutual repulsion among those parts, which would act in conjunction with the attraction of the spunge. So is the case between the electrical and common matter.

7. But in common matter there is (generally) as much of the electrical as it will contain within its substance. If more is added, it lies without upon the surface, and forms what we call an electrical atmosphere; and then the body is said to be electrified. . . .

9. We know that the electrical fluid is in common matter, because we can pump it out by the globe or tube. . . .

There follows a theory explaining the power of points to draw on and throw off electricity based on the concept of electrical atmosphere, and then:

18. These explanations of the power and operation of points, when they first occurred to me, and while they first floated in my mind, appeared

37 An 18th-century electrical experiment, by van Loo

38 Lecture on electricity, Amsterdam, 1801

perfectly satisfactory; but now I have written them . . . I must own I have some doubts about them. . . .

19. It is not of much importance to us, to know the manner in which nature executes her laws; it is enough if we know the laws themselves. It is of real use to know that china left in the air unsupported will fall and break; but how it comes to fall and why it breaks are matters of speculation. It is a pleasure to know them, but we can preserve our china without it.

The 'positivist' and near-pragmatist tenor of the last passage was in striking contrast to the metaphysical views of many of Franklin's contemporaries. Unfortunately, there was 'one experiment more which surprises us, and is not hitherto satisfactorily accounted for; it is this . . . bodies having less than the common quantity of electricity [*i.e.* negatively charged bodies], repel each other, as well as those that have more'. Franklin's attempts to explain this fact with the hypothesis of an electric atmosphere were very unsatisfactory. The difficulty was not removed until 1759, when Franz Ulrich Theodor Aepinus put forward the hypothesis that, when molecules of 'common matter' are deprived of their normal 'electricity', they repel one another exactly like the particles of 'electrical matter'.

The advocates of Franklin's one-fluid theory of electricity engaged in violent disputes with the upholders of the two-fluid theory, which Robert Symmer propounded in the same year (1759). In fact, as Coulomb was quick to realize, there was little to choose between the two. Once the symmetry between the properties of 'electrical matter' and those of 'common matter' had been fully established by Aepinus' contribution, it should have been obvious that the two 'matters' are closely related. As it happened, this fact was not appreciated until a century later, when the electrical structure of all matter was generally appreciated.

This is also the reason why Franklin committed the serious error of identifying electrical matter with Du Fay's vitreous electricity. His error seems to have been founded on the belief that brush charges and electrical winds are visible manifestations of the flow of electricity from positively to negatively charged conductors. We know today that he was taken in by appearances, and that the flow consists of negatively charged electrons too small to be perceived.

Franklin made another blunder: like Watson and the Abbé Nollet, he confused 'electrical matter' with the 'electrical atmosphere' surrounding charged bodies, *i.e.* with their electric field. It was only after Aepinus and Coulomb had stated their views on the subject, and after Newton's ideas were generally recognized, that the primitive idea of electrical atmospheres was finally abandoned. That idea was later resuscitated by Faraday, but his formulation was far more accurate, and shorn of primitive materialist ideas.

The Lightning Conductor

Franklin as a scientist is chiefly known to laymen for his invention of the lightning conductor. In 1749, having observed the resemblance between lightning and electric sparks, he asked himself if lightning, too, might not be attracted by pointed conductors. To test this assumption, he suggested that a man standing on the floor of a kind of sentry-box placed on a high steeple ought to be able to draw sparks from clouds containing lightning, by means of a pointed rod.

An experiment performed in May 1752, by Jean François Dalibard, proved this assumption correct. In October, Franklin himself carried out his famous kite experiment, as a result of which he was able to develop a lightning rod to 'secure houses, churches, ships, from lightning . . . by drawing the electrical fire out of a cloud silently, before it could come near enough to strike'.

Franklin's Contemporaries and Successors

Franklin's theory of the Leyden jar had explained virtually all electrical induction phenomena in terms of electrical effluvia. Aepinus and his pupil J. C. Wilcke (1759) were the first to explain them exclusively in terms of attraction, repulsion and the flow of electricity in conductors, thus raising electricity to a Newtonian, though still qualitative, science.

Aepinus was led to this explanation by his discovery of pyro-electricity. When tourmaline crystals are heated, they develop opposite electric charges at the ends of their polar axes. This discovery of electric poles also convinced Aepinus that there must be a close connection between electrical and magnetic induction. As a single electrical fluid flows in electrical matter, so a single magnetic fluid flows in magnetic matter; its particles repel one another but are attracted by common matter. Whenever bodies contain their natural quantity of these fluids, 'the universal gravitational attraction of Newton can remain unaffected'. Aware that his concept of natural repulsion would be repugnant to physicists, Aepinus called it a 'working hypothesis'.

The two-fluid theory, propounded by Symmer in 1759, was given a more rigorous form by the Swedish physicist Torbern Bergman in 1765. According to Bergman, equal quantities of the two electrical fluids exist in all neutral bodies; when an electrified body is brought close it attracts one and repels the other, thus producing the observed induction phenomena. This theory was later extended by Joseph Priestley, Franklin's direct successor and pupil.

MEASUREMENT OF ELECTRIC AND MAGNETIC FORCES

In 1749, Le Roy and d'Arcy invented the first instrument for measuring electric forces: the floating electrometer. They placed a float supporting a metal rod and plate into water, and brought a second plate, connected to an electrical machine, near it. As a result the float was lifted up; the weights needed to restore it to the original level measured the attractive force.

In 1760, Daniel Bernoulli used this instrument to measure the variations of electric attraction with increasing distance between the plates. He failed to verify the inverse square law, simply because the phenomena involved were too complex to be understood at the time.

Priestley's Contribution

Priestley's great classic, *The History and Present State of Electricity, with Original Experiments*, appeared in 1767. Its contribution to the science of electricity was twofold: first, it contained the first (rough) measurements of conductivity, and second, it gave the far more important proof that an electrified hollow metal vessel has no charge on the inner surface. Priestley concluded:

> May we not infer from this experiment that the attraction of electricity is subject to the same laws with that of gravitation, and is therefore according to the squares of distances; since it is easily demonstrated that were the earth in the form of a shell, a body in the inside of it would not be attracted to one side more than another?

He left this question unanswered, for his brilliant inference was not a demonstration. Newton's theorem is, in fact, valid only for hollow spheres and it fell to Cavendish to provide the necessary experimental proof.

John Michell

We have not yet mentioned the important contribution of John Michell, whose *Treatise of Artificial Magnets* (1750) marked the first important advance in 18th-century magnetic theory. Like Franklin and Aepinus, Michell was a convinced Newtonian, and stated the principle of magnetic theory as follows:

> 'Each pole [of the magnet] attracts or repels exactly equally, at equal distances, in every direction', and the 'attraction and repulsion of magnets decrease as the square of the distance from the respective poles increases'.

However, the experiments by which he tried to establish his laws were rather inaccurate and inconclusive.

THE WORK OF CAVENDISH

Though Franklin had defined the concepts of electric charge or quantity of electricity, neither he nor his successors had been able to measure it. In fact, apart from those few attempts which we have mentioned, all the experiments and theoretical explanations remained purely quantitative. The transformation of electricity into a quantitative science was the work of Cavendish and Coulomb.

Henry Cavendish (1731–1810) published only a single memoir (*Philosophical Transactions*, 1771), which he intended to form the first part of a book. But he cared far more for research than for renown, so that his other writings remained unknown until 1879, when Maxwell first published them. Here are the main arguments of his first paper:

1. Cavendish began by assuming that the law of force between electric charges is 'inversely as some less power of the distance than the cube'. He then showed that it is 'likely that it is inversely as the square', for only on that assumption could one explain the absence of electrical forces inside a hollow sphere, or the surface charges of spheres and plane parallel plates, and the phenomenon of electric induction.

2. His theory introduced the 'degree of electrification' (which was, in fact, our electric potential).[1] When two bodies of different shape are connected by a conducting wire, they do not carry the same charge, though they are electrified to the same degree. The two fundamental concepts of electrostatics—charge and potential—had at last been discriminated.

Cavendish's later papers, which, because they lay buried among his personal effects for a century, played no role in the history of physics, dealt mainly with the following four problems:

1. The experimental verification of the inverse square law (1772–1773), and that all points inside an electrified hollow sphere are electrically neutral: 'the redundant fluid [*i.e.* electric charge] is lodged intirely on its surface'.

2. The definition of electrostatic capacity: the charges of two conductors which are electrified 'to the same degree' are proportional to the capacities. These can be measured directly by discharging the conductors by means of a proof plane.

3. The discovery that the capacities of condensers of equal dimensions (which were square tin plates separated by non-conducting material) vary according to the substance employed to separate the plates. Cavendish was thus able to anticipate modern measurements of capacity, and Faraday's work on specific inductive capacity.

[1] Du Fay had previously defined the 'degree of the electrical force', and measured it with his wire-electroscope, but he had left it at that.

4. The accurate comparison of the electric conductivities of various bodies:

> Iron wire conducts roughly 400 million times better than rain or dishwater; that is the electricity meets with no more resistance in passing through a piece of iron wire 400,000,000 inches long, than through a column of water of the same diameter only one inch long. Sea water ... conducts 100 times, and a saturated solution of sea salt about 720 times, better than rain water.

We cannot discuss all of Cavendish's ingenious experiments in detail; suffice it to say that, once the concepts of charge and potential had been clearly defined, it was but a short step to the definition of the intensity or rate of flow of the electric current and of electrical resistance.

Charles Augustin Coulomb: the Fundamental Laws of Magnetism and Electrostatics

We shall begin our discussion of Coulomb's work with a quotation from Maxwell:

> It is remarkable, that not one of his [Coulomb's] experiments coincides with any of those made by Cavendish. The method by which Coulomb made direct measurements of the electric force at different distances, and that by which he compared the density of the surface charge on different parts of conductors, are entirely his own and were not anticipated by Cavendish. On the other hand, the very idea of the capacity of a conductor as a subject of investigation is entirely due to Cavendish, and nothing equivalent to it is to be found in the memoirs of Coulomb.

Like Cavendish, and unlike so many of Newton's successors, Charles Augustin Coulomb (1736–1806) was steeped in Newtonian thought. Most of his papers follow a set pattern: a theoretical summary of past contributions, a series of working hypotheses, a description of the instruments used, an account of the experiments made and of the numerical results obtained, a discussion of their theoretical consequences, a description of further experiments based on the new data, a conclusion, and finally a list of practical applications.

In 1773, while still a military engineer, Coulomb studied the resistance of materials; six years later he propounded his theory of simple machines and the laws of friction. He was attracted to the problems of electricity and magnetism by a competition (1777) for the best method of constructing a ship's compass. As a result, he published a paper which was not so much concerned with practical methods as with the study of the basic phenomena. Quoting

Musschenbroek's old experiments together with his own, he established the following two fundamental principles:

1. In a given place, the earth has a uniform magnetic field.

2. A magnet placed in that field will experience a couple proportional to the sine of the angle the magnet makes with the direction of the earth's field.

From these principles, Coulomb deduced the 'general corollary' that 'the deflection of a magnetized needle cannot result from the flow of a fluid. . . . Experiment shows that the different magnetic phenomena are not produced by vortices, but arise from attractive and repulsive forces of the kind treated by gravitational and celestial physics.'

Coulomb then showed how the periods of oscillation of a magnetic needle can be used to determine the 'momentum of the magnetic force' and also to compare the magnetic moments of different magnets. To do so, he made a series of measurements of the oscillations of magnets suspended from fine wires. Afraid that his results might have been falsified by the torsion of the wires, he allowed for torsional effects by a method which was very nearly correct. Finally, he defined what we call the *demagnetizing field* and showed how its effects on a magnetic needle can be reduced.

In 1784, Coulomb resumed his studies of torsion and corrected his slight error of 1777. He then propounded the very simple theory of the effects he had discovered.

In 1785, he published his first fundamental paper on electricity: the *Construction et usage d'une balance électrique* . . ., in which he described his well-known torsion balance for measuring electric forces of as little as one thousandth of a dyne. (He constructed an even more accurate balance later on.) The book also described his classic experiments on electrical *repulsion*, which provided the first rigorous proof—except for Cavendish's, which had remained unpublished—of 'Coulomb's law'.

In a second paper, also published in 1785, Coulomb described his investigations of the law of electrical *attraction*. To establish this law, he had suspended an insulated needle, with a gold leaf fixed to one end, horizontally by a silk thread in the vicinity of a large insulated spherical conductor. The needle was given an opposite charge to the sphere and the needle was set into oscillation at various distances from it. (The torsion balance would have broken down in this case, because, when torsion and attraction are in equilibrium, the system is unstable.) The same paper described Coulomb's measurements of magnetic forces by means of a suspended needle, and also by means of a torsion balance. Coulomb made due allowance for the various disturbing factors.

In a third paper of 1785, Coulomb dealt with the leakage of electricity.

Finally, in three papers published, respectively, in 1786, 1787 and 1788, he discussed the distribution of charges in various conductors.

In the first of these papers, he described an experiment proving that 'the electrical fluid does not distribute itself in any body because of chemical affinity . . . but is shared out between different bodies in contact, solely because of its repulsive action' and that 'having reached a state of equilibrium it distributes itself over the surface without penetrating into the interior'.

To establish this principle, he covered an insulated metal sphere with two hemispherical cups, fitted with insulated handles. By means of this instrument he also proved Cavendish's theory, *viz.*:

> If a fluid is contained in a body in which it can move freely, and if all its elementary particles repel one another with a force greater than the inverse of the cube . . . the fluid must spread over the surface of the body and cannot remain in its interior. (Abridged from Cavendish's paper of 1771.)

Coulomb's other two papers gave approximate solutions of various problems connected with the distribution of charges over various systems of conductors. In particular, they dealt with measurements of the 'electric density' by means of the proof plane and the torsion balance, and included remarkably precise theoretical calculations based exclusively on the laws of attraction and repulsion.

Coulomb's work had brought electrostatics to a high degree of perfection, so much so that his successors—Poisson and Lord Kelvin —had merely to follow the paths he had indicated.

We must, however, stress one point. While Coulomb's law defined the 'electric mass', *i.e.* the electric charge of a body, and while Coulomb was the first to measure that charge, he, like all his contemporaries, was unable to define its nature. Thus he was rather cautious when it came to choosing between the one-fluid theory of Franklin and Aepinus and the two-fluid theory of Symmer and Bergman:

> Since the two suppositions differ only in being more or less probable, I should like to make it clear that by adopting two electrical fluids, I intend only to present the results of my calculations and experiments with the least number of elements, and not to explain the true causes of electricity.

In his last papers (1789–1801) Coulomb returned to the study of magnetic phenomena, and tried to calculate the distribution of magnetic fluid in a cylindrical steel needle. To do so, he was forced to introduce, in addition to attraction and repulsion, 'a coercive force, comparable to friction, which stops the fluid from running from one part of the needle to the other'.

Finally, experiments with broken magnets led him to propound the molecular theory of magnetism, though not, of course, in modern terms:

> I believe that the experimental results can be made to agree with calculations . . . if, for instance, we assume, in the system of M. Aepinus, that the magnetic fluid is contained in every molecule . . . so that every molecule has two poles, and that while the fluid is carried from one end [of the magnet] to the other, it cannot pass from one molecule to the next.

* * *

With Franklin, but above all with Cavendish and Coulomb, electricity and magnetism had become a modern science, albeit a century later than celestial mechanics, statics, hydrostatics and mathematical optics. This delay was due largely to the experimental difficulties—Newton himself made no original discoveries in electricity or magnetism—but also to the persistence of mechanistic and qualitative concepts which, as Coulomb was able to show, were based on so many delusions.

It was only during the 18th century that physicists began to realize that contact actions, though more familiar, are not more directly intelligible than action at a distance. Thus Musschenbroek was able to write in 1739:

> One objection against the system of attraction has been that it is inconceivable that two bodies can act on each other without touching. While I agree with this objection, I must confess that I, for my part, have absolutely no idea of the reciprocal action of any body whatsoever. In fact, the human intellect cannot grasp the mutual action of two contiguous bodies: it can have no idea of the force which causes them to act, of how this force passes from one to the other, of the manner in which it is produced, or finally how it ceases to act. This is a mystery which passes human understanding.

The 18th century ended with the discovery by Galvani and Volta of the battery and of current electricity, two altogether unsuspected phenomena, which represented a clear break with the past, and whose consequences were not fully developed until the discovery of electrolysis and electromagnetism.

This is why we have decided to defer the discussion of these discoveries to a later volume, dealing with the 19th century.

CHAPTER 5

The Birth of Modern Chemistry

THE CHEMISTRY OF GASES

THE MOST IMPORTANT DEVELOPMENT in chemistry from about 1650 to 1750 was the discovery that the air is not a simple substance, for it was largely by this that Lavoisier was led to his famous experiments and to his reform of the chemical system.

THE STATUS OF CHEMISTRY

In the 17th century, and even in the early 18th, the work of chemists was generally despised. Chemists had to stoke furnaces, they worked with evil-smelling substances, their clothes were generally covered with burns and stains, and their experiments were the source of many public complaints. All this was gradually changed as the study of chemistry began to offer increasing financial rewards, and as laboratories became better equipped.

In the course of this development, alkaline salts began to be distinguished, alkaline bases and earths were identified, new metals and some metalloids, their salts, were discovered.

ALKALINE COMPOUNDS AND ALKALINE EARTHS

Two salts of the alkaline metals enjoyed particularly great renown from the beginning of the 17th century: sodium sulphate and potassium chloride. Glauber called the former the 'admirable salt' and described its preparation; Geoffroy (1732) determined its composition. On the other hand, the composition of potassium chloride, or 'sylvine' (*sal digestivus Sylvis*), whose 'digestive virtues' were greatly appreciated, remained a mystery. Potassium salts in a good state of purity were prepared by Glaser and by Tachenius, and became known as 'salts of tartar'. Sodium potassium tartrate (Rochelle Salt) was first prepared by Seignette in 1672, and the method of its preparation was published in 1731 by Geoffroy and by Boulduc.

In 1736, Duhamel was the first to prepare sodium oxide by heating sodium nitrate with carbon. The distinction between soda and potash was drawn by Brandt in 1746; Margraff distinguished their salts by the form of their crystals and by flame tests. He called soda 'fixed mineral alkali' and potash 'fixed vegetable alkali'.

Ideas on the composition of limestone varied a great deal, though limestone was generally considered to be a salt. The composition of gypsum was first explained by Macquer (1747) and confirmed by Margraff (1750). Black's studies of the fixation of carbonic acid gas and of the formation of calcium carbonate led to the general adoption in 1755 of the view that calcium is an alkaline earth.

At about the same time the nature of magnesia was explained. Barely fifty years earlier, apothecaries had spread the use of this powder, which they called white magnesia (*magnesia alba*) to distinguish it from black magnesia (*magnesia nigra*) or glaziers' earth (manganese dioxide), which had been known since ancient times. It seems that white magnesia was first prepared in Italy. In 1722, the German chemist Friedrich Hoffmann described a method of obtaining it from certain mineral springs. Joseph Black studied magnesium carbonate in order to settle a medical argument; as a result he identified magnesia and discovered 'fixed air' (carbon dioxide).

In this period also, chemists began to suspect the existence of barium compounds which had previously been mistaken for calcium sulphate. Margraff showed that the reduction of 'heavy spar', as the barium salt was then called, did not produce lime but a different earth. Nevertheless baryta was not fully identified until some thirty years later.

Lavoisier was the first to suspect that alkaline and calcareous earths might not be simple substances.

The Discovery of New Metals

The 18th century also witnessed the discovery of many new metals. Zinc had been used since time immemorial in the form of brass, but as zinc was not known as a separate metal, brass was considered a mixture of melted copper and calamine. The word zinc, though used by Paracelsus, did not become part of the chemical vocabulary until about 1720, when the metal was first obtained in Europe by roasting calamine. Various methods of obtaining it were suggested by the Swedish metallurgist Swab (1742), and by the German chemist Margraff (1746). Previously Europe had imported most of its zinc minerals from India. The nature of blende (ZnS) was first recognized by the Swedish chemist Funk. The industrial manufacture of zinc in Europe was begun towards the end of the 18th century.

The confused ideas on the nature of bismuth were dispelled by the work of Hellot (1737), Pott (1739) and Geoffroy the Younger (1753); Geoffroy's paper defined its properties correctly.

Cobalt and nickel were discovered at about the same time. In effect, their compounds, too, had been used for a long time, and had even been reduced, though the metals themselves had not been identified. Cobalt was isolated in 1742 by Brandt, who named it after the ore from which he had extracted it; nickel was isolated by Swedish chemists in ores resembling copper ores but yielding no copper (Kupfernickel). Cronstedt described the chemical and physical properties of metallic nickel and also its magnetic properties, which he attributed to the presence in the metal of a small quantity of iron. His study of nickel was completed by Bergman.

The discovery of platinum aroused keen interest, not only in chemical circles. Brownrigg brought back samples of this rare metal from Jamaica and presented them to the Royal Society in 1750; other samples were brought back from Peru by the Spanish mathematician Antonio de Ulloa. The first paper on platinum was published by the English assayer Charles Wood, in 1746. Swedish chemists discovered platinum in their own country. In 1758, William Lewis published an important work on what was then called platina, white gold, or the eighth metal. Among other chemists who studied platinum were Margraff, Macquer, Baumé and Bergman. In 1783, Lavoisier melted platinum with the hydrogen blowpipe, with which he later demonstrated the exact composition of water. Towards the end of the 18th century, platinum was used in the manufacture of reflectors and for making the standard metre and the standard kilogram.

The chemistry of minerals was completed by numerous studies of metallic salts. The composition of iron sulphate was established by Geoffroy the Elder in 1778, and that of alum in a series of works by Geoffroy, Pott, Margraff and Vauquelin. Prussian blue was discovered by Diesbach in 1710, as a result of a series of fortuitous circumstances. He managed to keep the manufacture of this famous pigment a close secret until 1724, when various methods of obtaining it were published in England. In 1752, Macquer showed that it was the result of the formation, in an alkaline medium, of a compound of iron and an unknown substance, 'Prussic acid', which Scheele was to isolate in 1783.

Towards the end of the 17th century, chemical recipes first mentioned the preparation of red oxide of mercury by the calcination of the metal, an operation which later played a great part in the history of chemistry. Previously, the red oxide had been obtained exclusively by the decomposition of the nitrate or precipitation from the chloride. Béguin was the first to mention the new method. Boyle decomposed the oxide by heat and so recovered the metal, whence Ettmüller spoke of 'the marvellous precipitation of mercury by itself', and the oxide became known as the *precipitate per se*.

Boric Acid and Phosphorus

Two other discoveries set off a long chain of investigations. The first was Homberg's preparation of boric acid from borax in 1702. This acid was studied by Louis Lémery, Geoffroy the Elder, Pott and Baron. The second was the discovery of phosphorus, probably *c.* 1674, when a Hamburg alchemist, Henig Brand, managed to prepare a mysterious substance which glowed in the dark. A few weeks later, J. Kunkel obtained the same substance by the calcination of the residue of evaporated urine; Homberg and Boyle discovered phosphorus independently. Phosphorus remained a laboratory curiosity until Scheele was able to obtain it from bones; its combustion was one of the first objects of Lavoisier's studies.

The Discovery of Gases

Side by side with the study of chemical compounds went the study of the newly discovered gases, and of the precise part played by air in combustion. That it played some part in combustion had been suspected for close on 150 years.

The Increase of Weight of Calcined Metals

Very much earlier still, it was known that lead and tin increase their weight during calcination—a phenomenon which was mentioned by Galen, by numerous medieval authors, and later by Scaliger, Cardan, Fasch, Libarius and Cesalpino, all of whom explained it as resulting from the addition to the metal of fire particles. A different explanation was given by Biringuccio (1540), according to whom fire expels the lighter parts of a metal much as death expels the spirit from animals, increasing their dead weight. Until the correct solution was discovered, all explanations hinged on one or other of these two views.

In 1630, the French physician Jean Rey published a series of *Essays* in which he contended that fire expels the lighter parts of the air adhering to all metals. This explanation, which was based on dialectical arguments and not on observation, was really on a par with Biringuccio's, so that the many claims that Rey was a precursor of Lavoisier need not be taken seriously.

It was at about the same time that van Helmont coined the term 'gas' to refer, not so much to an aeriform substance, as to a subtle spirit in the traditional sense of the word. Van Helmont found that this spirit appears during the combustion of carbon, during the explosion of gunpowder, during fermentation, and when certain salts are attacked by acids. He also called it the cause of the mephitic air in wine barrels and in some caves. He was probably the first to mention the fact that when a lighted candle is placed in an upturned bell-jar over a pneumatic trough, the flame is extinguished and the volume of air in the jar decreases.

Von Guericke's invention of the pneumatic pump attracted further attention to the properties of air and became the signal for the appearance of a vast number of works which were to play a fundamental part in the study of gases.

The Theories of Boyle, Hooke and Mayow

Robert Boyle, who formulated the famous gas law to which his name is attached, also invented the method of collecting gases over a pneumatic trough. Boyle himself collected the gas (then still unidentified) which is released when iron is acted upon by dilute sulphuric acid. He also showed that combustion ceases as the air is withdrawn from a closed vessel, and that a glowing splint is rekindled when the air is readmitted. From these experiments, and others on the respiration of birds and mice, he concluded that only a part of the air is involved in combustion or respiration.

Boyle was less successful in his attempts to explain the calcination of metals. Though he carefully weighed the metal before and after calcination and though he verified by a separate experiment that the weight of the vessel in which the metal was calcined remained unchanged, he never thought of weighing the metal in a *sealed* vessel before and after calcination. As a result, he failed to observe that the total weight remains unchanged, and that the increase in weight of the metal is accompanied by a corresponding decrease in the weight of the residual air—Lavoisier's great discovery a century later. Boyle himself concluded that the increase of weight resulted from the metal's absorption of heat through the wall of the vessel.

At about the same time, Hooke suggested that the combustion of a substance in air is similar to its combustion in saltpetre. This idea was taken up by John Mayow, who believed that air and saltpetre must contain a common 'spirit' necessary to combustion; this he called the *nitro-aerial spirit*. He also believed that the same spirit was responsible for transforming venous into arterial blood.

The Collection of Gases. Mayow and Hales

Mayow was an exceptionally skilled experimeter, and much more clear-sighted than his contemporaries. He perfected the technique of collecting gases by introducing a host of special troughs and flasks as well as new methods of igniting substances in upturned test-tubes.

Mayow died at an early age and his theories were quickly forgotten, mainly because his successors lost interest in the problems that had occupied him. His techniques, however, lived on, and were described, for instance, in a small book published in 1719 by the otherwise unknown physicist Moitrel d'Élément. Even so, later chemists took their gas-collecting apparatus mainly from Stephen Hales (1677–1761).

Hales carried out a large number of experiments on the respiration of plants, on fermentation, and on the generation of gases. He communicated his results to the Royal Society and also published his findings in his *Vegetable Staticks* (1727). From this book it appears that Hales had succeeded in preparing most of the gases that were to be identified during the next fifty years, and which he himself failed to distinguish simply because he believed that all gases were basically forms of the same 'spirit'. In addition, he lagged behind his contemporaries in believing that air loses its respirable properties because of a loss of elasticity.

The fact that chemists continued to be baffled by the problem of combustion has often been attributed to their adherence to Stahl's phlogiston theory. This is certainly not true. Admittedly that theory was built on traditional misconceptions, but these would have prevailed in any case. That is the reason why the phlogiston theory remained unchallenged for so long, and why it collapsed so quickly once Lavoisier was able to challenge the premisses on which it was based. The nefarious influence of Stahl's theory on the progress of chemistry is pure legend; in particular, the theory proved no obstacle to the discovery of gases, which was, in fact, made by some of its most ardent supporters.

Fixed Air

When the problem of combustion was finally solved, the first positive results did not accrue from the study of respirable air, but from Joseph Black's discovery that calcareous earths, alkalis and magnesia contain a large quantity of 'fixed air'[1] (carbon dioxide), and that this fixed air can be liberated by the action of heat or of acids. Black also found that 'when slaked lime is mixed with water, the fixed air dissolved in the water is attracted by the lime and saturates a small portion of it, which then becomes incapable of dissolution'.

When Black asserted that fixed air differs from ordinary air, he was challenging the traditional foundations of chemistry; though the Aristotelian elements had lost much of their former importance, chemists continued to look on water and air as elementary substances. No wonder, therefore, that his views gave rise to animated discussions. The Italian chemist G. A. de Saluzzo, who, shortly before

[1] Gases were generally described as 'airs' until Van Helmont's term was resurrected by Macquer in the *Dictionnaire de chimie* (1766).

Black's discovery, had studied the gas released by gunpowder, now published his own conclusions. A few years later the Scottish chemist David Macbride identified the air released during fermentation with Black's fixed air.

Black's theory was opposed in 1764 by a German apothecary, Friedrich Meyer, who introduced a new principle, *acidum pingue*, which, he claimed, was absorbed by calcium carbonate during calcination, transforming the carbonate into quicklime; conversely, quicklime was calcium carbonate deprived of *acidum pingue*. Meyer's principle was keenly defended, particularly by German chemists and by other obstinate proponents of outworn chemical ideas.

Inflammable Air

While these discusssions were taking place, Henry Cavendish identified hydrogen (1765), which, like carbon dioxide, had been prepared long before its identification. Cavendish determined the density of the gas and discovered its chief chemical properties, and particularly its explosive power, because of which he called it 'inflammable air'. Cavendish also conducted experiments on Black's 'fixed air', measuring its density and its solubility in water.

Finally, Cavendish invented the method of storing gases over mercury, thus enabling chemists to collect many gases that had previously escaped them.

Joseph Priestley

The phlogiston theory found its most obstinate advocate in the person of Joseph Priestley (1733–1804), a Unitarian pastor from Leeds, whose passionate interest in gases earned him the title of 'father of pneumatic chemistry'. Priestley was not a rigorous scientist, but strayed wherever his fancy took him. He began his studies of gases by repeating his predecessors' experiments on fixed air, and published a small work on the preparation of soda water in 1771. He then studied the effects of carbon dioxide on respiration and combustion, thus beginning the series of brilliant experiments which culminated with the discovery of oxygen.

Having realized that respiration and combustion cannot take place in stale air, he tried to discover under what circumstances respirable air is turned stale. In 1772, he collected 'acid air' (hydrochloric acid) and 'nitrous air' (nitrogen peroxide); in 1773 he collected 'dephlogisticated nitrous air' (nitrous oxide) which, he found, was able to support combustion.

Meanwhile, all chemists continued to consider ordinary air as a simple 'principle'. The subsequent discovery of oxygen gave rise to most violent priority disputes between the disciples of Priestley and

Lavoisier, though Lavoisier himself never denied that Priestley's contribution was crucial. Priestley's work was published in six volumes from 1774 to 1777 under the title *Experiments and Observations on different kinds of Air*.

Lavoisier's Early Studies of Oxidation

In about 1771, Lavoisier turned his attention to the part played by atmospheric air in the combustion of a diamond, of sulphur and of phosphorus, and towards the end of 1772 he became convinced that air is absorbed in all types of combustion. During the next year, he carried out numerous experiments on the calcination of zinc, tin and lead, and on the reduction of their oxides, methodically repeating and then modifying all the experiments of his predecessors. In 1774, he published the *Opuscules physiques et chimiques* which contained all the papers he had read to the *Académie des Sciences*. By then, he was convinced that calcination is equivalent to the fixation of a part of the air, though he had not yet been able to collect or identify that part, largely because he still believed that it must be identical with Black's 'fixed air'.

It was Priestley who first isolated the fraction of the air which is absorbed by metals during oxidation, *i.e.* oxygen, when, on 1st August 1774, he heated *precipitate per se* (red oxide of mercury) by means of a burning-glass and observed that a colourless gas was expelled in which a candle burned with a remarkably brilliant flame. He concluded that this gas was identical with nitrous oxide, a gas he had discovered less than a year before. During his stay in Paris in October 1774, he discussed this discovery with Lavoisier.

The French chemist did not immediately repeat Priestley's experiments, for he was busily preparing an important paper on the calcination of tin for the *Académie des Sciences*. In this paper, which he presented on 12th November 1774, he was able to show that the increase in weight of tin after calcination was due to the fixation of air from the vessel and not to particles of fire, as Boyle had thought. Lavoisier incidentally isolated nitrogen, which he called 'residual fire air'.

It was only in February 1775 that he found time to look more closely at Priestley's experiment. Both chemists were now working on the same problem. On 8th March 1775, Priestley discovered that oxygen (which he called 'dephlogisticated air') supports respiration; Lavoisier made the same discovery a few days later.

In fact, the study of oxygen had by then aroused the curiosity of most chemists. In France, the apothecary Pierre Bayen precipitated mercuric oxide from solutions of its salts and then heated it to obtain mercury, but without suspecting that he was preparing an unknown

39 Lavoisier and his wife, by Jacques-Louis David

Late 18th-century model of a chemical laboratory

40 Reconstruction of Lavoisier's laboratory, with original instruments

gas. In Sweden, Scheele carried out independent investigations, in the course of which he succeeded in preparing oxygen from manganese dioxide, arriving at the same results as Lavoisier and Priestley at the beginning of 1775.

The Work of Scheele

Carl Wilhelm Scheele (1742–1786), a poor Swedish apothecary, could study chemistry only in his spare time, and with meagre resources. Even so, he isolated chlorine, and was an independent discoverer of oxygen, ammonia, hydrogen chloride, and of many inorganic and organic acids. His work was recognized by Swedish scientists from 1775 onwards, but the rest of Europe did not learn of his fame until two years later, when it became generally known that he had discovered that the air consists of 'two kinds of elastic fluid', only one of which 'has an affinity with phlogiston'. He identified oxygen as the fraction of the air which is absorbed by 'liver of sulphur' and phosphorus, and determined its properties. However, since he continued to adhere to the phlogiston theory, and since, in any case, his *Chemical Treatise on Air and Fire* was not translated into German until 1777 and into French until 1781, he played no part in the major theoretical developments that sprang from the discovery of oxygen.

The Interpretation of the Properties of Oxygen

Though Priestley was the first to recognize the part which dephlogisticated air plays in the respiration of plants and mice, and though he and Lavoisier gave an almost complete description of oxygen and nitrogen, it was Lavoisier alone who appreciated the full importance of the new discovery. His name for oxygen at this time was 'vital air'.

For Priestley, as for most other chemists of his day, atmospheric air was a simple substance; oxygen was merely atmospheric air that had surrendered its phlogiston to metal oxides (whence its name of dephlogisticated air), and nitrogen (phlogisticated air) was that portion of the atmospheric air which refused to surrender its phlogiston. In other words, most chemists saw no reason for abandoning the phlogiston theory because of the discovery of oxygen.

It was only in 1776, when Lavoisier carried out his famous experiment, in the course of which he first combined a measured volume of oxygen with mercury and later recovered the same volume of the gas by heating the mercuric oxide, that the phlogiston theory was seriously challenged.

The story of oxygen shows better than anything else how a scientific discovery is made in stages. It is only completed when the newly-discovered phenomenon has been fully analysed, and when its properties are given a correct theoretical interpretation. Hence it is idle to call either Priestley or Lavoisier the 'real' discoverer of oxygen.

The Transformation of Chemistry

The Life of Lavoisier

Antoine Laurent Lavoisier was born at Paris on 26th August 1743. After studying law, he became a *Fermier Général*. In 1768, he married Marie-Anne Paulze, the thirteen-year-old daughter of the Director of the French East India Company. He quickly proved his administrative skill and played a leading part in improving French agricultural methods and the lot of agricultural labourers. In 1775, he was appointed Commissioner of Powder, and went to live at the Arsenal, where he later made his great discoveries. It was largely thanks to the reforms he introduced into the manufacture of gunpowder that the revolutionary armies proved so successful in the field. Lavoisier was one of many well-to-do people who sympathized with the objects of the French Revolution at first. His arrest and execution were due not to his political views but to his having been a *Fermier Général*—not even his scientific reputation could save him from the opprobrium in which these private collectors of taxes were generally held. It is incidentally untrue that Coffinhal, the president of the tribunal which tried him, made the much-quoted remark that 'the Republic has no need of scholars'.

It was in about 1770 that Lavoisier first felt that the phlogiston theory had brought chemistry to an impasse. He read everything he could on the subject and was particularly interested in his predecessors' studies of gases. He was quick to realize that the part played by air in chemical reactions was the most urgent problem to be solved and that the solution would have profound repercussions on chemical theory.

Lavoisier's Experiments

What distinguished Lavoisier from all his contemporaries was his freedom from preconceived ideas and his general intellectual independence. In that respect, he was everything that Descartes could have wished a true scientist to be. But admitting none but experimental evidence was one thing; designing conclusive experiments was another. It was in this sphere that Lavoisier really excelled.

One of Lavoisier's earliest experiments (1768) was devoted to Boyle's contention that, if water is heated for a long time in a vessel, a small part of it is transformed into earth. After careful weighing,

Lavoisier was able to show that the 'earth' was produced by the vessel and not by the water. (Scheele came to the same conclusion after a chemical analysis of the residue.)

Lavoisier soon realized that there was no need to explain combustion with hypothetical entities. As a result, he completely ignored Stahl's phlogiston, even when other chemists objected that this omission made all his findings suspect. He probably knew he could not ignore this problem for ever, but felt that before he could engage in public controversy he must first be able to muster all the facts.[1]

Acids and Gases

We saw that the discovery of oxygen was not by itself sufficient to supplant the prevailing phlogiston theory. Lavoisier therefore carried out a remarkable series of experiments on the composition of acids (1775–1777), by which he was able to show that the transformation of metals into their calces and of non-metals into acids was due to their combination with oxygen and not with phlogiston. He coined the word 'oxygen', which means 'acid-former', a misconception which was later corrected by Berzelius. At about the same time, he laid the foundation of the theory of gases which he was to define a year later, and he gave the name 'azote' to nitrogen.

According to that theory, all gases contain substances rich in caloric. Oxygen, for instance, is an acidifying principle associated with caloric. Though Lavoisier's theory of gases was therefore still based on traditional qualities, it did not lead to the same absurd contradictions as the phlogiston theory (see below), so that it could be quietly abandoned without endangering the entire theoretical structure of chemistry. Lavoisier's new theory seemed so baseless that few of his adversaries felt threatened by it.

Guyton de Morveau later published a letter by Macquer, one of the most respected chemists of the time, who, having read one of Lavoisier's papers, expressed his relief as follows:

> Where should we have been with our old chemistry if we had had to build an entirely different edifice? For my own part I don't mind admitting I should have given up the game. . . . However, M. Lavoisier has just published this discovery of his, and I can tell you that since that time I have had a great weight removed from my breast.

[1] In 1756, the Russian chemist M. A. Lomonosov, who propounded such advanced ideas as the atomic constitution of matter and the kinetic energy of molecules, also came to the conclusion that the phlogiston theory must be rejected because metals increased their weight during calcination. Unfortunately he wrote in Russian, and his work was therefore not accessible to Western chemists. Familiarity with his ideas would undoubtedly have given chemistry a tremendous impetus at the time.

This phrase sums up the general attitude of most 18th-century chemists, and explains their desperate resistance to a theory that seemed to make nonsense of all their efforts.

The Nature of Water

Much as the composition of the air had given rise to polemics ten years earlier, so a violent quarrel was set off in 1783 when it was shown that water, too, was not a simple substance. This view was first suggested by Macquer's assertion that the combustion of hydrogen causes the formation of droplets of water. Sporadic attempts to explain this phenomenon had led to no result. When Lavoisier tried, he failed at first because of his belief that the combustion of hydrogen must lead to the production of an acid compound.

It was Henry Cavendish who, by combining hydrogen and oxygen by means of an electric spark, was able to show that the two gases combine to produce water. When news of that experiment reached Paris in June 1783, Lavoisier and Laplace repeated it at once and affirmed on the same day that water is composed, weight for weight, of inflammable and vital air.

The phlogiston school was not dismayed by this new discovery; according to them water was formed in the experiment simply because inflammable air surrenders its phlogiston to dephlogisticated air, which is water deprived of its phlogiston. Cavendish himself tended to adopt this view, so that, as in the case of the constitution of air, Lavoisier was once again the only chemist to appreciate the true facts. The similarity between the circumstances surrounding the two discoveries became greater still when it was learned that Gaspard Monge had managed to synthesize water in June, *i.e.* before he could have heard of the experiments of Cavendish, Laplace and Lavoisier.

It was in 1783, also, that the brothers Montgolfier made use of the buoyancy of an envelope filled with hot air to achieve human flight. The physicist J. A. C. Charles was the first to make a human ascent in a hydrogen balloon and the *Académie des Sciences* set up a commission charged with improving balloon flights. Meusnier and Lavoisier thereupon investigated efficient methods of preparing hydrogen, studying the decomposition of water by red-hot iron, and setting the stage for one of the most spectacular experiments in the history of science. This experiment was performed on 27th and 28th February 1785 and again on 1st March, in Lavoisier's laboratory in the Arsenal and before a large number of spectators. The two scientists allowed water to drip through a sloping iron gun-barrel, heated to redness in a furnace. The hydrogen collected was then ignited by an electric spark in a balloon flask with two inlets, when a liquid was produced. Measurements of the volumes and weights involved showed beyond the shadow of a doubt that that liquid must be water.

Even then the phlogiston theory continued to hold full sway. The first converts to Lavoisier's doctrine were not chemists but mathematicians—Laplace, Cousin and Meusnier—to whom chemical theories were, in any case, a matter of indifference, and who were far more interested in another aspect of chemistry, the theory of chemical affinity. The first chemists to join them were Chaptal and Fourcroy, and later Berthollet and Guyton de Morveau.

Modern Nomenclature

At the beginning of 1787, Guyton de Morveau, a prominent lawyer from Dijon, working in conjunction with Lavoisier, Berthollet, Fourcroy and a number of mathematicians who frequented the Arsenal, set about revising the whole nomenclature of science. As a result, a new system was presented to the *Académie des Sciences* in the same year, and also published under the title *Essai de nomenclature chimique*. This work provided chemists with a terminology basically the same as that used today.

Lavoisier's Later Work

The later work of Lavoisier was devoted almost exclusively to the development of de Morveau's system, and to the application of chemical discoveries to biological processes.

Lavoisier had previously considered the respiration of animals as part of his studies of the properties of oxygen; in particular, his work with Laplace on calorimetry had led him to measure the heat produced during this process. After the publication of his *Traité élémentaire de chimie* (1789), Lavoisier turned definitely to physiological chemistry, having first mapped out a comprehensive programme with the young chemist Armand Séguin. The two scientists communicated their first results (on respiration and transpiration) to the *Académie des Sciences* in 1790. Drawings by Madame Lavoisier have immortalized their collaboration. In 1792, Lavoisier was forced to ask Séguin to continue the work by himself, and thus to abandon his plan to go on to a study of digestion.

The Opposition to Lavoisier's Doctrine

The disappearance of the phlogiston theory represents a landmark in the history of chemistry, for with it disappeared principles that went back to the earliest origins of science. Mechanics had undergone a similar transformation in the 16th century, and physics in the 17th. Chemistry came last because its experimental problems were much more difficult to solve. Even Lavoisier was not entirely immune from outworn ideas—his use of the caloric shows clearly how difficult it was for even the most independent thinker to discard all the traditional misconceptions.

Lavoisier's contemporaries hung on desperately to the phlogiston theory, which, they considered, had brought chemistry to such a stage of perfection that little remained to be done. True, Stahl's theory failed to explain the increase in weight of metals during calcination, but 17th-century chemists felt they could safely ignore this 'minor' shortcoming. Later, when Lavoisier forced them to take notice of just that aspect, the collapse of the phlogiston theory was merely a question of time.

Phlogiston and Weight

Though the weight of phlogiston was the subject of the most varied hypotheses, all were in line with established chemical thought: the fiery element of the ancients had simply been given a new name. In 1763, Chardenon introduced the distinction between specific and absolute gravity, and asserted that phlogiston tended to decrease the absolute gravity of all bodies with which it combines. Other authors adopted this argument with slight variations. Venel contended for more than twenty years that phlogiston has a negative weight, and that it is therefore repelled by bodies. This was also the view of many other chemists, including Black, Leslie and Guyton de Morveau, who spoke of the specific 'levity' of phlogiston. In 1776, de Morveau made a fresh attempt to reconcile the discovery of 'fixed air' with phlogiston, in which he confused carbon dioxide with oxygen. In the same year, Berthollet offered a similar explanation. Macquer, Bergman, Scheele and Priestley invariably interpreted every new discovery by Lavoisier in terms of the phlogiston theory.

Lavoisier's Attacks on Phlogiston

Lavoisier first voiced his doubts about the existence of phlogiston in 1777. Even so, he remained very cautious, for he was anxious to avoid the criticism that, like his opponents, he was putting forward an unsubstantiated hypothesis. Only when he was certain of all his facts did he present his outspoken *Réflexions sur le phlogistique* (1785) to the *Académie des Sciences*.

Once the first French chemists had rallied to his side, Lavoisier felt free to sanction the publication of a number of further attacks on the phlogiston theory. Chief among these were the *Nomenclature* which we have mentioned earlier, and a translation by Madame Lavoisier of Richard Kirwan's *Essay on Phlogiston*, to each chapter of which Lavoisier or one of his friends had appended a refutation. After reading their comments, Kirwan, too, joined the anti-phlogiston camp and managed to carry most English chemists, excepting Priestley, with him. Cavendish contended that the new phenomena were explained as well in one theory as in the other.

In January 1789, Lavoisier published his *Traité élémentaire de chimie*, which ran to many editions and was translated into numerous languages. This book, which differed radically from any chemical textbook of the past, proved an invaluable aid to the teaching of chemistry.

French and German Opposition

However, the older chemists continued to resist. In France, Macquer died before he could rally to the new doctrine, while Baumé and Sage remained intransigent opponents of Lavoisier. Since de la Metherie, the editor of the *Observations sur la physique*, the only French scientific monthly journal, proved an obstinate Stahlian, Lavoisier and his friends were forced to found the *Annales de chimie* in 1789.

The sharpest attacks on Lavoisier were written by Lamarck, who opposed Lavoisier's oxygen theory with a pyrotic theory of his own (*Réfutation de la théorie pneumatique*, 1796). According to Lamarck, oxygen was a pure abstraction.

Orthodox German chemists also put up a last-ditch stand against Lavoisier. As in France, these were the older chemists—Wiegleb, Crell and Gmelin, and when S. F. Hermbstädt translated Lavoisier into German, the new idea gained ground rapidly.

Nevertheless, the spirit of the old chemistry was still not dead. A Hungarian chemist, J. J. Winterl, imagined a new 'universal substance' which he called *andronia*, an idea which was taken up by Oersted in 1803 but attracted few followers. In the same year the Dutch chemist J. B. van Mons made hydrogen the principle of combustion; Davy ascribed a similar role to nitrogen. But all these theories were doomed to failure, and in the end Lavoisier's ideas triumphed completely.

CHEMICAL AFFINITY AND ATOMIC THEORY

Affinity Tables

Long before they made it an object of special study, chemists implicitly assumed the concept of chemical 'affinity', a term borrowed by Guyton de Morveau from Conrad Barchusen's *Pyrosophia sive elementa chemiae* (Leyden, 1698). In fact, chemistry had always been the study of the tendencies of various bodies to attract or repel one another.

However, the nature of these tendencies had never been discussed. Before Descartes, they were generally considered to result from 'sympathies'—one body expelled a second from its union with a third because the first was more sympathetic with the third than was the second. These notions were used in chemical language not so much to explain as to describe the phenomena involved by means of familiar images.

In 1648, Glauber established an order of affinity of different metals for mercury; that is, of the ease with which amalgams can be formed.

The Cartesians frowned on chemical affinities as impermissible qualities. However, since their own scheme failed to explain chemical reactions, even Cartesian chemists were forced to introduce them, albeit implicitly, in their practical investigations.

Newton devoted Query 31 of his *Opticks* to the problem of the attraction between the smallest particles of matter. In order to explain this, and also why some chemical actions are more violent than others, he assumed that the attractive virtue varies from one substance to the next. Acid particles are more strongly attracted by iron than by copper, and by copper than by silver; the dissolution of a salt in water is the result of the repulsive force between the particles of the salt and those of the water; crystallization and capillary phenomena are also caused by attraction.

Newton's ideas brought chemists face to face with the kind of corpuscular conception which had already been adopted by philosophers and physicists, and which chemists had been able to ignore because it played no part in the chemistry of principles. Newton now forced the pace with an irrefutable argument: when matter wears away, its particles must remain whole, for if the particles themselves broke into pieces, all Nature would be changed. 'Water and Earth composed of old worn Particles and Fragments of Particles, would not be of the same Nature and Texture now, with Water and Earth composed of entire Particles in the Beginning. And therefore, that Nature may be lasting, the Changes of corporeal Things are to be placed only in the various Separations and new Associations and Motions of these permanent Particles.'

Geoffroy's Affinity Tables

The first chemist to speak of affinity in terms of fixed attractions between different bodies and to prepare tables of these attractions (1719) was E. F. Geoffroy. Geoffroy made the assumption that if one acid has a greater affinity for a certain base than another, then the former acid will displace the latter from a salt formed by its combination with that base. In Geoffroy's tables, metals are precipitated in saline solutions by lime, lime by ammonia, and ammonia by potash and soda. Since what happens in fact is that lime precipitates ammonia, chemists were quick to criticize his system. Nevertheless his tables had the merit of proposing a general system of relations between chemical reactions.

Boerhaave's *De Menstruis*

In the first half of the 18th century the notion of affinity had another outstanding exponent in Hermann Boerhaave, a Dutch physician, who devoted his *De Menstruis* (1732) to this subject.

> 'In explaining the actions of *menstrua* (solvents),' he wrote, 'one need not introduce mechanical actions, violent propulsions, or natural antipathies, but rather a kind of amity, to wit a tendency to union.'

He accordingly defined chemical affinity as an attractive virtue, much as Newton had done before him, explaining that the attractive virtue causes dissolved particles to remain in homogeneous suspension irrespective of their density.

> 'This virtue', he asserted, 'causes the elements of one body to be attracted by those of the other and hence to be separated from their original mass. As a result, they can form an infinite number of new bodies.'

This concept may be called a rudimentary theory of double decomposition.

Advances in the Theory of Affinity

At about that period many chemists, especially in Germany, began to publish new affinity tables in which chemical substances, including phlogiston, were arranged more methodically. Even so, all of them shared Geoffroy's erroneous belief that chemical reactions are constant, no matter under what conditions they take place. Not until the work of Berthollet appeared was this idea finally abandoned.

Discussions on the existence of chemical affinities were pursued until about 1780. According to Venel's article on chemistry in the French Encyclopedia, affinities must be rejected because chemistry admits of only two great principles: chemical connections and heat. By chemical connections he meant the mutual actions between elementary corpuscles of matter, which, he contended, depend exclusively on such properties as their homogeneity or heterogeneity and not on repulsion or attraction, and hence not on their masses.

Clairaut and Buffon

In about 1745, Clairaut put forward the idea that the inverse square law did not apply to the attraction of chemical corpuscles. This view was attacked by Buffon who dealt with the subject at length in his *Secondes vues de la Nature* (1765). According to Buffon, one and the same law governs the attraction of all bodies, large and small. Moreover, that law could even be used for discovering the form of chemical corpuscles. Lavoisier, though absorbed by other problems, indicated that affinity theory alone could help to give chemistry the mathematical precision of an exact science. Accordingly he established affinity tables for oxygen. In 1772, Guyton de Morveau made a calculation of the affinities of various metals for mercury, in which he confused adhesion with chemical reaction.

Bergman and Elective Attractions

Other chemists studied affinity in specific reactions. A. Baumé showed that chemical affinities vary according to whether the reactions are carried out in solutions at ordinary temperatures (the 'wet way') or by heating the substances together at higher temperatures (the 'dry way'). T. O. Bergman, professor of chemistry at Upsala, distinguished between simple and double affinities.

Bergman studied a wide range of substances for almost ten years before he published his famous *Dissertation on Elective Attractions* (English translation, London, 1785). In this work he used the following approach:

> Suppose A to be a substance for which other heterogeneous substances *a*, *b*, *c*, *d etc.* have an attraction; suppose that A, combined with *c* to saturation (A*c*) should, upon the addition of *b*, tend to unite with it to the exclusion of *c*, A is then said to attract *b* more strongly than *c*, or to have a stronger elective attraction for it; lastly let the union of A*b* be broken on the addition of *a* to the exclusion of *b*, it will follow that *a* exceeds *b* in elective power, and we shall have a series *a*, *b*, *c* in respect of efficacy.

The tables constructed by Bergman on these principles consisted of 59 columns. One of the columns was devoted to the affinities of 'vital air' (oxygen), and two separate columns covered 'dry' and 'wet' reactions. Bergman also established tables of double affinities, amounting to 64 columns. Though he considered his tables as generally valid, he realized that the temperature of the reaction might affect the results.

From Affinity to Atomic Theory

Bergman also adopted the scheme of John Elliott (1747–1787) of expressing affinities numerically, *e.g.* potash ⟷ sulphuric acid = 9; silver oxide ⟷ nitric acid = 2; nitric acid ⟷ potash = 8; sulphuric acid ⟷ silver oxide = 4. From these values Elliott could predict that, when a solution of silver nitrate is mixed with a solution of potassium sulphate, potassium nitrate and silver sulphate will be formed, since the combined affinity of the last two salts (8+4) is greater than the combined affinity of the first two salts (9+2).

Further Research on Affinities

Without Elliott's contribution, all the long discussions on affinity would have remained completely useless. His numerical method paved the way for the laws of proportion by which chemistry was turned into an exact science. Until the search for these was begun, chemistry was an essentially qualitative study. Even Lavoisier's quantitative measurements were exclusively meant to help determine the number of elements forming a given compound, or to show that a given substance is simple and not compound. But by the time Lavoisier had made his great discoveries, that approach no longer met the needs of the day—the possibilities of qualitative chemistry had been largely exhausted.

The Strength of Acids

In 1775, Bergman established the respective weights of sulphuric, nitric, hydrochloric and carbonic acids which combined with a given quantity of soda or potash. However, all his and other calculations remained useless approximations, until a suitable standard substance was introduced.

The solution was provided by Kirwan, to whom Priestley's paper on hydrochloric acid (1772) had suggested the idea of using that gas for preparing a standard solution. He saturated a measured quantity of water with hydrochloric acid gas, measured the volume of the gas absorbed, and determined the increase of weight of the saturated solution. He then established the relationship between the densities of various acid solutions and their real acid content. Finally, he standardized carbonate solutions by means of a standard solution of acid, and then compared the strength of other acids. Between 1782 and 1792, he was also the first to establish the composition by weight of a number of salts.

At about the same time, Karl Friedrich Wenzel (1740–1793) determined the strength of acids by a different method: he plunged identical metal cylinders into various acids for one hour, and then determined their loss in weight, and hence their affinity for the various acids. Fourcroy argued that affinity must be measured not by the formation of compounds but by the propensity for decomposition, for, though nitrate of mercury, for instance, is obtained most readily by dissolving mercury in nitric acid, mercury has a much higher affinity still for hydrochloric acid, since the nitrate is also easily decomposed by heat whereas the chloride is not.

Double Decompositions and Proportions by Weight

Wenzel's subsequent studies of double decomposition led him to the important result that solutions of neutral salts give a neutral solution, even if one of the salts is precipitated. Hence he concluded that that portion of a base which neutralizes the acid of one salt will also neutralize the acid of another.

For instance, if one mixes solutions of barium nitrate and sodium sulphate, the sodium will exactly neutralize that proportion of the nitric acid which was combined with the barium; conversely, the barium will neutralize the exact quantity of sulphuric acid combined with the sodium. Fixed quantities of sodium and barium will therefore neutralize the same quantity of nitric or of sulphuric acid.

Wenzel published the results of his many analyses in his *Lehre von der Verwandtschaft der Körper* (Dresden, 1777), a book on which Guyton de Morveau commented at length in his article on affinity in the *Encyclopédie méthodique*. However, neither Wenzel nor de Morveau appreciated the full importance of the new discovery; Wenzel even suggested that neutrality was not maintained in all reactions, and de Morveau found that Wenzel's, Bergman's and Kirwan's theories of neutralization led to different results for reasons that escaped him. The prevailing confusion helps to emphasize what great obstacles had to be overcome by chemical analysts. Every time a new problem was posed, the whole framework of chemistry had apparently to be re-examined.

The next chemist to make a major contribution was the German mineralogist J. B. Richter (1762–1807), who ignored the question of affinity and concentrated instead on the numerical proportions in which chemical substances combine. He began by studying Wenzel's work on neutralization, and was able to establish, much more rigorously than Wenzel, the law of neutrality, namely that two neutral salts on double decomposition yield neutral compounds. Thence he concluded that there must be fixed quantitative relations between the constituents of these salts. He also affirmed that the various weights of the bases which neutralize a fixed weight of one acid also neutralize another fixed weight of a second acid, and that the weights of alkalis which neutralize a fixed weight of different acids always stand in a fixed ratio.

The First Laws of Proportions

Richter's main works, the *Anfangsgründe der Stöchyometrie oder Messkunst chemischer Elemente* (1792–1794) and the *Über die neuern Gegenstände der Chymie* (1791–1802), were not widely read because Richter's style was extremely obscure, and also because at times he wrote in terms of the oxygen theory and at others in terms of the phlogiston theory.

Nevertheless, commentaries on them were published by G. E. Fischer, whence Berthollet learned of Richter's ideas. Dalton knew nothing about Richter's work until September 1803.

At the end of the 18th century, the concepts of the laws of definite and multiple proportions were therefore known. However, they were not given the status of laws until the end of the 19th century, mainly because they had been propounded in the abstruse language of Wenzel and Richter. When Berthollet developed similar ideas more rigorously in his *Statique chimique* (1803), he too wrote in far too clumsy a style to attract the attention of the early 19th-century chemists.

Discoveries at the End of the 18th Century

Beside the great theoretical discoveries we have been discussing, 18th-century chemists also introduced a host of practical advances. Most of these were made by the Swedish school of chemists, led by Bergman. Between 1767 and 1768, Scheele's brilliant researches led him not only to the independent discovery of oxygen and chlorine, but also to the discovery of barium (1774), and of molybdic and tungstic acids (1778 and 1781). (These discoveries were intimately linked with the discovery of manganese by Bergman, molybdenum by Hielm and tungsten by Fausto de Elhuyar.) Scheele also succeeded in isolating a great number of organic compounds, the most important of which were glycerine (1783) and tartaric (1769), formic (1774), uric (1776), lactic and mucic (1780), benzoic and tannic (1782), citric, oxalic (1784), malic (1785) and gallic (1786) acids.

Two hydrocarbons were discovered at about the same time: methane, which Volta obtained from marsh gas in 1778 and which Berthollet studied in 1785, and ethylene, which was discovered in 1796 by four Dutch chemists, Boudt, Deiman, van Troostwyk and Lauwerenburg. They called it 'olefient' or 'oil-making' gas because they noticed that in the presence of chlorine it forms an oily liquid, the so-called 'Dutch liquor' (ethylene dichloride).

Dalton's Theory

By their work on chemical affinity, the 18th-century chemists had prepared the field for Dalton, whose atomic theory we shall be discussing in a later volume. As early as 1781, the Irish chemist William Higgins (*A Comparative View of the Phlogistic and Antiphlogistic Theories*) had propounded the view that all bodies are constituted of atoms which combine in simple proportions into different compounds. Higgins realized clearly that the various oxides of one and the same element must differ from one another by the number of their oxygen atoms, but since he was mistaken in thinking that all atoms are of equal weight, his conclusions could easily be disproved. As a result, his hypothesis was generally ignored and Higgins himself was forced to abandon it in the end. Fifteen years later, the scientific climate had changed so radically that Dalton's hypothesis met with little opposition.

BIOLOGICAL AND GEOLOGICAL SCIENCES

CHAPTER 1

General Biology

CLASSIFICATION AND DESCRIPTION

Antecedents

Though the idea of putting some order into the apparent confusion of living forms had already occurred to the older naturalists, J. P. de Tournefort (see p. 364) (1656–1708) was probably the first to establish a really natural system of classification, based on 'the objective reality of species, genera and classes' (J. F. Leroy). A similar attempt was made by John Ray (*Historia plantarum generalis*, 1686–1704), who also tried to define the concept of species more precisely.

The Work of Linnaeus

Their work was continued and developed by Linnaeus, who proposed a 'sexual system' of classifying plants by their stamens. Though this system proved most useful for distinguishing species, its exclusive concentration on only one floral part made it rather artificial and hence less advanced than many earlier systems (see p. 554).

Linnaeus was fully aware of this shortcoming, and therefore made a further attempt to divide the plant kingdom into *ordines naturales* and, in particular, to classify animals in the most 'natural' way possible in his day, *i.e.* by considering not only their external but also their internal structure, and especially the structure of the heart and the respiratory and sexual organs.

One of Linnaeus' greatest contributions was his *binary* nomenclature, in which a noun represents the genus and an adjective the species. Each of his genera formed a natural group. For example, the genus *Felis* embraced the species *Felis domesticus* (cat), *Felis catus* (wild cat), *Felis leo* (lion), *Felis pardus* (panther) and *Felis tigris* (tiger).

This simple nomenclature proved so useful that it is used by biologists to this day, though the general system proposed by Linnaeus proved too inflexible to be retained. This fault was repaired by Linnaeus' successors, and especially by Bernard de Jussieu, Antoine Laurent de Jussieu and Michel Adanson, who stressed the importance of natural *families*, a concept previously used by Pierre Magnol (1689).

Buffon's Opposition to Linnaeus

Linnaeus' illustrious contemporary, Georges Louis Leclerc, Comte de Buffon (1707–1788), was appointed Keeper of the *Jardin du Roi* in 1739 and thereafter devoted himself exclusively to writing a natural history. Buffon was not only a zoologist but also a physicist, mathematician, geologist, mineralogist, philosopher and great stylist. His main works included the *Théorie de la Terre* (1749), the *Époques de la Nature* (1778), the *Histoire des Quadrupèdes* (12 volumes, 1755–1767), the *Histoire des oiseaux* (9 volumes, 1770–1783) and the *Histoire naturelle de l'Homme* (1749). Buffon was implacably opposed to Linnaeus, and scoffed at a system which lumped the ass and the zebra together with the horse:

> Is it not far better to place the horse before the dog, which runs after it in nature, than before the zebra, of which we know little, and which, perhaps, has no connection with the horse other than that it, too, is a soliped? (*Histoire naturelle*, Vol. I.)[1]

In his subsequent writings, and notably in his elegant *Histoire des oiseaux*, Buffon was willy-nilly forced to introduce a methodical classification and to consider structural affinities rather than 'practical and familiar' relationships. Even so, he continued to claim —whether he acted upon it or not—that 'genera, classes and orders exist only in our imagination' and that 'nature consists only of individuals'.

Buffon and the Description of the Animal Kingdom

Despite his bias, his obstinacy and certain crude misconceptions which Flourens has attributed to his having been a mathematician before he became a naturalist, Buffon was an outstanding observer of animal forms. Unlike Linnaeus, he concentrated less on structural detail than on living entities, on synthesis rather than analysis. Beyond that, he had the unfortunate tendency to sacrifice accuracy for stylistic effect, though d'Alembert probably went too far when he called him a 'great phrasemonger'. He rendered a great service to zoology not only by his elegant descriptions of quadrupeds and birds, and by the brilliance of his style, which convinced many ordinary people of the charms of that science, but also by introducing a novel approach to the subject.

[1] In this connection, Linnaeus wrote to a friend: 'I cannot wait to see M. Buffon's new volumes. By way of a natural method, he begins with the horse and with the dog. This is quite enough for me; I have seen the theory; now I want to see its practical consequences.'

41 Linnaeus in Lapp costume, by Martinus Hoffman

Comte de Buffon, by François Hubert Drouais

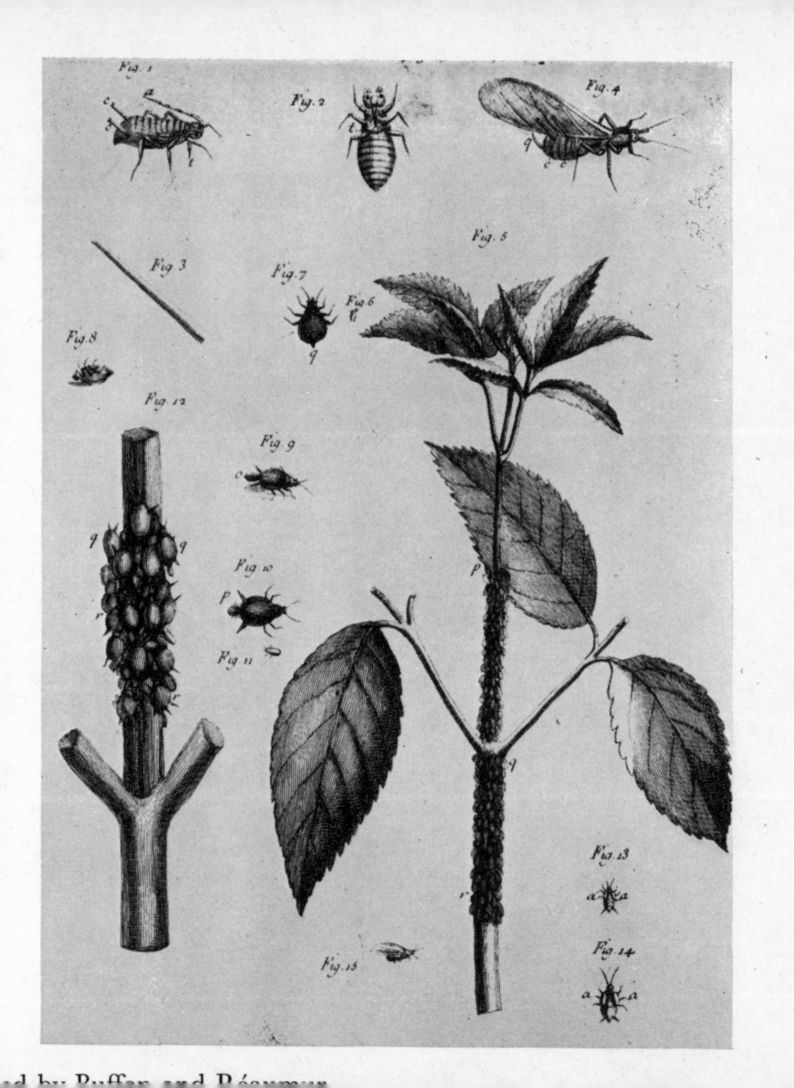

12. Zoological plates used by Buffon and Réaumur

For every animal he described, he gathered such specific data as the rate of growth, the age of maturity of the male and the female, the duration of gestation, the size of the litter, the termination of fertility in either sex, the sex ratio, the tendency to hybridization, racial variability, maternal care, habits, instincts, voices *etc.*

Buffon tried to establish connections between fertility and size and degree of domestication, and also between hydridization and sex ratio. Far from being an armchair naturalist, as some have called him, he lived in close contact with the animals he wrote about. At Montbord he kept birds, bears, and lions; to study the meaning of 'species' more closely, he tried to cross dogs with wolves, rabbits with hares, and goats with sheep.

Buffon's 'Zoological Philosophy'

According to Cuvier, some of Buffon's ideas were, in fact, true discoveries. Among these were his stress of the unity of nature, his views on extinct species, and on the differences between the New and the Old World faunas (A. L. de Jussieu had previously drawn attention to the existence of such differences in the distribution of plants). Finally, he was one of the first to include man in zoological classifications, when he said that the orang-utang is either first among the apes or else the last among men (*Nomenclature des singes*).

Buffon was, on the whole, a pantheist, and ridiculed the musings of those who, like Réaumur, imagine that 'there is a God who concerns himself with such matters as the way in which beetles fold their wings'.

Daubenton

Buffon's chief collaborator was Louis Daubenton (1716–1800), who carried out Buffon's dissections, prepared all the specimens, and put them on display in the *Jardin du Roi*, which was soon afterwards thrown open to the public.

Daubenton, one of the founders of descriptive anatomy, also turned his attention to breeding an improved strain of sheep by selection.

Other Zoological Studies

While Buffon and Daubenton studied the natural history of the higher vertebrates, other naturalists concentrated on the lower orders. Artedi examined fishes, Adanson molluscs, Pallas worms, and Müller protozoa.

Lyonet (1707–1789) wrote a remarkable paper on the 'caterpillar which devours willow-wood' (1750), a marvel of micro-morphology in which he distinguished more than 4,000 muscles.

J. A. Peyssonel (1694–1759), a Marseilles physician, was one of the first to recognize that corals are not plants but animals. This view was challenged by many zoologists and especially by Réaumur.

THE FORMATION OF SPECIES

The Fixity of Species

Ray, and above all Linnaeus, had introduced the view that every species is fixed and immutable. Thus Ray asserted that 'no species is ever born from the seeds of another' and Linnaeus (*Fundamenta botanica*, 1736) declared that nature has as many species now as were created in the beginning. As Leroy has put it so correctly, 'far from being an obstacle to the progress of science, this idea fulfilled a pressing need and introduced some order where utter confusion had reigned before'.

It must be remembered that, before Linnaeus and Ray, it was generally believed that any species could give rise to practically any other species. Even in the 18th century, the English surgeon Nathanael de Saint-André still believed the story that a woman had given birth to a rabbit, and so able a microscopist as J. T. Needham maintained that a mould could turn into an animal.

Partial Transformism

However, despite its many advantages, the theory of the fixity of species failed to explain certain variations which undoubtedly occurred within the same species. Ray therefore conceded that a species might occasionally 'degenerate', so that a cauliflower, for instance, might produce an ordinary cabbage, or a *Primula veris major* a *Primula pratensis inodora*.

Linnaeus, for his part, attributed 'serious' differences between plants to God's infinite wisdom, and less 'serious' and transitory differences (*e.g.* monstrosities) to Nature herself.

However, in 1742, when a student showed him a *Linaria* which Linnaeus was unable to identify, he was forced to modify his views, and to accept the 'stupefying' conclusion that new species, and even new genera, can appear in the plant kingdom either by sudden variation or by hybridization.

> Are all species the daughters of time? Or has the Creator, at the beginning of the world, limited this development to a fixed number of species? I do not dare to pronounce on this subject with certainty.

In other words, the chief advocate of the fixity of species had begun to waver.

A few decades earlier (1715–1716), the botanist J. Marchant had come across two species of Mercury which differed from the typical species by the arrangement and serration of their leaves. Since the new species produced like descendants, Marchant concluded that he had found a new species and felt free to put forward the following hypothesis:

> This observation would suggest that once the Almighty created individual plants of every conceivable structure and nature as models of every genus, these models produced varieties among which those which have remained constant and permanent have become species. In the course of time, these have multiplied to such an extent that some genera are known to contain up to a hundred, a hundred and fifty, and even more than two hundred distinct and constant species. . . . ('Observations on the nature of plants', *Mem. de l'Ac. roy. des Sciences*, 1719.)

Similar opinions were expressed by Duchesne, an amateur botanist of great renown, who had observed the sudden appearance of a new type of strawberry (*Fragaria monophylla*). Duchesne was too cautious to call the new type a 'species' and merely concluded that all strawberries must have sprung from a common stock. In his *Histoire naturelle des Fraisiers* (1766), he went on to argue that the genealogical order of plants is all that the botanist need study—'everything else is arbitrary and futile'.

Michel Adanson (*Histoire des familles des plantes*, 1763) also argued against the absolute fixity of species, alleging that he had himself heard of eight cases of the appearance of new species, three of which, in particular, were 'very remarkable and highly authenticated, and vouched for by reliable botanists, who knew how to use their eyes'. According to Adanson, these transformations were produced by the action of such external factors as domestication, climate *etc.*

Buffon and Transformism

Buffon, who devoted much of his time to the problem of species, finally decided in favour of limited variability. However, he appreciated the complexity of the problem, which he called 'one of nature's profound mysteries which man cannot plumb except by making repeated, long and difficult experiments'. Writing on mules and the problems of hybridization he says:

> How, except by the results of thousands of unions, can we determine the relationship between animals? . . . At what distance from man must we place the large apes, which resemble man so perfectly by the structure of their bodies? Have animal species not changed since the beginning; has their number not increased or diminished; have weak species not been destroyed by the stronger or by the tyranny of man . . .? What connection is there between the interrelationship of species and the

better-known interrelationship of races belonging to the same species? (*Des mulets.*)

Buffon expressed his transformist ideas most clearly in his discussion of the *degeneration* of animals under the influence of climate, nutrition and domestication.

He asserted that these influences explained variations in size, in the colour and quality of the fur, in the thickness of the skin, in the size of the paws, and in the voice, all of which suggested the possibility 'that a degeneration in very early times' may have produced differences between species of one and the same genus.

From a comparison of quadrupeds, Buffon then concluded that the 200 species known to him can definitely 'be reduced to a very small number of families or principal types'. Of these, he named 24 in the Old and 14 in the New World, adding that since the tapir resembles the elephant, the peccary the pig, the llama the camel, the jaguar and the ocelot the panther, the skunk the polecat, *etc.*, the number of original types may have to be reduced still further. However, he was careful not to appear as an official advocate of the transformist theory, possibly because he was afraid of the Church.

The Transformism of Maupertuis

The first to adopt transformist ideas openly was not a biologist but a mathematician, Pierre Louis Moreau de Maupertuis, whose *Essai sur la formation des corps organisés* (1754) represents a landmark in natural history.

According to Maupertuis, generation is the result of the combination of 'seminal molecules'. When these molecules combine in the normal way, the young resembles its parents, but when they combine abnormally, as they sometimes do, the young is a unique, abnormal individual. Species may well have arisen from the handing down of such abnormal characters.

By these ideas Maupertuis clearly foreshadowed the modern concept of mutation. He had previously written in his *Vénus physique* (1745):

> Those who try to satisfy the demands of the curious often become discoverers of new species, revealing the existence of unsuspected breeds of dogs, pigeons and finches, which were at first no more than odd individuals, but which repeated acts of generation have turned into species.

Similarly, discussing polydactyly in man, Maupertuis wrote, 'I fully believe that the supernumerary digits were originally no more than accidental varieties. . . . But these varieties, once consolidated by a sufficiently large number of generations by two sexidigital parents, became the foundations of new species, and it is perhaps in this way that all species have multiplied' (Letter XVII).

The Precursors of Speculative Transformism: Benoist de Maillet and J. B. C. Robinet

At about the same time that Maupertuis presented his remarkable views, the philosopher Benoist de Maillet (1659–1738) published the *Telliamed* (printed in 1735 but not released until 1748), in which he developed a kind of fabulous transformism that he himself may not have taken seriously. Since the Biblical story of the Flood was apparently corroborated by the existence of 'petrified bodies'—fossil shells and fish—in mountains, de Maillet argued that the first living creatures must all have been marine animals, and that all terrestrial species, man included, arose from these primordial creatures by sudden transformations.

He went on to explain that just as a caterpillar turns into a butterfly, so a fish can turn into a bird by transforming its fins into wings, its scales into feathers, *etc.*, or even into a bear, an elephant or, finally, man. While these sudden transformations must have killed off millions of animals, 'so long as only two survived, the existence of the new species was assured'.

Another 'speculative transformist' was Jean Baptiste Charles Robinet (1735–1820), who described the principle of continuity as a 'new manner of contemplating nature'. For him, all living creatures belong to a single kingdom, forming a 'continuous chain' and being but variations on an original 'prototype', whose progressive development resulted from a growing predominance of force over matter. Man represents the upper limit of the chain, and is the aim and object of all Nature's efforts.

> With each variation of the prototype, Nature meditates the human form. . . . Nature advances step by step towards the excellent creature crowning her work. . . . There are as many intermediate variations between the prototype and man as there are rough drafts which Nature had to make before reaching the perfection towards which she constantly strives. (*De la nature*, 1766.)

Erasmus Darwin

Much more important was the work of Erasmus Darwin (1731–1802), grandfather of the great Charles, whose *Zoonomia or the Laws of Organic Life* (1794) contained a complete theory of the gradual transformation and perfection of the animal kingdom.

According to Erasmus Darwin, all organic life originated from a single primal filament, on which the 'Great First Cause' bestowed the power of acquiring new parts and new potentialities, and hence 'the faculty of continuing to improve by its own inherent activity and of delivering down these improvements by generation to its posterity....'

These 'improvements' resulted from responses to a variety of external stimuli: climate, habitat, food, diseases, domestication *etc.* The snout of the pig enables it to root in the ground, the trunk of the elephant enables it to feed on high branches and to draw up water without bending its knees, and so on. These and other specialized organs must have been acquired gradually by successive generations of animals in the effort to obtain suitable nourishment.

Apart from this 'Lamarckian' idea, the *Zoonomia* also contained the germ of such 'Darwinian' notions as protective coloration, sexual selection *etc.* For example, Erasmus Darwin contended that the spurs of birds did not serve to defend them against other species, for in that case, the females would have had them as well as the males. Nature's aim was rather to make sure that only the strongest and most active male birds would participate in the production of offspring.

By the end of the 18th century, the new doctrine of transformism was firmly entrenched. It received support both from naturalists, who considered it an adequate explanation of the variations they had observed, and from philosophers, who were no longer satisfied that the Biblical account of the Creation explained all the known facts.

THE PROBLEM OF GENERATION

The Heritage of the 17th Century. Preformationists *v.* Epigenesists

Seventeenth-century preformationist views, according to which every germ contains a complete being in miniature, had a large number of supporters in the 18th century. This was not surprising, since preformationism simply did away with the embryological problem. As one of its leading advocates put it, all generation does is to magnify previously invisible parts.

The preformationist camp was, however, divided into two factions: one which placed the germ in the ovum (the 'ovists'), and another which placed it in the spermatozoon (the 'spermatists' or 'animalculists'). In addition, preformationism was often associated with the fantastic theory of *emboîtement*, according to which the germ contained a foetus which, in turn, contained the germ of the third generation, and so on *ad infinitum*.

Another associated and equally far-fetched theory was that of 'dissemination', according to which the germs are all-pervading, and seize the first chance of insinuating themselves into any man or woman who provides them with a domicile.

Since all these ideas were so extraordinary, many biologists rejected preformationism in favour of epigenesis, or the gradual formation of the embryo from a newly produced substance and not a pre-existing germ. The resulting controversy had considerable repercussions on the subsequent history of biology. As happened with so many scientific disputes, each side was partly correct. The Epigenesists were right to criticize the naïve idea of *emboîtement*; the preformationists were right to insist that *ex nihilo nihil fit*. The solution did not appear until the 19th century, when it was shown that the germ cell, though inherited and highly organized, bears no resemblance to the future foetus.

The Discovery of Parthenogenesis

The *emboîtement* hypothesis had a most brilliant and staunch advocate in Réaumur's pupil, the Swiss naturalist and philosopher Charles Bonnet (1720–1793). Bonnet first attracted the attention of naturalists when, at the age of twenty, he discovered a phenomenon which had previously been merely suspected (by Leeuwenhoek and Réaumur), that of parthenogenesis.

He placed a single unfertilized aphis on a plant and covered it with a bell-jar. After a month, he found that the unfertilized female had produced 95 aphids, all born alive. This discovery, which Réaumur communicated to the *Académie des Sciences* in 1740, caused a great sensation and was hailed quite generally as convincing proof of the ovist thesis.[1]

Bonnet's Explanation

From this experiment, Bonnet concluded that when male fluid or semen enters the ovum—*i.e.* the preformed foetus—it merely helps the fluid by its 'nourishing molecules'. Now these 'molecules' are able to act selectively on given parts of the foetus, which explains the resemblance of the young to the father, particularly in the case of such hybrids as mules. (The resemblance of a child to both its parents had been the great stumbling-block of ovists and spermatists alike.) Thus when the sperm of the ass enters the foetus of a mare, its molecules tend to increase the size of the eyes and the neck; when the sperm of the horse enters the foetus of a female ass, its molecules tend to increase the size of the tail.

Though Bonnet knew that semen contains 'animalcules', he denied that they played any part in fertilization.

[1] The only notable dissentient was Erasmus Darwin, according to whom Bonnet's aphis had been a male and not a female. He therefore concluded that animals could be born without a mother, but never without a father.

Maupertuis' 'Seminal Particles'

Chief among Bonnet's many opponents was Maupertuis, who, in the *Vénus physique* and in his letters, argued convincingly that the single-germ theory was refuted not only by the existence of hybrids, but also by the transmission of human anomalies.

Maupertuis had, in fact, discovered a Berlin family (that of the surgeon Jacob Ruhe) in which polydactyly was transmitted from generation to generation. By delving back into the history of this family, he found that the anomaly was handed on by parents of either sex. He concluded that Nature's own experiments proved conclusively that particles from both parents contribute equally to the formation of the various organs.[1]

Buffon and the Theory of Organic Molecules

This hypothesis was developed by Buffon, according to whom all living beings were built up of animated and indestructible molecules, stemming from both parents and organized by an 'internal mould'.

With the help of the famous microscopist, John Turberville Needham (1713–1781), Buffon was able to produce 'direct proof' of his theories. He claimed that the microscope actually reveals the birth of animalculae from male semen, and of 'active globules similar to animalculae' in the fluid from the female glands, which he also called 'testicles'. He obtained these fluids from crushed animal organs contaminated with vegetable matter, and had, in fact, confused animalcules with infusoria, so that his whole system was based on an elementary error.

At about 1760, the great Swiss physiologist, Albert von Haller, who originally held epigenesist views, concluded from his own observations that the germ of the chick is produced by the hen and that the chick embryo is formed before fertilization. Charles Bonnet's ovist theory had apparently been vindicated.

C. F. Wolff and the Beginnings of Descriptive Embryology

But that theory, and all other preformationist doctrines, were completely destroyed by the work of Caspar Friedrich Wolff (1733–1794), who, after patient microscopic studies, discovered that the blood-vessels of the chick blastoderm appear where no blood-vessels have existed before. He described this discovery in his *Theoria generationis* (1759). In a later work (*De formatione intestinorum*, 1768), he was able to prove further that the chick intestine is formed by the folding back of a sheath of tissue which is detached from the ventral

[1] The transmission of paternal characters was also demonstrated by Kölreuter, working with tobacco-plants (1761), and by Trembley, working with maize.

surface of the embryo, and that the folds produce a gutter which in time transforms itself into a closed tube.

Though Wolff may be called the first descriptive embryologist, and though he turned biologists from their idle speculations to the detailed study of the complex phenomenon of animal embryogenesis, his theory left the problem of the respective contributions of the ovum and the spermatozoon unsolved. Wolff's view that embryonic growth is governed by a *vis essentialis* was challenged by Bonnet:

> If the substance which the essential force organizes is in no way preformed, why should that force tend to produce an animal rather than a plant, and one animal rather than another? Again, why should the essential force produce one organ rather than another in a determined place?

Bonnet's criticism was quite fair, for though the epigenesists were right to hold that the embryo is formed gradually, they explained its evolution by the vaguest of hypotheses: Maupertuis' attractions, Buffon's inner mould, and Wolff's essential force.

Spallanzani and the Experimental Study of Fertilization

The Italian biologist, Lazzaro Spallanzani (1729–1799), one of the foremost physiologists of his day, took the study of animal generation one step further when he made an experimental study of fertilization. Although he thought that his observations supported the ovist theory, he was open-minded enough not to let that theory blind him to the real facts.

From experiments with frogs, Spallanzani concluded that the eggs (which he took for miniature tadpoles) never develop if they are removed before they are laid, and that they must therefore be fertilized outside the female's body.

He therefore dressed male frogs in small trousers and left them with females. Unlike Réaumur and Nollet, who had tried the same experiment earlier, Spallanzani managed to abstract some transparent liquid and to moisten the virgin eggs with it. The eggs hatched out into normal tadpoles, and Spallanzani was therefore one of the first to achieve artificial insemination under laboratory conditions. (In 1763, Jacobi had fertilized fish-eggs with milt, and according to some authors, the artificial insemination of mares was an old Arab practice.)

A little later, Spallanzani managed to inseminate a bitch, and in 1799 Hunter applied the method to women.

Spallanzani also attempted the artificial cross-breeding of cats and dogs, in which he was, of course, unsuccessful. In addition, he made many carefully controlled experiments, often with the help of Bonnet, to demonstrate the role of the thick albuminous coat surrounding the frog's eggs, and to show that semen can be diluted without losing its fertilizing power. He also studied the comparative resistance of different ova and of semen to variations in temperature and to a number of chemical substances, and attempted to cross-breed tailless and tailed amphibians.

By a convincing experiment he destroyed the common belief in 'remote fertilization' (*aura seminalis*) and showed that fertilization depends on semen coming into direct contact with the ovum. Further, he proved that filtration robs semen of its fertilizing power, but he failed to draw the correct conclusion, that the fertilizing fraction of semen is contained in the residue. It was not that he denied the existence of spermatozoa, which he had, in fact, studied at great length in about 1717, but that, like Buffon, he believed that every ovum was a foetus in miniature, and thought that the animalculae could play no more than the subsidiary role of stimulating the ova.

On the other hand, the very misconception which prevented Spallanzani's correct interpretation of his own experiments suggested to him the possibility of artificial parthenogenesis. If semen is no more than a stimulating agent, then a purely physical agent (electrical fluid) or some organic substance (salamander poison, lemon juice *etc.*) might serve equally well. Spallanzani himself made no progress along these lines, but his idea, although based on an error, led to fruitful experiments in the 19th century.

ANIMAL REGENERATION

The problem of generation was intimately connected with the problem of regeneration, or the replacement of injured or lost parts. This problem was introduced into biological discussions in 1712, when Réaumur discovered that a crayfish can grow new legs, and carefully described the stages of regeneration.

Trembley's Experiments

A far more fundamental discovery was made in 1740, when Abraham Trembley (1700–1784) described the extraordinary regenerative powers of *Hydra*, a very small creature found in ditches and stagnant ponds.

Trembley was only an amateur naturalist, and it was sheer curiosity which first caused him to look at the tiny creature more closely. Uncertain whether *Hydra* was an animal or a plant, it occurred to him to cut it in two and see if the two halves would live; if they did, the natural conclusion would be that *Hydra* is a plant.

However, though he found that the parts did grow, he also found that they devoured live water-fleas, so that he was no wiser than before. It was only after further studies, lasting for more than three years, that he finally concluded that *Hydra* was, in fact, an animal. (*Mémoire pour servir à l'histoire d'un genre de Polypes d'eau douce à bras en forme de cornes*, 1744.)

Trembley showed that small segments of *Hydra* can grow into complete polyps, that two complete polyps can be grafted together, and finally that polyps can be turned inside out without suffering any damage (*ibid.*).

Like parthenogenesis, Trembley's *Hydra* was generally acclaimed as a 'marvel of nature'. Another marvel was Needham's and Spallanzani's discovery that apparently dead vinegar eels, rotifers and tardigrades have the power of reviving when placed in water.

Discussion of Animal Regeneration

Trembley's discoveries were quickly confirmed by Baker, Réaumur and others,[1] who showed that the phenomenon of animal regeneration was far more common than had at first been thought.

Charles Bonnet discovered the regenerative powers of certain freshwater worms, and Spallanzani (1768) of earthworms, snails (which can grow new mouth-parts, tentacles and eyes) and tritons (which can grow four new legs complete with bone, muscle and nerves). Voltaire immediately started collecting and decapitating snails in his garden.

Regeneration, like generation, was explained by preformationists and epigenesists in terms of their respective theories. Thus, Charles Bonnet contended that preformed germs are found not only in the ovary but in every part of the body, so that *Hydra*, for instance, is formed of 'an infinite number of small polyps which emerge when conditions are favourable'. Bonnet also gave the following explanation of the partial regeneration of worms:

> I see no objection to assuming the existence of germs containing anterior parts and others containing posterior parts. This hypothesis seems to me less difficult to maintain than that of the partial obliteration of germs.

According to Bonnet, the leg of the crayfish consists of a chain of germs with decreasing potentialities:

[1] Voltaire, who was often sceptical when there was no need to be, denied that *Hydra* was an animal. 'Though my eyes and my reason may play me false, I must confess that I have been unable to see in these polyps anything but fine reeds which seem to be of the nature of sensitive plants. . . . It would be well to suspend judgment . . . the truth can never suffer from waiting' (*Singularités de la nature*, 1768).

> In each leg of the crayfish is lodged a series of germs which contain parts similar to those which nature intends to replace. I therefore believe that the germ from which the old leg originates contains an entire leg with five articulations, the next a leg with only four articulations, and so on.

Moreover, since the second leg can also be regenerated, it 'follows' that the new, like the old, leg 'contains germs for producing further legs' which 'need not stagger the imagination'.

Once again, preformationism had become bogged down in the disastrous doctrine of *emboîtement*.

Nor were the epigenesists more successful. To explain regeneration by their theory they were forced to introduce 'mechanical' and other inexplicable forces.

THE ORIGIN OF MONSTERS

The scientific study of abnormal or monstrous animals was begun in the early 18th century. By then, it was appreciated that monsters were not caused by the devil or by special acts of God, but that they were objects of scientific observation, and subject to natural laws.

Still, scientific opinion remained divided as to their origin. While some biologists, led by Lémery, assumed the existence of monstrous germs, others, led by Winslow, claimed that abnormality resulted from 'accidental causes' (compression, diseases, maternal stresses *etc.*) affecting the normal development of the embryo in the womb.

The two parties to what became known as the 'monster controversy' placed their respective views before the Paris Academy of Science and the ensuing discussions laid the foundations of 19th-century studies of teratology.

Oddly enough, the problem was not at first considered part and parcel of the wider problem of generation. Thus, though von Haller, as a convinced preformationist, affirmed the existence of monstrous germs in his *De monstris*, Bonnet, who was an equally staunch defender of preformationism, rallied to the environmental theory.

SPONTANEOUS GENERATION

The Animalcule Problem

Despite the work of Redi and Vallisnieri, biologists continued to believe in the spontaneous generation of microscopic organisms, and especially of infusoria. It was generally known that if organic matter was left in tepid water for a few days, the water would turn turbid and begin to teem with innumerable microscopic organisms, including animalcules.

Once again, epigenesists confronted preformationists. While the former saw no reason why animalcules should not be formed spontaneously out of the medium by 'mechanical' or 'vegetative' forces, the preformationists called these views an insult to the human intelligence. Mere smallness of size was no reason for excluding animalcules from the laws governing the generation of animals.

The Advocates of Spontaneous Generation

Among the chief advocates of the theory of spontaneous generation were the 'prince of micrographers', O. F. Müller, who had made a special study of infusoria, and Buffon, according to whom spontaneous generation was not restricted to microscopic animals alone. All animals, he maintained, are formed of 'organic molecules' and when an animal, however large, dies, these molecules are released to produce such small animals as worms, crustaceans, maggots, caterpillars, or even such plants as mushrooms. Again, if a living animal has an excess of these molecules, the result is tapeworms, threadworms, fluke-worms, lice, *etc.*

'My experiments', Buffon wrote, 'show very clearly not only that there are no pre-existent germs, but also that the generation of animals and plants is not univocal: there are perhaps as many animals or plants produced by the fortuitous combination of organic molecules as there are animals and plants reproduced by a constant succession of generations. . . . Corruption and decomposition produces an infinite number of organized animals and plants.'

The Opponents of Spontaneous Generation

Réaumur and Bonnet were two of the chief opponents of the theory of spontaneous generation.

'All nature', Bonnet wrote, 'argues against *equivocal* generation. . . . While I know that we must constantly guard against general rules . . . I also know that we must only admit those exceptions that are established beyond any doubt, especially when they run counter to the most universal, the most constant, and the most invariable of all the laws we know. . . . When the appearance of certain animalcules in a liquid is explained by *productive* forces and *vegetative* virtues, are we not offered mere words instead of facts? What idea are we given of these forces; how can they conceivably organize matter, transform inanimate molecules into living beings . . .? We have laughed at Epicuros who peopled his world with atoms: is turning mutton gravy into an animal less of an insult to sane philosophers?'

Spallanzani's Objections to Needham's Experiments

By this last remark, Bonnet was alluding to an experiment which Needham had performed in about 1740 and which had caused preformationists great embarrassment. Needham had poured some boiling mutton broth into a flask, which he immediately corked and sealed with mastic to exclude external germs, assuming that the germs from the broth had been destroyed by the boiling. Upon opening the flask a few days later and discovering that it teemed with living organisms, he concluded that these organisms could only have originated spontaneously in the liquid.

Though the preformationists heaped abuse on Needham, they were unable to refute his findings until 1770, when Spallanzani repeated the experiment under more carefully controlled conditions. As a result, he was able to show that the porous cork Needham had used did not exclude all the germs and that, moreover, Needham had not boiled the broth long enough. When an infusion was boiled for a much longer period in a hermetically sealed flask, no new germs appeared.

Needham objected that the prolonged heating destroys not only the germs but also the virtue of the infusion for generating life spontaneously, or the virtue of the air for supporting it. And there the matter rested until the 19th century, when Schwann and Pasteur were able to vindicate Spallanzani completely.

* * *

To sum up, 18th-century biology was dominated by the struggle between the preformationists and the epigenesists, and by their clash of views on three cardinal problems: the problem of the formation of the individual, the problem of the formation of the species, and the problem of the formation of life.

The preformationists were necessarily opposed to the theory of spontaneous generation, and generally believed in the fixity of species. The epigenesists, on the other hand, defended the theory of spontaneous generation and generally inclined to transformist views.

Both schools of thought have affected subsequent developments. Thus modern biology has adopted epigenesis while yet retaining the organized germ, and transformism while yet retaining the fixity of living species. It has rejected the theory of spontaneous generation, while yet admitting the spontaneous formation of life in the distant past.

CHAPTER 2

Animal Physiology

New Factors in Research

Eighteenth-century advances in physics and chemistry had direct repercussions on physiological research. Thus electricity was used to study the behaviour of vital forces, pneumatic chemistry led to a better understanding of gaseous exchanges between living organisms and their environment, and new physical instruments like the thermometer and the calorimeter enabled biologists to determine a number of biological constants. It is therefore not surprising that most 18th-century physiological discoveries were made by such non-medical scientists as Hales, Priestley, Lavoisier, Réaumur and Spallanzani.

On the other hand, the teaching of physiology was still left in the hands of professors of medicine, the most illustrious of whom were the 'great systematizers', Boerhaave (1668–1738), Stahl (1660–1734) and Hoffmann (1660–1742).

RESPIRATION

The study of respiration hinged on the solution of two problems: the mechanical problem of how the air enters the lungs, and the chemical problem of the constitution of the air-blood mixture. The first problem was partially solved when Borelli explained how the intercostal muscles are capable of altering the volume of the thorax. After Musschenbroek, Daniel Bernoulli and Hamberger had investigated the problem more fully, Haller was able to provide a complete solution in his *De respiratione experimenta anatomica* (1746–1747).

The second problem was studied by so many biologists that we can mention only the most important of them. From Robert Boyle's *Nova experimenta physicomechanica de vi aëris elastica et ejusdem effectibus* (1669), John Mayow concluded, about 1674, that animal respiration involves the fixation of an aerial 'spirit' and hence the exhaustion of respirable air in a confined space. In his *Experiments and Observations on different kinds of Air* (1774–1777), Priestley reported that a sprig of mint will release enough dephlogisticated air (oxygen) to support combustion in an upturned bell-jar. In 1775 he informed the Royal Society that dephlogisticated air obtained in that way also supports the respiration of a mouse.

Lavoisier's Discoveries

Lavoisier's first investigations of the 'principle' with which metals combine during calcination had much the same aims as Priestley's studies: the analysis, detection and identification of various kinds of gases. However, his more systematic studies of the respiration of birds (1775–1776) and of guinea-pigs (1777) enabled him to present to the *Académie des Sciences* a definitive paper on changes in the blood during respiration (*Mémoire sur les changements que le sang éprouve dans les poumons et sur le mécanisme de la respiration*, 1777). From comparative measurements of the volume of gas absorbed and the quantity of heat released by guinea-pigs during respiration, he and Laplace were later able to show that respiration is a form of slow combustion (1780). They were wrong, however, in assuming that it is merely the combustion of carbon, but Lavoisier corrected this error in his *Sur les alterations qu' éprouve l'air respiré* (1785). They were also wrong to describe the lung as the centre of combustion, and the function of the blood the distribution of the heat produced.

Finally, after measuring energy exchanges in human beings, with Séguin as the experimental subject, Lavoisier summed up his views on the respiration and transpiration of animals as follows:

> The animal machine is controlled by three principal governors: respiration, which consumes hydrogen and carbon and which supplies caloric; transpiration, which fluctuates with requirements of caloric; and finally digestion, which restores to the blood what it has lost by respiration and transpiration.

These conclusions put an end to an age-long controversy. Among Lavoisier's more immediate predecessors, the 17th-century chemists had attributed animal heat to fermentations in the heart (like van Helmont), to the effervescence of venous blood and chyle (like Sylvius), or to the mechanical action on the blood of air pressure and friction (like Stahl). Von Haller had taken a similar view, though he had added that, since internal friction and air pressure cannot raise water to blood heat, the lungs must play some part in regulating the temperature of animals.

The Seat of Animal Heat. Spallanzani

The end of the discussion on the *causes* of animal heat coincided with the beginnings of new discussions on the *seat* of the phenomenon. In

43 Natural history rooms in the Jardin du Roi (18th century)

44 Vaccination caricatured; French school, early 19th century

1791, Lavoisier's view that animal heat is produced in the lungs by the action of oxygen on a hydrocarbonic fluid was challenged by Jean Henri Hassenfratz, a former assistant of Lavoisier, who pointed out that if Lavoisier were right, the lungs would have to be at a higher temperature than the rest of the body, which they are not.

According to Hassenfratz (and to Lagrange, whose views he was propounding), animal heat is liberated throughout the body because the oxygen dissolved in the blood combines with carbon and hydrogen all along its path. (This explanation—which was correct, except that oxidation takes place not in the blood but in the cells—was proved experimentally in 1837 by Gustav Magnus, who used a mercury pump to extract free gases from venous and arterial blood.)

From Jean Sénebier's posthumous *Mémoires sur la respiration* (1803), we know that Spallanzani (1729–1799) devoted the last years of his life to making thousands of systematic experiments on the respiration of invertebrates and vertebrates, from which he, too, concluded that oxygen is absorbed and carbon dioxide released by all the tissues, and that amphibians and reptiles may absorb more oxygen through the skin than through the lungs.

DIGESTION

Theoretical Differences

Early 18th-century discussions of digestion continued the disputes between the iatromechanists and the iatrochemists. While the iatromechanists, and especially Borelli, Pitcairn and Hecquet, considered digestion a kind of grinding process, the iatrochemists, and van Helmont (*Sextuplex digestio alimenti humani*) in particular, attributed digestion to the action of an acid ferment from the spleen—and later from the gall and the liver—on food particles in the stomach. When Steno discovered the excretory duct of the parotid (1662) and explained the part played by that gland in the production of saliva, Sylvius propounded the view that digestion takes place under the action not of acids but of digestive juices related to saliva. His view received experimental support when de Graaf managed to tap pancreatic juice from the pancreatic ducts of a dog (1664).

In the 18th century, Boerhaave combined the mechanical and the chemical theories when he explained that, though digestion starts as a mechanical phenomenon (mastication and gastric peristalsis) it is completed by the chemical processes of solution and putrefaction under the action of saliva and gastric juice.

Boerhaave's pupil, von Haller, described the stomach as a sort of pressure cooker in which food is subjected to heat, humidity and air. Heat produces putrefaction, while the gastric juice and saliva—

'liquids which tend to alkalinity'—prevent the food from turning sour. 'There can be no ferments [in the stomach] which are contrary to the character of these liquids and to the ends of nature.' Though von Haller appreciated the mechanical action of the gastric muscles, he denied that it resembled the trituration of graminivorous birds. He also asserted that bile destroys the natural acidity of food particles, preparing them for putrefaction and stimulating intestinal peristalsis, and that pancreatic juice dilutes the bile and plays a part similar to that of saliva.

Réaumur's Experiments

Réaumur, who was already famous as a result of his *History of Insects*, examined the existing theories of digestion—grinding (trituration), putrefaction, dissolution—in his *Sur la digestion des Oiseaux* (1762). He described how he had induced a kite to swallow small metal tubes, closed by fine mesh on both ends and filled with various food-substances, relying on the kite's habit of rejecting from its stomach whatever it cannot digest. The rejected food showed no sign of putrefaction, but meat (though not vegetable food) was partly dissolved, even in the absence of trituration. Moreover, the tubes contained a yellowish fluid, acid in taste; having obtained a sufficient quantity of it by making the kite swallow metal tubes filled with sponge, Réaumur found that meat dissolved in the fluid did not putrefy, whereas meat left by itself did. After similar experiments with other animals, including dogs and ducks, Réaumur concluded that there must be two types of digestion: trituration in herbivores and granivores, and chemical dissolution in carnivores. Though he failed to determine the precise nature of the juice he had obtained, he had nevertheless invented an ingenious method of experimental research.

Spallanzani's Contribution

Réaumur's work on digestion was continued by Spallanzani, who obtained gastric juice by Réaumur's sponge method and also by opening the stomachs of birds he had starved for a few days. He poured the juice into tubes containing meat or grain, carried them under his armpits for two or three days, and found that the food in both had dissolved but not putrefied. In other words, he showed that the digestion of both granivores and carnivores involves the action of gastric juices. However, he too failed to discover the true composition of the gastric juice; its acidity was established by Carminati (*Ricerche sulla natura del succo gastrico*, Milan, 1785); its hydrochloric acid was first isolated by Prout (1834).

Edward Stevens (*Dissertatio physiologica inauguralis de alimentorum concoctione*) published the results of his studies of human digestion one year after Spallanzani's *Opusculi di fisica animale et vegetabile* (1776). Unlike Réaumur and Spallanzani, Stevens obtained his juice not from birds but from a professional stone-swallower.

THE CIRCULATION

The Earliest Measurements

In his *De motu Cordis,* Harvey had calculated the weight of the blood propelled by the heart simply in order to show that so large a quantity of blood could not possibly be produced continuously by any organ. The first to consider the circulation of the blood as a hydraulic phenomenon was Borelli, who calculated the force of the systolic contraction on the assumption that the contractive force of a muscle is proportional to its volume. Having estimated that the volume of the human heart is equal to the combined volume of the masseter and the temporal muscles, and having established that the contractive force of these two can balance 3,000 Roman pounds (1 Roman pound $=11\frac{1}{2}$ oz.), he gave that figure as the force of the contraction of the heart. As for the pressure the heart communicates to the blood, his deductions led him to the figure of 135,000 lb.!

In 1718, James Keill (1673–1719) devoted three essays of his *Tentamina medico-physica* to the calculation of the total quantity of blood, the velocity of its flow, and the force of the heart. He estimated that the blood of a man accounts for $\frac{5}{8}$ of his total weight, that the blood in the aorta travels at the rate of 5 ft. 3 in. per hour, and that the force of the heart is 12 oz. (The modern figures are: weight of blood $=\frac{1}{3}$ body-weight; flow of blood in the aorta $=20$ in. per second; work of contraction wave of left ventricle $=3\frac{1}{2}$ oz.)

Stephen Hales's *Haemastatics*

The Rev. Stephen Hales made an important contribution to the theory of blood circulation when he published his *Statical Essays, containing Haemastatics etc.* in 1733. Hales had previously written his important *Vegetable Staticks* (1727) in which he described a method of measuring variations in sap pressure. From that it was but a short step to measuring the blood pressure of horses, dogs and sheep by means of a special manometer. Hales was able to establish that the blood pressure is lower in the veins than it is in the arteries (the blood rose to 9 ft. when the manometer was connected to the crural artery of a horse, but only to 15 in. when it was inserted in the jugular vein); that it fluctuates with the systole and the diastole; and that it is characteristic of a given animal species. Since Hales's work was not bettered for an entire century—the next work of equally great importance was Jean Poiseuille's *Recherches sur la force du cœur aortique* (1828)—the contributions of his immediate successors have often been ignored. Daniel Bernoulli, professor of anatomy at Basle from 1733 to 1751, was the first to calculate the work of the heart from the weight of the blood expelled and the systolic displacement; he also made comparative studies of the flow of liquids in rigid pipes and in living vessels (*Hydrodynamica*, 1738). His pupil, Daniel Passavant (*De vi cordis*, 1748) used Hales's figures to arrive at a more accurate evaluation of the work of the heart.

Late 17th-century physiologists posed the special question of the movement of the blood in the veins, which are not directly connected to the arteries. Borelli, though admitting the force of the heart, denied that it was sufficient to drive the blood in the veins. Hence, the microscopic examinations by Malpighi (1661) and Leeuwenhoek (1690) of the capillary circulation in the mesentery of frogs and the tail of tadpoles assumed a very great importance, and so did Cowper's investigations of the mesentery of a cat (1697). Von Haller (*De Motu sanguinis*, 1752) was the first to show that the arteries and the capillaries transmit the same pulse from the heart. His theory of irritability then enabled him—as the theory of tonicity enabled Stahl—to ascribe to the tunic of the capillary vessels an independent contractility, and hence an additional impulsive effect on the blood. Spallanzani was another to deal with this problem in various special papers.[1]

MUSCULAR CONTRACTION

Muscular contractions and their effects on posture and locomotion had been described in mechanical terms ever since antiquity. While Descartes had turned Aristotle's comparison of the limbs of animals to levers into a dogma, other physiologists adopted the view of Erasistratos and Galen that, since muscular paralysis follows the ligature of the corresponding nerve, the contraction of muscles must be governed by an influx of animal spirits from the brain.

17TH-CENTURY THEORIES

In his *Traité de l'homme* (1664), Descartes asserted that muscular contraction results from the mechanical congestion and pressure of these spirits. This view was challenged by Thomas Willis (*Cerebri anatome*, 1664; *De morbis convulsivis*, 1667; *De motu musculari*, 1670), who showed that the convulsive or tetanic muscular contractions which occur in certain pathological conditions cannot possibly result from purely mechanical actions. Willis called muscles 'special

[1] Tourdes' French translation of these papers (1800) contains a life of Spallanzani which, with Jean Sénebier's, is considered the best biography of this great biologist. *Cf.* also Jean Rostand, *Les origines de la biologie expérimentale et l'abbé Spallanzani*, Paris, 1951.

combustion engines in which the subtle spirits introduced by the nerves combine with the blood'.

In his *Elementorum myologiae specimen sive musculi descriptio geometrica* (1667), Steno showed that muscles are composed of simple elements —the motor fibres—and that the contraction of muscles affects their form but not their bulk.

Borelli (*De motu animalium*, 1680–1681) used the laws of the lever to make systematic measurements of the force of contraction of the skeletal muscles. Beyond that, he agreed with the iatrochemists that the initial cause of the contraction was a local ebullience, and hence a swelling, of a mixture of nerve fluid and blood.

In 1734, a new edition of Borelli's *De motu animalium* appeared, with two appendices by Jean Bernoulli, the *De effervescentia et fermentatione* (1690) and the *De motu musculorum*. According to Bernoulli, muscular contraction is caused not by the blood itself, but by the influx into the muscle of oxygen from the blood corpuscles. He also tried to apply the theory of curves and differential analysis to muscular contractions, but failed to make any great headway.

The Influence of Newtonian Science

Though physiologists applied Newton's theory of attraction mainly to the study of secretions, they also considered its repercussions on the theory of muscular movement.

Thus James Keill (*Tentamina medico-physica*, 1718) tried to explain that muscle fibres swell up as a result of the attraction which animal spirits exercise on the blood. George Cheyne (1671–1743), who studied muscle contractions in conjunction with nervous diseases (*The English Malady or a Treatise of Nervous Diseases of all Kinds*, 1735) much as Willis had done in the 17th century, explained that muscle fibres vibrate in sympathy with the aether in the nerves. Cheyne claimed the authority of Newton when he rejected all speculations on the essence of this phenomenon. Bryan Robinson (*Treatise of the Animal Œconomy*, 1734) also explained muscle movement in terms of the vibrations of an animal aether.

It is worth mentioning that early 18th-century physiologists clung to these theories simply because they were ignorant of Swammerdam's demonstration that purely mechanical excitations can cause contractions of the muscles of a frog, long after the nerve supply to them has been cut off. Swammerdam also showed that muscle contractions involve no changes of volume, and hence no influx of any fluid whatsoever. Swammerdam's experiments were made in 1658, but did not become generally known until 1737, when Boerhaave first described them in his edition of Swammerdam's *Bible of Nature*.

Boerhaave and Hoffmann

It was only to be expected that Boerhaave, Hoffmann and Stahl would explain muscle contractions in terms of their all-embracing theories.

Boerhaave took muscle fibres for fine branches of nerve fibres. Like Descartes, he believed that they were capable of vibrating with different amplitudes depending on their tension, and of conducting spirit from the brain into the muscles, which contract under the resulting pressure.

Hoffmann, on the other hand, explained that muscle contractions are caused by the pressure of the blood inside the muscle fibres. He, too, believed that aether is an essential component of the nerve fluid.

Stahl's Animism

Both theories were criticized by Stahl, who argued that living beings cannot be reduced to a sum of mechanical effects (*Disquisitio de mecanismi et organismi diversitate*, 1706; *De vera diversitate corporis mixti et vivi*, 1707; *Theoria medica vera*, 1708). Instead, he re-introduced Aristotelian teleological precepts into physiology: all parts of the body combine to preserve total equilibrium; the body's natural tendency to decompose is opposed by the soul's action on the tonic motion of the humours.

The idea of tonic motion had been suggested earlier by Galen (*De motu musculorum*, I, VII, 8), Fabricius da Aquapendente, Borelli and Francis Glisson (*De natura substantiae energetica*, 1672; *De ventriculo et intestinis*, 1677). But whereas Glisson had distinguished between *perceptio naturalis*—direct tissue excitability—and *perceptio sensitiva*—tissue excitability transmitted to the brain by the nerves—Stahl made no such distinction; every local response, he maintained, is produced and perceived by an indivisible vital principle: the soul.

Von Haller's Doctrine of Irritability

It is only against this background that we can appreciate why von Haller's physiological doctrine found such ardent supporters and why it held sway for almost a century.

Von Haller based his theory on hundreds of experiments with decapitated animals, and on observations of anencephalic foetuses, from all of which he concluded that animal spirits can play no part in muscle contractions. He considered that irritability must be a specific property of muscle tissue, because it is absent in connective tissue, ligaments, tendons, or the skin, and because it persists in muscle preparations from which all nerves have been severed.

This force [of irritability] differs completely from all other known properties of the body; it does not depend on gravity, attraction or electricity, and is found exclusively in soft fibres. (1747.)

Like Stahl, von Haller therefore assumed that the contraction of muscles is due to an inherent property and not to external mechanical causes. But while Stahl had subordinated contractility and sensibility to the soul, von Haller established that the two are, in fact, separable, and that the soul plays no part in irritability. Stahl's vitalism was based on animistic speculations, von Haller's on experimental studies.

Subsequent Work on Muscle Contractions

In 1753, the Prussian Academy offered a prize for the best essay on muscular motions, and this was won by Claude Le Cat (1700–1768). From the title of his paper, *Traité de l'existence, de la nature et des propriétés du fluide des nerfs et principalement de son action dans le mouvement musculaire* ('Treatise on the existence, the nature and the properties of the nerve fluid and particularly on its action in muscular movement'), we gather that the independence of nerves and muscles was not generally accepted even in von Haller's day.

Earlier, the Royal Society had inaugurated a series of Croonian Lectures (so called in honour of W. Croone) on muscular action, the first three of which were delivered by Alexander Stuart in 1737.

P. J. Barthez (1734–1806) applied Stahl's theory to the study of the muscular actions governing running, jumping, swimming, flying *etc.* (*Nouvelle mécanique des mouvements de l'homme et des animaux*, 1798). Barthez denied Borelli's claim that animal motion is produced by elastic reactions of the environment.

Before concluding, we must stress that, by his theory of irritability and by the overthrow of mechanistic explanations of muscular actions, von Haller had prepared the field for Galvani's experiments on animal electricity, for Lavoisier's studies of respiration and vital energy exchanges, and finally for Regnault and Reiset's measurements of the chemical reactions involved in respiration (*Recherches chimiques sur la respiration des animaux*, 1849).

THE NERVOUS SYSTEM

Though von Haller's theory represented a major advance in muscle physiology, his belief that muscles function quite independently of the nervous system greatly obscured the problem of involuntary muscle contractions.

Now, involuntary motions had been discussed by Aristotle, Galen and many of their successors, who had tried to explain them by a host of different hypotheses. Those who considered the brain or the soul as the seat of animal spirits had nevertheless to admit that there were certain purely automatic responses in which the brain could play no more than a mechanical role. That was the view of Descartes in the 17th century and of Astruc in the 18th.

Others took the opposite view, that movements of separated organs, of decapitated animals and anencephalic foetuses showed clearly that animal movements could be produced independently of any cerebral control. That view was shared by von Haller, Le Cat, Winslow and Prochaska. From their lengthy disputes there eventually emerged the concept of reflex motions.

Reflexes

In his *Description du corps humain* (1664) Descartes had taught that the soul cannot cause the motion of organs unless they are predisposed to respond to its orders. Moreover, 'when all the organs tend towards a given motion, the body has no need of the soul to produce it'. As instances of this tendency, Descartes cited what have since been called the pupillary and palpebral reflexes.

Thomas Willis based his definition of reflex action on a study of what Sherrington called the scratch reflex. According to Willis, all reflex actions are instantaneous responses to local stimuli:

Motus est reflexus qui scilicet a sensione praevia, tamquam causa evidenti aut occasione immediatius dependens, illico retorquetur. (*De motu musculari*, 1670.)

(Movement is a reflex action stimulated by a previous sensation, as if a manifest cause or occasion were immediately sent back [to its place of origin].)

Willis assumed that all muscular motions are caused by a centrifugal flux of animal spirits from the brain, but he distinguished between voluntary motions governed by the cerebrum, *e.g.* locomotion, and the natural or involuntary motion governed by the cerebellum or the rhachidian bulb, *e.g.* respiration and heart-beat. Hence he distinguished between two souls—a sensitive and reasonable soul, which was characteristic of man alone, and a sensitive and vital soul, which man shares with the animals (*De anima brutorum*, 1672).

Among the many 18th-century anatomists who associated various movements with various regions of the brain were Vieussens (1641–1715), Boerhaave, Le Peyronie (1678–1747), Lorry (1725–1785) and von Haller, to mention only the most important.

While the great anatomist S. T. von Sömmering (1785–1830) placed the *sensorium commune* in the serous fluids of the ventricles of the brain (*Organ der Seele*, 1796), Jean Astruc (1684–1766) placed it in the white matter of the brain. Hence he was able to 'explain' how it came about that stimulation to, or injury of, one part of the organism produces a reaction in another part. When agitated animal spirits are carried by one nerve into the medulla, they may be reflected into another (motor) nerve, according to the optical laws of reflection. He explained the sneezing reflex by contractions of the diaphragm, in sympathy with nasal irritations. Other reflexes 'are due to similar rapid, simple and convenient mechanisms'.

Robert Whytt

An entirely novel explanation was put forward by Robert Whytt (1717–1766) in his *Essay on the Vital and Other Involuntary Motions of Animals* (1751). According to Whytt, all motions are caused by the soul. 'The general and wise intention of all involuntary motions is the removal of everything that irritates, disturbs or hurts the body.' Thus he attributed the contraction of the pupils in strong light not to the action of the light on the iris, but to the irritation which the retina and optic nerve transmit to the soul. Because all animal motions (like the moral sense, 'whence we approve of some actions and disapprove of others almost instantaneously and without previous reasoning') are vital, they cannot be caused mechanically. However, Whytt would not be called a Stahlian, 'one of those who hold that the mind presides over, regulates and continues the vital motions'. While he firmly believed that the sentient is identical with the rational principle—there are no two minds—he also held that the mind may eschew calculation and reason and hence remain unconscious. In any case, muscles do not contract unless they are innervated and stimulated by the senses. The reason why decapitated animals continue to move is that the spinal cord, like the brain of which it is an extension, is capable of producing nerve fluid.

Whytt returned to this subject in 1754 in a work on hypochondria and hysteria. Here, he cited A. Stuart's experiments (1736) as further evidence for his theory. Stuart had found that, though the legs of decapitated frogs jerk when they are pricked with a needle, the jerking ceases the moment the spinal connection is broken.

Though Whytt did not speak of reflexes as such, he was the first to consider the spinal cord as a reflex centre.

Unzer's Objections

One of Whytt's severest critics was J. A. Unzer (1727–1799), who explained that, being mechanical systems, living beings can readily dispense with a brain and a soul. Movement takes place whenever the nerve ganglia reflect an external stimulus to a given organ. In this way, he was able to explain the movements of *Hydra*, an animal without a brain, and also of decapitated vertebrates (*Erste Gründe einer Physiologie der eigentlichen thierischen Natur thierischer Körper*, 1771).

Prochaska's Synthesis

The theories of Whytt and Unzer were combined by G. Prochaska (1749–1820), professor of anatomy and ophthalmology at Prague and Vienna, who explained that, because the sensory nerves are connected to the motor nerves in the spinal cord, they can produce movements without the intervention of the brain (*De functionibus systematis nervosi commentatio*, 1784). Unlike Unzer, Prochaska did not consider reflexes as purely physical phenomena governed by the optical laws of reflection; like Whytt, he took them for biological reactions serving the preservation of the organism as a whole. He defined the connection between reflex movements and consciousness much better than his predecessors had done, for he based his distinction between automatic and voluntary reactions on his studies of comparative anatomy. As we go up the animal scale, we find that, though the brain assumes increasing importance, it never controls any action completely; all actions spring directly from the nerves. In other words, Prochaska ended where Descartes had begun: the mind or soul presides over an apparatus that can function without its co-operation and permission. However, unlike Descartes, Prochaska described the nervous system not 'in general' but as an increasingly complicated and hierarchical structure, of which the human brain is the highest development though not the characteristic type.

Whytt, Unzer and Prochaska discarded mechanistic explanations because they realized that physiological functions cannot be explained by means of mechanical analogies. And they were perfectly right, for their work on the nervous system of the frog yielded far more important results than any theoretical speculations on the mind-body problem would have done.

The Birth of Electrophysiology

It was also through the frog that Galvani came to study the functions of nerves by means of an entirely new method: electrophysiology. The physiological effects of an electric spark were one of the great curiosities of the century. The Abbé Nollet had used a Leyden jar to give an electric shock to 180 Royal Guards, and later 700 monks, holding hands. Less spectacularly, Caldani, of Padua, had used a Leyden jar to study electric effects on the heart (1745) and on muscles (1756); Whytt used it to study the contractile and tropic effects of electricity on paralysed muscles (1751). In 1772, Walsh established that the torpedo fish produces electrical shocks, as von Haller and Borelli had suggested previously. In 1775 Cavendish exhibited a model of the torpedo fish, made of wood and leather, to John Hunter, Priestley and three others. It was submerged in salt water and in some manner charged from a battery of 49 Leyden jars so as to provide '481,000 inches of electricity'. All five visitors were persuaded to receive severe shocks to convince them that electricity can travel from a fish through salt water.

It was therefore not mere chance which led Galvani to study the effects of electric sparks on the leg muscles of frogs (1780), and to observe that the muscles jerked, even in the absence of electric sparks, whenever they were brought into contact with strips of different metal. From this he concluded that electricity is an inherent property of the organ, and tried to determine which of the two—muscle or nerve—is the seat, and which the conductor, of the phenomenon (*De viribus electricitatis in motu musculari commentarius*, 1791). The ensuing polemic between Galvani and Volta, who contested the existence of animal electricity, led to a host of further studies, the most important of which were made by Valli and von Humboldt. All these early studies began to bear fruit in the early 19th century, when Legallois was able to demonstrate the functional segmentation of the medullary centre (1809–1812), and when Charles Bell (1811) and Magendie (1822) distinguished the respective motor and sensory functions of the anterior and posterior roots of the spinal nerves.

SURVEY OF 18TH-CENTURY PHYSIOLOGY

By about 1780, physiology had finally outgrown the iatromechanical theories. Unfortunately, the reaction was too violent: Barthez (*Nouveaux éléments de la science de l'homme*, 1778) argued that the vital principle of man should be conceived by keeping the ideas of the body and soul distinct, while Bichat (1771–1802) insisted on the complete autonomy of biological methods (*Recherches physiologiques sur la vie et la mort*, 1800). Cournot explained more tolerantly that:

> Vitalism seizes upon the analogies which all manifestations of life exhibit in such astonishing variety, and takes them for its guide, but does not pretend that it can penetrate the very essence of life. (*Considérations sur la marche des idées et des événements dans les temps modernes.*)

To study this 'astonishing variety', 18th-century physiologists looked at the whole animal kingdom—from the polyp to man. If classicism is a rigorous approach combined with mathematical generalization, that term cannot be applied to 18th-century physiology, which took all living matter for its subject and which, if it generalized at all, did so by playing an infinite number of variations on its chosen themes. It was a picturesque science, as prolific in its images as nature herself.

CHAPTER 3

Medicine

ANATOMY AND PHYSIOLOGY

Macroscopic Anatomy

In the 18th century, the considerable body of anatomical knowledge handed down by the Renaissance and the 17th century was put into some sort of logical order.

Some of the most important contributions to this development were made by: B. S. Albinus (bones), G. D. Santorini (muscles), A. C. Thebesius (coronary circulation), P. Mascagni (lymphatics), J. Sénac (heart), A. Ferrein (liver and kidneys), J. N. Lieberkühn (function of intestinal villi), T. de Bordeu (glands and connective tissue), M. Bichat (membranes), J. Lieutaud and J. Douglas (peritoneum), F. Vicq d'Azyr (brain), A. Pacchioni (cerebral membranes), K. A. Bergen (arachnoid membrane), A. Scarpa (nerves), H. A. Wrisberg (abdominal nerves), J. G. Zinn and P. Demours (eyes), A. M. Valsalva (ears), and A. Monro the Younger (seminiferous tubules). The most important anatomical textbooks were written by P. J. Desault, R. B. Sabatier, J. L. Petit and J. R. Tenon (France); W. Cheselden, A. Monro the Elder and John Hunter (Britain); J. E. Hebenstreit and L. Heister (Germany); J. Palfyn (Low Countries); A. von Haller (Switzerland); and J. B. Winslow (Denmark).

Microscopic Anatomy

Microscopic anatomy, which was born in the 17th century, marked time in the 18th. Bordeu described the fine structure of mucous (*i.e.* connective) tissue and Bichat the membranes. The word 'tissue' was somewhat loosely used and did not acquire its full histological meaning until the 19th century.

Other microscopists produced results which have been called far-sighted by some and far-fetched by others. In 1700, N. Andry explained that all diseases are caused by eggs in the atmosphere which penetrate the body through the skin, the lungs or the digestive tract, and hatch out into worms. These ideas earned him the nickname of '*Homo vermiculosus*'. In 1722, J. B. Goiffon blamed the plague on insects in the blood, but gave no tangible proof of this hypothesis. A. Deidier attributed venereal diseases to worms, and the Viennese physician M. A. Plenciz suggested that all diseases are caused by micro-organisms but provided no evidence.

Pathological Anatomy

Morbid anatomy was truly born in the 18th century when J. B. Morgagni brought his long experience and vast erudition to bear on this subject in his comprehensive *The Seats and Causes of Diseases Investigated by Anatomy* (Engl. transl. 1769). By his clear descriptions of the hundreds of cases he had treated, and by his stress of the connection between certain symptoms and lesions discovered at autopsy, Morgagni rendered a great service to pathology.

In France, J. Lieutaud published a less authoritative work on morbid anatomy, and Vicq d'Azyr wrote an excellent article on this subject for the French Encyclopedia. Although he was not a pathologist himself, Bichat stressed the relevance of autopsies to clinical practice. C. F. Ludwig in Germany, and M. Baillie in England put auscultation on a sound footing after R. Vieussens had given an accurate description of aortic insufficiency.

Physiology

Though physiology was gradually split into two branches, human and animal physiology, research in the latter continued to have repercussions on the former.

Important advances in physiology included Margagni's discovery of arterio-venous anastomoses in the lungs, Lavoisier's discovery that respiration is a form of combustion, Spallanzani's demonstration that gaseous exchanges take place in all the tissues, and the more general appreciation of the role of the diaphragm in respiratory movements.

Gastaldy discovered that the hearts of dogs continue to beat after severance of the vagus and intercostal nerves. J. C. A. Helvetius and P. Chirac continued to believe in the existence of neuro-lymphatic capillaries. While digestion was studied seriously by Réaumur and Spallanzani (see preceding chapter), other physiologists preferred idle discussions on the role of the brain and its membranes, though Santorini did show that the dura mater has no independent movements.

While the study of the sense organs made little progress, Ferrein was able to dispel many common errors when he demonstrated that the voice is produced by the vocal cords. Embryologists made more detailed studies of the ovum and its membranes, but failed to produce any striking results.

MEDICAL SYSTEMS

At the beginning of the 18th century two medical systems fought for supremacy: iatrochemistry and iatromechanics. Convinced that neither system could be absolutely right, the Dutchman Hermann Boerhaave (1668–1738) and the German Friedrich Hoffmann (1660–1742) tried to take the best from both and developed two entirely new systems, which were to gain many adherents.

Boerhaave's 'Solidism'

According to Boerhaave, the human body is composed of solids immersed in humours. Both have characteristic vital movements; if either ceases, death ensues. Boerhaave did not deny the existence of the soul, but held that, since it is immaterial, it falls outside the province of biology, which is properly concerned only with measurable effects.

Boerhaave considered digestion a mechanical process, during which digestive juices are mixed with food substances and turned into chyle. The chyle is then cooked by animal heat until it can be absorbed by the blood, which carries it to the brain. Here the chyle and the blood are turned into vital spirits, which agitate the nerves and hence produce movements.

Under normal conditions, the solids are kept in equilibrium by the external air and the internal humours. If the normal functioning of these factors is in any way disturbed, the result is ill health.

Since the air is subject to changes in temperature, humidity and pressure, specific conditions must be associated with hot, cold, humid, dry, heavy and light air.

Other diseases are caused by mechanical or chemical changes producing alterations in the fluidity, viscosity or alkalinity of the humours, or in variations in the pressure exerted on the nerve fibres by the vital spirits.

All that the therapist could hope to do was to re-establish equilibrium by means of alteratives, purgatives, sedatives, tonics and hygienic measures. Boerhaave's system was particularly popular in Holland, Austria and Germany.

Hoffmann's System

According to Hoffmann, the human body is a machine, and movement the expression of life. He, too, ignored the soul without denying its existence.

Hoffmann's system was based mainly on the flow of the humours —blood, lymph and nerve fluid. The initial cause of the flow was nutrition; air played no part in it. When assimilated food particles reached the brain through the blood, the brain secreted a nerve fluid which controlled the further flow of the humours, and hence the contractions of the heart, the movements of the dura mater (Hoffmann firmly adhered to 17th-century Italian theories on this subject), secretion, excretion and intestinal peristalsis.

Hoffmann believed that most diseases are caused by disturbances of the humours at given points along the digestive tract. The humours then begin to disturb the nerve fluid which, in turn, disturbs the blood circulation, the secretions, *etc*.

While nature herself invariably provides the correct remedy, Hoffmann preferred to give her a helping hand by prescribing sedatives, tonics, purgatives and alteratives, including his famous anodyne liquid, and such proven remedies as camphor, quinine, iron and nitre, but not opium. He also prescribed cold and hot baths. Hoffmann had many followers in Germany but few in England and Italy.

Irritability and Associated Doctrines

Many of the other medical theories that appeared at about this time were based on Glisson's theory of irritability, or on its extension by Albert von Haller.

Being an anatomist first and foremost, Glisson contended that 'fibre' is the essential constituent of all living organisms. Since fibre can move for some time after death, its movements cannot be controlled exclusively by the soul, but also by external stimuli, proprioceptive impulses, or voluntary impulses from the brain. The brain can also modify the intensity of external stimuli by altering the conductivity of the nerves. In response to a stimulus, the fibre contracts; once the stimulus ceases, it 'dilates' and returns to its 'passive phase'. Life as a whole is the sum of these 'irritabilities'.

Contractility, which Glisson had considered a specific property of fibre, was identified with irritability by von Haller. He also showed that precisely because contractility persists after death, it cannot be a characteristic of life. Haller went on to study the respective irritabilities and sensibilities of various organs, and concluded that, whereas some could be irritated by the humours, others responded exclusively to external factors.

G. B. Gaub (1705–1780) tried to fuse Haller's theory of irritability with Hoffmann's humoral doctrine. According to him, all diseases are due to the effects of humoral disequilibrium on the general irritability of the fibres.

William Cullen (1712–1790) raised the nervous system to the paramount position which Hoffmann had ascribed to the spinal cord. But while Hoffmann had asserted that all diseases are communicated to the nervous centres by the humours, Cullen believed that pathogenic causes act directly on the nervous system. Fever is not a disease but a reaction against it. He divided diseases into four categories: pyrexia, adynamia, cachexia and surgical obstruction.

In his therapy, Cullen had a marked predilection for quinine, sedatives and antiphlogistics. However, like Boerhaave, he would often forget his theories and prescribe specifics whose efficacy he had learned to appreciate in practice.

John Brown (1735–1788) was first a disciple and later an adversary of Cullen. He considered irritability a characteristic of life, and asserted that a certain number of stimuli are essential for its maintenance. Diseases are due either to excessive stimulation (sthenic conditions) or, more often, to deficient stimulation (asthenic conditions). Accordingly Brown divided fevers into sthenic (pyrexia) and asthenic (true fevers), and also spoke of sthenic and asthenic inflammations. 'Brownian' or 'stimulist' therapy consisted of sedatives (blood-lettings, purgatives, vomitives *etc.*) or, more often, of stimulants (wine, alcohol, electricity *etc.*).

One of Brown's bitterest opponents was his former disciple, Giovanni Rasori (1766–1837), who used the same premisses to arrive at opposite conclusions. Thus he described as sthenic diathesis a case that Brown would have called asthenic. Rasori diagnosed diathesis by blood-letting: if the patient's state of health improved, he was suffering from stimulant diathesis; if not, he was suffering from contrastimulant diathesis. His therapy was much the same as Brown's.

The complex system propounded by F. J. V. Broussais (1772–1838) was to have very harmful effects on French medicine. According to Broussais, health is the result of the normal action of the external heat on the humours and hence on the tissues. Any alteration in the local effects of heat automatically engenders disease in a particular tissue. In his anti-Hippocratic therapy, Broussais ignored the reactions of the organism as a whole, and hence prescribed copious blood-lettings and the applications of an unusually large number of leeches to the head and the stomach.

Animism

Though they did not deny the existence of the soul, the founders of all the systems we have been discussing tried to reduce biology to simple mathematical, chemical or mechanical laws. It was in opposition to their views that Stahl (1660–1734) propounded his doctrine of animism, according to which the soul presides over all living movements—voluntary and involuntary. It does so in three main ways: through the circulation, through secretion and through excretion, though Stahl did not explain how.

Since all diseases are due to disturbances of the soul, the soul can safely be trusted to produce its own remedies; all the physician can hope to do is to aid it. (Stahl's 'soul' was clearly identical with Hippocrates' 'Nature'.) Stahl considered the bleeding of haemorrhoids beneficial, called fever the soul's reaction against diseases, and paid special attention to the pulse.

Stahl had many followers, especially in Germany and England. His most famous French disciple was F. Boissier de Sauvages (1706–1767).

Vitalism

Animism has often been coupled with vitalism because both theories reject the view that biological phenomena can be explained in purely mechanical terms. However, unlike the animists, the vitalists rejected the soul as the controller of organic processes and introduced instead a 'vital principle', intermediate between the soul and the body.

Vitalism was founded by Théophile de Bordeu (1722–1776), who considered that all life is based on the combined lives of individual glands. Hence, therapy must be concerned with restoring glandular balance. Among the external causes of diseases, Bordeu gave a very special place to inflammation.

Henri Fouquet (1727–1806), a pupil of Bordeu, contended that contractility and sensibility act like a couple of forces, and that it was the normal action of that couple in the living fibre which ensured perfect health.

P. J. Barthez (1734–1806) made this couple subject to a higher force which he called the 'vital principle'. Like Bordeu, he placed it half-way between the body and the soul, but he rejected Bordeu's glandular lives—his vital principle was indivisible.

Barthez believed that all diseases result from disequilibrium between the forces of sensibility and motility. He made a thorough analysis of all the observed symptoms to decide which of the two forces must be aided to restore balance, and put forward the novel hypothesis that efficacy is the only test of a remedy. Barthez's originality was that he treated symptoms rather than 'temperaments' and that, ignoring systematic views, he introduced a measure of logic into therapy.

Barthez's disciple Xavier Bichat (1771–1802) introduced two new couples, one governing external reactions, and the other internal functions. He placed the former in the neuraxis, and the latter in the sympathetic nervous system. He also believed that every tissue has a specific vital force related to its specific function.

Though a peculiarly French system, associated chiefly with Montpellier, vitalism had a number of followers in Germany and England, who were attracted to it because it seemed to offer a synthesis of all the best elements in the earlier systems.

Homoeopathy

An entirely new system—homoeopathy—was propounded by Samuel Hahnemann (1755–1843), who had observed that an overdose of quinine produces the very malarial symptoms the drug is supposed to cure. After many experiments in which he himself was generally the subject, he adopted the 'hair of the dog' axiom of the ancients—*similia similibus curantur*—adding as a rider of his own that the more diluted a drug is, the more effective is its action. In 1806, he reported that he had obtained successful cures by administering as little as one-millionth the normal dosage of a drug.

The related doctrine of isopathy was propounded in America by C. Herring, who believed that diseases must be treated by the administration of the causative agent or its products.

ADVANCES IN PRACTICAL MEDICINE

Neo-Hippocratic Medicine

Though 18th-century medicine was generally bogged down in the various systems we have been discussing, many physicians were far more interested in practical studies than in deep metaphysical discussions. It was they who laid the foundations of modern semeiology and clinical practice.

Semeiology

Contributions to semeiology in the 18th century were mainly restricted to pulsimetry and percussion. Though pulsimetry had been studied by the ancient Chinese, by the Greeks, by Galen and by medieval authors, and though Galileo and Santorio had invented a special *pulsilogium*, the subject had been largely forgotten in the West until it was revived by the Spanish physician Solano de Lucques (1685–1736), who distinguished three types of pulse: dicrotic, intermittent and *inciduus*.

Théophile de Bordeu claimed that all impaired organs have characteristic pulses and gave a list of these. His view, although quite false, nevertheless drew the attention of physicians to the relationship between the pulse and various diseases. Bordeu was also the first to popularize the method of taking the radial pulse with four fingers. In England, S. Hales invented the sphygmometer.

The use of percussion was introduced by Leopold Auenbrugger in about 1761, but its importance was not fully appreciated until the beginning of the 19th century, when J. N. Corvisart (1755–1821) and R. Laënnec (1781–1826) used percussion to diagnose chest complaints.

Clinical Teaching

Though Sylvius de la Boë had lectured on clinical methods in the 17th century, and though a number of Dutch and Italian physicians had followed his example, the first to make clinical teaching a part of the normal medical curriculum was Boerhaave, whose lectures at Leyden became renowned throughout the world. As a result, clinical centres were opened in Vienna, Göttingen, Erlangen, Pavia and in many other large cities, and medicine ceased to be a matter of mere book-learning. From a practical study of symptoms, Boissier de Sauvages, the first of an ever-growing number of nosologists, was able to divide diseases into 10 classes, 44 orders and 315 genera; Linnaeus, Pinel and Richerand worked along similar lines.

Pathology and Epidemiology

The many diseases studied in the 18th century included phlegmonous angina (particularly in England), œdema, angina pectoris, colic, scurvy, exophthalmic goitre, venereal diseases, diseases of women, pellagra, and a number of skin diseases, which are still named after 18th-century physicians. In 1720 Kramer, an Austrian army doctor, asserted that lime or orange juice would cure scurvy. It was when the British Navy began to include lime-juice in the stores of all vessels undertaking long voyages that the British were dubbed 'Limeys' by the Americans. Still more attention was paid to chronic diseases, and though no new knowledge of fevers was gained, quinine treatment was greatly improved.

At the same time, some progress was made in epidemiology. The plague continued to ravage Europe, and was particularly disastrous in Marseilles in 1720; its cause remained unknown in spite of the shrewd observations of Antoine Deidier. Malaria was studied and fought effectively, particularly by M. J. Lancisi (1654–1720). Other epidemiologists studied diphtheria, which raged in England and to a lesser extent in the rest of Europe, typhoid fever, rabies, influenza, whooping-cough and the new scourge—yellow fever—which had reached the rest of Europe from Spain. However, the most striking results of all were made in the study and treatment of smallpox.

Inoculation and Vaccination

Long before the 18th century, the Chinese had discovered a means of protecting themselves against smallpox: they blew the powdered scabs that had fallen from the skin of an infected person into the nostrils of a healthy one. Other Eastern countries seem to have used similar methods. In Turkey and Greece it was common practice to prick the skin in three different places with a needle that had previously been pushed into a fresh smallpox pustule. Lady Mary Wortley Montagu, wife of the British ambassador to the *Sublime Porte*, brought this method back to Great Britain, preaching it by example when she had her own son inoculated in 1717. The method caught on quickly, and became known as 'variolation'. Though some died of it, the number of people who gained immunity from smallpox was so much greater that Germany, Switzerland, Holland and Sweden soon followed Britain's example; France did so very much later. The most famous inoculators were Theodore Tronchin (1709–1781), who helped to spread the method in Switzerland, D. Sutton and T. Dimsdale.

Variolation had hardly been adopted when Edward Jenner (1749–1823) introduced his far less dangerous method of vaccination, on account of which he has rightly been esteemed one of the greatest of English physicians. Having observed the immunity from smallpox of cowhands who had contracted cowpox in the course of their work, Jenner carried out patient research for twenty years before he was ready, on 14th May 1796, to inoculate a human being with matter from a cowpox pustule. His success was so complete that vaccination quickly replaced the practice of variolation.

The Beginnings of Electrotherapy

Ever since the invention of the first electrical machine in the 17th century, physicians had tried to use electricity to cure all sorts of diseases, and especially nervous complaints.

The first success was obtained in 1740, when Louis Jallabert (1712–1768) succeeded in curing a case of paralysis. The first theses on electrical therapy submitted to the Montpellier Medical School in 1749 dealt with the electrical treatment of hemiplegia and with the relationship between the nervous and electrical fluids. At the same time, the Leyden jar was replaced by the far less dangerous 'static bath'. G. F. Pivati made his patients hold a phial containing drugs, and then applied an electric discharge on the assumption that the drugs were absorbed through the hand. The Abbé Bertholon classified diseases into electrical and non-electrical, and tried to treat them accordingly. Volta, who constructed the first electric pile, was also the first to use current electricity in medicine.

Mesmerism

'Magnetic therapy' was adopted by Franz Mesmer (1733–1815), who practised the laying-on of hands and held collective seances round a tub filled with acidulated water. Spectacular lighting effects, 'mesmeric passes', weird music, added to his effects. Mesmer even used 'magnetism' to bestow curative effects on trees. Mesmerism was all the rage in Europe and particularly in France, where Benjamin Franklin undertook to investigate it at the request of Louis XVI. He had no difficulty in showing that its claims to 'magnetic' influence were false and in 1784 mesmerism was officially condemned by a joint Commission of the Paris Medical Faculty and the *Académie des Sciences*. Mesmer had to flee France and was quickly forgotten.

Tropical Diseases

As long voyages became more common, tropical diseases received increasing attention. Yellow fever, which took so heavy a toll in San Domingo that a war had to be called off for lack of combatants, was studied at close hand. Augustus II of Poland and Frederick IV of Denmark sent medical missions to the Barbary Coast and to the Near East; other studies were pursued in Asiatic Russia and on Minorca.

The countries which had contributed most to the development of tropical pathology in the 17th century were overtaken by England and France in the 18th. Apart from yellow and other fevers, English and French pathologists also studied exanthematous typhus, leprosy, the dysenteries, yaws, leishmaniasis, filariasis *etc*. Some advances were also made in climatology.

Neuro-psychiatry

Neuro-psychiatry became an independent branch of medicine in the 18th century, when mental illnesses ceased to be attributed to the devil and mental patients were no longer thrown into dark pits. One of the greatest pioneers in this field was Philippe Pinel, who was responsible for releasing many poor wretches from their chains, and who distinguished between four types of mental illness: mania, melancholy, dementia and idiocy. Pinel also described neuroses, which had previously been studied by Cullen, Boissier de Sauvages and Stahl. In Italy, V. Chiarugi re-organized the existing lunatic asylums and began treating psychotics by medical techniques.

Hygiene

The 18th-century physicians took a keen interest in social and personal hygiene, and were largely responsible for introducing public health measures into hospitals, schools and prisons, and for opening public baths in England and public lavatories in France. General treatises on the subject were written by J. P. Frank and S. Tissot, and particularly by Bernardini Ramazzini (1633–1714), whose *De morbis artificum* (1700) covered a vast field. Army hygiene was studied by J. Pringle and hospital hygiene by John Howard, who gathered his material from all the corners of Europe; M. Thouret and H. Haguenot warned against the common practice of burying corpses in churches; Lancisi drained some of the worst parts of the Pontine Marshes. In France, more and more draconic laws were imposed during times of pestilence. Finally, the Republic of Venice promulgated a series of laws to prevent the spread of tuberculosis.

Forensic Medicine

Forensic medicine made little progress in the 18th century because of the persisting influence of Paolo Zacchias (1584–1659). In France, there was keen discussion on the extreme limits of pregnancy. The surgeon Antoine Louis (1723–1792) gave expert evidence in numerous court cases; other authors studied legal problems connected with asphyxia. The creation of three chairs of forensic medicine in the *Écoles de Santé* of the French Republic marked a turning-point in the history of that science.

SURGERY

General Surgery

In the 18th century, surgery ceased to be a despised trade and surgeons became gentlemen. In France, this development was hastened by the renown of three successive Royal Surgeons—Georges Mareschal (1658–1738), François de Lapeyronie (1678–1747) and Pichaut de Lamartinière (1696–1783). The *Académie royale de Chirurgerie* was founded in 1731, following the reorganization of the Paris College of Surgeons in 1727, and preceding the restoration and extension of its ancient privileges in 1743. Henceforth, French surgeons were allowed to teach their skills to medical students free from medical supervision, and to wear the highly-prized long robe.

In Denmark, surgery broke its medical shackles largely through the efforts of Simon Cruger. An Academy of Surgery was founded in Copenhagen, with Heinrich Callisen as one of its most brilliant teachers. In Britain, Colleges of Surgery sprang up in London, Edinburgh and Dublin, all of which produced surgeons of renown.

Though surgical colleges were founded in Berlin and Vienna, surgery remained a subsidiary branch of medicine in the rest of Germany and Austria. The same was true of Italy and Holland, despite the fact that the traditional gulf between physicians and surgeons had never been particularly great in these countries.

The 18th-century surgeons concentrated especially on the study of superficial wounds, abscesses, phlegmons, suppurations, gangrene, head injuries and gunshot wounds. Amputations were generally performed by the coat-sleeve method, and the indications for such operations were more clearly defined. Surgeons also removed tumours, including malignant tumours of the breast, performed high ligations of arteries affected by aneurysmal swellings, and even operated on the stomach and the esophagus. Inguinal hernias were generally treated by closing the wall of the containing cavity and by prescribing the use of a truss, and no longer by castration. Attempts were also made to operate on crural and other secondary hernias. Anal fistulas and hydroceles were removed, though surgeons were not generally agreed on the best methods. The treatment of fractures and dislocations made little progress apart from some detailed improvements in the methods of reduction and retention. On the other hand, 18th-century surgeons had a very clear idea of ossification, and were therefore able to refute the erroneous theories of their predecessors. They also practised vertebral and orthopedic surgery, which was first introduced by N. Andry and A. J. Venel.

Various surgical operations and techniques, and various anatomical regions, still bear the names of their 18th-century discoverers. Among these are Desault's apparatus, Louis's angle, Petit's hernia, Monro's line, Douglas's line, Pott's fracture, Hunter's operation, Scarpa's shoe, Richter's hernia, Heister's valves *etc.*

Of the many specific contributions made by 18th-century surgeons, we can mention only F. Chopart's method of amputating the foot; Petit's differentiation between compression and concussion in cranial injuries, and his remarkable description of cholecystitis; John Hunter's description of the canal bearing his name; Lapeyronie's resection of strangulated hernia; the description by Pott and David of Pott's disease; the study by H. L. Duhamel du Monceau and B. Vigarous of osseous regeneration; and T. Goulard's descriptions of urethral and venereal diseases.

The Work of Specialists

Some operations, and particularly lithotomies, which had previously been performed by itinerant surgeons or 'specialists', were gradually taken over by the professional surgeons. Stones from the bladder were increasingly removed by lateral lithotomy, an operation which owed much of its success to Jean Baseilhac or 'Frère Jacques' (F. Côme, 1703–1781). In England, surgeons also revived Franco's suprapubic or perineal lithotomy, which was generally adopted in the 19th century.

At the same time, surgeons began to take far more interest in ophthalmology. In particular, the time-honoured method of couching cataractous lenses was abandoned when J. Daviel (1696–1762) invented the extraction method which is used to this day.

While some advances were made in otorhinolaryngology—the removal of nasal polyps and abscesses in the jaw, and the treatment of various buccal lesions and of hare-lip *etc.*—Tagliacozzi's method of rhinoplasty was completely forgotten.

Dentistry, too, was largely taken out of the hands of itinerant quacks. Surgeons and physicians published some of the earliest textbooks on the subject, perfected the existing instruments and invented new ones. Caries began to be treated, and false teeth were introduced. Dental hygiene was taught in the Republic's *Écoles de Santé* in Paris, Strasbourg and Montpellier.

Obstetrics

Obstetrics had become a branch of medicine in the 17th century, when midwives were relegated to second place and surgeons and physicians began to vie for supremacy in this field. The first specialists appeared in the 18th century, and began to make a detailed study of the female reproductive organs, particularly during pregnancy.

Pelvimetry made great progress, thanks largely to A. Levret and J. B. Beaudelocque. F. L. J. Solayres de Renhac gave a clear description of the successive positions of the foetus during its descent and of its various presentations at birth. W. Smellie advised podalic version in the case of *placenta praevia*.

J. R. Sigault discovered symphysiotomy, which many preferred to Caesarean section. The forceps was no longer a medical secret, and many surgeons tried to perfect it. Maternity hospitals sprang up everywhere, and the first journal of obstetrics appeared in Germany at the end of the century.

PHARMACOLOGY

The 18th-century advances in pharmacology were meagre; no drugs were discovered that could rival the great medicaments of the past. Even so, the old drugs were put to many new therapeutic uses. A. von Störck re-examined the properties of conium, datura, aconitum, colchicum *etc.*; Charles Darwin (1698?–1778) prescribed digitalis against dropsy, and F. Torti studied the posology of quinine.

Cod-liver oil was the only animal product introduced by 18th-century pharmacologists. Mineral products, on the other hand, were greatly prized. Thomas Fowler prepared the arsenic solution which bears his name (*liquor potassii arsenitus*); T. Goulard prepared various products containing Goulard's extract (a mixture of lead acetate and oil of camphor); Berthollet prescribed potassium chlorate, and T. Henry prescribed magnesia. Mercury continued to be used in the treatment of syphilis (which was not yet clearly distinguished from blennorrhoea) and as a salivant. Bottled mineral waters were sold in increasing quantities following Bordeu's praises of the therapeutic effects of the mineral springs of Barège. G. F. Venel began to manufacture artificial soda water shortly afterwards, and many physicians prescribed it as a suitable substitute for the natural product.

ACADEMIC DEVELOPMENTS

Metaphysical systems played a far less important part in the history of 18th-century medicine than they had at any time in the past. In France, the Revolution swept away the last vestiges of the ancient privileges enjoyed by the Paris Medical Faculty, and granted autonomy to medical schools all over the country. A host of medical journals sprang up all over the world, in which physicians and surgeons could exchange their views freely.

Latin teaching was abandoned in many German colleges but was revived in Latin America. Those who could do so frequented the famous medical schools at Leyden, Halle, Göttingen and Montpellier, or the clinical schools at Leyden, Vienna, Edinburgh and Pavia, which continued to enjoy their former renown, or the somewhat less famous schools at Paris, Leipzig, Padua, Pisa, Bologna, Basle and Upsala. In Eastern Europe, new medical schools were founded at Moscow and Vilna. As in the 17th century, teachers would often move from one medical school to another, according to which offered them better opportunities. Though chemistry and botany had become independent branches of science, they were still taught almost exclusively in the medical schools. At the same time, pharmacists so improved their social status that, in France at least, they were allowed to share the deliberations of their former superiors, the physicians.

* * *

From the preceding discussion it will have become clear that, though the 18th century failed to make a particularly great or original contribution to medicine, it nevertheless helped to consolidate those trends which were to turn medicine into a true science in the next two centuries.

CHAPTER 4

Botany

CAROLUS LINNAEUS (Carl von Linné, 1707–1788), most famous of all the 18th-century botanists, was the son of a Swedish clergyman. He first discussed the problem of plant classification in his *Hortus uplandicus* (1730), which he wrote while he was still a student at Lund and Upsala. In the course of his subsequent travels he met the great lawyer George Clifford, who sponsored the publication of the *Systema naturae* (1735), in which Linnaeus presented the principles of a new method of classification. This work, which began as a simple pamphlet of a dozen or so pages, ran to twelve editions, of which the last, consisting of four volumes (1766–1788), was translated into many languages. Linnaeus' next work, the *Genera plantarum*, described 995 genera of plants in the first edition (1737) and 1,767 genera in the 1789–1791 edition. Among Linnaeus' other works, the most important were the *Bibliotheca botanica* (1736), the *Corollarium generum plantarum*, the *Methodus sexualis*, the *Critica botanica* (1737), the *Classes plantarum* (1738), the *Philosophia botanica* (1751) and the *Amœnitates academicae* (1749–1769). Linnaeus' system of plant classification has been called the 'sexual system' because it employed the reproductive organs of plants as critical characteristics. It was based on the number of stamens (monandria, diandria, . . . polyandria), on their arrangements into whorls (monadelphia, diadelphia, . . . polyadelphia) and, finally, on the general distribution of the sexual organs. Plants were said to be hermaphrodite when the male and female organs are found in the same flower, monoecious when the two organs are found in separate flowers but in the same plant, dioecious when the organs are found in separate plants, and polygamous when the same or different plants of a given species bear hermaphrodite as well as male or female flowers.

Despite its many flaws, Linnaeus' system was superior to those of his predecessors. Far more important, it led to his binary system of nomenclature, in which all plants and animals are distinguished by a Latin noun (genus) and a Latin adjective (species). Unlike his 'sexual system', Linnaeus' nomenclature is used to this day, and earned him so much renown that he was appointed professor of botany at Upsala, knighted by the King of Sweden, and buried by the side of kings in Upsala Cathedral.

The de Jussieus and Adanson

What Linnaeus had set out to do was completed by Bernard de Jussieu (1699–1777), who managed to classify the plants in the Royal Garden at the Petit Trianon by the first truly natural system of classification. That system was described in the *Genera plantarum* (1789) by his nephew Antoine Laurent de Jussieu (1748–1836).

The de Jussieus introduced the distinction between acotyledons, monocotyledons and dicotyledons, subdivided the monocotyledons into hypogynous, perigynous and epigynous, and the dicotyledons into apetalous, monopetalous, polypetalous and diclinous, and then into families of which more than half have been retained to this day.

At about the same time, Michel Adanson (1727–1806) made an independent attempt to seek the correct principle of classification 'in nature herself'. After studying the similarities and dissimilarities between various species, he was able to classify plants into 58 natural families in his famous *Famille des plantes* (1763). Although Adanson has been accused of copying de Jussieu's ideas, he was, in fact, an independent discoverer of a system that was very much 'in the air' at the time.

Other Works

When R. L. Desfontaines (1750–1833) was appointed professor at the *Jardin du Roi* (1736), he compiled a famous herbal from various local collections, after eliminating duplicates. His herbal gave a great impetus to systematic studies, even though he himself remained an advocate of Tournefort's outdated system. Desfontaines also wrote a study of monocotyledons (1798) and published a *Histoire des arbres et arbrisseaux qui peuvent être cultivés en pleine terre sur le sol de France* ('History of trees and shrubs that can be grown on French soil'). His lectures were attended by audiences of more than 500 people.

Whereas Boissier de Sauvages published a classification of plants according to the form and arrangement of their leaves in 1751, his pupil A. Gouan adopted and explained Linnaeus' system. Charles L'Héritier de Brutelle published a detailed classification of exotic plants and N. Duchesne a *Histoire naturelle des Fraisiers* (1766), which was one of the first works to discuss mutation.

In Germany, J. Gärtner founded the science of carpology and described more than a thousand fruits in his *De fructibus et seminibus plantarum* (1789–1794); G. Bose wrote a paper in defence of Tournefort's system; C. Knaut tried to modify Rivinus' system; G. Kramer combined the two; J. G. Gleditsch published his *Systema plantarum a staminum situ* (1764), which was used by A. L. de Jussieu; C.Schmiedel wrote the important *Icones plantarum* and G. D. Ehret the equally important *Plantae selectae*. In a letter to Leibniz, J. H. Burckhard suggested, before Linnaeus, that plants could be classified very simply according to the position of their reproductive organs. (This letter was published in 1750 by L. Heister, a bitter opponent of Linnaeus.)

In England, Richard Bradley studied the generation of plants and particularly of tulips, and John Ellis made a special study of exotic plants; in Austria, N. Crantz, J. Schreber and S. Miller made a detailed study of many families of plants and types of flowers; in Holland, A. von Royen and E. J. van Wachendorff took a keen interest in classification. In Sweden, the home of systematics, Linnaeus' pupil P. Artedi classified umbellifers according to their involucres. Switzerland produced not only the great von Haller, but also such famous scholars as J. Scheuchzer, J. König and J. Gesner. In Italy, P. Micheli studied the glumellae of grasses, and described more than 1,400 species of plants. In Spain, botanical studies were pursued chiefly by Gomez de Ortega and A. J. Cavanilles, the founder of the *Anales de historia natural*.

Floras

Many 18th-century botanists made detailed studies of the flora of their native countries. The Parisian flora was studied particularly by J. Guettard and P. Bulliard who, apart from his *Flora Parisiensis* (1774), also published the *Herbier de la France* and the *Histoire des plantes suspectés et vénémeuses* (1794).

English floras were published by J. Hill, J. Edwards, J. E. Smith and W. Hudson. The flora of Belgium was described by Gorter and Necker, that of Germany by Hoffmann, Borckhausen and Rohr. Jacquin performed the same service for Austria, Oeder for Bohemia and Denmark, Swartz for Sweden, Linnaeus for Lapland, Gunner and Vahl for Norway, Gilibert for Iceland, Greenland and Poland. The flora of Russia was studied by Deschizeaux, Buxbaum, Gmelin and many others; the flora of Switzerland by A. von Haller and J. J. Scheuchzer (whose *Herbarium diluvianum*, 1734, was one of the first books on paleobotany), and by H. B. de Saussure *et al.* The Italian flora was compiled by G. A. Scopoli, the author of the *Flora carriolica* (1772); the flora of Spain by Cavanilles, Quer y Martinez and Gomez de Ortega, and the flora of Portugal by Brotero de Avelar.

Cryptogamy

Many of these floras reflected 18th-century interest in cryptogamy, a branch of botany that had previously been neglected and misunderstood. Ferns were studied by Swartz, Bolton, Hedwig, Gmelin and many others; mosses were discussed by the great cryptogamist J. Dillen (1687–1747), who was the first to distinguish the genera *Bryum*, *Hypnum* and *Sphagnum*, and who described hundreds of mosses and mushrooms. Hedwig, who was attacked by Linnaeus for calling spores what Linnaeus mistook for anthers packed with pollen, made a detailed study of the Bryophyta in his *Fundamentum historiae naturalis muscorum frondosorum* (1787–1797). Among other botanists working in this field, Necker and Buxbaum deserve mention.

Adriatic marine algae were studied by V. Donati; *Fucus* by S. Gmelin, by Réaumur (who believed that their reproductive organs resembled those of the higher plants) and by John Ellis, who also made a special study of coral zoophytes.

C. Persoon published a number of fundamental papers on the morphology and classification of mushrooms, as also did P. Bulliard (1742–1793), the author of the *Herbier de la France* and of the beautifully illustrated *Histoire des champignons de France*. Mushrooms were also discussed by J. Paulet (1775) and by Gleditsch.

Lichens were the subject of fundamental papers by the Swedish botanist Acharius (1757–1819), who divided them into 40 genera and 800 species. General works on cryptogams were published by Micheli, Hoffmann, Dickson and Kölreuter, who applied Linnaeus' sexual system to the lower plants.

PLANT ANATOMY AND PHYSIOLOGY

Plant Anatomy

Plant anatomy made far less progress in the 18th century than it had in the 17th. In his *Theoria generationis* (1759), C. F. Wolff compared the tissues of young plants to rising dough, and suggested that their branches and floral parts are made up of leaf tissue. This idea was taken up fifty years later by Goethe and then by Mirbel. Hedwig studied xylem and phloem patterns, Duhamel du Monceau the structure of wood and the anatomy of the pear, R. Bradley the structure of thick-leaved plants, and H. B. de Saussure the structure of the stomata. J. H. D. Moldenhawer was the first to describe the structure of lactiferous plants.

Fertilization

In the 17th century, Camerarius had shown that plants, like animals, have reproductive organs and that fertilization is an essential prerequisite of generation. The 18th-century students were profoundly divided on this subject. Among the opponents of Camerarius' ideas were such famous botanists as Tournefort, Linnaeus, Kramer (who called it misleading, impudent and impious), Pontedera and Spallanzani (who had carried out interesting but difficult experiments on the fertilization of basil, hemp and spinach, which neither he nor his collaborator F. Moeller was able to interpret correctly).

Among the growing number of studies corroborating Camerarius' views, C. J. Geoffroy's *Mémoire sur la structure et sur l'usage des diverses parties des fleurs* deserves special mention, for it was the first to depict various types of pollen grain. R. Bradley was able to cross a sweet-william and a carnation, F. W. von Gleichen (Russworm) was the first to describe a pollen tube (in *Asclepias*).

G. Kölreuter (1733–1806) showed that pollination is effected by the wind, insects, or by movements of the stamens. He counted 4,863 pollen grains in a hibiscus flower and showed that 50 would suffice to fertilize more than 30 ovules. He also showed that crossing is successful only if it takes place between related individuals. His work was continued by K. Sprengel, who was able to demonstrate in 1793 that most hermaphrodite flowers cannot be self-pollinated because their stamens and ovules do not mature at the same time. He also showed that insects are attracted to flowers by special colours and scents, and that plants lacking in attractive devices are usually wind-pollinated, and produce large quantities of light pollen. J. T. Needham (*New Microscopical Discoveries*, 1745) claimed that he had observed pollen grains bursting in water and releasing germs. The Italian physician R. Vallisnieri discussed the curious fertilization of the aquatic plant bearing his name (*Vallisneria*), and J. Wallerius published the results of his studies of artificial fertilization (1752).

The Circulation of Sap

The circulation of the sap was studied by the French Jesuit N. Sarrabat (1698–1737), who plunged the tip of a branch into the red juice of *Phytolacca* and observed its rise in the vessels of the branch. Far more important was the work of Stephen Hales (1677–1761), who reported in his *Vegetable Staticks* (1727) more than 140 experiments on the rise of sap under the action of strong light, and who measured the quantities of water absorbed by the roots and 'perspired by the leaves'. Hales's work was translated into many languages and his ideas caught on very quickly, particularly in France, where Guettard spread them in his *Mémoire sur la transpiration insensible des plantes*. Charles Bonnet (*Recherches sur l'usage des feuilles*, 1754) dealt more specifically with the absorption of water by the leaves, though the experimental evidence on which he based his conclusions was rather unconvincing. Duhamel du Monceau distinguished between 'sensible transpiration' in the form of water droplets and 'insensible transpiration' in the form of vapour. Like Bonnet, he failed to distinguish between descending and ascending sap. Martin van Marum compared the circulation of the sap to that of the blood, and G. Bazin the vessels of plants to the tracheae of insects. N. L. Vauquelin began his systematic studies of the subject in 1799.

Respiration

The first papers on plant respiration were published soon after Lavoisier's discovery of the composition of air. Lavoisier himself demonstrated how plants build up living matter from the air, from water and from mineral salts, and how they restore their waste products to the atmosphere. In 1771, J. Priestley showed that whereas green plants cause water to become carbonated in the dark, they have the power of 'reviving' it in sunlight.

Jan Ingenhousz (1730–1779) established the respiration of plants and was also the discoverer of photosynthesis, for he showed in his *Experiments upon Vegetables* (1779) that sunlight enables plants to synthesize their carbohydrates from atmospheric carbon dioxide. His belief that all carbohydrates are obtained in this way was challenged by J. Sénebier (*Mémoires physico-chimiques sur l'influence de la lumière solaire*, 1782), who argued that plants also suck up dissolved carbonic acid through their roots; this view was shared by T. de Saussure.

Plant Movements

Botanists also studied the movements of plants and particularly of the leaves and flowers. Linnaeus planted a 'floral clock' in Upsala in which various flowers opened and closed at different times of the day; he also discussed plant movements in his *Somnus plantarum* and the *Calendrium florae*. Sénebier showed the effect of artificial light on the movements of the leaves of leguminous plants; Duhamel du Monceau studied the movements of Mimosa leaves; J. F. Gmelin the movements of *Hedysarum* leaves; dal Covolo movements of the stamens in the Berberidaceae; Adanson the movements of algae; P. Willemet the behaviour of etiolated plants; J. Ustroff of bent plants; Starken of climbing plants; Buffon and Duhamel du Monceau studied the tensile strength and the imbibition of wood; Cortit discovered the movement of the cytoplasm in cells of the stonewort (*Chara*). The Abbé Bertholon was the first to discuss the action of electricity on plant movements (1783).

General Works

Among the general botanical textbooks which were published in the 18th century the following deserve special mention: Rousseau's *Essais élémentaires sur la botanique* (1771) and *Lettre sur la botanique* (1793–1795), which helped to spread the general appeal of the 'amiable science'; Claret de la Tourette's *Démonstrations élémentaires de botanique*, which Gilibert and Rozier turned into a profusely illustrated botanical encyclopedia (1788); Necker's *Elementa botanica*; Bulliard's *Dictionnaire élémentaire de botanique*; de la Métherie's *Vues physiologiques sur l'organisation végétale et animale*; Séguier's *Bibliotheca botanica*; N. Jolyclerc's *Dictionnaire* and *Cours de botanique*; Maria Merian's *Neues Blumen Buch*, famed for its beautiful plates; and the *Vegetable System* by Bryant, Pulteney and Hill, a vast work profusely illustrated with more than a thousand plates. The first botanical journal, the *Magasin für die Botanik*, was founded by Römer in 1787.

APPLIED BOTANY

Medical Botany

Progress in the study of vegetable drugs was retarded by the absence of efficient methods of organic analysis. In France, A. de Jussieu's *Cours de matière médicale* was published in 1722, and Chomel's work of the same name in 1761. Medical botany was also discussed by J. Barbeu du Bourg, E. F. Geoffroy, B. de Jussieu, A. Gouan, J. E. Gilibert and J. Gautier d'Agoty. In Germany, books on medical chemistry included the works of F. Cartheuser, who distinguished six 'principles which can be extracted from vegetables', and the *Icones plantarum medicinalium* by Plenk and Zom. Similar works were written in England, Holland, Italy and Sweden, where Linnaeus published his *De materia medica e regno vegetabili* in 1749.

Botanical Gardens

Botanical gardens continued to play a very important part in the development of botany. In particular, they provided material for many illustrated catalogues, including P. Ventenat's *Jardin de la Malmaison*, a splendid work commissioned by the Empress Josephine in 1803. Exotic plants, brought back by sailors from abroad, were cultivated in special gardens in Toulon and Brest. The famous Roule Nursery, which was opened in 1669 and existed until 1828, contained more than 50,000 plants collected by travelling botanists.

In England, the famous Kew Gardens were founded in 1759 and W. Aiton, the first curator, was able to cultivate many plants that had not previously prospered in Europe. In 1789 Solander and Dryander helped him to publish a catalogue of them. P. Miller compiled a catalogue of the plants in the Chelsea Physic Garden and also a beautifully illustrated *Gardener's Dictionary*.

In Germany, catalogues were published of the plants in the botanical gardens of Altdorff, Frankfort and Göttingen; J. Kerner published the *Hortus sempervirens*, consisting of seventy-one volumes of elephant folio size, each containing twelve original hand-coloured plates; D. Ehret (1710–1770), one of the greatest botanical draughtsmen of all time, provided the illustrations for Linnaeus' *Hortus*

Cliffortianus, for B. de Jussieu's catalogue of the plants in the *Jardin du Roi*, and for Trew and Vogel's *Plantae selectae* (1750–1760). In Austria, J. Jacquin published numerous magnificently illustrated books on various Viennese gardens; in Holland, H. Boerhaave (1668–1738) published his beautifully illustrated *Index alter plantarum;* in Sweden, Linnaeus compiled a catalogue of the plants in the botanical gardens of Upsala; Italian botanists compiled catalogues of the plants in the Florence, Pisa, Padua and Bologna gardens.

The first botanical garden in America was opened in 1784 by M. G. J. de Crèvecœur, French consul in New York, who had obtained many of his seeds from the Abbé Nolin. In 1786, A. Michaux opened two further gardens in the New World, one near New York on the right bank of the Hudson and the other in South Carolina. Seeds from these gardens were sent to the Abbé Nolin, who distributed them to various French gardens and nurseries.

EXOTIC FLORAS

Botanical Explorations

The study of exotic plants made considerable headway during the 18th century, particularly in France, where Louis XV encouraged the work of explorers.

The flora of North America was studied by M. Sarassin who arrived in Canada in 1685, lived there for forty-five years—he discovered the plant which Tournefort named *Sarracenia* in his honour—and later by P. Charlevoix, who reported his findings in his *Description des plantes principales de l'Amérique équinoxiale*. André Michaux (1746–1803) explored the flora of Carolina, Florida, Pennsylvania, Maryland and Canada, and described 1,700 American plants and 40 new genera in his *Flora boreali-americana*. His son, François André Michaux, who visited America first in his father's company (1785–1790), and again in 1801, in 1806 and in 1809, published an account of his travels and a number of books on American trees, including the *Histoire des arbres forestiers de l'Amérique septentrionale* (1810–1813), which contained 76 plates of unknown species of trees.

The British explorer Mark Catesby visited Carolina, Virginia, Florida and the Bahamas from 1712 to 1719, and wrote a natural history of Carolina. James Sherard's *Hortus britanno-americanus* (1767) described 85 American trees that could be transplanted to England. J. Clayton, who spent his entire life in Virginia, made an important collection of plants which was described by F. Gronovius (1743). P. Browne improved Plumier's classification and introduced new genera. The end of the 18th century produced a further spate of works on North American plants, the most important of which were by G. Howston, T. Walter, S. Barton and F. C. Medicus.

The flora of South America was studied by Father L. Feuillée (1660–1732), who visited the Antilles and explored the coast round Caracas (1703–1706), and later Chile and Peru. *Fuchsia* was one of the many new genera he described.

The flora of Latin America was studied by J. Dombey (1742–1794), the leader of a French scientific mission. Though Dombey was harassed by the Spanish authorities, who seized part of his collection and threw him into gaol at Montserrat, where he died in 1794, his herbarium containing 1,500 plants (including 60 new genera) nevertheless reached the Paris Museum. The Spanish botanists H. Ruiz and J. Pavon, with whom Dombey had gone on a previous voyage, published a flora of Peru and Chile in four volumes (1798–1802). The flora of South America was also studied by Joseph de Jussieu, who arrived in Peru with La Condamine's expedition in 1735 and stayed there for thirty-five years. James Petiver's remarkable collection of exotic plants was bought by Sir Hans Sloane and exhibited in London. Apart from a catalogue of that collection (1692–1703), Petiver also wrote a book on American ferns and a flora of Peru. Towards the end of the 18th century, further works on American plants were published by the Swedish botanist O. Swartz, the Norwegian botanist A. Vahl and the Spanish botanist J. C. Mutis.

The flora of the Antilles was studied by the great British botanist Sir Hans Sloane (1660–1753), who collected and described 800 plants (London, 1707–1725). Sloane, who succeeded Newton as President of the Royal Society, left his collections of natural history specimens, one of the largest of his day, to the nation.

Father J. B. Labat, who lived for seven years in Martinique and later in San Domingo, published an account of his travels in 1722. G. Hughes studied the plants of Barbados (1750) and J. Jacquin those of the Caribbean Islands (1760); Jacquin also introduced many American plants and animals into the gardens of Schönbrunn Palace. The flora of Guiana was studied by P. Barrère, who stayed there in 1722, by de Préfontaine (1763) and by P. Fusée-Aublet, who described 800 plants, half of which were unknown. Guiana was also visited by Charles Sonnini de Manoncourt (1751–1812), whose journal was consulted by Buffon. Claude Richard returned to France from a journey to the Antilles, Guiana and Brazil with a herbarium containing 3,000 plants.

The flora of Africa was studied by many French botanists, including Michel Adanson, who worked as a clerk in the *Compagnie des Indes* at Fort St. Louis (1749–1754), where he gathered the material for his famous *Histoire naturelle du Sénégal* (1757). This work earned him a fellowship of the *Académie* at the age of only thirty years. In particular, he described the baobab and the rubber tree.

Pierre Poivre succeeded in smuggling spice trees out of the Moluccas to Mauritius and Réunion, though the export of these trees was a capital offence. As Governor of Réunion, Poivre also visited Madagascar and the Philippines, establishing superb gardens wherever he lived.

A. Lippi (1704) and C. Sonnini de Manoncourt (1799) described the flora of Egypt; J. Houtou de la Billardière headed a botanical mission to Syria (1786). T. Shaw made a collection of 600 plants, including 200 new species, in Numidia, Syria and Egypt, and published an account of his travels in 1738. The flora of Turkey was explored by J. C. Buxbaum (1728–1740); that of Greece by J. Sibthorp of Oxford. The Swedish botanist P. Forsskål made an important collection of Egyptian and Middle-Eastern plants; F. Hasselquist's collection of Palestinian plants was described by Linnaeus. The flora of Tunisia and Algeria was studied by E. Hebenstreit (1731), by J. Burmann (1738) and by R. L. Desfontaines, whose *Flora atlantica* described 1,520 plants including 300 new species. Among other works worth mentioning were L. Rauwolff's *Floria orientalis*, published by Gronovius in 1755, J. Mariti's account of his travels in the East (9 vols., 1769–1776) and J. de la Roque's travel book (1716), which contained a description of the coffee shrub.

Another interesting travel book was written by P. Sonnerat, who visited Mauritius, Réunion, Madagascar, the Seychelles (where he came across *Erythroxylon coca*), Manila, the Philippines and the Indies. The flora of the Cape of Good Hope was studied by J. Bergius (1767), P. Thunberg (1772–1775) and F. Mason (1772). The Swedish botanist A. Sparrman left for China in 1765, joined Captain Cook's expedition, where he renewed his friendship with Forster and Thunberg, and then went on to South Africa. He described the Cape flora in 1787. The flora of the East Indies was studied by the German botanist B. Valentin, the Dutch botanist F. Valentyn and the British botanist C. Milne. J. Burman studied the flora of Ceylon, Amboina, Malabar and America from various herbaria. His son, N. Burman, began to compile a flora of India in 1766, the work being completed by J. G. Koenig. The Swedish botanist O. Torén, who visited the Comoro Islands, the Malay Peninsula and Canton, communicated his findings to Linnaeus, who helped to publish them in 1757; the Danish botanist C. F. Rotboell studied the flora of Surinam (Dutch Guiana); the Portuguese Jesuit J. de Loureiro studied the flora of Cambodia, Malabar and Mozambique and published an excellent flora of French Indo-China (1790). The flora of Java was studied by

J. C. M. Radermacher, and the flora of China by the French Jesuit N. Chéron (or d'Incarville, 1706–1757), who sent B. de Jussieu a collection of 300 plants, including *Ailantus*, *Cedrela* and *Incarvillea*, but not, as has often been claimed, the China-aster which was first described by Dillenius in 1732. The flora of China was also studied by A. Sparrmann, the flora of Japan by C. P. Thunberg and by P. Charlevoix, and the flora of New Holland (Australia) by Fenyl and Schott.

A French naval expedition to the South, led by Bougainville, was given model instructions on the collection of botanical specimens by P. Commerson. Commerson himself left France in 1766 on board the frigate *Étoile* and visited Brazil, Tierra del Fuego, Tahiti, New Guinea, Australia and Batavia, collecting plants wherever he could. He also made an important collection of plants in Mauritius, Madagascar and Réunion, where he died in 1773. (His collections and his drawings of new species were used by de Jussieu and Lamarck.) Another expedition, led by d'Entrecasteaux, to rescue the French explorer La Pérouse, included Ventenat, La Billardière and many other naturalists. It visited the Canaries, the Cape of Good Hope, Australia, Tasmania, New Caledonia and the Moluccas. In 1798, La Billardière published an account of this sensational voyage and, later, a number of very important studies on the plants he had gathered.

In Britain, Sir Joseph Banks (1743–1820) devoted his entire fortune to the study of exotic plants. He made a botanical expedition to Newfoundland in 1763; in 1768–1771, with the Swedish botanist D. Solander, he accompanied Captain James Cook (1728–1779) on his voyage round the world in the *Endeavour*, visiting the Canaries, the Cape Verde Islands, Brazil, Tierra del Fuego, Australia, New Zealand, a number of Pacific islands and New Guinea. In 1722, he made a trip to the Hebrides and Iceland, and was instrumental in bringing to public notice the marvels of Fingal's Cave on the island of Staffa. He became President of the Royal Society and formed a valuable collection which he bequeathed to the British Museum.

The German naturalist Johann R. Forster and his son Georg joined Cook's second voyage on board the *Resolution*. The expedition rounded the Cape of Good Hope, reached New Zealand, the Society Islands and the Friendly Islands, and discovered New Caledonia. On his return to England in 1775, J. R. Forster was able to describe 75 new genera of plants, while Georg Forster published a special study on *Autocarpus incisa*, a description of the medicinal plants he had gathered on the Pacific islands, and a general account of his voyage (1777). A journal of the voyage was also published by J. C. Lettsom, the author of a paper on the tea plant.

CHAPTER 5

Earth Sciences

Until the French Revolution, geologists were still so much under the influence of the Church that few dared to question the Biblical story of the Flood. Even so, 18th-century students made a considerable contribution towards the development of paleontology, stratigraphy, orography and mineralogy.

GEOLOGY

The Italian School

In 1711, Galeazzi observed that the fossils of Monte San Lucca, near Bologna, resembled Indian rather than Mediterranean species. Ten years later, Vallisnieri made a general survey of the distribution of marine deposits in Friuli, Vicenza, Verona and Bologna, and decided that these could not have been laid down during the Flood. He also wrote an account of Monte Bolca, famous for its fossil fish.

In 1740, Anton Lazzaro Moro published his *De' crostacei e degli altri marini corpi che si truovano su' monti* ('Of crustaceans and other marine bodies found on mountains'), in which he put forward the view that fossil shells were thrown up from the ocean by volcanic actions of the kind that had caused a new island to appear in the Greek Archipelago in 1707.

Moro's theory, which was presented to the Academy of Cremona in 1749, was the first of many attempts to explain prehistoric in terms of historic phenomena. Thus G. Arduino challenged the story of the Flood when he distinguished between primary, secondary and tertiary deposits near Verona and Vianza.

Fossils also attracted the attention of the Italian naturalist G. B. Beccari, who, in 1729, described a foraminifer which Linnaeus named *Nautilus Beccarii* and which is now known as *Rotalia* (*Turbinularia*) *beccarii*. Ten years later, G. Bianchi (J. Plancus) announced that he had discovered a fossilized 'Ammon's horn' on the beach of Rimini; Soldani subsequently described many other ammonites. At the end of the century, Serafino Volta published the 'Veronese Ichthyology' in which he described 123 species of fossil fish from Lacastra, near Monte Bolca, of which he claimed 12 were extinct.

fig. 34 Imprints of fossil plants.
(J. J. Scheuchzer: 'Herbarium diluvianum', 1709.)

In 1751–1752, Targioni published his 'Travels in Tuscany', in which he showed that valleys are not formed by ocean currents, as Buffon had taught, but by rivers.

The Swiss School

Johann Jacob Scheuchzer (1672–1733) is famous for his observations on his native Switzerland, to which he devoted his entire life. One of his earliest works, the *Piscium querelae et vindiciae* (1708), described a meeting of fossil fish to protest against the malicious libels of men who called them freaks of nature, when, in fact, they were the ancestors of living fishes. The book contained many beautiful plates of German and Italian fossils.

One year later, Scheuchzer published the *Herbarium diluvianum*, in which he described and depicted many fossil plants and animals from England, Switzerland and Italy, including fossil ammonites, whose septa had previously been mistaken for the veins of leaves. A study of carboniferous strata convinced Scheuchzer that the Flood must have taken place in the month of May!

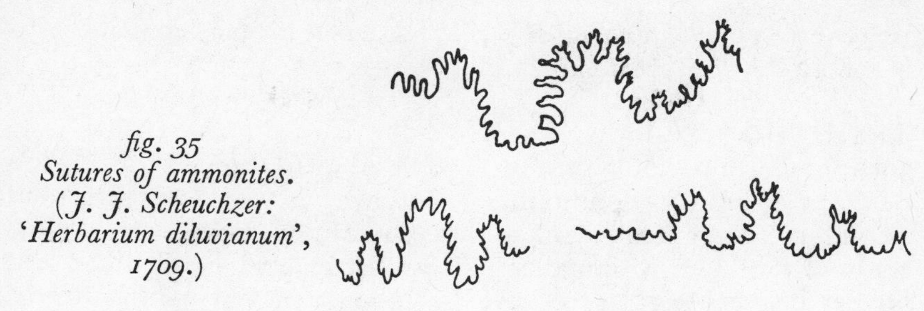

fig. 35
Sutures of ammonites.
(J. J. Scheuchzer:
'Herbarium diluvianum',
1709.)

In 1716, he published a catalogue of his collection of 1,500 fossils, including 149 ammonites, which he classified into spiny and spineless, and further into smooth and wrinkled, bifurcate and trifurcate, *etc.*

Scheuchzer's work was continued by Johann Gesner, who observed that when fossil shells split they invariably reveal the planes of a calcium carbonate crystal. Petrifaction was studied by Louis Bourget, who published a treatise on the subject in 1742.

In his *Lettres physiques et morales sur les montagnes et sur l'histoire de la terre et de l'homme* ('Physical and moral letters on mountains and on the history of the earth and of man'), which he addressed to the Queen of England, Jean André de Luc (1727–1817) distinguished between primitive volcanic mountains, secondary marine mountains and primordial or inexplicable mountains. In his subsequent letters to Blumenbach (1798), he described the continents as domes of marine sediment, folded and broken by a great upheaval and drained during the general retreat of the oceans. De Luc professed that his chief aim was to prove the correctness of the Biblical account of the Flood. In the *Journal de physique*, he likened nummulites to cuttle-fish, and observed correctly that the nummulites from Bayonne, Italy and India are identical.

Horace Benedicte de Saussure (1740–1799), professor of philosophy at Geneva, was one of the greatest geologists of his day. His *Voyages dans les Alpes* (1786–1796) contained the results of studies pursued during thirty years. De Saussure was the first to appreciate the full importance of the bedding of strata, when, having observed the great fold on the flank of Nant d'Arpenaz, he saw that the strata could not have been deposited on a curved surface but were originally laid down in a horizontal position and later folded by an unknown force.

In the first volume of his *Voyages dans les Alpes*, de Saussure stated that he would give an overall explanation of geological phenomena and their causes, but at the end of Volume IV he admitted that he had set his original aim too high:

In my youth, when I had crossed the Alps only a few times, I believed I had grasped all the facts. . . . Since then further explorations of different parts of the mountain chain have shown me that the only constant thing in the Alps is their great variety.

The German School

Johann Gottlob Lehmann (d. 1767) adopted Steno's distinction between primitive mountains laid down at the Creation, and secondary or sedimentary mountains containing fossils. After a close study of the Harz Mountains and the Erzgebirge, he distinguished further between eight successive formations: primary with mineral veins, old red sandstone, coal measures, new red sandstone, blue limestone, copper-bearing shales, marl-slate and Zechstein limestones.

Two further series were distinguished by J. C. Füchsel (*Historia terrae et maris*, 1762, and *Entwürfe der ältesten Erd- und Völkergeschichte*, 1773): the mottled sandstone and the Muschelkalk. Füchsel also noted the kinds of fossils associated with different strata and was one of the first to illustrate his work with a geological map. The first coloured geological map was produced by Gottlieb Gläser at Leipzig in 1775.

Peter Simon Pallas (1741–1811), a native of Berlin, did for the geology of Russia what de Saussure did for the geology of Switzerland. Under the auspices of the Empress Catherine II, he explored almost the whole of Russia and made a study of two of Asia's greatest mountain ranges, the Urals and the Altai. He brought back many important observations, and was the first to discover in the Siberian ice 'the remains of great animals of India, bones of elephants, rhinoceroses, monstrous buffaloes . . .' He also discovered the Yenisei meteorite.

In a paper to the St. Petersburg Academy of Science (1707), Pallas put forward the view that the highest mountain ranges of the world are composed of granite, a massive rock containing no fossils, and this is flanked by crystalline schists succeeded and overlain by calcareous rocks. Though this explanation may strike one as rather simple, it must be remembered that Pallas published his work before de Saussure and Werner.

Werner and Neptunism

Abraham Gottlieb Werner (1750–1817) was born in Prussia and published his first geological work, the *Von den äusserlichen Kennzeichen der Fossilien*, when he was only 24 years old. In 1755, he was appointed lecturer in mining and metallurgy at the Freiberg School of Mines, and began his special studies of the geology of Saxony, on which he intended to base a new science: 'geognosy'.

Twelve years later, he published his 'Brief Classification and

Description of the Different Kinds of Rocks', followed by his 'New Theory of the Origin of Mineral Veins' (1791). Werner, who adopted the ideas of Steno, Lehmann and Füchsel, had the great advantage over them of being able to put his ideas to a large number of students, who flocked to his lectures from all parts of Europe.

Like his predecessors, Werner believed in the regular recurrence of certain formations, and distinguished between primitive, transitional and secondary rocks. He believed that primitive rocks are formed by the crystallization of material dissolved in the oceanic water, transitional rocks by chemical precipitation, and secondary rocks by mechanical sedimentation during alternate advances and retreats of the sea. In the face of a great deal of evidence to the contrary, Werner even maintained that basalt is not volcanic but of aqueous origin. This doctrine, which became known as 'Neptunism', was opposed by Hutton's 'Plutonism'. While both theories explained that coal was a deposit of plants, Hutton attributed their carbonization to heat and pressure, and Werner to the action of the sulphuric acid liberated from pyrites.

On the assumption that all true veins were originally rents, open in their upper part and afterwards filled in from above, Werner was able to establish a criterion for distinguishing the age of veins: 'Every vein which intersects another is newer than the one traversed, and is of later formation than all those which it traverses.'

The British School

In Britain, as elsewhere, many people, including geologists, devoted their efforts to proving the historical accuracy of the Scriptures, and particularly of the Flood. John Wesley (1703–1791) taught that volcanoes and earthquakes had not existed before the Fall, and in 1708, the astronomer W. Whiston explained 'by science' that the Flood had started on Wednesday, 28th November.

Nevertheless, much excellent work was being done in England, where the first geological map was made at this time. That such maps should be made was suggested by Martin Lister as early as 1683, but it was not until 1743 that Christopher Packe (1686–1749) published *A New Philosophico-Chorographical Chart of East Kent*. Other British workers were engaged in collecting fossils, and they included Thomas Pennant (1726–1798), author of *British Zoology* and *Tours Through the British Isles*, the Rev. Clayton Mordaunt Cracherode (1730–1799) and William Martin (1767–1810), author of *Petrificata Derbiensia*. James Sowerby was also busy collecting at this time, and J. T. Needham deduced that the presence of fossils in the rocks showed that the strata were originally fluid and horizontal, and that all mountain chains consist of concentric layers of equal thickness.

Gustavus Brander (1720–1787), though a Swede, must also be counted in the British school for he was born in London, became a Fellow of the Royal Society, and for the last twenty-six years of his life was a Trustee of the British Museum. His principal geological work was done in Hampshire, where he made a collection—still extant—of 124 Tertiary fossils. This collection was described by C. Solander, a pupil of Linnaeus and an officer of the Museum, in *Fossilia Hantoniensia* (1766).

James Hutton and Plutonism

The Scottish physician James Hutton (1726–1797) gave up medicine for geology and devoted his life to scientific observation. His *Theory of the Earth*, which he presented to the Royal Society of Edinburgh in 1785, attracted little attention until John Playfair (1748–1819) published his *Illustrations of the Huttonian Theory* in 1802.

Hutton believed that the earth's interior contains 'a fluid mass, melted but undamaged by the action of heat', and explained many geological phenomena on the assumption that some of this molten material had been forced up from the interior, intruding into various strata from below. According to Hutton, such intrusive rocks include basalt, porphyry and granite. Whereas Werner had contended that primitive rocks were chemical precipitates, Hutton took the view that they had been fused by the action of the fiery force in the earth's interior, and were later thrown up by the expansive force of the heat. The older a formation, the steeper is its slope. Unlike Werner, therefore, Hutton believed that the veins in eruptive rocks are filled from below. He also asserted that, since granite can be shown to have intruded into sedimentary rocks, it must be the more recent of the two. Hutton's plutonic theory won a complete victory over Werner's neptunism when it was adopted by von Humboldt and von Buch.

William Smith

William Smith (1738–1839), the 'father of English geology', was the first to give an adequate account of the nature and succession of geological formations in his *Tabular View of the Order of Strata in the vicinity of Bath with their respective remains* (1799). Among his most intimate friends and closest collaborators were the Rev. Benjamin Richardson and the Rev. Joseph Townsend, the author of a book bearing the title *The Character of Moses established for Veracity as an Historian, recording events from the Creation to the Deluge*. In 1815, Smith published his famous 8′ 9″ × 6′ 2″ map, entitled *A Map of the Strata of England and Wales with a part of Scotland, exhibiting the Collieries, Mines and Canals, the Marshes and Fenlands originally overflowed by the sea and the varieties of soil according to the variations in the substrata*. Smith's two other important works, marking the beginning of stratigraphical paleontology in England, are mentioned in a later volume of this series, covering the 19th century.

The French School

In 1708, J. Astruc described some fossils found near Montpellier as Mediterranean shells. In 1720, Réaumur published a paper on the shell marl of Touraine, in which he propounded the view that the shells in it had been carried there by a current from the Channel. His paper was read to the *Académie des Sciences* by Fontenelle, who had this to say about it:

> Though the Flood described in Holy Scripture must have, and indeed has, left many traces on earth, the shells of Touraine are certainly not among them. They must have been deposited there very slowly and gently over a much longer period than a year.

Fontenelle, when introducing Scheuchzer's paleontological findings to the Academy, also made the famous remark which has since become classical: 'We have here a new species of coin which can be dated with much more certainty, and is of far greater importance, than any Greek or Roman coin.' He went on to suggest that these shells might well help geologists to prepare accurate maps of the various formations.

In France, as elsewhere, there was much opposition to the new ideas. Their most illustrious critic was Voltaire, who claimed that shells found on mountains had been placed there by pilgrims returning from Syria or Spain. The Encyclopedists, on the other hand, warmly embraced paleontology as supporting their struggle against the Church.

B. de Maillet (Telliamed, 1748) timidly hinted at the extinction of species, and put forward the view that all living species are descendants of plants and animals which survived the Flood. E. Guettard (1715–1786) published a work entitled *Mémoire et carte minéralogique sur la nature et situation des terrains qui traversent la France et l'Angleterre* (1746), which may be described as the first geological survey. In it, he put forward the view that the minerals and rocks round Paris are arranged in concentric 'bands' of sand, marl and schist, which are continued on the other side of the Channel. He indicated many fossil localities in his *Atlas et Description Minéralogiques de la France* (1780), which he prepared with the help of Monnet, and was one of the first to identify the trilobite fossils in the slates of Anvers, mammalian remains in the Parisian gypsum, and nummulites in the Dauphiné (1779). Even more important was a discovery he made while collecting material for his survey. His curiosity was aroused by the milestones at Moulins, which, he was told, had been obtained from Volvic, near Clairmont, and on 10th May 1752, he told the *Académie des Sciences* that he had immediately suspected that Volvic was an abbreviation for *volcani vicus* ('volcanic village'), and that many mountains in Central France must be volcanic. Nobody believed him, and he himself failed to realize that basalt is of volcanic origin.

It fell to Nicolas Desmarest (1725–1815) to make a detailed volcanic map of the Auvergne, to demonstrate the volcanic nature of basalt, and to identify the deposits of active and extinct volcanoes. Desmarest was probably the first to make a clear distinction between synclines and anticlines, though the terms themselves were not coined until 1822, by Conybeare and Buckland.

Special mention must be made of the Abbé Palassou's *Essai sur la minéralogie des Monts-Pyrénées* (1781). Palassou was the first to recognize the general parallelism of the strike of the strata with the chain of the Pyrenees and, like Targioni before him, he attributed the formation of valleys to erosion by rivers and not by the ocean (as was generally believed). His *Essai* contained a geological map of the northern slopes of the Pyrenees.

Buffon

Like Descartes, Newton, Steno and Leibniz, Buffon believed that the earth and the other planets had originally been part of the sun.

In his *Théorie de la Terre* (1749), he showed that the abundance of fossil shells in all parts of the earth was clear evidence that the sea must have covered them in the past. He distinguished pelagic from littoral species and noted that some forms, such as the ammonites, are extinct.

Like Desmarest, he recognized the volcanic origin of basalt. Having no desire to fall out with the Church, Buffon wrote that 'the earth was very much as it is now, even before the Flood'. At first, he attributed the appearance of mountains to the action of the ocean, but in a second edition of his work he asserted that 'mountains are not formed by the waters but by the earth's central fire. Water merely lends the fire a helping hand.'

In 1778, he published his far more important *Époques de la nature*, a work which, though obscure and encumbered by philosophical speculation, nevertheless contained many original ideas, some of which were condemned outright by the faculty of theology of the University of Paris. In this work, Buffon tried to explain the past by the present, but, knowing little about either, he was forced to rely largely on his own imagination. He was the first to express definite opinions on the duration of geological time. 'Strata are formed by the action of water over millennia, and not over the forty days of the Flood.'

He divided the history of the earth into six epochs, covering a total period of at least 75,000 years, a figure at which he arrived after establishing that every tide lays down 1/12 of a *ligne* of clay, or 5 inches of clay a year, so that a 6,000-ft. mountain would take at least 14,000 years to form.

Buffon was also the founder of paleogeography. His comparative studies of Old and New World mammals convinced him that the two hemispheres must have been linked in the past, at least until his sixth epoch. All in all, his ideas opened up many new horizons, which were not fully explored until the 19th century.

Dolomieu

In 1796–1798, Dieudonné Dolomieu (1750–1801) visited a part of the Alps, and succeeded in verifying many of de Saussure's observations. In a report to the *Journal des Mines*, he explained the phenomenon of overthrust in so remarkable a way that we shall quote it in full, despite his many confused ideas:

> An explanation of this phenomenon . . . can be found only if we postulate a violent force which, on striking the hard crust of the earth obliquely, compressed it, displacing some of the strata and forcing them to buttress one another in the air, as in the case of Mont Blanc, and others to drop down and to override the masses below, not very far from their original position, as in the case of Monte Rosa.

Giraud-Soulavie

Jean Louis Soulavie (1752–1813), who joined a monastic order under the name of Giraud, was the real founder of stratigraphical paleontology and a precursor of the theory of transformism.

In 1772, he discovered that lava flows along river-beds and that volcanic material had been transported far downstream by the Rhône. He therefore attempted to determine the chronological sequence of rocks from the formation of valleys, and arrived at figures (hundreds of millions of years) that did not in any way tally with Scripture.

Soulavie came to Paris in 1778, intending to write a physical geography of France in seven volumes (*L'histoire naturelle de la France méridionale*). However, he was so violently attacked, not only by the clergy but also by Buffon, that he was forced to suspend the publication of the last two volumes. Shortly before, he had written that sedimentary rocks can be classified according to their fossil content:

The unknown plants contained in the most ancient slates, and the marine shells enclosed in primitive limestone, were the first to inhabit the oceans and the earth. . . . Among the shells, there are some families which have existed before others. . . . Nature has multiplied and perfected these families, beginning with the simplest and ending with the most complex. . . .

He accordingly distinguished between five types of sedimentary strata: the first and oldest with fossils of extinct species only (orthoceras, ammonites, belemnites); the second containing fossils of extinct species together with such extant species as *Nautilus*; the third 'with recent shells, the descendants of which still live in soft and calcareous stones in the oceans'; the fourth with plant-beds (Miocene shales of Coiron); the fifth with conglomerates containing elephants' teeth. He stressed the fact that the extinction of old and the rise of new species are due to environmental influences (soil, temperature, food *etc.*).

Though his enemies forced Soulavie to keep silent for many years, the French Revolution made it possible for him to be heard again. In 1793, when he declared that traces of volcanic eruption could persist for more than six million years, he had broken finally with the Book of Genesis.

PREHISTORY

Prehistory may be called a branch of geology, for it reconstructs man's evolution during the last million years by the study of fossils and stone implements in sedimentary rocks. Since this study brought geologists and archaeologists into conflict with the Church, very little progress in it was made in the 18th century.

Comparative Ethnography

Flint arrowheads, to which a 'fairy' or magic origin was popularly ascribed, and which were also sometimes called 'thunderbolts', were first intelligently described in a posthumous work by Michele Mercati (1541–1593), the *Metallotheca* (1717):

'While most men', Mercati wrote, 'believe that *céraunies* are produced by lightning, historians hold that they have been chipped off by violent blows from very hard flints, at a time long before iron was put to use for the follies of war. The most ancient of men knew no blades other than flakes of flint.'

A few years later, A. de Jussieu, Father Lafitau (1724) and N. Mahudel (1734) compared arrowheads to the stone weapons of existing primitive tribes, and stressed their similarity.

In 1715, Conyers, a London pharmacist and antiquary, discovered a flint axe together with elephant remains in river gravel. An explanation for this remarkable find was suggested by his friend Bagford: the axe had been used by an ancient Briton to kill one of the Emperior Claudius' elephants. At the end of the 18th century, John Frere made a further discovery of animal remains and prehistoric implements at Hoxne, in Suffolk, and declared that his find probably dated from prehistoric times. This astonishing observation passed unnoticed in the 18th century—it was the first mention of man's coexistence in the past with animals that have become extinct.

Giants

Because the Bible was rarely questioned, the existence of fossil man was not even postulated until the very end of the 18th century. What human fossil remains were discovered before then were commonly attributed to giants. Was it not written:

> There were giants in the earth in those days; and also after that, when the sons of God came in unto the daughters of men, and they bare children to them, the same became mighty men which were of old, men of renown. (Gen. 6: 4.)

In the 16th century, a church in Valencia displayed an elephant tooth as a relic of St. Christopher, and in another Spanish church the femur of a fossil elephant was worshipped as the arm of a saint. In 1714, the Royal Society received a paper from Cotton Mather, of Boston, in which the remains of mastodons, discovered in Albany in 1705, were described as 'the bones of the accursed race before the Flood'. In the 18th century, Scheuchzer still described fragments of a large animal, dug up near Lucerne in 1577, as the bones of a giant. Felix Platter, professor of medicine at Basle, attributed the same remains to a man 17 feet tall.

So little was known of the anatomy of prehistoric man that Scheuchzer, though a talented naturalist, described the skeleton of the great fossil salamander discovered at Oeningen in Switzerland as *Homo diluvii testis* ('human witness of the Flood'). His view was shared by A. J. d'Argenville, and it was only in 1787 that Pieter Camper described the skeleton correctly. The question of fossil man was mentioned by Buffon in his *Époques de la Nature* (1778), where he stated that man is more recent than the fossil elephants and rhinoceroses found in the Seine alluvium, a mistake which was, however, an expression of current opinion. It was not until 1797 that John Frere affirmed the great antiquity of man and considered that the human race flourished contemporaneously with some animals which are now extinct.

MINERALOGY

In the 18th century, mineralogy had not yet become a distinct science, for though Wallerius and Werner had attempted to classify minerals, and though Bergman, Cronstedt and von Born studied their chemical composition, the results were rather meagre. Felspar, for instance, was called a 'siliceous earth combined with clay and a little magnesium'.

Torbern Bergman (1735–1784) has often been called the precursor of Haüy because of his explanation that prismatic calcite breaks into the rhombohedra of Iceland spar. In fact, while Bergman merely noted the phenomenon, Haüy made it the basis of a new branch of science.

In 1735, Linnaeus suggested that all crystals of the same geometrical form have similar chemical compositions. In 1783, Romé de l'Isle (1736–1790) and his pupil A. Carangeot discovered the law of constancy of angles between crystals of the same substance.[1] De l'Isle, who coined the word 'crystallography', prefaced his *Essai de cristallographie* (1772) as follows:

> This work, which I here present to the public, is not only as complete a crystallography as the present state of our knowledge permits, but also a lithology, which, as an associated branch of mineralogy, offers a general explanation of the theory of the earth, for which no systems other than crystals can account. . . .

De l'Isle's views were challenged by Buffon, according to whom crystals play a relatively unimportant part in geological processes:

> One might say, in all strictness, that there is but a single primitive glass—quartz—which may be discoloured by iron to take the form of jasper and mica . . .; larger quantities of iron and other heterogeneous substances turn quartz into felspar and schorl. It is to these five substances that Nature seems to have limited the number of glasses produced by the primitive fire, and it is from these that all the vitreous substances of the mineral kingdom have originated.

According to Buffon, the important characteristics of minerals are hardness, density, homogeneity, fusibility and combustibility—their crystalline form is merely accidental.

[1] That law was first propounded in 1745 by Lomonosov, whose works, as we saw, were published in Russian and were therefore not available to Western scientists.

René Just Haüy

In 1770, René Just Haüy (1743–1822), a young theologian, began to attend the lectures of the mineralogist Louis Daubenton (1760–1800) at the *Jardin du Roi*. Haüy, who was a keen botanist, was puzzled by the fact that whereas flowers of the same species always have the same number of petals, minerals of the same species assume different crystalline forms. Upon discovering that prismatic calcite can always be split into rhombohedra, he assumed that cleavage may be continued down to the crystal elements, which he called 'integrant molecules'. On 21st February 1781, he submitted to the *Académie des Sciences* a preliminary paper on the structure of garnet crystals, which he followed with another preliminary paper on the structure of spar on 22nd December. In 1748, he was ready to present his full theory in his *Essai d'une théorie sur la structure des cristaux appliquée à plusieurs genres de substances cristallines*, which has rightly become famous. One year before, his work had already earned him membership of the *Académie des Sciences* (botanical section); in 1795 he was made a member of the *Institut national*, and in 1802 he became professor at the School of Mines and professor of mineralogy at the *Musée de l'histoire naturelle*. Among his later works were the *Traité de mineralogie* (5 vols. including an atlas, 1801) and the *Traité de cristallographie* (3 vols., 1822).

Having discovered the laws governing the structure of crystals, Haüy went on to their classification. He established that the integral molecules of all minerals belonging to the same species have an 'invariable form in which the faces lie in the direction of the natural joints indicated by the mechanical division of the crystals'. He then divided mineral species into five classes: stony and sandy, non-metallic, metallic, igneous and volcanic.

The Microscopic Study of Minerals

Optical methods were first applied to geology in the 17th century, mainly as a result of the pioneer work of A. van Leeuwenhoek, the father of protistology, and of Robert Hooke, who was the first to study the comparative anatomy of living and fossil plants. Huygens observed polarization in Iceland spar in 1678.

Despite the construction of better microscopes, microscopy marked time during most of the 18th century. However, in 1782, Louis Daubenton published an interesting paper on microscopic mineralogy, in which he explained the true nature of dendrites. Dolomieu discussed microscopic mineralogy in 1794, and Fleuriau de Bellevue analysed volcanic deposits in the neighbourhood of Rome in 1800.

Conclusion

ALTHOUGH ITS CONTRIBUTION was less revolutionary than that of its great predecessor, the 18th century nevertheless left a considerable mark on science.

We have only to read the work of Lacroix, Monge, Lagrange and Laplace to realize how far mathematics, mechanics and astronomy had progressed since Leibniz and Newton. While optics stood relatively still, heat, sound, magnetism, electricity, chemistry and biology moved rapidly towards their present state.

More important still, 18th-century science was largely responsible for the rise of rationalism and for the shedding of much theological lumber. Scientists began to play an increasing part in furthering human progress, and were generally acclaimed for doing so. They also paved the way for that ever-closer union between science and technology which is so characteristic of our own age.

BIBLIOGRAPHY

General

Bibliographies by POGGENDORFF, RUSSO, SARTON.

Works already cited of BOLL, BUTTERFIELD, DAUMAS, D'IRSAY, ENRIQUES and SANTILLANA, HALL, HANOTAUX, MAINDRON, MASON, PLEDGE.

C. H. ALEXANDER, *The Leibniz-Clarke Correspondence*, Manchester, 1956.

G. BACHELARD, *La formation de l'esprit scientifique*, Paris, 1938.

J. R. CARRÉ, *La philosophie de Fontenelle, ou le sourire de la raison*, Paris, 1932.

P. HAZARD, *European Thought in the Eighteenth Century*, London, 1954.

G. LEFEBVRE, *La Révolution française* (Vol. XIII in the series 'Peuples et Civilisations'), new ed., Paris, 1951.

H. METZGER, *Attraction universelle et religion naturelle chez quelques commentateurs anglais de Newton*, Paris, 1938.

D. MORNET, *Les origines intellectuelles de la Révolution française*, new ed., Paris, 1947.

La Pensée française au XVIIIe siècle (Vol. V in the series 'Histoire générale des civilisations'), Paris, 1951.

L. RÉAU, *L'Europe française au siècle des lumières*, Paris, 1938.
L'Encyclopédie et le progrès des sciences et des techniques, Paris, 1952.

P. SAGNAC, *La fin de l'Ancien Régime et la Révolution Américaine* (Vol. XII in the series 'Peuples et Civilisations'), Paris, 1952.

H. PRESERVED SMITH, *A History of Modern Culture*, Vol. II (1687–1776), New York, 1934.

A. WOLF, *A History of Science, Technology and Philosophy in the XVIIIth Century*, 2nd ed., London, 1952.

Mathematics

Works already cited of AMODEO, ARCHIBALD, BALL, BECKER and HOFMANN, BOUTROUX, BOYER, BRAUNMÜHL, BRUNSCHVICG, CANTOR (Vol. III, 1668–1758, Leipzig, 1901; Vol. IV, 1759–1799, Leipzig, 1908), CHASLES, COOLIDGE, DICKSON, GEYMONAT, HOFMANN, KÄSTNER, LORIA, MONTUCLA, SMITH, TODHUNTER, TROPFKE.

E. FUETER, *Geschichte der exakten Wissenschaften in der schweizischen Aufklärung* (1680–1780), Aarau, 1941.

J. F. SCOTT, *A History of Mathematics*, London, 1958.

N. NIELSEN, *Géomètres français du XVIIIe siècle*, Paris, 1935.
Géomètres français sous la Révolution, Paris, 1929.

J. B. DELAMBRE, *Rapport historique sur les progrès des sciences mathématiques depuis 1789*, Paris, 1810.

F. CAJORI, *A History of the Conceptions of Limits and Fluxions in Great Britain from Newton to Woodhouse*, Chicago, 1931.

T. MUIR, *The Theory of Determinants in the Historical Order* . . . Vol. I, 2nd ed., London, 1906.

G. LORIA, *Il passato e il presente delle principali teorie geometriche*, 4th ed., Padua, 1931.
'Perfectionnements, évolution, métamorphoses du concept de "coordonnées"' in *Osiris*, VIII, 1948, pp. 218–288.
Storia della geometria descrittiva, Milan, 1921.

R. BONOLA, *Non-Euclidean Geometry*, Chicago, 1912.

J. L. COOLIDGE, *History of Conic Sections and Quadric Surfaces*, Oxford, 1945.

D. J. STRUIK, 'Outline of a History of Differential Geometry' in *Isis*, XIX and XX, 1933–1934.
Der Briefwechsel von Johann Bernoulli, Vol. I, Basle, 1955.

H. AUCHTER, *Brook Taylor*, Würzburg, 1937.

C. TWEEDIE, *James Stirling*, Oxford, 1922.
'The "Geometria Organica" of Colin Maclaurin' in *Proc. Roy. Soc. Edinburgh*, XXXVI, 1916.

L. G. DU PASQUIER, *Léonard Euler et ses amis*, Paris, 1927.

R. FUETER, *Léonard Euler*, Basle, 1948.

P. BRUNET, *La vie et l'œuvre de Clairaut*, Paris, 1952.

R. TATON, *L'œuvre scientifique de Monge*, Paris, 1951.

G. SARTON, 'Lagrange's Personality' in *Proc. Amer. Phil. Soc.* LXXXVIII, 1944.

M. STECK (ed.), *J. H. Lambert. Schriften zur Perspektive*, Berlin, 1943.

Works by EULER (in course of publication since 1912), LAGRANGE (14 vols., Paris, 1867–1892), LAPLACE (13 vols., Paris, 1878–1904), RUFFINI (3 vols., Palermo, 1915–1954).

Mechanics

Previously quoted works by DUGAS, DUHEM, JOUGUET, MACH, TODHUNTER.

J. BERTRAND, *D'Alembert*, Paris, 1889.

P. BRUNET, *Maupertuis*, 2 vols., Paris, 1929.
Étude historique sur le principe de la moindre action, Paris, 1938.
L'introduction des théories de Newton en France au XVIIIe siècle (avant 1738), Paris, 1931.

P. E. B. JOURDAIN, *The Principle of Least Action*, Chicago, 1913

R. MARCOLONGO, *Il problema dei tre corpi da Newton (1686) ai nostri giorni*, Milan, 1919.

Astronomy

Previously quoted works by ABETTI, ANDRÉ and RAYET, BAILLY, BIGOURDAN, BOQUET, DANJON and COUDER, DELAMBRE, DOUBLET, HOUZEAU and LANCASTER, KING, LALANDE, MACPHERSON, REPSOLD, WOLF, ZINNER.

H. ANDOYER, *L'œuvre scientifique de Laplace*, Paris, 1922.

F. BRUNNOW, *Lehrbuch der sphärischen Astronomie*, 4th ed., Leipzig, 1881.

R. GRANT, *History of Physical Astronomy*, London, 1852.

E. GUYOT, *Histoire de la détermination des longitudes*, La Chaud-de-Fonds, 1955.

F. R. HELMERT, *Die mathematischen und physikalischen Theorien der höheren Geodäsie*, 2 vols., Leipzig, 1880–1884.

P. S. LAPLACE, *Précis de l'histoire de l'astronomie*, Paris, 1821.

A. A. A. LESUEUR, *La Condamine*, Paris, 1911.

A. MARGUET, *Histoire de la longitude en mer au XVIIIe siècle*, Paris, 1935.

J. MASCART, *La vie et les travaux du chevalier de Borda*, Paris, 1919.

W. I. MILHAM, *Time and Time-keepers*, New York, 1923.

C. A. F. PETERS, 'Recherches sur la parallaxe des étoiles fixes' in *Ac. Imp. Sc. St. Petersburg; Maths. and Phys. Sc.*, V, 1848.

F. TISSERAND, 'Tentatives faites pour déterminer la parallaxe du Soleil' in *Proc. Obs. Paris*, XVI, 1882.

Traité de mécanique céleste, 4 vols., Paris, 1889–1896.
I. TODHUNTER, *History of the Mathematical Theories of Attraction and the Figure of the Earth . . .*, 2 vols., London, 1873.
R. WOLF, *Handbuch der Astronomie, ihrer Geschichte und Litteratur*, 2 vols., Zurich, 1890–1893.

Physics

Previously quoted works by CAVERNI, CAJORI, DAUMAS, GERLAND and TRAUMÜLLER, HOPPE, LASSWITZ, MAGIE, POGGENDORFF, ROSENBERGER, USHER, VOLKRINGER.
T. S. ASHTON, *The Industrial Revolution, 1760–1830*, Oxford, 1948.
P. BRUNET, *Les physiciens hollandais et la méthode expérimentale en France au XVIIIe siècle*, Paris, 1926.
P. MANTOUX, *The Industrial Revolution in the Eighteenth Century*, London, 1928.
T. M. C. SHELBY, *French Inventions in the XVIIIth Century*, Univ. of Kentucky, 1952.
Works on the history of optics quoted in the bibliography of Part II, p. 388.

Heat

E. MACH, *Prinzipien der Wärmelehre*, Leipzig, 1923.
D. MCKIE and N. H. DE V. HEATHCOTE, *The Discovery of Specific and Latent Heats*, London, 1935.

Electricity and Magnetism

Works already cited of BAUER, DAUJAT, GLIOZZI, HOPPE, MOTTELEY, PRIESTLEY, SARTIAUX and ALIAMAT, TURNER, WITTAKER.
D. and D. H. D. ROLLER, *The Development of the Concept of Electric Charge*, Harvard Univ. Press, 1954.
J. TORLAIS, *L'abbé Nollet*, Paris, 1954.
C. VAN DOREN, *Benjamin Franklin*, New York, 1938.
I. B. COHEN, *Benjamin Franklin's Experiments*, Cambridge, 1941.
Franklin and Newton, Philadelphia, 1956.
C. WILSON, *Life of Henry Cavendish*, London, 1951.
H. CAVENDISH, *Scientific Papers*, Cambridge, 1921.
A. J. BERRY, *Henry Cavendish*, London, 1960.

Chemistry

Previously quoted works by DELACRE, DUVEEN, FERGUSON, FIERZ-DAVID, HOLMYARD, JAGNAUX, LEICESTER and KLICKSTEIN, VON LIPPMANN, METZGER, OSTWALD, PARTINGTON.

J. R. PARTINGTON and D. MCKIE, 'Historical Studies on the Phlogiston Theory' in *Annals of Science*, II–IV, 1937–1939.
H. METZGER, *Newton, Stahl et Boerhaave*, Paris, 1930.
T. E. THORPE, *Priestley*, New York, 1906.
H. GUERLAC, 'Joseph Black and Fixed Air' in *Isis*, XLVIII, 1957.
J. R. PARTINGTON, *The Composition of Water*, London, 1928.
D. MCKIE, *La chimie au XVIIIe siècle avant Lavoisier*, Paris, 1958.
M. BERTHELOT, *La révolution chimique. Lavoisier*, Paris, 1890.
E. GRIMAUX, *Lavoisier*, 3rd ed., Paris, 1899.
D. MCKIE, *Lavoisier*, New York, 1952.
M. DAUMAS, *Lavoisier, théoricien et expérimentateur*, Paris, 1953.
D. I. DUVEEN and H. KLICKSTEIN, *A Bibliography of the Works of Antoine-Laurent Lavoisier*, London, 1954.

Zoology

Previously quoted works by ALMQUIST, CANGUILHEM, CHOULANT, COLE, CUVIER, FULTON, GUYÉNOT, LOCY, NEEDHAM, NORDENSKIÖLD, RÁDL, ROSTAND, ROTHSCHUH, SINGER.
M. CAULLERY, *Les Étapes de la biologie*, Paris, 1941.
L. C. MIALL, *The Early Naturalists*, London, 1912.
D. MORNET, *Les sciences de la vie au XVIIIe siècle*, Paris 1931.
J. ROSTAND, *La formation de l'être*, Paris, 1930.
L'évolution des espèces, Paris, 1932.
La genèse de la vie, Paris, 1943.
Les origines de la biologie expérimentale et l'abbé Spallanzani, Paris, 1951.
L'atomisme en biologie, Paris, 1956.
P. OSTOYA, *Les théories de l'évolution*, Paris, 1951.
R. SAVIOZ, *La philosophie de Charles Bonnet*, Paris, 1948.
E. BASTHOLM, *The History of Muscle Physiology* . . ., Copenhagen, 1950.
H. BORUTTAU, 'Geschichte der Physiologie' in T. PUSCHMANN, *Handbuch der Geschichte der Medizin* (ed. NEUBURGER and PAGEL), Vol. 1, Jena, 1903.
S. M. FORSTER, *Lectures on the History of Physiology*, Cambridge, 1901.
J. F. FULTON, *Muscular Contraction and the Reflex Control of Movement*, Baltimore, 1926.
V. KRUTA, *Med. Dr. Jiri Prochaska*, Prague, 1956.
A. E. CLARK-KENNEDY, *Stephen Hales*, Cambridge, 1929.
J. TORLAIS, *Réaumur*, Paris, 1936.
J. R. BAKER, *A. Trembley*, London, 1952.
S. D'IRSAY, *Albrecht von Haller*, Leipzig, 1930.
P. FLOURENS, *Histoire des travaux et des idées de Buffon*, Paris, 1844.
R. HEIM (ed.), *Buffon*, Paris 1952.
J. PIVETEAU, *Buffon. Œuvres philosophiques*, Paris, 1953.

Botany

See also previously quoted works by ARBER, BLUNT, DAVY DE VIRVILLE, GAGER, GREEN, NISSEN and SACHS.

H. F. ROBERTS, *Plant Hybridization before Mendel*, Princeton, 1929.

H. REED, *J. Ingenhousz*, Waltham, 1949.

A. CHEVALIER, *Michel Adanson*, Paris, 1934.

K. HAGBERG, *Carl Linnaeus*, London, 1952.

N. SANDBERG and W. HEIMANN, *A Catalogue of the Works of Linnaeus*, Stockholm, 1957.

B. H. SOULSBY, *A Catalogue of the Works of Linnaeus . . .*, London, 1933.

Catalogue of the Linnaeus exhibition, Muséum national d'histoire naturelle, Paris, 1957.

Medicine

In addition to the general works quoted in the bibliographies of Parts I and II, pp. 176 and 390, see also:

P. J. G. CABANIS, *Sketch of the Revolutions of Medical Science, and Views relating to its Reform*, London, 1806.

P. DELAUNAY, *Le monde médical parisien au XVIIIe siècle*, Paris, 1906.

F. G. D. DREWITT, *The Life of Edward Jenner*, 2nd ed., London, 1931.

N. F. J. ELOY, *Dictionnaire historique de la médicine*, 4 vols., Mons, 1778.

J. LORDAT, *Exposition de la doctrine médicale de P. J. Barthez*, Paris, 1818.

Geology

Previously quoted works by ADAMS, GEIKIE, VON GROTH, MATHER and MASON, MEUSNIER and VON ZETTEL.

L. AUFRÈRE, *La relief et la sculpture de la Terre. Soulavie et son secret*, Paris, 1952.

J. C. DE LA MÉTHERIE, *Théorie de la Terre*, 5 vols., Paris, 1797.

'Commemoration of the 150th Anniversary of the Death of James Hutton' in *Proc. Roy. Soc. Edinburgh*, LXVIII, 1950.

A. LACROIX, C. MAUGUIN, J. ORCEL, 'René-Just Haüy, Centenaire' in *Bull. Soc. fr. Minéralogie*, LXVII, 1944.

J. ORCEL, 'Essai sur le concept d'espèce et les classifications en minéralogie et pétrographie', *ibid.*, LXVII, 1944.

R. HOOYKAAS, 'Les débuts de la théorie cristallographique de R. J. Haüy . . .' in *Rev. Hist. Sci.*, VIII, 1955.

PART IV

Science outside Europe

HAVING EXAMINED SCIENTIFIC PROGRESS in Western Europe from 1450 to 1800, we must now turn to the development of science outside it. To be sure, the Western contribution was so important during this period that, by comparison, that of the rest of the world shrinks almost into insignificance. Moreover, the policy of exploration, expansion and colonialization pursued by the principal Western European powers brought in its train a wide spread of Western science and technique; this, in turn, was the prelude to the emergence in the course of the 19th and 20th centuries of a practically universal science. However, some independent developments outside Europe are sufficiently characteristic and important for their study to be justified.

While in the Far East there was some occasionally fruitful competition with Western science from indigenous work, in the countries under Indian influence the preponderance of traditional theories led to a general fossilization of science in its medieval form. In various parts of America the European colonists, after destroying the pre-Columbian civilizations, undertook the exploration and exploitation of the immense natural riches of the continent, and gradually introduced cultural institutions which would enable the New World to participate in active scientific life.

We shall restrict ourselves in this volume to the study of three regions of major importance and exclude from consideration the contributions of the Islamic world, which, though of some interest, were incomparably less important than they had been in the brilliant medieval period. The awakening of the Moslems to modern science will be dealt with in a later volume, where we shall endeavour to give a general account of the spread of contemporary science in the various regions where it had previously been unable to take root.

CHAPTER 1

Science in the Far East from the 16th to the 18th Century

Until the end of the 16th century, Chinese science, despite many more cultural contacts with the West than are often supposed to have existed, retained all the characteristics of Chinese culture. It was only from 1583, the date of the arrival in China of the Jesuit astronomer and mathematician Matteo Ricci, that Western science began to penetrate into China and, later, into Japan. As a result, the Far East began the slow and difficult process of integration into the modern scientific world, a process which took quite different forms in China and Japan, as we shall see when we deal with these countries individually.

CHINA

The Jesuit Contribution in the 17th and 18th Centuries

Modern science was introduced into China by Jesuit missionaries, whose policy it was to demonstrate their intellectual superiority in secular matters, and then to use the prestige they had gained in this way for the purposes of religious conversion.

The example was set by Matteo Ricci (1552–1610), who first settled in Southern China and later (1601) went to live at the court of the Ming emperors in Peking, where he worked on mathematical translations, cartography and astronomy. Scholars whom he had converted helped him to publish the first modern scientific works in Chinese.

Ricci died in 1610, but his successors remained on good terms with the Ming emperors and continued to translate and to teach the precepts of modern science. In 1644, when the Manchu dynasty of the Ta-Chhin—the 'Great Pure'—replaced the Ming, these good relations were maintained and a German, Father Johann Adam Schall von Bell, was put in charge of the *Chhin Thien Chien* (Imperial Bureau of Astronomy). Despite the efforts of Moslem astronomers, whose influence had until then been predominant at court, von Bell's colleague Ferdinand Verbiest was allowed to take over from him in 1669, and the office of director of the bureau remained in Jesuit hands till the end of the 18th century.[1] At the court of the great Manchu emperors Khang-Hsi (1662–1723) and Chhien-Lung (1736–1796), it was mainly Italian, German, Polish and French Jesuits who constructed astronomical instruments, prepared maps of the empire, and published new translations. Father Fontaney treated Khang-Hsi with quinine brought from France, and Father Gerbillon was even charged with negotiating, in the name of the emperor, the treaty of Nerchinsk with Russia (1689). In exchange, their efforts at evangelization were tolerated, though it does not seem that they were nearly as successful in these as they were in their scientific activities.

However, the dissolution of the Society of Jesus at the end of the 18th century, combined with the restrictions which the Chinese government began to impose on foreigners, put an end to the dissemination of Western science by Jesuits, which had lasted for two centuries.

As we pointed out in an earlier volume,[2] the Chinese of the Middle Ages had developed positional astronomy into an advanced science on the basis of the celestial equator instead of the ecliptic, but had maintained their ancient ideas of a vast and empty sky containing points of light. The Jesuits, on the other hand, in their lectures and translations, introduced Ptolemy's ecliptic system, to which they remained faithful throughout their stay despite the advances of European astronomy in the 17th and 18th centuries. Thus the Chinese treatise on astronomy published in 1738 by Fathers Koegler and Pereira was based on the same Ptolemaic principles as von Bell's astronomical encyclopedia of nearly a hundred years before (1645).

In the technique of astronomical observation, the Jesuit contribution was considerable and included more accurate methods for the calculation of eclipses, the construction of telescopes (the first was introduced in 1618 by Father Schreck, or Terrentius) and of many other instruments, the establishment of celestial planispheres like those of von Bell or, later, of Koegler, and the revision of the Chinese calendar according to a mixed luni-Gregorian system. But sometimes, as in the construction of armillary spheres based on the ecliptic, these innovations by the Jesuits were not a real scientific

[1] The principal Jesuit directors of the *Chhin Thien Chien* were: Verbiest (1669–1688), Grimaldi (1688–1712), Koegler (1720–1746), von Hallerstein (1746–1774) and d'Almeida (1783–1805).

[2] *Ancient and Medieval Science* (ed. R. Taton).

advance; rather were they a retrograde step from the equatorial astronomy practised by the Chinese.[1]

The Jesuits also published great numbers of Chinese translations and compilations of mathematical texts. In 1609, Ricci, in collaboration with the Christian scholar Li Chih-Tsao, published a small treatise on the rectangular triangle. With the help of Paul Hsü Kuang-Chhi, he also translated the first six books of Euclid (*Chi Ho Yuan-Pên*).

Father Rho wrote a treatise on Napierian analysis in 1628, to which Smogulecki and Hsüeh Fêng-Tsu added new logarithmic tables in 1654. Terrentius published a treatise on trigonometry in 1631. The best 18th-century Jesuit mathematician was Pierre Jartoux, who put forward nine remarkable formulae on infinite series in 1701.

In other branches of science, too, the Jesuits did their utmost to spread many of the new acquisitions of the Renaissance. In 1625, Terrentius published a short treatise on the human body, and Parrenin, at the beginning of the 18th century, a series of plates known as the 'Manchu Anatomy', inspired by the engravings in the *Anatomie de l'homme suivant la circulation du sang* by Dionis (Paris, 1690). The missionaries installed a pharmaceutical laboratory in Khang-Hsi's palace, where they followed the principles of pharmacology expounded in a textbook by the Frenchman Moyse Charas (1619–1698).

They also translated or compiled treatises on perspective (1626), on earthquakes (1626 and 1679), on the thermometer (1671), on light and sound (1682), on hydraulic machinery (1612), and on other engines (1617), and it was through the medium of the last that Archimedes' screw, previously unknown in China, was introduced. To amuse Khang-Hsi, the missionaries also constructed a mechanical nightingale, which sang as jets of steam were forced through organ pipes, as well as a chariot and a small boat, both moved by steam turbines (made in 1671 by Father Grimaldi), and many clockwork mechanisms.

For political reasons, Khang-Hsi and Chhien-Lung attached particular importance to the Fathers' geographical abilities. A group of Jesuit cartographers travelled with Khang-Hsi through Tartary, and

[1] The controversy between the Jesuits von Bell and Verbiest and the Moslem astronomers of Peking at the beginning of the Manchu dynasty bore on this point. The Jesuits blamed the Moslems for errors in the calendar which, based as it was on equatorial data, had necessarily to differ from theirs which was based on the ecliptic. The young emperor Khang-Hsi, impatient to shake off the tutelage of his regents and hoping to discredit the official Moslem astronomers of the court who supported them, sided with the Jesuits in 1669 for purely political reasons and in spite of the intrinsic defects of their system.

all China was covered by triangulation in 1708–1717. In 1702, Father Thomas measured the degree of longitude in China and a map of China consisting of 35 woodcuts was published in 1718. Under Chhien-Lung, six Jesuit cartographers prepared a large map of Central Asia in 104 folios (1769) which, until the 19th century, remained superior to any European maps of that region.

The Limits of the Jesuit Contribution

If the Jesuits' scientific contribution was impressive in its scope, it nevertheless had a predominantly religious aim. The missionaries introduced modern Western science solely because they hoped thereby to convert the Emperor and the leaders of the empire more easily. It was their fundamental belief that the value of modern science lay in its Christian origin and not in its intrinsic superiority over medieval Chinese science. Von Bell called his great astronomical encyclopedia of 1645 *Hsi-Yang Hsin Fa Li Shu* ('Treatise on Astronomy and Calendrical Science According to Western Methods'), but when this text was republished in 1669, Khang-Hsi demanded that the title be changed into *Hsin Fa Suan Shu* ('Treatise on Mathematics and Astronomy According to the New Methods'). In this way, the Emperor showed his desire to profit by the knowledge of the West, but only because it was more up to date than that of the Chinese and not because he thought the West generally superior.[1]

However, because the missionaries continued to identify their science with the Christian religion they hesitated to keep the Chinese informed of current scientific developments in Europe (which were, after all, considerable during these two centuries). This was the reason for their obstinate adherence to the Ptolemaic doctrine. Galileo's system (which was condemned by the Church) came later than Ricci's Chinese work and there was the risk that it might raise doubts about all Ricci's teachings, including his religious ones. It is a remarkable paradox that at the very moment when Tycho Brahe abandoned the ecliptic armillary sphere for the equatorial, Ricci had just succeeded in persuading the Chinese to renounce the latter, which they had known for centuries, and to adopt the ecliptic. This incapacity on the Jesuits' part to follow the scientific movements of the West was to manifest itself on many occasions. Thus in 1710, when Father Foucquet wished to make use of the new planetary tables of P. de la Hire in Peking, the Father-Visitor would not permit

[1] In a letter dated November 1640, von Bell wrote: 'The word *hsi* [western] is very unpopular [with the Chinese] and the Emperor in his edicts never uses any word other than *hsin* [new]; in fact the former word is employed only by those who want to belittle us.' (Quoted by H. Bernard-Maître, *Monumenta Serica*, 1937, 3.)

it, for fear of 'giving the impression of a censure on what our predecessors had so much trouble to establish and occasioning new accusations against religion'.[1] As a result of this bigoted attitude,[2] the real contribution of the Jesuits to Chinese science in the 18th century was restricted to the practical field: triangulation, quinine, Grimaldi's steam chariot, and anatomical tables.

Moreover, the tactics of religious penetration chosen by the Jesuits tended to restrict their scientific work to the Imperial court. In order to have influential converts, they concentrated on amusing the Emperor Khang-Hsi (who was a remarkably talented man) with ingenious machines, on demonstrating new cures, on giving sound political advice, on making better maps and a better calendar. But all this never went beyond Peking, or even beyond the mandarins and eunuchs of that city.

Thus, their influence did not reach those sections of Chinese society among which the seed of modern science would have fallen on the most fruitful soil. This is all the more surprising because Ricci, before arriving at the Imperial court, had chosen Canton and Kuantung, which were the most economically advanced of all the provinces, as the centres of his activity; it was for the merchants of Tshao-Tshing Fu, near Canton, that he had constructed his first planisphere. In his letters, he wrote that these merchants flocked to him in great number, together with many scholars from these livelier provinces. His best Chinese collaborators came from them, in particular Paul Hsü Kuang-Chhi. However, Ricci soon afterwards left these promising regions and went to Peking. His successors all followed his example and the steam chariot constructed by Grimaldi in 1671 had no effect other than to pander to the idle curiosity of the court. In brief, the very nature of the Jesuits' work prevented Western science from making anything but a superficial impression on Chinese life.

The Spread of Jesuit Scientific Influence

To what extent did Chinese scientists really assimilate the scientific knowledge of the West brought to them by the Jesuits, and to what extent did they incorporate it in their own work and scientific practice? For lack of adequate texts, it is much more difficult to answer this question than to list the contributions of the Jesuits themselves—all we have to go by are a few fragmentary accounts.

[1] Quoted by L. Pfister, *Notice biographique et bibliographique sur les Jésuites de l'ancienne mission de Chine*, Shanghai, 1932, p. 551.

[2] This point of view is also that of J. J. L. Duyvendak (*T'oung Pao*, 1928, p. 328): 'China, when it received Western science, received it in a form which was already antiquated.'

At Peking, the Chinese astronomers of the Imperial Bureau of Astronomy had certainly assimilated their Western colleagues' methods. The first purely Chinese work containing logarithms was written in 1650 by Hsüeh Fêng-Tsu, a pupil of the Jesuit Father Smogulecki. The Chinese also learned how to use the new astronomical instruments brought from Europe and, in 1757, a catalogue of 3,083 fixed stars was published in Peking. This was the result of a joint project carried out by Fathers Koegler and da Rocha, but the Chinese astronomers also compiled an original catalogue. In 1641, Hsi Chan criticized the Ptolemaic system in his 'Analysis of the Motions of the Five Planets' (*Wu Hsing Hsing Tu Chieh*) and propounded a system resembling, but probably independent of, Tycho Brahe's, in which the planets revolve about the earth and then the earth about the sun. Shêng Pai-Erh adopted this system in the 18th century.

Chinese scientists were therefore not purely and simply tied to the apron-strings of their Jesuit masters. Another instance of this was the great encyclopedia compiled by the scholar Chhen Mêng-Lei in the reign of Khang-Hsi, the 'Compilation of Books and Images, Ancient and Modern' (*Thu Shu Chi Chhêng*), which reproduced the *Hsin Fa Li Shu* of von Bell and Verbiest but also contained star catalogues agreeing with ancient Chinese cosmological ideas, ancient lists of eclipses and comets, and a history of ancient Chinese astronomical instruments.

In other fields also, Chinese traditions continued to exist side by side with Western contributions. Paul Hsü Kuang-Chhi, a Christian scholar and a friend of Ricci's, wrote a treatise on agronomy in 1639 (later editions appeared in 1742 and 1843), which was based on ancient Chinese manuals of agriculture but also referred to a work on Western hydraulic machines by Father de Ursio. Similarly, some Chinese painters in the 17th century, including Tshiao Ping-Chhên, tried to paint according to the Western rules of perspective introduced by the Jesuits, while the great majority of painters remained faithful to the traditional Chinese style.

In mathematics, too, the great scientific encyclopedia published in 1723 at the behest of Khang-Hsi himself, the *Yü-Ting Li Hsiang Kao Chheng* ('Complete Calculations of Astronomy and the Calendar'), the fruit of the labours of Ho Kuo-Tsung and Mei Ku-Chhêng as well as of many others, gave pride of place to Western work. The second part was devoted to progressions, arithmetical operations, square roots, trigonometrical calculations and logarithms in the European manner; the third part, relating to the theory of Chinese music and of Chinese and Western musical instruments, was written by Fathers Pereira (a Jesuit) and Pedrini (a Lazarist).

The great philosopher Tai Chen (1724–1774) published a treatise on machines based on the examination of Archimedes' screw. At the age of twenty, he also published a treatise on Napierian counting rods. Ming An-Thu, a Manchu, who in the 18th century was president of the Bureau of Astronomy, produced a 'Quick Method for Determining Segment Areas' (*Ko Yuan Mi Lü Chieh Fa*). In it, he put forward the following formula for finding the chord of an infinitesimal arc:

$$a = c + \frac{1}{3 \cdot 4} c^3 + \frac{9}{5 \cdot 4^2} c^5 + \frac{225}{7 \cdot 4^3} c^7 \ldots$$

Similarly, Tung Yu Chhêng (1791–1823), also with the help of Jartoux's formulae, calculated the perimeter of the ellipse as:

$2\sqrt{(a^2 - b^2) + (\frac{1}{2} b \pi)^2}$ (where a is the major, and b the minor, axis)

Renaissance of Traditional Science

However, as a reaction against Western ideas, a number of scholars revived the work of the great mathematicians of the Han, Thang and Sung periods, who had reached the stage of working out a reasonably exact value of π, the theory of negative numbers, arithmetical triangles, and an original and very adequate algebra, the *Thien Yuan*. Their work had been generally neglected until Wên-Ting (1635–1721) examined the forgotten texts of the Sung mathematicians, for example on algebra, and decided that the Jesuits had not brought any startling innovations. In the 18th century, his manuscripts were published by his grandson Mei Ku-Chhêng under the title: 'Pearls Recovered from the Red River' (*Chhih Shui I Chhen*).

Following the example of the two Mei, many mathematicians examined and restored to an honoured place other great works of the past. Li Jui's treatise (18th century) on real and imaginary roots was based on the principles of *Thien Yuan*. Khong Ki-Han republished an arithmetical treatise from the Han period, and Lo Shih-Lin discovered and published an old copy of the *Ssu Yuan Yü Chien* ('Precious Mirror of the Four Elements'), a mathematical treatise from the Mongol period.

In medicine and geography the Jesuit influence was smaller still. True, Father Parrenin (1665–1741) published the plates of the 'Manchu Anatomy', but medical encyclopedias (*e.g.* the 'Golden Mirror of Medicine', 1749) dealt with nothing other than acupuncture, pulse-taking and other traditional techniques. In 1734, an Imperial decree obliged court physicians to make ritual sacrifices to their departed predecessors.

Geographical works, too, became virtually devoid of European influence. Among the many hydrographic treatises which appeared in the 18th century, the most famous were the *Shui Tao Tin-Kang*

45 Jesuits teaching astronomy in China; Beauvais tapestry, 17th century

46 Old instruments of the Peking Observatory

('Complete Description of Waterways') by Chhi Shao-Nan (1776), a work without equivalent in the contemporary Western literature, and the 'Historical Account of the Coastal Protection Works of Chekiang Province' (1751). The 'Treatise on Tides' (1781) by Yü Ssu-Chhien was an original account of the moon's influence on the tides, but it also included excerpts from ancient books on this subject, such as the *Hai Thao Chih* by Tou Chu-Mêng (8th century). Most geographies of China, as a whole, *e.g.* the *Ta Chhing Hui Tien*, or of particular provinces and districts, of which many appeared in the 18th century, were modelled on ancient texts.

Internal Obstacles to Scientific Progress

The reason why China did not make a more original contribution to the progress of modern science is not to be found exclusively in the inherent defects of the Western (Jesuit) contribution; it was due no less to the slow development of Chinese society.

In the absolutist and bureaucratic China of the 17th to 18th centuries, Confucianism remained the official philosophy. Mandarins and scholars were recruited by competitions which called for nothing but knowledge of classical Chinese thought, and none at all of science. Thus, the work of the Sung mathematicians was allowed to fall into oblivion for six centuries, while every student was expected to know the ancient maxims of Confucius and Mencius by heart. Most Confucian scholars felt a profound disdain for scientific research and for what they considered 'interventionist activities' (A. G. Haudricourt) in the world of nature. At the beginning of the 19th century, Fêng Chen, the son of the then Prime Minister and himself a high dignitary of the state, wrote a significant poem devoted to the microscope:

> With a microscope you see the surface of things.
> It magnifies them but does not show you reality.
> It makes things seem higher and wider,
> But do not suppose you are seeing the things in themselves.

(Quoted by H. Bernard in the *Yenching Journal of Social Studies*, August 1941.)

This attachment to the philosophies of the past, this lack of interest in science and its possibilities, were the inevitable result of China's economic backwardness, of the predominance of a feudal and agrarian economy based on traditional techniques. It is characteristic that the small number of scholars who showed a true interest in science (such as the compilers of Khang-Hsi's scientific encyclopedia) were for the most part natives of Eastern China, which was economically much more advanced. The most famous of these scholars were the geographers Tsi Chou Nang of Tche Kiong and Fang Kuan-Chhêng of Anhwei; the great philosopher and mathematician Tai Chen, one of the few original minds of China in the 18th century and the son of an Anhwei merchant; and the mathematician Li Jui, who re-established the ancient *Thien Yuan* algebra and was a native of the rich commercial centre of Suchow on the Lower Yangtze Kiang.

From Suchow also came the astronomer Fêng Kuei-Fên who, in about 1850, published accurate tables of the transits of a hundred stars. It was at Yangchow, another large commercial and industrial city in that region, that Lo Shih-Lin, at the beginning of the 19th century, republished the works of the mathematicians of the Mongol period. The two Meis, grandfather and grandson, also belonged to an old Anhwei family.

It is for the economic historians to explain why these provinces of the Lower Yangtze never became the 'Netherlands' of China, and why their economic progress failed to stimulate scientific research to the extent that it did in the Low Countries of Europe.

JAPAN

Indigenous Science

In the Middle Ages, Japanese civilization developed in the shadow of China, borrowing from the latter its ideographic script, its political and religious conceptions (Buddhism and Confucianism) and its basic techniques. Similarly, Japanese science was at first nothing but a branch of Chinese science: *Thien Yuan* algebra (*Ten zan* in Japanese), medicine and astronomy were all taken over piecemeal. It was only in the 17th century, under the feudal dynasty of the Tokugawa (1620–1868), who may be said to have acted as hereditary prime ministers to successive feeble emperors, that Japan began to make a contribution of her own, particularly to mathematics and medicine.

Early Japanese calculators used nothing but bamboo sticks (*sangi*) borrowed from their Chinese colleagues. The abacus, familiar in China since about the 3rd century, was not introduced to Japan until the end of the 16th century, when it became known under the name of *soroban* (from the Chinese *Suan Phan*, calculating plate). It generally consisted of 21 wires or rods, divided by a cross-bar into two sets, the wires in one set carrying unit beads and those in the other, beads representing five units each (see *fig. 36*). Though all mathematical operations could be carried out with the help of this *soroban*, mathematicians tended to despise it and to prefer bamboo sticks for their own theoretical work.

Then, within a century, Japanese mathematicians began rapidly

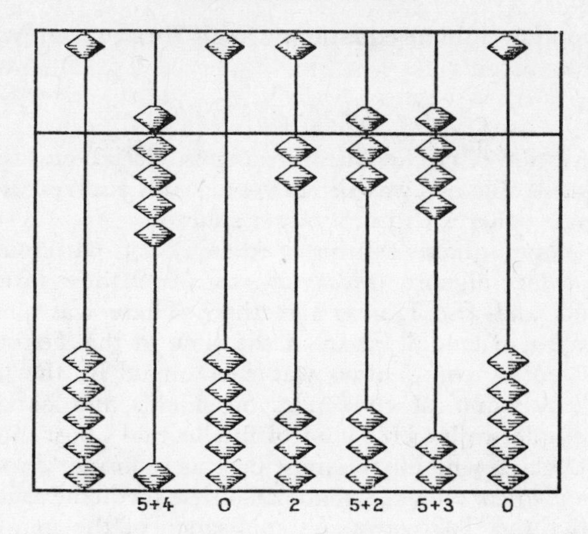

fig. 36 The number 90,278 on the 'soroban'.

to surpass their Chinese colleagues. The impetus came from Seki Kōwa (Takakazu, 1642–1708), who belonged to a Samurai family. He was more of a patron than a true mathematician, but the school which he founded, and the rival schools which soon arose, tackled the most varied problems. They arrived at very close values of π. In 1639, Imamura Chisho had got as far as 3.162, and Aida Ammei (1747–1817) established the series:

$$\frac{\pi}{2} = 1 + \frac{1!}{3} + \frac{2!}{3 \times 5} + \frac{3!}{3 \times 5 \times 7} + \frac{4!}{3 \times 5 \times 7 \times 9} + \ldots$$

Sakabe Kōhan (1759–1824), another Samurai turned *ronin* or knight errant, established the series:

$$\frac{\pi}{4} = 1 - \frac{1}{5} - \frac{1 \times 4}{5 \times 7 \times 9} - \frac{(1 \times 3)(4 \times 6)}{5 \times 7 \times 9 \times 11 \times 13} - \frac{(1 \times 3 \times 5)(4 \times 6 \times 8)}{5 \times 7 \times 9 \ldots \times 15 \times 17} - \ldots$$

At the beginning of the 19th century Japanese mathematicians obtained a value of π correct to 26 decimal places.

A sort of integral calculus was developed under the name of *yenri* (or *enri*: principle of the circle). Its invention is attributed, perhaps wrongly, to Seki and is more probably due to his pupil Takebe Kenkō (Katahiro), another Samurai. In the 18th century, *yenri* was developed further by the Samurai Ajima Shokuyen, whose work was in turn perfected by Wada Yasusi (1787–1840), a Samurai from the Harima province, who also computed the area of a sphere by differencing the volumes of two concentric spheres.

Work on indeterminate equations was also begun, and Aida Ammei studied the equation:

$$x_1^2+x_2^2+x_3^2+x_4^2+x_5^2=y^2$$

The inscription of circles within triangles, circles, and sectors (the so-called 'fan problems') was also in vogue. Ajima solved the problem of inscribing *n* spheres within a larger sphere.

Chinese magic squares continued to enjoy a great popularity and so did the *tenzan* algebra (*endanzitu*), by which Seki foreshadowed determinants and also Horner's method. There was a climate of active research in feudal Japan at the time of the Tokugawa. For example, scientific competition was encouraged by the practice of inscribing mathematical challenges on shields and hanging them from the temple walls. This kind of intellectual 'joust' appealed to Japanese scholars, who for the most part were former Samurai.

Japanese medical science also took Chinese medicine as its starting-point. Under the Tokugawa, a renaissance of the neo-Confucian Sung philosophy brought in its train a revival of Sung medicine. Many Japanese physicians continued to hold the view that the human being consists of the five elements of Nature (wood, fire, earth, metal, water). However, as a reaction, the Ko-i-Hō school advocated a return to proto-Confucian medicine. Thus Gotō Gonzan (1659–1733) attributed diseases to bad circulation of the 'vital breath', and a pupil of Gotō studied the therapeutic effects of thermal springs on the *pneuma*. In the 18th century, Kagawa Ginetsu published a treatise on obstetrics, the *Sanron*, which, though still based on ancient theories and apparently quite free of Western influences, contained many shrewd observations on the development of the embryo and on post-natal conditions.

The First Contacts with Western Science

Japan, like China, came into continuous contact with European science at the end of the 16th century. Western influence was brought to bear on Japan in the course of three clearly distinct phases: a Portuguese Jesuit phase (up till 1630), a period of clandestine Dutch influence (1630–1720), and a period of overt Dutch influence (1720–1868).

The first Europeans to arrive in Japan were Portuguese Jesuits, whom the Japanese called *Nambanjin* ('barbarians from the Southern seas'). They were active in many branches of science, published new works on astronomy, and introduced those which their colleagues were issuing in Peking. Father Almeida opened a hospital, where he taught the 'Surgery of the Southern Barbarians' (*Namban Ryū geka*). Portuguese physicians planted 3,000 trees and medicinal plants imported from Europe near Kyoto. A great many medical works were written by their Japanese pupils—55 were published before 1600, including ten on surgery, eight on diseases of the eye and five on gynaecology.

Even more than in China, modern science was to suffer from being identified with Christian doctrine. In 1630 the *Shogun* (the hereditary commander-in-chief of the Japanese army) banned all Western scientific works as tools of Jesuit propaganda. Existing works were destroyed and the import of others was proscribed. Pro-Western astronomers like Hayashi Kichiuyemon and Koboyashi Kaneseda were put to death in 1637.

17TH- TO 19TH-CENTURY DUTCH SCIENCE IN JAPAN

As a result, Japanese scholars were forced to study science clandestinely, in which task they were greatly helped by Dutch merchants, who, in 1641, were authorized by the *Shogun* to establish a trading post on the island of Deshima, off Nagasaki. Their presence helped to spread Western knowledge in two ways. On the one hand, Japanese interpreters employed by the Nagasaki trading houses, who had no scientific training but were in constant touch with the superior techniques of Dutch medicine, navigation and engineering, did not fail to take an interest in these; on the other hand, the Dutch traders were forced to send an annual deputation to pay homage to the *Shogun* in Yedo, and many Japanese astronomers and mathematicians in the capital did not fail to take advantage of this opportunity to talk to the Dutch, and particularly to the physician attached to the trading station, who regularly accompanied the deputation.

In spite of government prohibition, this resulted in an active and widespread interest in *rangaku* or 'Dutch science', so much so that in 1720 the *Shogun* Yushimune decided to lift the ban on Western scientific works; only political and religious works were henceforth proscribed. The physician and librarian, Aoke Bunzo, who was appointed 'Professor of Dutch science', devoted himself first of all to compiling a Dutch-Japanese scientific dictionary, which he published in 1761 and thanks to which many *rangakusha* (students of Dutch science) were able to consult Dutch works directly, and to spread Western scientific ideas as never before.

Modern Western medicine had spread even during the period of clandestine contacts—the Dutch physician in Deshima, Caspar Schambergen, who arrived in Japan in 1649, had trained Japanese pupils, and a Japanese edition of the works of Ambroise Paré had circulated at the beginning of the 18th century; but the liberal decree of Yoshimune (1720) opened much wider possibilities. On 4th March 1741, a pupil of Aoki, Mayeno Royōtaku, with some friends, took part in a body-snatching raid with the complicity of the executioner. Their aim was to check the accuracy of the Kulmus' anatomical tables which they had bought at Nagasaki, and they were able to establish beyond any doubt that the facts completely belied the traditional Japanese beliefs. Mayeno and his friends, after their exploit, edited these Dutch tables and published them in 1775. Another *rangakusha*, Hoshino Ryoetsu, constructed a wooden skeleton in 1798. The physicians of the Dutch trading post in Deshima, and especially P. F. von Siebold (who arrived in Japan in 1822), taught many pupils, including Hanaoka Seishū (1760–1835), how to excise tumours and anal fistulae, how to perform amputations, and how to administer narcotics. But these physicians 'in the Dutch manner' (*ran-pō-i*) were the exception and not the rule; the accounts of Thunberg (a physician in Deshima from 1775) show that the vast majority of their colleagues were still exclusively engaged in acupuncture, moxibustion and other traditional techniques.

Astronomy, by virtue of the civil and religious importance of the calendar, was an affair of state in all Eastern countries. The *Shogun* Yoshimune encouraged the astronomer Nakane Genkei to pursue his studies in *rangaku* astronomy (which Nakane had begun even before the 1726 decree) and appointed him director of the observatory at Yedo. A Nagasaki interpreter Motoki Ryoei (d. 1794) was the author of the first work expounding heliocentrism in the Far East; Hoashi Banri, a scholar from Osaka, another great centre of astronomy, was so enthusiastic about the Copernican system that he gave it out as his own discovery. Other Japanese astronomers, influenced by Jesuit works published in Peking in the 17th century, remained stubborn adherents of Ptolemaic geocentrism.

In mathematics, it is more difficult to disentangle the respective contributions of *rangaku* and indigenous Japanese science. We know, for example, that the great 18th-century Japanese mathematician Ajima was familiar with Western spherical trigonometry, and that logarithms reached Japan in 1767 through the translation of a Chinese treatise.

The *rangakusha* applied themselves with zeal to the study of many other branches of science imported from Europe. Noro Genjō, who started to learn Dutch at the behest of the *Shogun* in 1720, published his 'Japanese Explanations of Dutch Botany' in 1750. In 1783, Shiba Kohān (1738–1818), another illustrious *rangakusha*, published the first copper plates to appear in Japan since the expulsion of the Jesuits in the 17th century. He also published astronomical maps and, in 1781, a geographical description of the West. In 1785, the cartographer Hayashi Shihei published one of the first Japanese maps showing longitudes and latitudes.

Comparison with China

Modern science made incomparably greater progress in Japan than it did in China, particularly after the middle of the 18th century. A Japanese work on the microscope appeared in 1801, at the very time that the Chinese scholar Fêng Chen expressed his poetic disdain for that instrument. This situation was due first of all to the differences between the teaching of the Dutch and that of the Jesuits. The Dutch scientific contribution did not result from a systematic desire to establish the superiority of the West, but rather from the wish to satisfy the appetite for science evinced by the scholars themselves. Moreover, the Dutch merchants (apart from the physician of the trading post) were neither qualified nor willing to give the Japanese an education of the same standard as that given to the Chinese by the missionary mathematicians and astronomers of Peking. The *rangakusha* were left to their own devices and had painstakingly to decipher the treatises written in a language of which they had only the rudiments. It is truly by their own efforts that they assimilated modern science.

Even though the question raises general problems beyond the confines of the history of science, we must ask ourselves why Japan under the Tokugawa was so much more receptive to new ideas than Chhing China. The answer must undoubtedly be sought in social and economic distinctions. Japan made far greater economic progress during the 18th and 19th centuries than China, especially in centres like Yedo, Osaka and Nagasaki, which are precisely those where *rangaku* flourished. On the other hand, we have seen that many Japanese mathematicians came from Samurai families; this reflected the breakdown of the ancient feudal society, and the rise of a cast of dissatisfied warriors, who had to take to the liberal professions.

Modern science in 19th-century Japan was therefore linked with the forces which stood for political and social progress and which threatened the traditional structure of the state. In the 19th century, the Japanese government became more and more aware of this threat and began to take belated repressive measures, thus reversing the liberal trend set in the 18th century. The career of Takano Nagahidi (or Chōei), the most distinguished *rangakusha* of his time, who wrote on botany, mineralogy and geography, was typical. He was a member of a reform club and was arrested a number of times on this account. In 1840, he was given a life sentence for having 'deceived the people' by his modern scientific teaching. The 'Japanese Giordano Bruno' made this proud affirmation of his faith in science to his accusers:

We do not know that anyone has gone up to the heavens, but we have astronomers. We do not know that anybody has gone down into the earth, but we have geologists. . . . There is an inner eye with which such things can be seen. (Quoted by G. B. Sansom, *The Western World and Japan.*)

He escaped from prison in 1844 but was recaptured and committed *harakiri* in 1850.

* * *

If modern ideas did not penetrate more deeply into the Far East, it was because they came up against the opposition of the entrenched order. It was only when that order was swept away in the course of the 19th and 20th centuries that China and Japan begin to play their full part in the development of modern science.

BIBLIOGRAPHY

Chinese Science

H. BERNARD-MAÎTRE, 'Les adaptations chinoises d'ouvrages européens' in *Monumenta Serica*, 1945.
'Ferdinand Verbiest', *ibid.*, 1940.
Matteo Ricci's Scientific Contribution to China, Peking, 1935.
'Notes on the Introduction of Natural Sciences into the Chinese Empire' in *Yenching Journal of Social Studies*, II, 2, 1941.
La science européenne au tribunal astronomique de Pékin, Paris, 1951.
P. D'ELIA, *Galileo in Cina*, Rome, 1947.
W. FUCHS, 'Materialen zur Kartographie des Mandju-zeit' in *Monumenta Serica*, 1935 and 1938.
L. PFEISTER, *Notices biographiques et bibliographiques sur les jésuites de l'ancienne mission de Chine*, 2 vols., Shanghai, 1932–1934.
A. H. ROWBOTHAM, *Missionary and Mandarin*, Univ. of California Press, 1942.
A. WYLIE, *Notes on Chinese Literature*, Shanghai, 1902.
Chinese Researches, Shanghai, 1897.
See also:
A. W. HUMMEL, *Eminent Chinese of the Ch'ing Period*, Washington, 1944, and particularly
J. NEEDHAM, *Science and Civilization in China*, Vols. I–IV (Vols. V–VII are in preparation), Cambridge University Press, 1954–1962.

Japan

C. R. BOXER, *Jan Company in Japan, 1600–1817*, The Hague, 1936.
Christian Century in Japan, 1549–1650, London, 1951.

Y. FUJIKAWA, *Geschichte der Medizin in Japan*, Tokyo, 1911.

D. KEENE, *The Japanese Discovery of Europe. Honda Toshiaki and Other Discoverers (1720–1798)*, London, 1952.

A. KOBORI, *Les étapes historiques des mathématiques au Japon*, Paris, 1957.

A. KUWAKI, 'Western Science in Later Tokugawa Period' in *Cultural Nippon*, 1941.

Y. MIKAMI, *The Development of Mathematics in China and Japan*, Leipzig, 1913.

C. OKUMA, *Fifty Years of New Japan*, London, 1910.

G. B. SANSOM, *The Western World and Japan*, London, 1950.

D. E. SMITH and Y. MIKAMI, *A History of Japanese Mathematics*, Leipzig, 1914.

B. SZCZESNIAK, 'The Penetration of the Copernican Theory into Feudal Japan' in *Journal of the Royal Asiatic Society*, 1944.

I. VEITH, 'Medicine in Japan' in *Ciba Symposia*, 1950.

'Beginnings of Japanese Obstetrics' in *Bulletin of the History of Medicine*, XX, 1951.

CHAPTER 2

Indian Science from the 15th to the 18th Century

THOUGH SCIENCE CONTINUED to be cultivated in all the countries of India and even to spread into others under Indian influence, it made very little progress from the 15th century to the end of the 18th, when Indian scholars devoted most of their energies to defending their ancient traditions against Moslem encroachments. In peninsular India, where Dravidian culture predominated, the Moslem threat was felt less strongly and was, moreover, conterbalanced by a Brahmin renaissance from the 14th to 17th centuries.

The traditionalist Brahmin reaction was not, however, directed only against Islam and had, in fact, appeared long before the Moslem invasion, which, by facing it with a clearer danger, merely brought it out into the open. Apart from such heterodox movements (from the Brahmin point of view) as Buddhism and Jainism, two trends had begun to turn men's minds from the Brahmin tradition of giving rational explanations for natural phenomena. One of these, Tantrism, revelled in esoteric symbolism; the other, *bhakti* or 'devotion', explained everything by the love of a Supreme Being who transcends all natural phenomena. All these conceptions were so many obstacles to scientific progress, so that when the classical Brahmin tradition finally reasserted itself it had to begin where the medieval commentators had left off.

MATHEMATICS AND ASTRONOMY

Indian astronomical texts written from the 15th to the 18th centuries were generally based on the *Sūryasiddhānta*, or on works derived from it. They were mainly intended to help in astrological computations which had become more and more popular and complex. Among these texts were the *Makaranda*, written at Benares in 1478 (a commentary on which was said to have been written in 1620), the *Makarandavivaraṇa* by Nṛsiṃha, and the *Grahalāghava*, a summary of calculations of the position of planets by Gaṇeçadaivajña (1520).

Gaṇeçadaivajña was also the author of two texts, one short, the other fuller, on the calculation of the lunar day (*tithi*, *Tithicintāmaṇi*). Both reflect the Central Indian tradition of the *Âryabhaṭiya* modified by Lalla.[1] The South, on the other hand, followed the tradition of the *Âryabhaṭiya* (in Tamil, *vâkkiyam*) alongside that of the *Sūryasiddhānta* (*çittāndam*).

Foreign Influence

In the 17th century, some Indian astronomers began to introduce Arabic and European ideas, despite the traditional objections. Thus the *Siddhāntaviveka* by Kamalākara (1658) borrowed freely from the Arabs. In the early 18th century the Maharaja Sawi Jai Singh II (1699–1743) gave a great impetus to astronomy when he collected astronomical documents from India, Arabia and Europe (notably La Hire's tables), and established observatories in Jaipur, in Ujjayinī (Ujjaim), through which ran the traditional standard meridian of Indian astronomers, in Benares, Delhi and Mathurā (Muttra). These observatories contained enormous mural instruments, may of which have been preserved.

18th-century European Interest in Indian Astronomy

From the late 17th century onwards, Europeans began to take a keen interest in Indian contributions to astronomy and mathematics and Louis XIV sent a special mission to Siam for information.

Throughout the 18th century, French astronomers, above all the Cassinis, studied Indian astronomy and its offshoot in Siam from documents collected by travellers and missionaries. Le Gentil studied it on the spot, in Pondicherry.

They found that most Indian astronomers made skilful though mechanical use of mathematical tables, without ever observing the sky and without any profound ideas of cosmography, and concluded that Indian astronomy was not original and was, in any case, exclusively concerned with predicting eclipses and casting horoscopes. Though Bailly spoke of the existence of learned Indian astronomers in the past, whose teachings had been preserved, the more general opinion was that Indian astrologers had obtained their astronomical data exclusively from China, Greece and the Middle East. As we have seen, this belief was false, since the *nakshatra* system[2] existed in India long before the Greeks introduced zodiacal astronomy. Europeans were right, however, to assert that India's original contribution to astronomy in the 18th century was negligible.

[1] Cf. Taton, *Ancient and Medieval Science*, p. 422.

[2] Cf. *Ancient and Medieval Science*, pp. 136 *ff*.

CHEMISTRY AND MEDICINE

Indian chemistry, too, made few advances in the 17th and 18th centuries. Collections of recipes multiplied, but all were based on ancient works, though some of the traditional terms were changed. The same is true of medicine, in which ancient doctrines were retained with little modification.

Under the reign of the Emperor Akbar (1555–1606), Raja Todar Mall, who served the Mogul empire but was anxious to preserve Indian culture, commissioned a number of treatises on various subjects, including a *summa medica*. These treatises he intended to be a kind of encyclopedia of genuine Indian knowledge.

Other books on medicine, pharmacology and alchemy were inspired by foreign notions, superficially Indianized. Thus the *Arkaprakaça* (Sanskrit for 'Light of the Sun') had nothing to do with the sun but dealt with *arak*—the Arabic for strong spirit. The *Bhāvaprakāça*, a 16th-century medical treatise which otherwise followed ancient Sanskrit texts very closely, also contained references to syphilis, which it called *phirangiroga*, 'the disease of the Frangi or Franks'—in this particular case, the Portuguese.

The medical writings called *yūnānī*, which exist in Sanskrit, Tamil and various modern Indo-Aryan languages, were a separate category of medical literature. They dealt with Arabic medicine, described by a name which originally meant 'Greek' (Sanskrit: *yāvananī*), but later came to denote anything pertaining to the Moslems who had, taken the place of the ancient Greeks as great scholars.

Expansion of Indian Science

Despite its loss of creative activity under Mogul domination, India continued to exercise some scientific influence over certain regions. Thus, Indian medicaments and ideas went on being exported to the Indonesian archipelago, in part by Moslems travelling from India.

It was, however, on Tibet that Indian science continued to have a particularly great influence, even in this later period. In the 17th century, a great commentary by Rgyud-bzi, including a translation of the *Amṛtahṛdaya*, was published under the title of *Vaiḍūrya-sngon-po*. This work displayed a profound knowledge of the Indian medical tradition. Even more important, the 17th century saw the completion of the translation from the Sanskrit of the great Tibetan collection of canonical Buddhist commentaries and technical treatises, the *B'stan-'gyur* (*Tanjur*). This translation, which was greatly encouraged by the reigning Dalai Lama, gave a great impetus to Tibetan science, for it introduced many important texts that had previously been inaccessible to the Tibetans.

CHAPTER 3

Science in Colonial America

THE HISTORICAL FRAMEWORK

AFTER THE DISCOVERY OF AMERICA by Columbus, Europe poured shiploads of emigrants into the new continent, which, though it was the home of indigenous races and civilizations at the time of its discovery, eventually adopted a European way of life.

South America and Central America, which were rapidly but unevenly explored, populated and exploited, assumed their new character less than fifty years after the conquest. North America, on the other hand, was slower to conform, and it was not until the 17th century that the white population could truly be said to have established itself there.

SPANISH AMERICA

The Spaniards, who were the first to arrive in America, quite naturally seized the lion's share. Driven on by the lust for gold and spices and the mirage of the Indies, they plunged farther and farther inland. By 1550 the area which was to remain Spanish had been almost entirely conquered. In the following century they penetrated farther still, establishing new colonies wherever they went. Their immense West Indian empire extended from Tierra del Fuego to California; it included Mexico and Florida in North America and all Central and South America with the exception of Portuguese Brazil.

The destruction of the great Aztec and Inca empires and the enslavement and conversion to Christianity of the Indian masses led to the almost total disappearance of the indigenous civilizations. Meanwhile, the ties between Spain and her empire became increasingly firm, both politically and economically. They were weakened again as Spanish power receded and finally broke in the first half of the 19th century.

The West Indies were considered Crown lands and were governed direct from Madrid by the King and his Indies Council. This system of government was maintained, with very few changes, for centuries.

On the mainland of America, viceroys (first two and later four) governed very unequal kingdoms, of which New Spain and Peru were the oldest. (New Granada was established in 1717 and Plata in 1766.) Captains-General responsible to the viceroys had their headquarters in Guatemala, Venezuela and Chile. These high officials were almost invariably sent out from Spain.

The Europeans, who constituted a minority of the population, had considerable discretionary powers over the rest: half-breeds, Indians and Negroes. These powers increased as the central Spanish government found it more and more difficult to exercise its authority from a distance of several sailing weeks. The sincere efforts of certain religious orders to protect the Indians and win them over to European culture did not yield much result, though one consequence was the importing of African slaves.

Spain's tutelage had crippling effects on the economy of her colonies. Trade between the various Spanish possessions was forbidden and so, even more strictly, was trade between them and foreign countries. Their position was aggravated further by a chronic shortage of capital and manpower. However, at the end of the 18th century, Spain became involved in European wars and began to relax her control abroad. As a result, the colonists extended their trade with other countries and consolidated their own position. Moreover, the benevolent despotism of Charles III (1759–1788), although it did not immediately make itself felt in America, brought about an intellectual upsurge which paved the way for more liberal ideas. Discontent in the Americas, already very keen among the Creoles, was exacerbated by the ideas of the French Encyclopedists and later by the example of the young republic of the United States and the French Revolution. Ferdinand VII's reactionary policy after 1815 triggered off an uprising which led to the independence of many colonies. After more than three centuries, Spain was able to hold on only to Cuba and Puerto Rico in the New World, and was to lose even these before the century was out.

Portuguese Brazil

The accidental discovery of Brazil by Cabral in 1500 made it a Portuguese possession. However, the government was preoccupied with the East Indies, and left the colonization of the new country to individual initiative. It was only in 1534 that, following Spain's example, King John III tried to establish his authority more firmly by creating 13 captaincies, to which he appointed men of his own choice. The first Governor-General was appointed in 1578. During the time of the dynastic union between Spain and Portugal (1580–1640), an Indian council was established and Lisbon's monopoly became as complete as Seville's. In the 18th century, Brazil was governed by a Viceroy.

The Portuguese colonists, at first scions of noble families, traders and merchants, and later peasants from the Azores and Madeira, had no policy of racial discrimination and Brazil was quickly populated by a mixed race. Apart from the Europeans, a large number of black slaves were imported from the 16th century onwards. As for the primitive Indian tribes, their lot was much harder than in the Spanish colonies. They were pursued by bands of fanatics and reduced to cruel bondage. Only the Jesuits, who at first enjoyed the support of the Crown, protected them and settled them in reserves over which the Fathers had complete jurisdiction. But, yielding to the pressure of the large plantation owners who needed slaves, the government withdrew its support from the Jesuits and many of the reserves had to be closed. In the 18th century, under the enlightened Pombal government, slavery for the Indians was abolished. The Jesuits were expelled from Brazil in 1759.

In the 16th century, the Portuguese occupied a narrow strip of the Atlantic coast which they had first of all to defend against the French, who were finally eliminated at the end of the 16th century, and then against the Dutch, who arrived with Maurice, Prince of Orange, in 1637, but were driven out in 1654.

As a result of wasteful methods of agriculture, which led to progressive erosion of the soil, and under pressure from gold prospectors and slave hunters, the Portuguese colonists had to expand their dominion westwards as far as the Andes and southwards as far as the countries which were theoretically Spanish. New frontiers were established in 1777–1778, giving Brazil its present surface area of 3,288,000 square miles. But despite an increase in population in Minas Geraes, which is rich in minerals and diamonds, the bulk of the population continued to be concentrated in the port areas: Bahia, Recife (Pernambuco), Natal and Rio de Janeiro.

John VI turned Brazil into an autonomous kingdom when he fled there from Portugal, then under French occupation. After his return to Lisbon, the Brazilians feared a reversion to their former colonial status, and encouraged by the example of the Spanish colonists, they proclaimed the Constitutional Empire of Brazil in 1821.

The French Colonization of America

The French, who were occupied with the Italian wars and with their struggle against the Hapsburgs, took no part in the great voyages of discovery. Francis I, nevertheless, claimed the right of establishing his rule in all places discovered by the French and not under the effective rule of other Christian monarchs. However, the kings of

France, even if they took some interest in expeditions meant to discover new Eldorados or a passage to Cathay, did little to support their new colonies.

In Brazil, French settlers did, for some time, enjoy official support but it was insufficient and, despite their tenacious resistance, 'Antarctic France' disappeared at the end of the 16th century under the blows of the Portuguese.

French settlers fared no better in Florida, where a Spanish expedition exterminated them all the more zealously because a number of them were Huguenots.

But even before tropical America was completely closed to them, the French had already begun to penetrate into North America. Verrazzono, in 1524, had tried to find a passage to Cathay in that direction. Jacques Cartier, who had the same aim, reached the St. Lawrence estuary in 1534 and sailed up-river as far as Montreal. The first efforts at colonization were made in 1541, but ended in complete failure.

In 1603, at the orders of Henri IV, Champlain followed Cartier's route and a handful of Frenchmen settled in Canada. Quebec was founded in 1608 and the missionaries, above all the Jesuits, arrived in large numbers to convert the natives. The French, who maintained very good relations with certain Indian tribes, including the Hurons, nevertheless had to wage a bitter struggle against the Iroquois.

As New France provided neither gold nor spices, the kings and ministers, including even Colbert, took little interest in it most of the time. Moreover, the idea of colonization did not fire the public imagination. This was not surprising because estates abroad were usually farmed out to the gentry, who leased out small parcels of land to tenant farmers. What colonists there were came mainly from the west of France; many were soldiers who stayed behind when their regiments returned home. Canada's great weakness was always its small population.

However, few though they were in numbers, the colonists cleared the forests, founded towns, pushed towards the west in search of furs —Canada's chief export—reached the Great Lakes, sailed down the Mississippi and thus returned to colonial America, where they founded Louisiana in 1682. After exploring the entire prairie, they reached the Rocky Mountains in 1738.

At the beginning of the 18th century the French colonies in America comprised the St. Lawrence basin and Acadia (Nova Scotia) in Canada, and Louisiana and Illinois in what is now the United States. Their geographical position was such that they hemmed in the English colonies on the coast, preventing their

47 Jai-Singh Observatory, Delhi

48 Flying fish. Water-colour by John White (*c.* 1587)

expansion westwards and setting off a ferocious war long before France and England were in conflict in Europe. The English were vastly superior in numbers: in 1760, the thirteen colonies mustered 1½ million Englishmen against 60,000 Frenchmen in Canada and 20,000 in Louisiana. Moreover, during the war of the Spanish Succession and the Seven Years War, the French in America were practically left to their own devices while England regarded America as the most important scene of operations. The unequal struggle ended, despite Montcalm's efforts, in the fall of Quebec and Montreal in 1760–1761. By the Treaty of Paris of 1763, France renounced her possessions in North America to England. Louisiana was ceded to Spain, and France was left with nothing more than a part of Guiana and some islands in the Antilles. Here the French had been entrenched since 1635 and an economy had developed similar to that of Spanish America, based on Negro slaves, large colonial estates and a commercial monopoly for the mother country.

The English Colonies

The English, seized by the same gold fever as all other European countries in the 16th century, tried to succeed where Christopher Columbus had failed. The Italians John and Sebastian Cabot were commissioned by London merchants to find a North-west passage and discovered Labrador and Newfoundland. Like the French, the English were driven out of Central and South America by the Spaniards, who were, however, powerless to prevent the expeditions of Drake and Hawkins, a constant danger to their commerce.

When the power of Spain declined in the 17th century, England could no longer be kept away from the unoccupied territories of North America. As early as 1585, Walter Raleigh had made an unsuccessful attempt to found a colony in Virginia; the first secure English colony was established in Chesapeake Bay in 1607.

From then on, ever-increasing numbers of immigrants came to America from England, driven out by religious and political persecution and economic crises, or prompted by a sense of adventure and the lure of easy riches. The government, for its part, helped in the process of colonization by transporting convicts to America. Commercial companies and groups of landowners who had been granted concessions by the King set about recruiting colonists in England, Germany and other Protestant countries.

These immigrants, on disembarking in North America, found immense forest tracts peopled by primitive Indian tribes, who lived principally by hunting. The early colonists settled on the coast, where they formed isolated nuclei from which they later went forth to found new colonies. By the end of the 18th century there were altogether thirteen of these, all very different from one another. In the northern colonies, or New England, the Puritan spirit of the Pilgrim Fathers was predominant; here the colonists lived by agriculture carried on in the European way, and by commerce and industry. The central colonies had a mixed population, with the English in the minority, and lived mainly by trade. The southern colonies were dominated by the aristocracy owning the great tobacco and rice plantations, and in them the number of black slaves grew constantly.

At first these colonies were administered in a variety of ways, but by the end of the 17th century a certain degree of uniformity had been reached. Each had a Governor representing the King, a Council of State appointed by the King, and a House of Representatives elected by inhabitants with special voting qualifications. The House voted the budget and ratified the acts of the Council.

The English colonists had to fight not only against the Indian tribes but also against the Dutch and the French. The Dutch were finally driven out from New Amsterdam in 1667, but the French extended their domain and barred the route to the west all the way from the Great Lakes to the Mississippi. A decisive struggle took place between 1754 and 1763, and ended in complete victory for the English.

During the 17th century, the French danger had been one of the British Crown's main arguments for maintaining the colonies in a state of dependence. When this danger had disappeared, the colonists no longer required protection by England, and, moreover, felt able to manage their own affairs without outside interference. There were a number of good reasons for their resentment of colonial rule, and matters were made worse by the English government's authoritarian policy under George III. This led to the revolt of 1775, and to the Declaration of Independence on 4th July 1776. In the War of American Independence which followed, the thirteen colonies, now the United States of America, forced England to recognize their independence in 1782. England, however, was not completely driven out from North America: Canada remained British and the Crown retained the Caribbean possessions.

SPANISH AMERICA

During the two centuries which followed the *conquista*, the immense West Indian empire had practically no contacts with any country other than Spain. Because of this, and also because of the complete destruction of the pre-Columbian civilizations, the culture that developed was essentially Spanish and Catholic. It was introduced, spread and narrowly controlled by the secular and regular clergy of all orders—Franciscans, Dominicans and Jesuits—and was limited mainly to the Creole and Spanish population, although the Indians were not systematically excluded from it and many colleges were founded especially for them, including the famous college of Tlaltelolco in Mexico.

Intellectual Life

There was a good deal of intellectual activity in Spain at the time of the conquest and this had an effect on America, where universities (there were 20 by the beginning of the 19th century) as well as many religious colleges were soon founded. The main centres of scientific activity were Mexico and Lima, the seats of the first two Viceroys. In the 17th and 18th centuries, other universities—Charcas (now Sucre), Santa Fé de Bogotá, Buenos Aires *etc.*—came to the fore but concentrated more on the arts than on science.

Because books were free of all export and import duties, they poured into Spanish America in great numbers. All books had to be submitted to censorship by the Inquisition, which seems to have been quite liberal in practice, at any rate outside the strictly religious field.

Mexico, the capital of New Spain, attained a remarkable intellectual level in the 16th century. The first printing works in the New World were set up there in 1539, followed by three others before 1579. Newspapers, however, did not appear regularly until 1722.

The University of Mexico, the *Real y Pontificia Universitad de Mexico*, was able to celebrate the fourth centenary of its foundation in 1851, but in fact regular courses of lectures did not begin until 1533. The first chair of medicine was founded in 1580 and three others followed before 1666; a chair of mathematics was founded in 1637.

The University of San Marcos in Lima, founded in 1571, enjoyed enormous revenues which allowed it to maintain 32 chairs, including one of medicine founded in 1638. A printing press was set up in Lima in 1584 and a periodical paper began to appear in 1594.

In the 18th century, in the reign of Charles III, Spanish America experienced a veritable intellectual rebirth. The property which the Jesuits had been forced to leave behind when they were expelled was not only used to build a school of mining in Mexico, an *amfiteatro anatomico* in Lima, and an observatory in Sante Fé de Bogotá, but also to establish various scientific societies and publications, including the *Seminario de Nueva Granada*, the *Mercurio Peruano* (1791), the *Telegrafo mercantil* (Buenos Aires, 1801) *etc.*

Mathematics

Most of the arithmetical books published in Spanish America before the beginning of the 19th century were mainly concerned with practical problems of local importance: mining transactions, computations of the respective values of gold and silver, and calculations of the *quinto* due to the King of Spain.

The first of these works, the *Sumario compendioso de las quentas* (Mexico, 1556) by Juan Diez, dealt with the conversion of coins, gave rules for commercial transactions, and also tackled many algebraic problems on a level comparable with that of contemporary European school textbooks. Two similar works were the *Libro general de las reducciones de plata y oro* (Lima, 1597) by Juan de Belveder, and the *Libro de plata reduzida* (Lima, 1607) by F. Guarreguilla. The first general arithmetic published in the New World, the *Arte para aprender todo el menor del arithmetica, sin maestro* (Mexico, 1623) by Pedro Paz, accountant to the Chapter of Mexico Cathedrals, was based on earlier Spanish texts. It was followed in 1649 by the *Arte menor de arithmetica* by A. Reaton. The treatise on practical arithmetic by J. J. Padilla (1732), published in Guatemala, was more complete and contained a study of decimal fractions. Manuals answering the needs of mining and, later, of military academies, appeared in increasing number.

Francisco Diego Rodriguez, who corresponded with many European scientists and was appointed to the chair of mathematics founded at the University of Mexico in 1637, published an essay on the comet of 1652. His most eminent successor, Don Carlos de Sigüenza y Góngora, was extremely well read in the work of contemporary European scientists and published a study of the comet of 1680. In the course of a controversy with an Austrian Jesuit who was passing through Mexico, he maintained that comets had no influence on terrestrial events, a point of view which does credit to the scientific teaching of the New World. At the end of the 18th century, the School of Mines in Mexico introduced the teaching of the differential calculus.

In geometry, a study on the duplication of the cube, published in 1696 by a professor at the University of Lima, is almost the only work worth mentioning.

Metallurgy and Chemistry

Mining played a very important part in the development of the New World. As mines known to the Indians were rapidly exhausted, the Spanish set about prospecting for more productive ones. The fabulous Potosi silver mine was discovered accidentally in Alto Peru (now Bolivia) in 1645, and the Zacatecas, Santa Barbara and other

Mexican mines became the source of the flood of precious metals which transformed the economy of Europe in the 16th and 17th centuries.

At first the Spaniards used the mining methods of the Indians, who had developed the fairly advanced technique based on the solubility of the silver in the lead present in the ore and eliminating the lead by oxidation. This was done in small furnaces pierced with holes and heated by wood or charcoal.

An improved amalgamation process was introduced into Mexico in 1556 by Bartolomes de Medina who had, it seems, learned it from a German who was later expelled as a heretic. It consisted of grinding crushed ore fine with water and thoroughly mixing it with common salt, then adding and incorporating mercury and magistral (roasted pyrites consisting of crude sulphates of copper and iron). The silver was obtained by distilling the mercury from the amalgam which formed. This method allowed the exploitation of low-grade ore and was very economical of fuel. From Mexico, the process spread to the rest of America, and by about 1580 it was the only one used in the Potosi mines, which enjoyed great prosperity as a result. Other technical advances were also made: the use of metallic cones to recover the mercury vapour from the amalgam, improved furnaces *etc.*

In 1591, Juan de Cárdenas of Seville, a graduate and later a teacher of the University of Mexico, published a famous work, the *Primera parte de los problemos y secretos maravillosos de las Indias*, which contained many original contributions to mineralogy and an interesting account of the reactions in the amalgamation process. In 1640, a very important treatise on metallurgy appeared, the *Arte de los metales* by Alonso Barba. This book was republished several times in Spain, Mexico and Peru, and in a number of German translations.

Technology continued to make progress in the 18th century by profiting from European advances. Several of the principals of the Mexico School of Mines studied in Europe, at Freiberg and Upsala, and took miners back with them from Saxony to New Spain. The interest that was taken in chemistry is best shown by the fact that it was in Mexico that the first Spanish translation of Lavoisier's *Traité élémentaire de chimie* was published. 'A traveller would no doubt be surprised', Humboldt wrote, 'to meet in the interior of a country on the edge of California, young Mexicans who argue about the decomposition of water during the process of amalgamation. . . .'

Medicine

Chairs of medicine were founded in Mexico in 1580 and in Lima in 1638. As in Europe, 16th-century American medicine was entirely traditional, and so were the first medical books published in Mexico:

the *Opera medicinalia* (1570), by the Spanish-born physician F. Bravo, and the textbook (Mexico, 1727) of Marcos José Salgardo, the first American-born writer on medicine. However, several works described the therapeutical value of indigenous plants used by the Indians. Thus, the second edition (Mexico, 1592) of the *Tractado breve de anathomía y chirurgía* by Augustin Farfan, formerly physician to Philip II, recommended a number of Indian remedies. The *Milicia y descripcion de las Indias* (Madrid, 1600) by the soldier Vargas Machuca (1557–1622), which may be described as a sort of 'general guide for conquistadors' dealt with all the problems a Spanish invader may meet and, in particular, with first-aid in the field. Among its quick cures were many Indian remedies.

Despite this preoccupation with traditional and Indian remedies, the practice of inoculation had spread on a vast scale in New Spain by the end of the 18th century. Vaccination was introduced in 1804.

Botany

The flora of Spanish America was studied chiefly by European scholars, first immediately after the conquest and then again in the 18th century, when a great many expeditions were sent out from Europe.

It is well known that Spanish America gave Europe many plant products, some of which revolutionized the economic life of the Old World. The most striking examples were cinchona, from which quinine was later obtained, coca, maté, Peru balsam, sarsaparilla, tobacco, rubber, maize, manioc, groundnut, tomato, cocoa and, above all, the potato.

Most of these products were known to the Indians; the Aztecs even maintained botanical gardens which the conquistadors quickly stripped. After the conquest, fantastic accounts were spread of the medicinal properties of a great many indigenous plants, and particularly of the sacred guaiacum wood (*lignum vitae*) which was supposed to cure syphilis.

Bernardino de Sahagún (1499–1590) gathered valuable information from the Indians and from Montezuma's botanical gardens in Oaxaca, but his *Historia de las cosas de Nueva España* was not published until 1829. Nicolas Monardes (1507–1588), who traded with the Indies, took a passionate interest in the New World flora. He managed to acclimatize a number of American plants in his garden in Seville, and in the years 1565–1574 published a *Historia medicinal* which became very popular and was translated into a number of languages.

In 1570, the Council of the Indies launched an enquiry consisting of 50 questions, a number of which bore on natural history and the plants and medicaments employed by the Indians. In 1571–1577, the physician Francisco Hernandez, on the instruction of Philip II, toured New Spain gathering information from the Aztecs. He returned to Spain with 16 volumes of drawings and descriptions. A copy which remained behind in Mexico was summarized by Francisco Ximenes in the *Cuatro libros de la naturaleza y virtudes de las plantes* (Mexico, 1615). N. A. Recchi, physician to Philip II, also wrote a summary of Hernandez' work (Rome, 1628), an amended version of which was published by the *Accademia dei Lincei* under the title of *Rerum medicarum Novae Hispaniae Thesaurus* (1651). Hernandez' original drawings were deposited in the *Escorial*, where they were destroyed in the fire of 1671.

Cárdenas's treatise, which has already been mentioned, also contained references to the flora of New Spain and mentioned maize, tobacco, coca and some narcotic plants. A manuscript written in about 1552 in the native vernacular by the Indian physician, Martin de la Cruz, and translated into Latin by an Indian graduate of Tlaltelolco College, Juan Badiano, also provided useful information. It was rediscovered in the Vatican library in 1929 and published in 1940. The Spanish Jesuit, José de Acosta (1539–1600), after a long stay in Peru and Mexico, published a *Historia natural y moral de las Indias* (Seville, 1590), of which the chapter devoted to natural history mentioned various American plants, including maize, potato, pineapple, banana, cocoa, agave and coca.

In the 18th century there was a general renewal of interest in American plants. By then the cinchona bark was used to cure tertian and quartan fever in most European countries, and it was hoped that further research might reveal other equally potent drugs.

Many scientific expeditions set out for South America at that time. The coast of Peru and Chile was explored by Louis Feuillée in 1707–1712 and by Amédée François Frézier in 1712–1714. In 1735, the Paris *Académie des Sciences* sent an expedition led by Bouguer and La Condamine, to measure the arc of the meridian near the equator. The botanist of the expedition, Joseph de Jussieu, was so fascinated by what he saw that he remained in South America for thirty-five years, during which he sent his brothers copious notes and lists of plants and seeds. La Condamine himself, in 1738, gave the *Académie des Sciences* a description of a tree which he called *quinquina* (cinchona). After completing his geodesic work, he sailed up the Amazon and went to Guiana. On his return, in 1751, he read the Academy a paper 'on the elastic resin newly discovered in Cayenne', which he called *cahuchu*. A young Spanish officer, Antonio de Ulloa, who was attached to La Condamine's expedition by the King of Spain, published his account of their adventures, the *Relación historica del viaje a la America meridional* in 1748.

At about the same time, the Chilean Jesuit J. I. Molina (1738?–1829) studied the natural resources of Chile. After the expulsion of the Jesuits in 1768, he published the results of his researches, including a flora of Chile (Bologna, 1782). The famous expeditions led by Bougainville and by Cook also called on the coasts of South America. In the reign of Charles III a number of botanical missions were sent out to Peru, Chile, New Granada (Colombia), and, finally, to Mexico. The expedition to Peru and Chile (1778–1788) was led by H. Ruiz and J. Pavon, who were accompanied for a part of their journey by the Frenchman J. Dombey, whose misadventures have already been mentioned. Accounts of some of the results of their expedition were published in Madrid from 1798 to 1802. F. C. Mutis, who was sent to New Granàda in 1760, remained there for some time and collected and made drawings of many specimens of plants, some of which he sent to Linnaeus.

The expedition to New Spain led by M. Sesse, which reached Mexico in 1787, had two main objects: first, to establish a botanical garden and a chair of botany (1788), and second, to study the documents Hernandez had left behind and to prepare the publication of his complete works, which came out in three volumes (Madrid, 1790). A lively controversy developed on that occasion between the Spanish mission and the Creole botanists on the subject of Linnaeus' classification and the botanical knowledge of the Aztecs. Sesse and his Mexican assistant, J. M. Mociño, subsequently continued their travels in Spanish America, covering over 2,000 miles. They collected a rich herbarium and made a remarkable set of coloured drawings, some of which were published by the Swiss botanist A. de Candolle.

Mention must also be made of the botanical explorations at the end of the 18th century by Luis Née and Thaddaeus Haenhe, an account of which was published in Prague in 1825, and, above all, of the great voyage of Alexander von Humboldt and Aimé Bonpland from 1799 to 1804. These two travellers, who visited a good many parts of Spanish America, made exceptionally valuable observations of the fauna, the floral geography and the ethnography of South America. Their results were published in a series of works, including the *Essai sur la géographie des plantes* (1805) and especially the *Plantae æquinoctiales* . . . (Paris, 1805–1818), which opened up a new era in the exploration of the natural wealth of South America.

PORTUGUESE BRAZIL

There was relatively little intellectual activity in Brazil during the colonial period, partly because Brazil was completely subjugated to Portugal and partly because its urban centres were scattered. Brazil had neither a university nor a printing works; all schools were in the hands of the Jesuits, with the result that science was completely ignored.

Some French travellers in the 16th century described Brazil and the native Guarani tribes; Thévet made two journeys to Brazil, in 1550 and 1554; de Léri accompanied Villegagnon to Brazil and published an account of his journey in 1598. In the 17th century, scientific pursuits were encouraged by Maurice of Nassau, who was in Recife (Pernambuco) from 1637 to 1644. He established an observatory, a botanical and a zoological garden, and took with him a considerable number of scholars, who published accounts of Brazil on their return to the Netherlands. These included the Amsterdam physician, Willem Piso, who studied medicinal plants and snake venoms, and, more important, the German physician, Georg Marcgrav, who wrote a *Historia naturalis Brasiliae* (Amsterdam, 1648), in which he displayed a profound knowledge of the Brazilian flora and fauna. He also made important topographical, meteorological and astronomical studies and observed the eclipse of 1640. In 1643, Eckhout, a Dutchman, painted a series of portraits of Guarani tribesmen. However, all this scientific activity lasted no longer than the Dutch held on to Recife and, apart from it, there is hardly anything to record except a few botanical and topographical studies made by various foreign scholars: William Dampier in 1704, L. A. de Bougainville, who was in Rio de Janeiro in 1765, P. Commerson, who brought back an excellent collection of Brazilian plants, and Sir Joseph Banks, who was in Brazil in 1768.

Finally, we may mention that Bartholomeu Lourenço de Guzmão (1685–1724), who contributed to the development of the man-carrying balloon, was born at Santos in Brazil. His experiments, carried out in Lisbon in 1709, led some to consider him the direct precursor of the Montgolfier brothers, though, in fact, all he did was to send up a small balloon filled with hot air to a height of a few yards. The *Passarola*, a fantastic design for a flying machine, which aroused curiosity at the beginning of the century, was attributed to him. Guzmão, who was an Almoner-Royal, fell foul of the Inquisition in September 1724, and fled to Toledo, where he died two months later.

It was not until the end of the 18th century that science began to take root in Brazil, largely as a result of the revival of learning at the University of Coimbra under the influence of Pombal. Many Brazilians who graduated from Coimbra returned home with a taste for science, and founded a scientific academy and a literary society at Rio de Janeiro. The geographer Larceda e Almeida fixed the coordinates of many places in Brazil and made maps of several regions. The botanist Alexander Rodrigues Ferreira, the 'Humboldt of

Brazil', carried out scientific explorations in Amazonia and wrote a number of botanical and zoological studies. His manuscripts, brought from Lisbon to Paris after the occupation of Portugal in 1808, were consulted by Geoffroy Saint-Hilaire.

The mineralogist José Boifacio studied mining in Brazil before being appointed to the chair of metallurgy in Coimbra.

However, Brazil continued to be dominated by Lisbon and, in 1800, the Portuguese government forbade Humboldt to enter Brazilian territory. The French occupation of Portugal, which forced King John VI to take refuge in Brazil, was to transform the life of the colony, for it broke Portugal's commercial monopoly and thus exposed Brazil to foreign influence. As a result, many scientific and cultural institutions such as the Royal Press, the botanical gardens, the Royal Museum, a medical school and a military academy, were founded and a great impetus was given to scientific and technical studies. Even so, when Brazil finally gained her independence, she had a long way to go before she could make up for the ground she had lost during three centuries of Portuguese domination.

FRENCH CANADA

Under the French, Canada made very little intellectual or scientific progress. There were no printing presses or universities; metropolitan France purposely maintained a monopoly of higher education lest 'the sons of the quality lose their love for the motherland by not knowing it'. Secondary education for boys was in the hands of the Jesuit College in Quebec; the curriculum was classical and literary. There was, however, a school of hydrography attached to the Jesuit College, but it was taken over by the state in 1671. French-Canadian girls were educated by the Ursulines. Louisiana, which the French held for only a short time and which was underpopulated, lacked even secondary schools. Despite these handicaps, a number of French-Canadians and Creoles published books on American geography, plants and ethnography.

In 1545, Jacques Cartier published an account of his three voyages, to which he added a great many observations—some of them imaginary—on the Canadian flora. Lescarbot's *Histoire de la Nouvelle France* (Paris, 1612) was another valuable source book. Pierre Boucher, who was sent to Louis XIV to obtain help from the mother country, published a *Histoire véritable et naturelle des mœurs et du pays de la Nouvelle France* (Paris, 1663), but this was of little scientific value. More important scientific information was contained in the *Relations*, which the Jesuits sent to France every year. Those covering the period 1632–1673 contain interesting geographical, botanical and ethnographical studies. The following, too, are worthy of mention: L. Hennepin's *Description de la Louisiane* (1683), La Hontan's *Nouveau voyage dans l'Amerique septentrionale* (1703), and La Potherie's *Histoire de l'Amerique septentrionale* (1722).

BRITISH NORTH AMERICA

The fact that there was considerable scientific activity in the American colonies before independence is sufficiently impressive in itself at a time when one might have forgiven the colonists for concentrating exclusively on building up and expanding their new country. However, though the colonists had their work cut out in founding towns, clearing forests, cultivating fields, fighting the Indians, taking part in European wars and shifting their frontiers towards the west, they nevertheless found time to set up many scientific societies and to engage in multifarious research projects, some of which produced results of first-class importance.

Early Descriptions of the Flora and Fauna

On 17th August 1585, Thomas Harriot, the first Englishman to explore and describe the natural history of North America, arrived at Wingandacoa, Virginia (now North Carolina). After a stay of nearly a year, he published *A Briefe and True Report of the New Found Land of Virginia* (48 quarto pages, London, 1588), which was reprinted in 1590 with engravings of the fine watercolours made by Harriot's companion John White. This book will impress even a modern reader by its erudition, exactness and economy of statement. For example, Harriot stated that he was told the names of 28 animals but that he, personally, saw only 12 of them. His description of the American Cervidae was not surpassed for almost two centuries. Harriot also described 86 species of American birds, many previously unknown trees, shrubs and other plants, as well as fishes and crustaceans. He brought the tobacco plant and the potato back to Europe and he was perhaps the first smoker known to have died of lung cancer.

Captain John Smith, who arrived at Jamestown in 1606, entitled his report of his travels *A Description of New England* (London, 1660), thus giving that region its present name. He described for the first time many American mammals (including the moose), fishes, crustaceans, flowers, birds and trees. Other interesting descriptions were the *New England Prospect* by William Wood (London, 1634), and the *New English Canaan* by Thomas Morton (Amsterdam, 1637). By the end of the century, so much had been written on American plants and animals that John Josselyn felt the need to publish a special compilation of all the material amassed. It was called *New England's Rareties Discovered: in Birds, Beasts, Fishes, Serpents and Plants of that Country*, and contained so many sensational accounts that it is difficult to distinguish between fact and fancy. 'Barley', Josselyn wrote, 'commonly degenerates into oats', thus applying one of Pliny's more far-fetched ideas to the New World. Europeans accepted these absurdities fairly readily, perhaps because they believed that anything might happen in that remote region.

The Work of 18th-Century American Botanists

At the beginning of the 18th century, a good deal of work was done on botany in America, chiefly to supply the demand from England for new medicinal substances and for decorative plants. At the time, the principal preoccupation in England was agriculture and horticulture; gardens were built on the Dutch model and landscape-gardeners were employed in the parks of most large estates. American naturalists were in a position to supply the plants that were needed but they did not merely collect them; they also studied their anatomy and devised a number of important experiments in plant physiology.

The first great scientific achievement of the New World was a series of experiments on artificial or controlled plant hybridization which threw light on the theory of plant sexuality, a subject of keen discussion after Nehemiah Grew had read a paper on it to the Royal Society in 1676. Cotton Mather, a Fellow of the Royal Society, gave an account of these experiments in a letter to James Petiver, dated 24th September 1716. In it, he clearly described the result of the hybridization of *Zea mays* and *Cucurbita pepo*, noting the accompanying metaxenia and the appearance of dominants. Mather included the substance of this letter in his *The Christian Philosopher* (London, 1720), which, though it had a religious bias as the title implies, was the first general work on science to be published in North America. Mather, who accepted Grew's theory of the sexuality of flowering plants, found that a 'sort of male sperm' is needed to fertilize the seed. A little later Paul Dudley, Attorney-General of Massachusetts, independently discovered the possibility of hybridizing maize, and described his results in an article entitled 'Observations on Some of the Plants in New England with Remarkable Instances of the Nature and Power of Vegetation' (*Philosophical Transactions*, 1724). This article formed the basis of two entries ('Generation' and 'Maize or Indian Corn') in Miller's famous *Gardener's Dictionary*.

Other, still more important, experiments were carried out by James Logan in Philadelphia. Logan, who arrived in Pennsylvania in 1699 as secretary to William Penn, devoted a good deal of his time to mathematics, physics and astronomy, and even tried to base ethics on mathematical physics. His scientific library, the first in America, included the three editions of Newton's *Principia* and the works of Archimedes, Euclid, Ptolemy, Galileo, Kepler, Huygens, Flamsteed, Hevelius, Gilbert, Harvey, Leeuwenhoek, Malpighi, Linnaeus, Grew, Boerhaave, Sydenham, Boyle and Hooke. Logan is known to have lent his books to a number of people, including Benjamin Franklin and John Bartram. In 1730–1731, Thomas Godfrey, one of Logan's protégés, invented a type of maritime quadrant similar to that which Hadley constructed in England.

Though Logan's work on optics never attracted as much attention as he had hoped, his experimental studies of maize plants from which he had removed the stamens earned him the praise of Linnaeus, who read his letter on this topic in the *Philosophical Transactions* of 1736. With the encouragement of Gronovius, he published a fuller account in his *Experimenta et meletemata de plantarum generatione* (Leyden, 1738), which was widely read and aroused much comment. The fact that Linnaeus' system of classification was based on an analysis of the sexual organs of plants added to the importance of this work, for Logan's—as well as Mather's and Dudley's—experiments, in addition to being of tremendous value to the study of plant reproduction, also helped to confirm the soundness of the new system of classification. It may be noted that the ease with which the reproduction of maize could be controlled made it an exceptionally good subject for genetic studies. A number of scientists, who rediscovered the forgotten work of Mendel at the beginning of the 20th century, repeated Logan's experiments on maize as a means of testing Mendel's theories.

Another 18th-century American botanist worthy of mention was John Clayton, whose *Flora Virginica* was published by Gronovius with the help of Linnaeus (Leyden, 1793). Mark Catesby studied not only the plants but also the birds and animals of America, which he described and illustrated magnificently in his sumptuous *Natural History of Carolina, Florida and the Bahama Islands* (London, 1754–1771). Collecting plants was often attended with difficulty. For example, John Mitchell, a friend of Franklin and Linnaeus, who settled in Virginia in 1700 and who is best known for his *Map of the British and French Dominions in North America* (London, 1755), which marked the beginning of scientific cartography in North America, lost the rich collection of plants which he had made on his return journey to England in 1746. Writing to Linnaeus, he regretted that he could send him no plants, since of more than a thousand which he had collected, not one had been left intact by privateers or the bad effects on them of the sea voyage. Linnaeus, in a letter to Haller, wrote, 'All the plants which I have been sent from New York have fallen into the hands of the Spaniards, like those which Dr. Mitchell spent many years collecting in Virginia. He, himself, is back in England, but very disheartened. On the same ship, I have lost many specimens and descriptions sent to me by Governor Colden of New York.'

Cadwallader Colden was a Scottish physician who arrived in America in 1718; he became successively Surveyor-General and Lieutenant-Governor of New York. His daughter Jane, the first woman botanist in the New World, helped him to collect plants and to classify them according to Linnaeus' method. Colden published a *History of the Five Indian Nations of Canada* (1727) and also a work entitled *Principles of Action in Matter, with a Treatise annexed on the Elements of Fluxions or Differential Calculus* (New York, 1743). Another American naturalist, Dr. Alexander Garden of Charleston (South Carolina), was a friend of Linnaeus, who named the gardenia after him. John Bartram, whom Linnaeus called the greatest living 'natural botanist', was a self-taught man and was a farmer before he took to science. His reputation was so great that presents and honours came to him from all over the world. Bartram sent plants to Linnaeus and to British and French collectors. In order to prevent the destruction of his plants by privateers, he hit on the idea of marking his cases with the addresses of Dalibert, Buffon or Jussieu in Paris as well as those of the British consignees, with a request that they be sent to the former 'in case of capture'. Encouraged by Franklin and Logan, Bartram discovered and sent to England and France more specimens of American plants than any other contemporary botanist. He also studied the sexuality and hybridization of plants.

While botany thus made great advances in North America, zoology appears to have flourished less, and it is probably for this reason that men like Buffon and the Abbé Raynal were able, with little opposition, to put forward the theory that animals transported from the Old World to the New tend to become small and stunted. The English writer, Oliver Goldsmith, went so far as to claim that birds degenerated to such an extent in America that they ceased to sing. To give the lie to these theories, Thomas Jefferson sent an expedition to capture a moose, which he intended to send to Paris as clear proof that America had indigenous animals bigger than any to be found in Europe. The biological sections of his *Notes on Virginia* were also intended to clear up many mistaken notions prevalent in Europe.

Medicine

In the medical field, North America made a considerable contribution. In 1721, during a smallpox epidemic in Boston, Cotton Mather played a part in introducing inoculation. With remarkable courage, Mather, in the face of violent opposition from certain physicians and a large part of the public, advocated this new practice and managed to convince a local physician, Zabdiel Boylston, of its merits. Members of Mather's family were among the first to be inoculated, and Boston became the first city to implement the new procedure under controlled conditions. Moreover, the statistical report published by Mather and Boylston was one of the first historical examples of the quantitative analysis of a medical problem. They were right to assume that inoculation must stand or fall by a calculation of the deaths due to smallpox contracted normally, on the one hand, and to artificial infection produced by inoculation on the other. They proved that the latter were considerably outweighed by the former.

Other research in medicine was of smaller importance. John Lining of Charleston (South Carolina), who had studied medicine in Edinburgh, gave Europe the first exact description of the symptoms of yellow fever. He also studied the relationship between epidemic diseases and meteorological conditions, and took daily notes of his food intake and excreta, estimating the weight of his perspiration by changes in the weight of his clothing and correlating his measurements with temperature and weather fluctuations.

Interest in Science

Sermons preached in America during the 17th and 18th centuries, particularly in New England, throw considerable light on the state of science at the time. The preachers did not regard science as an enemy of Revelation; on the contrary, they believed that the Word of God is to be found in the planets, the plants and the stones, as well as in Holy Scripture. A handbook for intending ministers published in 1726 says, characteristically, that 'experimental philosophy is an essential part of the education of a minister and of other persons'. 'The incomparable Sir Isaac Newton' was held up as the model of experimental philosophy. Charles Morton, who in about 1675 had opened an 'Academy' at Newington Green, then in the outskirts of London, for dissenters whom the Test Act excluded from Oxford and Cambridge, later introduced the 'new science' of Galileo, Boyle, Hooke and Newton into American education. He arrived in America in 1688 with the manuscript of his *Compendium Physicae*, which was based on all the most recent scientific work in England and which served for many years as the basis of scientific teaching at Harvard (founded in 1663) and later at Yale (founded in 1701). As a result, teaching at the American universities had little of the scholastic and medieval flavour of their European counterparts. In 1737, the interest shown in science was confirmed by the endowment at Harvard of a chair of science: the Hollis professorship of mathematics and natural philosophy.

Astronomy

From 1659 Copernican astronomy was taught at Harvard, a fact scarcely less surprising than the foundation of a college in a new country less than twenty years after the arrival of the first colonists. In 1672, an astronomical telescope was presented to Harvard by Governor John Winthrop, who was mistaken in believing that he had discovered a fifth satellite of Jupiter with it. This telescope was also used by Thomas Brattle, whose observations of the great comet of 1680 were praised in Newton's *Principia*.

Apart from the observation of this comet, the main events in American astronomy were the various expeditions sent out to observe the transit of Venus and a number of eclipses. Franklin advised his fellow citizens of the transit of Mercury in 1753, but the only person to possess an adequate instrument and to have the advantage of being in the Antilles, which alone enjoyed favourable meteorological conditions at the time, made rather mediocre observations. In 1761, John Winthrop led the first American scientific expedition to be organized by a college, to observe the transit of Venus from Newfoundland. A government sloop took him there with his group of Harvard students, as well as telescopes and college clocks. The transit of Venus in 1769 was observed by William Smith and David Rittenhouse of Philadelphia.

An even more striking astronomical expedition was organized in 1780 by Harvard and the American Academy of Arts and Sciences at Boston, who sent the Rev. Samuel Williams of Harvard to Penobscot Bay to observe a total eclipse of the sun. America and England were then at war and the eclipse could be observed only from the territory occupied by the British, but hostilities were interrupted for as long as the operation lasted. Science again transcended national disputes when Franklin granted free passage to Captain Cook on his return from a voyage of exploration in the South Seas during the War of American Independence.

The Teaching of Science

In Harvard, which was the only North American college in the 17th century, an attempt was made in 1672 to open a botanical garden, an *ergasterium* (mechanical workshop) and a chemical laboratory. In 1727, Morton was appointed the first holder of the Hollis chair and he was given a valuable collection of scientific instruments; this collection was improved and kept up to date throughout the 18th century. At Yale, opened in 1701, science was cultivated from the very beginning. Scientific equipment was bought or built and, in 1714, the library was enriched by donations of their works by various English scientists, including Newton and Halley. The College of

William and Mary, founded in 1693, did not start university teaching until 1710; science was taught there and also at Princeton (founded in 1746) and Columbia (founded in 1754). The University of Pennsylvania, founded by Franklin (the first class graduated in 1757), also offered a science course; moreover, the first official American medical school was set up there. A little later, the first permanent American hospital, the Pennsylvania Hospital, was founded at Philadelphia. Nor were the sciences neglected in the remaining colleges founded and operating before 1775; Brown, which was recognized by the state in 1764, and Dartmouth, which was recognized as a college in 1769.

The First Scientific Societies

Another sign of the interest taken in science was the formation of many clubs and societies in which scientific subjects could be freely discussed. The first American scientific society, the Boston Philosophical Society, which was founded in 1683 by Increase Mather, the father of Cotton Mather, did not last long. In 1727, Benjamin Franklin founded the *Junto*, a secret fraternal and charitable association for the mutual improvement of its members; at its meetings, questions of ethics, politics and physics were discussed. In 1743, Franklin suggested the formation of a society of wider scope and influence to be composed of citizens of all the colonies who took an active interest in science, and so the American Philosophical Society was founded. In 1769 it was amalgamated with another, which had developed from the *Junto*, and assumed the official title it has maintained ever since: 'The American Philosophical Society held at Philadelphia for promoting Useful Knowledge'. The first major undertaking of the reconstituted society was the observation of the transit of Venus in 1769. It had no competitor until 1780, when the American Academy of Arts and Sciences was founded at Boston at the suggestion of John Adams, who had heard the praises of the Philadelphia society sung so much in Paris that he decided it was essential to form a similar one in Boston. Its first president was an amateur scientist, Governor James Bowdoin, and his first official act was to help to organize the expedition sent on the occasion of the total eclipse of the sun in 1780, which we have already mentioned.

Benjamin Franklin: the Importance of his Scientific Work

Of all the scientific activities in colonial America, the most important was the research into electricity carried out by Benjamin Franklin and his friends in the years preceding 1750. Known best for his famous kite experiment, Franklin was the first American to be elected a foreign associate of the *Académie Royale des Sciences* in Paris (1773), an honour conferred on no other American for more than a century. It was not until J. Willard Gibbs (1839–1903) that America produced another scientist whose contribution to physics was as important and as widely recognized as Franklin's. Franklin's *Experiments and Observations on Electricity carried out at Philadelphia* was first published in London in 1751 and ran to five English, three French, two German and one Italian editions in his own lifetime. For more than twenty-five years it was the most authoritative work on the subject and its influence was so great that even those who adopted a rival theory used the electrical terms which Franklin had introduced.

Franklin's experiments to demonstrate the electrical nature of lightning were very spectacular. In the first, he used a long, pointed and insulated iron rod. The lower end of the rod entered a kind of sentry-box where the experimenter, standing on an insulated stand, could join it to an earthed wire. Franklin thought that it was necessary to install the sentry-box on top of a high building and so he waited for the steeple of Christ Church in Philadelphia to be completed before he carried out the experiment. However, in 1752 the French naturalist Dalibard, the translator of Franklin's book on electricity, showed that the experiment would succeed even if the sentry-box was placed at ground level. The experiment was carried out in Dalibard's absence by a former dragoon, Coiffier, and the vilage priest Raulet on 10th May 1752, at Marly-la-Ville, during a thunderstorm. When describing the experiment and the results obtained to the *Académie des Sciences* on 13th May 1752, Dalibard said: 'In following the path which he [Franklin] has suggested, I have arrived at completely satisfactory results.' Equally convincing results were soon to reward the efforts of Buffon and Delor, Le Monnier and Nollet in France, Mylius and Ludolf in Germany, and Canton and Wilson in England.

In June 1752, before, apparently, he had received news of the success of his experiment in France, Franklin devised another experimental proof of the electrical nature of lightning discharges; this was his famous kite experiment. The importance of all these experiments lay in that they demonstrated that electrical phenomena did not result exclusively from artificial friction, but that they were also produced spontaneously in nature. From then on the physical sciences could no longer ignore electricity, or treat it as secondary to mechanics, heat, optics, magnetism and acoustics. Moreover, Franklin's analysis of lightning tended to eliminate the superstitious belief that it was a sign of divine wrath. Finally, this adventure in the field of pure science led to a very important application, the lightning conductor, and thus confirmed Bacon's belief that all good science must have practical results. This was, perhaps, the first time that a practical invention had resulted from disinterested research, aimed only at satisfying the experimenter's curiosity and at advancing pure knowledge.

Franklin was recognized as an outstanding scientist because his experiments made it possible to predict accurately the results of what had previously been considered mysterious processes. When he started on his experiments, the general scientific opinion was that electric discharges are governed by pure chance. Buffon, for example, wrote that 'the entire subject of electricity is far from having reached the stage where it is possible to establish a system of laws, or, for that matter, any kind of order at all'. But as a result of Franklin's work the situation was completely changed. Barbeu Dubourg has described Franklin's contribution as follows:

> Franklin, by distinguishing positive and negative electricity, by allotting its proper place to each, and by defining its characteristics, to the extent that the current state of physical knowledge made this possible, was the first to really illuminate the subject and to indicate the path that must be taken if new discoveries were to be made and related intelligibly to what was already known, if the limits of science were to be extended and the new discoveries, apart from agreeing with the old ones, were to produce useful results. He said, 'Do this, and that is what will happen; change this circumstance, and that is what will result from it. If you do this, you will succeed; if you do that, you will meet this obstacle.' When his suggestions were acted upon, everything took place in the way and in the order in which he had predicted it would; everything tallied, in Europe as in America, with his statements; everything, even celestial phenomena, confirmed the soundness of his theories, which, in his modesty, he never put forward as anything but simple conjectures.

Franklin's theory was based on the assumption that there is a single electrical fluid, of which all bodies possess a normal quantity, and that electrical effects are produced each time this normal quantity is increased or decreased, or whenever the distribution of the fluid in the conducting body is altered. According to Franklin, the electrical fluid is composed of particles which repel each other but attract particles of common matter. In this way, he was able to explain the action of lightning conductors, insulators, proof planes, the Leyden jar, and a host of other devices and phenomena, some of which he had discovered himself while others were already known but not properly understood.

If we regard Franklin's work from the point of view of our own age, we cannot help being impressed by the variety of the phenomena which he explained, and by the fact that most of the time we still use his theory, in a more or less modified form. As the discoverer of the electron, J. J. Thomson, has put it: 'The service which the one-fluid theory has rendered to the science of electricity, by suggesting and co-ordinating researches, can hardly be overestimated. It is still used by many of us when working in the laboratory. If we move a piece of brass and want to know whether that will increase or diminish the effect we are observing, we do not fly to the higher mathematics, but use the simple conception of the electric fluid which would tell us as much as we wanted to know.' Since Franklin's theory states that all electrical effects are due to a transfer of electrical matter and that what one body loses another gains, it implies the principle of the conservation of charge—that electrical charges always appear or disappear in equal and opposite quantities. This is as true in the case of large objects which are rubbed against each other as it is on the atomic or sub-atomic level, where, during the production or annihilation of pairs, the appearance or disappearance of every positron is accompanied by the simultaneous disappearance or appearance of an electron. Franklin's 'principle of the conservation of electric charge', like Wallis and Newton's 'principle of the conservation of momentum', is one of the great principles of modern physics. With it, Franklin had raised American science to a place of high honour.

The first official recognition of the new American nation by the world of science was accorded it in 1788, when James Bowdoin, the first president of the American Academy of Arts and Sciences, was elected a foreign member of the Royal Society.

* * *

In the light of American scientific achievements in the 18th century and the general interest taken in science, a great deal of scientific activity could reasonably have been expected in the century to follow. However, possibly because of their preoccupation with extending their frontiers into and beyond the Wild West, the United States did not, in the 19th century, produce any scientists or scientific discoveries on a par with Franklin's. It was not until the first half of the 20th century that American science once again succeeded in attracting the attention of the rest of the world.

BIBLIOGRAPHY

J. COMAS, 'Principales contribuciones indigenas precolombinas a la cultura universal' in *Cahiers d'histoire mondiale*, III, 1956.

J. REY PASTOR, *La ciencia y la técnica en el descubrimiento de América*, 2nd ed., Buenos Aires, 1945.

'A travers les Amériques latines' in *Cahiers des Annales*, IV, Paris, 1949.

C. PEREYRA, *L'œuvre de l'Espagne en Amérique*, Paris, 1925.

P. H. UREÑA, *Historia de la cultura en la America hispánica*, Mexico, 1947.

A. MIELI, *La ciencia del Renacimiento*, Vol. V, Buenos Aires, 1952.

L. C. KARPINSKI, 'Mathematics in Latin America' in *Scripta mathematica*, XIII, 1947.

J. J. IZQUIERDO, *La fisiologia en Mexico*, Mexico, 1934.

Montaña y los origines del movimiento social y cientifico de Mexico, Mexico, 1954.

'La botanique aztèque et la botanique mexicaine moderne' in *Arch. int. Hist. des Sci.* VIII, 1955.

F. VERDOORN (ed.), *Plants and Plant Science in Latin America*, Waltham, Mass., 1945.

J. BELL, Jr., 'Medicine in Sixteenth-Century New Spain' in *Bull. of the Hist. of Medicine*, XXXI, 1957.

E. BONNEFOUS et al., *Encyclopédie de l'Amérique latine*, Paris, 1954.

F. DE AZEVEDO, *A cultura brasileira*, Rio de Janeiro, 1943.

C. DE BONNAUT, *Histoire du Canada français, 1534–1763*, Paris, 1950.

A. VIATTE, *Histoire littéraire de l'Amerique française*, Paris, 1954.

M. GIRAUD, *Histoire de la Louisiane française*, Paris, 1958.

STEFAN LORANT (ed.), *The New World: the First Pictures of America made by John White and Jacques le Moyne . . . with Contemporary Narratives of . . . the Virginian Colony*, New York, 1946.

HENRY STEVENS, *Thomas Harriot, the Mathematician, the Philosopher, and the Scholar . . .*, London, 1900.

CONWAY ZIRKLE, *The Beginnings of Plant Hybridization*, Philadelphia, 1935.

OTHO T. BEALL, Jr., and R. H. SHRYOCK, *Cotton Mather, First Significant Figure in American Medicine*, Baltimore, 1954.

BROOKE HINDLE, *The Pursuit of Science in Revolutionary America, 1735–1789*, Chapel Hill, 1956.

WHITFIELD J. BELL, Jr., *Early American Science*, Williamsburg, 1955.

I. BERNARD COHEN, *Some Early Tools of American Science*, Cambridge, 1950.

Franklin and Newton, Philadelphia, 1956.

RAYMOND J. STEARNS, 'Colonial Fellows of the Royal Society' in *Osiris*, VIII, 1948, pp. 73–121.

THEODORE HORNBERGER, *Scientific Thought in the American Colleges, 1638–1800*, Austin, 1945.

Les botanistes français en Amérique du Nord avant 1850 (International Proceedings of the C.N.R.S.), Paris, 1957.

INDEX OF NAMES

Personal names appear in capital letters; geographical names are in roman type; the titles of books are in italics.

SUBJECT INDEX

  printing of, 154, 395

HISTORY OF SCIENCE

Edited by RENÉ TATON

of the Centre National de la Recherche Scientifique

The Contributors to this Volume:

GEORGES ALLARD University of Paris (Heat, 17th–18th centuries)
EDMOND BAUER University of Paris (Magnetism and electricity, 18th century)
GEORGES CANGUILHEM University of Paris (Animal physiology, 18th century)
JEAN CHESNEAUX École des Hautes Études (The Far East, 16th–18th centuries)
I. BERNARD COHEN Harvard University (British American Colonies)
PIERRE COSTABEL Catholic Institute, Paris (Mechanics, Sound, 17th–18th centuries)
MAURICE DAUMAS Conservatoire Museum, Paris (Chemistry, Renaissance and 17th–18th centuries)
ADRIEN DAVY DE VIRVILLE University of Paris (Botany, Renaissance and 17th–18th centuries)
PAUL DELAUNAY Société Française d'Histoire de la Médecine (Renaissance; humanism and encyclopedism, geology, biology, zoology, conclusion)
RENÉ DUGAS École Polytechnique, Paris (Mechanics, 17th–18th centuries)
DR LOUIS DULIEU University of Montpellier (Medicine, 17th–18th centuries)
JEAN FILLIOZAT Collège de France (India, 15th–18th centuries)
RAYMOND FURON Muséum National d'Histoire Naturelle (Geology, 17th–18th centuries)
ÉMILE GUYÉNOT Institut Français (Biology, 17th century)
JEAN ITARD Lycée Henri IV (Mathematics, 17th century)
ALEXANDRE KOYRÉ École des Hautes Études (The exact sciences during the Renaissance)
ROBERT LENOBLE (The scientific revolution, and magnetism and electricity, 17th century)
JACQUES LÉVY Paris Observatory (Astronomy, 18th century)
CHARLES MORAZÉ École des Hautes Études (18th century: general presentation)

JOSEPH NEEDHAM, F.R.S. Gonville and Caius College, Cambridge (The Far East, 16th–18th centuries)

JEAN ROSTAND (General biology, 18th century)

Mme JULIETTE TATON (The American Colonies, Spanish America and Canada)

RENÉ TATON Centre Nationale de la Recherche Scientifique (General Editor; Mathematics, 18th century)

Mme M.-A. TONNELAT University of Paris (Optics, 17th–18th centuries)

GÉRARD WALUSINSKI Lycée de Saint Cloud (Astronomy, 17th century)